An Introduction to

Physical Anthropology

"Brave New World"

Restoration of *Australopithecus*. From a painting by Maurice Wilson.
(Courtesy, British Museum [Natural History].)

An Introduction to
Physical Anthropology

THIRD EDITION

By

M. F. ASHLEY MONTAGU

CHARLES C THOMAS · PUBLISHER

Springfield · Illinois · U.S.A.

CHARLES C THOMAS · PUBLISHER

BANNERSTONE HOUSE

301-327 East Lawrence Avenue, Springfield, Illinois, U.S.A.

Published simultaneously in The British Commonwealth of Nations by

BLACKWELL SCIENTIFIC PUBLICATIONS, LTD., OXFORD, ENGLAND

Published simultaneously in Canada by

THE RYERSON PRESS, TORONTO

Library of Congress Catalog Card Number 59-14204

First Edition, 1945

Second Edition, 1951

Third Edition, 1960

With THOMAS BOOKS careful attention is given to all details of
manufacturing and design. It is the Publisher's desire to present books
that are satisfactory as to their physical qualities and artistic possibilities
and appropriate for their particular use. THOMAS BOOKS will be true
to those laws of quality that assure a good name and good will.

Printed in the United States of America

TO
WILLIAM KING GREGORY

PREFACE TO THE THIRD EDITION

THE DATA of physical anthropology continues to enlarge and accumulate at an accelerating rate. The nine years that have elapsed since the publication of the second edition in 1951 has witnessed some striking developments which have led to the re-evaluation of many once-solidly entrenched ideas. There has been a healthy shift of interest away from the statics of the subject to a dynamic functional approach. This is particularly evident in the micro-evolutionary studies of human populations which have begun to make their appearance.

The call for a new edition has enabled me to incorporate some of these changes in the present volume. A great portion of the book has been rewritten, and many new illustrations, tables, and references added.

As in the earlier editions it has been my object to make the subject matter of physical anthropology readably comprehensible to the beginning student. I hope that others may also find the book so.

For help with illustrative material I am much indebted to my colleagues Professor H. V. Vallois, Director of the Musée de l'Homme, Paris, Dr. C. Arambourg and also Messrs. P. Biberson and J. Signeux, of the Muséum National D'Histoire Naturelle, Paris, Dr. K. P. Oakley of the British Museum (Natural History), London, Professors I. Schour and M. Massler of the College of Dentistry of the University of Illinois, Chicago, Professor C. Snow, Department of Anthropology, University of Kentucky, Professors Raymond Dart and P. V. Tobias, Department of Anatomy, University of Witwatersrand, Johannesburg, South Africa, Dr. R. Singer, Department of Anatomy, University of Cape Town, Medical School, Observatory, Cape, Dr. Halbert L. Dunn, Chief, National Office of Vital Statistics, Professor W. W. Greulich, Department of Anatomy, Stanford University Medical School, Palo Alto, Mrs. H. M. Worthington, Denver Museum of Natural History, Denver, Dr. A. E. Mourant, The Lister Institute of Preventive Medicine, London.

To Dr. Edward Hunt, of the Department of Anthropology, Harvard University and to Professor Charles Snow of the Department of

[vii]

Anthropology, University of Kentucky, I owe many thanks for their helpful reading of the proofs. To Dr. N. A. Barnicot, of the Department of Anthropology, University College, London, I am obliged for several helpful suggestions.

To Dr. A. S. Wiener, Medical Examiner's Office, New York, I am greatly indebted, as in previous editions, for his helpful reading of the sections on blood groups and blood-typing. It should be made perfectly clear, however, that Dr. Wiener strongly disapproves of the views expressed in those sections on the relation between blood groups and disease, and thoroughly dissociates himself from them as contributing both to confusion and chaos. He has done his best to convince me of this, but I have obstinately resisted his efforts.

Finally, I wish to thank Dr. Richard Levins, Department of Zoology, Columbia University, and Professor Max Levitan, Department of Anatomy, Woman's Medical College of Pennsylvania, for their critical reading of Appendix C.

Princeton, New Jersey.

M. F. ASHLEY MONTAGU

PREFACE TO THE SECOND EDITION

THE second edition of this work brings up to date a volume first published in 1945. Since then many new and important discoveries have been made which throw new light upon the evolution of man. These are incorporated in the present edition. The whole work has been thoroughly revised and much new material and many new illustrations added.

Professor Gabriel Lasker of Wayne University, Detroit, read the manuscript and made many useful suggestions. Professor Gerhardt von Bonin of the University of Illinois, not only performed a similar service, but also read the galleys and lent his expert knowledge to the checking of the accuracy of the brain drawings. Professor Theodosius Dobzhansky of Columbia University gave the sections on the mechanism of evolution the benefit of his critical reading. Professor William C. Boyd of Boston University and Dr. A. S. Wiener of New York kindly read the sections on the blood groups, and Dr. Stanley Garn of the Forsyth Infirmary, Boston, read the section on anthropometry. Professor Donald Hager of Princeton University, Professor J. N. Spuhler of Ohio State University, and Professor W. S. Laughlin of the University of Oregon, each read the galleys. Professor Laughlin also contributed the section on blood typing technique in the Appendix. Professor W. E. Le Gros Clark of Oxford University has been most helpful in sending me copies of his writings, even before they were published. Dr. Kenneth P. Oakley of the British Museum (Natural History), London, generously helped in a similar capacity. Dr. L. S. B. Leakey of Nairobi, East Africa, Professor Claude Levi-Strauss of the Musée de l'Homme, and Professor Henri Vallois of the Institut de Paléontologie Humaine, both of Paris, Dr. L. J. Angel, of Jefferson Medical College, Philadelphia; Dr. Robert Broom of Pretoria, South Africa; Professor Raymond Dart, University of Witwatersrand, South Africa; Sir Arthur Keith of Downe, Kent; Dr. Geoffrey Morant of London; Dr. William H. Sheldon of the Constitution Laboratory, Columbia University; Mr. J. C. Trevor of Cambridge University; and Mrs. H. M. Worthington of the University of Denver, Colorado, very kindly supplied photographs. For these friendly services I am grateful to each of them. To R. T. Simmons of the Commonwealth Serum Laboratories, Melbourne, I am much indebted for keeping me abreast of research on blood typing in the Pacific. To Dr. Alfred Wood of the Philadelphia General Hospital I am grateful for his careful reading of the page proof.

M. F. ASHLEY MONTAGU

Department of Anthropology
Rutgers University
New Brunswick, New Jersey

PREFACE TO THE FIRST EDITION

THIS LITTLE BOOK has been written with the object of providing those who wish to learn something about the subject-matter of physical anthropology with a brief means of doing so. The work is not a text-book, but a general introduction to a rather young but enormously extended subject. Intended for the general reader, for the student, whether he be medical or interested in the social or anthropological sciences, I trust the work will also be found of value by students in the biological sciences, and finally by physicians, and psychologists.

Physical anthropology is a very large subject; to cover it all adequately would take a work as large as the *Encyclopaedia Britannica,* and almost as many contributors to write it. In the present modest volume it has been possible to present only part of the subject-matter with which the science deals, and that, for the most part, in a general rather than a detailed manner. I have, however, attempted to do more than merely introduce the reader to the subject. I have endeavored to give him a real grasp of the fundamental facts and problems which it is necessary for anyone to know who desires to understand man. I have not only set out these facts, but, wherever possible, have also explained their meaning.

The events of the last thirty years have made it abundantly clear that, if civilization is to continue, scientific thought must increasingly be applied to man himself. We stand badly in need of a saner distribution of scientific interests. If men of the scientific potentialities of those who today generally enter such fields as chemistry, mathematics, and physics, would apply their energies to the study of the social and physical sciences of man we should, I am convinced, be a great deal better off than we are at the present time.

At the base of all studies relating to man stands physical anthropology, the comparative science of man as a physical organism in relation to his total environment, social as well as physical. Those who are in any way concerned with the study of man do well to equip themselves with the facts it makes available. In this volume

I have endeavored to provide some of those essential facts and to interpret them.

The book has greatly benefited from the critical reading which it received from a number of distinguished scientists, each one an eminent and creative worker in the different, though related, fields of science with which this book deals. For this service I am most grateful to my colleagues: Dr. L. J. Angel, Jefferson Medical College, Philadelphia; Professor and Mrs. W. C. Boyd, Boston University; Dr. P. B. Candela, New York Medical College; Professor D. S. Davidson, University of Pennsylvania; Professor Th. Dobzhansky, Columbia University; Professor W. K. Gregory, American Museum of Natural History and Columbia University; Professor A. I. Hallowell, Northwestern University; Professor M. J. Herskovits, Northwestern University; Professor E. A. Hooton, Harvard University; Professor C. Kluckhohn, Harvard University; Professor W. M. Krogman, University of Chicago; Mr. R. M. Snodgrasse, University of Chicago; Professor J. H. McGregor, Columbia University; Professor M. Steggerda, Kennedy School of Missions, Hartford, Connecticut; Dr. A. S. Wiener, Medical Examiner's Office, New York; and Professor Conway Zirkle, University of Pennsylvania.

For all errors and omissions, and other deficiencies (of which I am conscious there are many), I alone am responsible, and it should be added that the readers of the manuscript named above should not be held responsible for views with which they may well disagree. Unless otherwise attributed these views are my own.

M. F. ASHLEY MONTAGU

"Never forget this when the talk is clever:
Wisdom must be born in the flesh or wither,
And sacred order has been always won
From chaos by some burning faithful one
Whose human bones have ached as if with fever
To bring you to these high triumphant places.
Forget the formulas, remember men."

MAY SARTON*

"When you are studying any matter or considering any philosophy, ask yourself only what are the facts and what is the truth that the facts bear out. Never let yourself be diverted either by what you would wish to believe or by what you think would have beneficent social effects if it were believed. But look only at what are the facts."

BERTRAND RUSSELL
March 1959

---

* From the poem "The Sacred Order," by permission of the author and Rinehart & Co., from May Sarton's *The Lion and the Rose*.

CONTENTS

An Introduction to

Physical Anthropology

Chapter I

INTRODUCTION

PHYSICAL ANTHROPOLOGY: ITS SCOPE AND DEFINITION

Aɴᴛʜʀᴏᴘᴏʟᴏɢʏ is the science of man, the science devoted to the comparative study of man as a physical and cultural being. The physical anthropologist studies man's physical characters, their origin, evolution, and present state of development, while the cultural anthropologist studies man as a cultural being in all the varieties which his cultures assume.[1] Both physical and cultural anthropology are conveniently recognized as separate, though interrelated and interdependent subdivisions of anthropology which should never be permitted to become too detached from one another.

The task of the physical anthropologist is not merely to study man as a physical being, but to round out the picture of man from the bio-

[1] *Ethnography* is the description of the cultural characteristics of a people.

Ethnology is the historical reconstruction of the cultural relationships of a people to other peoples; the comparative study of culture.

Social Anthropology is concerned with the phenomena or culture which can be summarized in terms of generalizations or laws, which are true of all cultures in which a specific phenomenon is manifested.

Society denotes that complex of fundamentally cooperative interactions or inter-relations which exist between and among the members of a group.

A society, as distinct from society, is a group the members of which consciously or unconsciously cooperate to maintain a common life.

By *social* is meant all those interactive relations between individuals or groups in which needs are satisfied.

Culture is the class of things and events, dependent upon the symbolic process, considered in an extrasomatic context.

A culture is the particular form which characterizes the learned, shared, and transmitted social activities of a group. In this connection it will be helpful to remember that society is a generic term and that culture is a species of society.

Archeology is the ethnology and ethnography of cultures which no longer exist—at least in precisely the same form—based on the study of, and inferences from, cultural products and subsistence remains recovered by excavation and similar means.

[3]

logical side which the cultural anthropologist endeavors to complete from the cultural side.

Since man, in all his variety, examined at any given moment, may be regarded as a complex of the effects of past causes and of the operation of present ones, it is possible to study him both from the historical and contemporary viewpoints. From the historical viewpoint the anthropologist asks: How did man come to be the kind of physical organism that he is, and how did he happen to develop his particular type of culture? From the contemporary viewpoint he asks: "What is the nature of the conditions which have made man what he is here and now in all his wonderful variety?" These, briefly, are the questions which, out of the great orbit of human inquiry, have fallen to the lot of anthropology for investigation and answer.

To learn more or less precisely how much of the biological enters into the expression of any social process, and how much of the social enters into the expression of any biological process is one of the principal aims of physical anthropology. Hence, the physical anthropologist must be something of a social biologist.

Man lives in a physical environment which varies in different lands and often in neighboring localities of the same lands. The seasons, sunlight, temperature, humidity, barometric pressure, rainfall, water, soil, foods, and a thousand and one other factors, are all to be taken into consideration in the study of the mental and physical development of man. Man, in short, must always be studied in relation to his environment, past as well as present.

Man's environments are cultural as well as physical, and cultural factors have undoubtedly played a role in the evolution of man and the differentiation of his varieties.

Physical anthropology, then, is the comparative science of man as a physical organism in relation to his total environment, social or cultural as well as physical.

Within the same ethnic group, and in different ethnic groups, striking differences may be present in skin and hair color, in hair form, eye color, stature, weight, and in numerous other characters. How did these different characters come into being, and what are the factors which account for their present distribution?

The attempt to return an answer to such questions is again one of the most important tasks of the physical anthropologist. Many methods have been utilized in this attempt with but moderate success. In recent years, however, a new instrument of investigation has become available in the form of the genetic methods of analysis. The

Figure 1. Edward Tyson (1650-1708). Father of Primatology, author of the first comparative anatomy of an ape, *Orang-Outang, Sive Homo Sylvestris*, London, 1699. (From the portrait in the Royal College of Physicians, London, probably by Sir Godfrey Kneller. Courtesy, Royal College of Physicians, London.)

LOUIS-JEAN-MARIE ,

DAUBENTON ,

Né à Montbard le 29 Mai 1716
Mort à Paris le 31 Décembre 1799

Figure 2. Louis-Jean-Marie Daubenton (1716-1799). Comparative anatomist who, in addition to many fundamental contributions, provided much of the basic data for Buffon's *Natural History.*

application of such genetic methods to the solution of the problems of human variability has already made something of a beginning, and holds great promise for the future. The investigation and analysis of the mechanism of heredity has steadily yielded valuable information concerning the individual as well as the species. By the use of genetic methods we may hope to solve the problems of the detailed causes of individual variation and the diversification of the different varieties of men. This involves the study of the biological variability of living populations.

Our purpose in such studies is to draw up a reasonably reliable history of the origin and evolution of the human species and all its varieties, and ideally of each living person. This we can ultimately hope to do by breaking down in greater and greater detail each of the problems confronting us, not so much by investigating the end-effects of evolution, such as the shape of the head or the nose, or the color of the eyes and hair, as by investigating the causes which produce those end-effects. The question of questions which the physical anthropologist asks is no less than this: What are the causes which produced, and which continue to produce, man in all his variety? It is a powerfully big question, but can there be one surpassing or even equalling it in interest? Many of the answers to the questions asked must remain conjectural, for the simple reason that they refer to events which occurred in remote prehistory. Much of physical anthropology is, therefore, devoted to the reconstruction of events for which the records, if any, are few and incomplete. The very incompleteness of the record makes this aspect of the physical anthropologist's activities all the more challenging.

Man is an animal whose closest kinship is with the apes and monkeys, and with them he is classed in the mammalian Order of Primates. The study of the monkeys and apes is known as the science of *primatology*. While man is distinctly a primate of the primates it is convenient to apply the term primatology to the non-human primates alone. This is merely an arbitrary distinction for the purposes of convenience and no more. The study of man as a purely zoological species may be recognized as the science of *human biology*, to be distinguished from *social biology*, the study of the interacting social and biological factors upon the development and functioning of man as an organism. Primatology is fundamental to the study of human biology. The study of the anatomy, physiology, and behavior of non-human primates throws an invaluable light upon the evolution of man. Without the knowledge obtained from these studies we should

Figure 3. Johann Friedrich Blumenbach (1752-1840). The "Father" of Physical Anthropology. (From an engraving by Wachsmann after a painting by Grimm.)

Figure 4. William Lawrence (1783-1867). Anatomist, surgeon, and physical anthropologist whose *Lectures on Physiology, Zoology, and the Natural History of Man,* first published at London in 1822, is one of the great classics of physical anthropology.

Figure 5. James Cowles Prichard (1786-1848). Physical anthropologist and alienist. Author of the celebrated work *Researches into the Physical History of Mankind,* London, 1813, and *The Natural History of Man,* London, 1843.

be virtually wholly in the dark concerning the pre-human history of man. Hence, primatology is an indispensable part of the equipment of every physical anthropologist.

Not only is the study of the living primates a necessary division of physical anthropology, but equally important, in another way, is the study of extinct or fossil primates which are ancestral or related to those living today, and which flourished many millions of years ago, long before the appearance of man upon the earth. This constitutes the study of *primate paleontology.*

Primate paleontology necessitates some knowledge of general paleontology, but particularly of stratigraphical geology and the various geological eras and periods. An important aspect of such knowledge is the study of prehistoric climatic changes and their effects upon the ecology * of man's precursors, and later upon man himself. This branch of knowledge, which is only just beginning to be the subject of inquiry might be called *geoecology*. The related discipline, *geochronology*, deals with the time-scales of man's prehistory. From primate paleontology to the study of prehistoric man, through his fossil remains, we are brought to the earliest history of man himself.

It is the principal ambition of the physical anthropologist, in his studies of prehistoric man, *paleoanthropology*, to trace the origin of mankind back to that non-human primate stock from which he emerged, and then from that stage to trace the evolution of man, in his different varieties, up to the present time. As we shall see in later chapters some progress has been made during the last forty years towards the realization of this ambition.

The proper evaluation of the status of the remains of fossil man in the evolutionary reticulum demands a good knowledge of human and comparative anatomy, including embryology or developmental anatomy, and the anatomy and physiology of growth.

From the study of our prehistoric ancestors to the study of the origins and relationships of the existing varieties of man is but a logical step. Very gradually we are beginning to untangle the strands which have entered into the evolutionary pattern of our species, and there is every reason to believe that we shall some day be able to provide a fairly complete account of the elements and conditions which, as vital dynamic reticulate processes, have gone into the making of mankind.

The study of the existing varieties of man is generally known as the study of *race*. But since this term has become more closely identified with social pathology rather than with scientific usage, modern physical anthropology is beginning to devote more and more attention to a re-examination of the meaning of this and related terms in the light of modern knowledge, and to re-study and analyze the varieties of man, in order that the real significance of such differences as they exhibit may be properly interpreted and clearly understood. Anthropology regards as unscientific and vicious the view that there can be one kind of history for ourselves and another kind for

---

* **Ecology** is the science of the relations of plant and animal communities, to their surroundings, animate and inanimate.

Figure 6. Charles Darwin (1809-1882). At the age of 45. Author of *The Origin of Species*, 1859. This photograph was taken in 1854. (By permission of the British Museum [Natural History].)

Figure 7. Thomas Henry Huxley (1825-1895). Comparative anatomist whose *Man's Place in Nature*, London, 1863, and numerous other writings place him in the forefront of 19th Century physical anthropologists.

Figure 8. Pierre Paul Broca (1824-1880). Neurosurgeon and physical anthropologist. Founded the first anthropological society in Europe at Paris in 1859. (Photo, Courtesy Musée de l'Homme, Paris.)

Figure 9. Alfred Cort Haddon (1855-1940). Cultural and physical anthropologist. Holder of the first chair in anthropology at Cambridge University. (From the portrait by Philip de Laszlo. Courtesy, University Museum of Archaeology and Ethnology, Cambridge, England.)

Figure 10. Karl Pearson (1857-1936). Principal founder and most distinguished worker in the modern school of biometrics. (From a pencil drawing made in 1924 by Miss F. A. de Biden Footner. Courtesy, Cambridge University Press.)

Figure 12. Sir Arthur Keith (1866-1955). Anatomist and physical anthropologist. Author of *The Antiquity of Man*, London, 1925. (Photo by J. R. Miller.)

Figure 11. Franz Boas (1858-1942). Cultural and physical an
Founder of the American school of anthropology. (Courtesy
Boas.)

Figure 13. Robert Mearns Yerkes (1876-1956). Psychologist, psychobiologist, and student of the comparative behavior of the anthropoids. (From a painting by Clarence A. Brodeur. Courtesy, Yale University.)

Figure 14. William King Gregory (b. 1876). Paleontologist, comparative anatomist, and primatologist. (From a painting by Charles G. Chapman, N.A. Courtesy, American Museum of Natural History.)

other peoples. It is, indeed, through the bold and untiring labors of anthropologists that the great truth has been discovered that the same evolutionary principles have governed the development of all men, past and present, and that such differences as the existing varieties now exhibit are not of a kind which, upon any scientific system of biological or even social values, would justify any one of them being distinguished as biologically superior or inferior to any other. If physical anthropology had achieved nothing else, this discovery alone would forever have justified its labors, for the concept of the natural unity of mankind provides a firm basis for the conception of the social unity of mankind, a conception which may some day be universally realized. In this connection, however, it should be clearly understood that equality of opportunity and equality in law in no way depend upon the concept of the natural unity of mankind, but rather that such equality depends upon the ethical principle which holds that by virtue of their humanity all human beings are entitled to equal rights for the realization of their potentialities.

Hence, physical anthropology has an important contribution to make towards the improvement of the social order. This is not simply because of the grandeur of the story it has to tell, but by virtue of the very appreciable contribution it makes to the better understanding of ourselves and of our fellow men, in a world in which such understanding is not too widely distributed. Furthermore, the value of physical anthropology for the analysis and ability to direct the growth and development of the individual here and now cannot be overestimated, not to mention the promise which science holds for the regulation and direction of human evolution in the future.

Writing in 1889 to a young man (A. C. Haddon, see Figure 9), who later became a distinguished anthropologist, T. H. Huxley (see Figure 7), penned the following words:

"I know of no department of natural science more likely to reward a man who goes into it thoroughly than anthropology. There is an immense deal to be done in the science pure and simple and it is one of those branches of inquiry which brings one into contact with the great problems of humanity in every direction."

These words will always remain true, just as the service of the physical anthropologist to humanity will, among other things, always be to show that the proper study of mankind is to discover man as a human being, no matter what the texture of his hair, the color of his skin or the shape of his skull.

FOR FURTHER READING, CONSULT:

BENDYSHE, T.: The history of anthropology. *Mem. Anthropol. Soc., London, 1:* 335-458, 1863.
An invaluable account of early thought on the origin and development of man, containing translations of the most important anthropological writings of the 17th and 18th centuries.

BOAS, F.: *Anthropology and Modern Life* (2nd edition). New York, Norton, 1932.
A valuable and interesting discussion of the problems of modern life in the light of the results of anthropological studies.

CASSON, S.: *The Discovery of Man.* New York, Harper, 1940.
An absorbingly interesting and authoritative account of the history of man's researches into his own origins.

GILLIN, J. (editor): *For a Science of Social Man.* New York, Macmillan, 1954.
Convergences in anthropology, psychology and sociology of especial interest to the student of anthropology.

HADDON, A. C.: *History of Anthropology* (2nd edition). London, Watts, 1934.
A short but remarkably full book. The first half is devoted to the history of physical anthropology and the second half to the history of social anthropology.

HALLOWELL, A. I.: Personality structure and evolution. *Am. Anthropol., n.s., 52:* 159-173, 1950.
An excellent presentation of the point that the definition of man involves more than morphological criteria.

————: The dimensions of human existence. *Quart. Rev. Biol., 31:*88-101, 1957.
A valuable study toward the definition of man.

————: Behavioral evolution and the emergence of the self. In B. J. Meggers (editor), *Evolution and Anthropology.* Washington, D.C., Washington Anthropological Society, 1959, pp. 36-60.
More on the definition of man and the emergence of the self.

HOYLE, L. E.: Physical anthropology and its instruments: an historical study. *Southwest. J. of Anthropol., 9:*408-430, 1953.
A brief history of anthropometric instruments.

HUXLEY, T. H.: *Man's Place in Nature.* New York, Appleton, 1896.
First published in 1863 this is one of the classics of physical anthropology which should be read not only for its historical interest, but also for its genuine contribution to the understanding of contemporary problems of physical anthropology. The 1896 edition is the best. A reprint of the 1863 edition is published by the University of Michigan Press, Ann Arbor, 1959.

KLUCKHOHN, C.: *Mirror For Men.* New York, Whittlesey House, 1949. Reprinted, New York, Premier Books, 1957.
An admirable introduction to anthropology.

KROEBER, A. L. (editor): *Anthropology Today: An Encyclopedic Inventory.* Chicago, University of Chicago Press, 1953.

TAX, S., *et al.* (editors): *An Appraisal of Anthropology Today.* Chicago, University of Chicago Press, 1953.
Two indispensable volumes representing a stocktaking of every branch of anthropology by fifty authorities, together with the discussion of these in the second volume.

LOWIE, R. H.: *The History of Ethnological Theory.* New York, Farrar & Rinehart, 1937.

A distinguished history of ethnology.

MEGGERS, B. J. (editor): *Evolution and Anthropology: A Centennial Appraisal.* Washington, D.C., The Anthropological Society of Washington, 1959.

A stimulating series of eight lectures on the influence of evolutionary theory on the various branches of anthropology.

MONTAGU, M. F. ASHLEY: *Edward Tyson, M.D., F.R.S., (1650-1708): And the Rise of Human and Comparative Anatomy in England.* American Philosophical Society, Philadelphia, 1943.

The history of the rise of human and comparative anatomy with special reference to the origin and development of the interest in the relation of the apes to man, written around the life of the founder of primatology, Edward Tyson (1650-1708). Useful background reading.

MÜHLMANN, W. E.: *Geschichte der Anthropologie.* Bonn Universitäts Verlag, 1948.

A brief but rather wide coverage of the whole field of anthropology from the viewpoint of the anthropologist interested in the history and development of the subject.

PENNIMAN, T. K.: *A Hundred Years of Anthropology* (2nd. edition). New York Macmillan, 1952.

A readable and informative history covering more than the last hundred years, with a useful chronological table, and lists of anthropological congresses, societies and periodicals, in various countries of the world.

ROBERTS, D. F. and WEINER, J. S. (editors): *The Scope of Physical Anthropology and its Place in Academic Studies.* London, Institute for Biology, 1958.

Ten authorities stimulatingly discuss the scope and subject matter of physical anthropology.

STURTEVANT, W. C.: *Anthropology as a Career.* Washington, Smithsonian Institution, 1958.

An informative pamphlet answering the questions likely to be asked by those interested in the possibility of anthropology as a career.

WASHBURN, S. L.: The new physical anthropology. *Trans. N. Y. Acad. Sci., 13:* 298-304, 1951.

A stimulating essay on the direction in which modern physical anthropology must develop.

WENDT, H.: *In Search of Adam.* Boston, Houghton Mifflin, 1956.

A most interesting account of man's search for his ancestors. Well-illustrated.

REFERENCE WORKS ON PHYSICAL ANTHROPOLOGY

KROGMAN, W. M.: *A Bibliography of Human Morphology, 1914-1939.* Chicago, University of Chicago Press, 1941.

A valuable bibliography covering most publications in the field of physical anthropology from the year 1914 to the year 1939.

LANGER, W. L. (editor): *An Encyclopedia of World History.* 3rd ed. Boston, Houghton Mifflin, 1952.

An indispensable revised and modernized version of Ploetz's famous *Epitome.* The biography of man from prehistoric times to the present day, chronologically arranged.

MARTIN, R.: *Lehrbuch der Anthropologie* (2nd edition), 3 vols., Jena, Fischer, 1928.

The standard reference work on the methods and subject matter of physical anthropology, profusely illustrated. The third volume is entirely devoted to the bibliography of the subject. A third edition, edited by Karl Saller, is in process of publication by the same publisher.

STEWART, T. D. (editor): *Hrdlička's Practical Anthropometry* (4th edition). Philadelphia, Wistar Inst., 1952.

A standard work on the measurement of the living body and of the skeleton.

Chapter II

THE PRIMATES AS A ZOOLOGICAL GROUP

WARM-BLOODED animals possessing a four-chambered heart, breathing by lungs, exhibiting a growth of hair over the body, and which suckle their young, are distinguished by taxonomists as belonging to the Class Mammalia. Within this Class eighteen living Orders of mammals are recognized. The two most important for our purposes being the Order Insectivora, which comprises the European hedgehogs, the shrews, and moles, and the Order Primates which comprises the lemurs, tarsiers, monkeys, apes, and men.

Zoological classifications are based almost entirely upon structural characters, and these characters are of such a nature in the lemurs, tarsiers, monkeys, apes, and men, as to leave no doubt about their common membership in the Order of Primates. Realizing this, Linnaeus, in 1758, took the bold step of putting them all into the same Order, a decision which subsequent researchers have fully justified. In giving this Order the name Primates, Linnaeus meant to suggest that the animals which it embraced ranked first in the order of importance of all the creatures of the animal kingdom. This, of course, is a purely anthropocentric view, to which the members of the rest of animated nature, could they be heard upon the subject, might demur. Certainly Linnaeus's bestowal of the term "sapiens," upon man, *Homo sapiens*, "man the wise," has not yet been fully merited, though in bestowing it Linnaeus had in mind the powers of discrimination and judgment in which man so much exceeds the rest of the animal kingdom.

It is, however, one of the merits of the study of our evolutionary history and genealogical relationships that it teaches us that there is hope for even such a sadly misunderstood, and misunderstanding, creature as man. Bearing this in mind, let us attempt to trace the story of his emergence into the world, for the problem of his origin is the principal reason for our interest, in this chapter, in the nonhuman primates.

Figure 15. Tree-shrew. (*Urogale everetti*) Philippines. (Courtesy, Dr. Ralph Buchsbaum.)

THE ORDER OF PRIMATES

The Tree-Shrews

Before proceeding with the description of the primates it is desirable to give an account here of a group of animals which stands at the base of the primate stem, and which many modern authorities would include within the primate group, but which other zoologists continue to describe as the oriental tree-shrews of the Order Insectivora. This group of tree-shrews is very squirrel-like in appearance, and comprises the single living Family Tupaiidae, including two subfamilies, of which there are six genera, some 32 species, and about 100 subspecies. While the tree-shrews are all arboreal to a varying extent, they are not nearly as much so as was at one time believed, the smaller species being more arboreal than the larger ones, the latter generally inhabiting the undergrowth in the bush or the lower branches of the trees. Almost all tree-shrews, however, spend most of their time on the ground. The smaller species (such as *Tupaia minor*) appear to be crepuscular or nocturnal animals, while the larger (e.g., *Tupaia ferruginea*) are diurnal in their habits. The typical dental formula for the group is I $\frac{2}{3}$, C $\frac{1}{1}$, PM $\frac{3}{3}$, M $\frac{3}{3}$.* The manus (hand) and pes (foot) are adapted for grasping, and both pollex (thumb) and hallux (big toe) show some degree of opposition to the other digits for the purposes of grasping. All the digits are provided with sharp curved claws. In the early Oligocene tupaioid *Anagale gobiensis*, discovered in Mongolia, the terminal phalanges of the fingers were provided with claws while those of the toes were almost certainly furnished with nails.

The tail, which is not prehensile, is used as a balancing organ, and is wholly bushy or close-haired in the subfamily Tupaiinae, the hairy-tailed tree-shrews, and naked but tufted at the terminal portion in the Ptilocercinae, the pen-tailed tree-shrews.

The skull bears a remarkable resemblance to that of the lemurs (see Figure 52) although the orbits are directed rather more laterally, as in the insectivores proper. As in the lemurs, the rhinarium or external nose is naked, moist, and glandular, and the commencement of the tear duct is situated outside the orbit on the face.

The average numbers of vertebrae are seven cervical, 13 thoracic, six lumbar, three sacral, and about 25 caudal (tail) in the Tupaiinae, and seven cervical, 14 thoracic, five lumbar, three sacral, and about 32 caudal in the Ptilocercinae.

The brain is of primitive form in the pen-tailed tree-shrews, and though of somewhat more complex form in the hairy-tailed tree-shrews the advance is very slight. In both subfamilies the olfactory lobes are well developed, though in comparison with other insectivores somewhat reduced in *Tupaia*. A shallow sylvian fissure is present in *Tupaia*. The occipital poles of the cerebral hemispheres fail to overlap all but the most anterior parts of the cerebellum.

The diet of tree-shrews is largely insectivorous and partly frugivorous, but in fact they are omnivorous and will eat anything that is digestible. Pregnancy lasts about five months, and two young usually, sometimes one, and sometimes four, are born at a birth. There are from one to three pair mammae at which the young are suckled for

---

* In the dental formula the letters I, C, PM, and M stand for incisors, canines, premolars, and molars respectively. The numbers above the line refer to one side of the upper jaw, the numbers below the line to one side of the lower jaw. The opposite side is, of course, identical.

several months. These animals appear to breed throughout the year.

The tree-shrews live in small groups or in pairs, and build their nests in hollow bamboos or fallen timber on the ground.

Tree-shrews are very lively, extraordinarily inquisitive, and remarkably intelligent.

A synoptic classification of the tree-shrews follows:

Synopsis of the Living Tree-Shrews

SUBORDER TUPAIOIDEA

THE ORIENTAL TREE-SHREWS

FAMILY TUPAIIDAE

SUBFAMILY TUPAIINAE

The hairy-tailed tree-shrews

Genus *Tupaia*. Malaysia, India, Burma, and China (15 species, 74 subspecies)

Genus *Anathana*. Indian Peninsula, South of Ganges (3 species, 3 subspecies)

Genus *Dendrogale*. Borneo, French Indo-China (3 species, 3 subspecies)

Genus *Tana*. Borneo, adjacent islands, and Sumatra (9 species, 16 subspecies)

Genus *Urogale*. Mindanao, Philippine Islands (1 species)

SUBFAMILY PTILOCERCINAE

The pen-tailed tree-shrew

Genus *Ptilocercus*. Borneo, Sumatra, and Southern Malaysia (1 species, 2 subspecies)

It will be noted from the above synopsis, and from others which are given in the following pages, that while sometimes used with suborders the names of superfamilies terminate in the letters "oidea," the names of families in "idae," and the names of subfamilies in "inae." Names of genera are given as proper names without adding any consistent termination to the stem, and in the Linnaean system of classification in universal use the name of the species follows the generic name. As a rule only the names of genera, species, and subspecies are written in *italics*. The name of the genus is written beginning with a capital letter, but the name of the species is written in lower case, as for example, *Ateles paniscus chamek*, or *Homo sapiens neanderthalensis*. The scientific designation of animals is uninominal (one name) for subgenera and all higher groups, binominal (two names) for species, and trinominal (three names) for subspecies.

It has already been remarked that the tendency among many modern authorities is to class the tree-shrews with the primates as the most primitive members of the order. But precisely how they are to be situated within the order is a matter which is still under debate. Wood Jones regards the tree-shrews as primitive lemurs, and unites them and the lemurs in a single group which he excludes from the assemblage of the primates. Carlsson, Le Gros Clark, and Simpson class the tree-shrews together as members of the lemuriform series within the primate order. But as Straus has pointed out, the fundamental differences between the tree-shrews and the lemurs in such characters as placentation, the chondrocranium (the cartilaginous skull), ankle and wrist bones, musculature, viscera, and many other features, render such jointures of these groups open to serious question. Straus suggests that the tree-shrews are best treated as constituting a separate primate suborder, the Tupaioidea, distinct from all other suborders of the primates.

The closest affinities of the tupaioids are with the lemurs of Malaysia. The many lemur-like characters of the tupaioids suggest that these were acquired after the line leading to the primates had become distinct. This line, in turn, arose from some insectivorous pre-primate. The appreciable number of lemur-like characters of the early Oligocene tupaioid *Anagale* supports the suggestion that the tupaioids arose from primitive lemuriforms, slightly diverging from the lemurs proper while retaining most of their ancestral characters.

The tupaioids would, then, appear to belong properly within the order of primates as a distinct suborder, the Tupaioidea. Since, how-

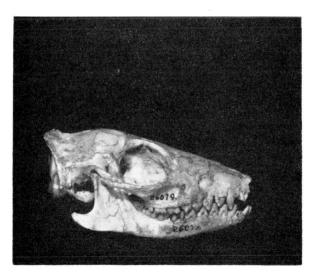

Figure 16. *Anagale gobiensis,* an Oligocene Tupaioid. (From Simpson, Courtesy, American Museum of Natural History.)

ever, this is a view which has not generally achieved complete acceptance we shall proceed with the description of the primates according to the conventions prevailing at the present time.

General Description of the Primates

The Order Primates embraces the lemurs, tarsiers, monkeys, apes, and man. These forms share the following features: relatively large and complicated brains, hands and feet prehensile or clearly derived from the prehensile type; the presence of a clavicle (collar-bone); free mobility of the digits, and opposability of either the thumb or big toe or both; flattened nails instead of claws on some or all fingers and toes; the presence of, as a rule, only two mammae.

Our present purpose in studying the non-human primates, as well as man himself, is to throw light upon the physical and social evolution of man. Even if the fossil record of the ancestry of man were complete—which it is not—it would still be necessary to study the living primates for the very good reason that while the fossil record yields us the bones alone of dead animals, the existing primates yield all the knowledge that we are capable of gleaning from living animals. Dead primates enable the primatologist to make detailed studies of their anatomy, so that this may be compared and evaluated for whatever light such comparisons may throw upon the significance of various characters in any or all of the primates, and upon the evolutionary relationships of these animals to one another, to earlier forms, and to man past and present. It may at once be said that such studies have richly fulfilled the purposes for which they have been undertaken, though a vast amount of work still remains to be done.

As many as 600 species of living primates, not counting synonyms, have been recognized by D. G. Elliot in his *A Review of the Primates* (1913). There can be little doubt that the true number is very considerably less. Sanderson, in his *The Monkey Kingdom* (1957) gives 244 species and 752 subspecies, grouped into 80 genera. The primates as a whole exhibit a high degree of morphological variability. This fact taken together with a mid-nineteenth century species concept which was for the most part based on the study of skins and skeletons in museums led to a regular orgy of classificatory speciation. Differences were sought rather than likenesses, and more and more refined morphological distinctions between groups were recognized. A single small difference, such as a darker ring of hair on the tail, was sometimes considered a sufficient peg upon which to hang a specific difference. The excesses thus committed led to the creation of numerous species in every animal group. Today careful field studies and analyses of their

findings by biologists with a fuller understanding of the nature of variation than the nineteenth century taxonomist could possibly have possessed, have been responsible for something of a reversal of this
tendency. "The "splitters" make way for the "lumpers."

Linnaeus's rather static morphological conception of a species
underwent a considerable enlargement in the nineteenth century as
a consequence of the publication of Darwin's epoch-making *Origin
of Species* (1859). It was not, however, until the first half of this
century, with the development of the science of genetics and the
refinement in our understanding of the processes of speciation which
this brought us, that we have been able to approximate a biologically
sound conception of a species.

To the modern biologist a species is a more or less temporary
eddy in the stream of evolution. A species is not a fixed, static, sharply
delimitable group, but a more or less definable result of the process
of speciation. This process is to some extent observable in the resulting variation presented by geographically but not reproductively
separated groups. Such groups were formerly described as species,
today they are recognized as geographic variant representatives or
types of a single species, that is to say as representatives of a single
polytypic species. Some species are *monotypic,* meaning, all their
members closely resemble one another. Monotypic species generally
occupy a limited range, and since there is an absence of geographic
barriers there is no opportunity for reproductive separation and
hence geographic variation. Whether a species is polytypic or monotypic can only be determined when populations are studied with
respect to their variability, their geographic distribution, and their
reproductive relationship to other groups. Few such studies have yet
been made on the primates, but there can be no doubt that most primates are members of polytypic species.

A species may be defined as a group of actually or potentially
interbreeding natural populations, which is reproductively isolated
from other such groups. The actually or potentially interbreeding
populations may be recognized as subspecies or geographic races.
It should be borne in mind that a species is not a fixed immutable
or unvarying group, and that the concept of a species is a relative
and subjective one, the reality is the component individuals constituting the common gene pool.

Classification

It has been well said that the principal purpose of classification
is to provide a simple practical means by which students of any

TABLE I

CHROMOSOME NUMBERS IN THE PRIMATES

Family	Genus and Species	Chromosome Number	Investigators
Lorisidae	Nycticebus coucang (Slow loris)	50	Bender & Mettler 1958
Callithricidae	Callithrix chrysoleucos (Golden marmoset)	46	Bender & Mettler 1960
"	Leontocebus illigeri (Maned marmoset)	46	" " "
Cebidae	Callimico (Goeldi's monkey)	48	" " "
"	Callicebus cupreus (Red titi)	46	" " "
"	Saimiri sciureus (Squirrel monkey)	44	" " "
"	Cebus apella (Cinnamon ringtail)	54	" " "
"	Cebus capucinus (Capuchin ringtail)	54	" " "
"	Cebus sp., (No species given)	56	Painter 1924
"	Ateles geoffroyi cucullatus (Hooded spider monkey)	34	Bender & Mettler 1958
"	Ateles paniscus chamek (Black faced spider monkey)	34	" " "
Cercopithecidae	Cercopithecus aethiops sabaeus (Green monkey)	60	Chu & Giles 1958
"	Cercopithecus aethiops tantalus (Tantalus)	60	" " "
"	Cercopithecus diana roloway (Palatine guenon)	60	" " "
"	Cercopithecus mona campbelli (Campbell's guenon)	66	" " "
"	Cercopithecus mona mona (Mona guenon)	66	Bender & Mettler 1958
"	Cercopithecus nicticans buettikoferi (Büttikofer's guenon)	66	" " "
"	Erythrocebus patas (Patas monkey)	54	Chu & Giles 1958
"	Cercocebus torquatus lunulatus (White-crowned mangabey)	42	" " "
"	Cercocebus torquatus torquatus (Red-capped mangabey)	42	Bender & Mettler 1958
"	Macaca mulatta (Rhesus monkey)	42	Darlington & Haque 1955; Chu & Giles 1958
"	Macaca nemestrinus (Pig-tailed macaque)	42	Darlington & Haque 1955
"	Papio papio (Typical baboons)	42	Chu & Giles 1958
"	Papio doguera (The Anubis baboon)	42	Bender & Mettler 1958
"	Papio sphinx (The Yellow baboon)	42	Painter 1924
Pongidae	Pan (Chimpanzee)	48	Bender & Mettler 1960
"	Pan (Chimpanzee)	48	Bender & Mettler 1958
Hominidae	Homo sapiens (Man)	46	Chu & Giles 1958

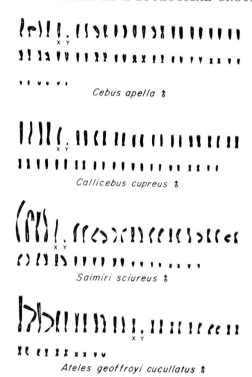

Figure 17. Mitotic chromosomes of representative species of four platyrrhine genera. The chromosomes are arranged by paired homologs and in
     order of size. (From Bender and Mettler. Courtesy, *Science*.)

group may know what they are talking about and others may find
out. It is with this end in view that the following revised classification is offered.

Two suborders of the primates are recognized, the Prosimii and
the Anthropoidea. The Prosimii include the three infraorders Lemuriformes (Madagascar lemurs), Lorisiformes (African and Asiatic lemurs), and the Tarsiiformes (Malaysian and Philippine tarsiers). The
Anthropoidea embraces the monkeys, apes, and man.

The suborder Anthropoidea is divisible into two main series, and
three superfamilies. The New World Monkeys comprise the series
Platyrrhini (= "broad" + "nose") and constitute the superfamily Ceboidea. The Old World Monkeys comprising the superfamily Cercopithecoidea, and the apes and man comprising the superfamily Hominoidea, constitute the series Catarrhini (= "down-pointing" + "nose").

In the Platyrrhini the nostrils are generally separated by a relatively broad external septum and tend to be directed forwards and sidewards and almost vertically parallel, while in the Catarrhini the septum is generally quite narrow, the nostrils tending to be directed slightly more downwards and to assume a "V" form (see Figure 27).

The apes together with man are often referred to as the Anthropomorpha as a synonym for the superfamily name of Hominoidea. The monkeys may be distinguished from the Prosimii on the one hand and from the Anthropomorpha on the other by the term Pithecoidea, without, however, recognizing them as a separate infraorder as the term might suggest.

Chromosome numbers in the primates are listed in Table I.

It may assist the reader to have this classification set out in schematic form. (See below and Table II.)

ORDER PRIMATES

SUBORDER: PROSIMII

LEMUROIDS, LORISOIDS, AND TARSIOIDS

SUBORDER: ANTHROPOIDEA

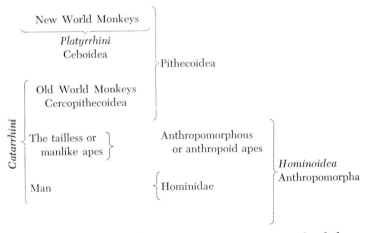

For the purposes of convenience one may speak of the prosimian group or of the prosimians, the pithecoid groups, the anthropomorphous group, and the platyrrhine and catarrhine series of the primates.

Each suborder is divided into families, and the latter are some-

TABLE II

CLASSIFICATION OF THE PRIMATES

Sub-order	Infra-order and Series	Super-family	Family	Subfamily	Genus	Common Name
PROSIMII	LEMURIFORMES		Lemuridae	Lemurinae	Lemur / Hapalemur / Lepilemur	True Lemurs / Gentle Lemurs / Sportive Lemurs
				Cheirogaleinae	Cheirogaleus / Microcebus / Phaner	Dwarf Lemurs / Mouse Lemurs / Fork-Crowned Dwarf Lemurs
			Indriidae		Indris / Propithecus / Lichanotus	Endrina / Sifaka / Woolly Avahi
			Daubentoniidae		Daubentonia	Aye-Aye
	LORISIFORMES		Lorisidae	Lorisinae	Loris / Nycticebus / Arctocebus / Perodicticus	Slender Loris / Slow Loris / Angwantibo / Potto
			Galagidae	Galaginae	Galago / Galagoides / Euoticus	Typical Bush Babies / Dwarf Bush Babies / Needle-Clawed Bush Babies
	TARSIIFORMES		Tarsiidae		Tarsius	Tarsier
ANTHROPOIDEA	PLATYRRHINI	CEBOIDEA	Callithricidae	Callithricinae	Callithrix / Cebuella / Mico / Marikina / Tamarin / Tamarinus / Leontocebus / Oedipomidas	Tufted Marmoset / Pygmy Marmoset / Naked-eared Marmoset / Bald-headed Tamarin / Black-faced Tamarin / Mustached Tamarin / Maned Tamarin / Pinché
			Cebidae	Callimiconinae	Callimico	Callimico
				Aotinae	Aotes / Callicebus	Night Monkey / Titi Monkey
				Pitheciinae	Pithecia / Chiropotes / Cacajao	Hairy Saki Monkey / Short-haired Saki / Ouakári Monkey
				Cebinae	Saimiri / Cebus	Squirrel Monkey / Capuchin Monkey
				Atelinae	Lagothrix / Ateles / Brachyteles	Woolly Monkey / Spider Monkey / Woolly Spider Monkey
				Alouattinae	Alouatta	Howler Monkey
	CATARRHINI	CEROPITHECOIDEA	Cercopithecidae	Cercopithecinae	Cercopithecus / Erythrocebus / Cercocebus / Macaca / Cynopithecus / Theropithecus / Papio / Mandrillus	Guenons / Red-haired Patas / Mangabey / Macaque / Celebes or Black Ape / Gelada Baboon / Typical Baboon / Mandrill and Drill
				Semnopithecinae	Semnopithecus / Colobus / Rhinopithecus / Nasalis	Langur / Guereza / Snub-nosed Langur / Proboscis Monkey
		HOMINOIDEA	Hylobatidae	Hylobatinae	Hylobates / Symphalangus	Common Gibbon / Siamang
			Pongidae	Ponginae	Pongo / Pan / Gorilla	Orang-Utan / Chimpanzee / Gorilla
			Hominidae		Homo	Man

Figure 18. Ring-tailed Lemur *(Lemur catta)*. (Photo, New York Zoological Society.)

Figure 19. Brown Lemur *(Lemur macaco fulvus)*. (Photo, New York Zoological Society.)

Figure 20. Galago or Bush Baby *(Galago crassicaudatus).* (Photo, New York Zoological Society.)

times further subdivided into subfamilies, these or the families are still further subdivided into genera, and the latter into species, species into subspecies or races, and the latter sometimes into clines and habitat forms.

All the living primates, save man, are limited to the tropical continents, to the Oriental, Ethiopian, and Neotropical (South American) regions. Man's habitat is the whole earth, and he now seeks to conquer extra-terrestrial space.

PROSIMII. *The Lemuriformes and Lorisiformes*

The lemurs are the most primitive of the existing primates; they are small creatures, the smallest, the mouse lemurs (*Cheirogale*), is only about four inches in body length; the largest, the endrinas (*Indri*), attain a body length of about 24 inches. Lemurs look not unlike squirrels with fox-like heads. There are five families, including some 18 genera, about 34 species, and about 100 subspecies. Morphologically the suborder exhibits a considerable range of variability. The lemurs are almost entirely arboreal creatures, and are mostly nocturnal in their activities, a fact which seems to be associated with their rather large eyes. The hands and feet are adapted for grasping, and the thumb and big toe are characterized by a high degree of mobility. All the digits of the hand and foot, with the exception of the second digit of the foot, which bears a sharp curved claw, are provided with flat nails. The typical dental formula is I $\frac{2}{2}$, C $\frac{1}{1}$, PM $\frac{3}{3}$, M $\frac{3}{3}$, though in the family of Indriidae this is modified to I $\frac{2}{2}$, C $\frac{1}{1}$, PM $\frac{2}{2}$, M $\frac{3}{3}$. In the typical lemurs, the anterior teeth in the lower jaw are procumbent, the incisors and canines being situated in a row at the front of the jaw; these are separated by a wide gap from the first premolars which are rather canine-like in form. The true canines are so much like incisors that many authorities have described them as such. The tail is not prehensile, but when functional is used as a balancing or stabilizing organ.

A unique and extraordinary lemuroid is the "aye-aye" (*Daubentonia*) of Madagascar. Not only are all the digits, save the big toe, provided with claws, but this unusual primate has incisor teeth which continue to grow as they wear, a characteristic which it shares with the rats and other rodents. The dental formula is I $\frac{1}{1}$, C $\frac{0}{0}$, PM $\frac{1}{0}$, M $\frac{3}{3}$, a total of 18 teeth. Furthermore, the third finger of each hand is elongated and thin and is used in skewering grubs, the favorite food of this peculiar species.

The jaws in the lemurs are generally elongated in a fox-like muzzle, but it is in the possession of the typical rhinarium and crescentic nostrils of less specialized mammals that the lemurs exhibit their truly primitive character and difference from all other primates. In other words, the rhinarium or skin around the nostrils is almost exactly like that seen in the dog or cat. Instead of completely ringed nostrils, there are two crescentic slits, and the surrounding skin, as well as the middle part of the upper lip, is naked, moist, and glandular. A septum on the deep surface binds the lip to the gum of the upper jaw for almost the whole of its length, a feature which determines the lemuroid method of drinking by lapping instead of sucking.

The commencement of the tear duct is situated outside the orbit on the face, but as in all other primates it opens within the nasal cavity.

In the skull there are many primitive mammalian features, such as the presence of a large palatine bone in the inner wall of the orbit, the general absence of an external auditory meatus, the complete absence of a post-orbital wall—rendering the orbit and the temporal fossae (the regions below the temple) confluent; the orbits, though directed somewhat laterally, have eyeballs mounted in them in a manner such that the eyes look forward and not to the side, a distinct advance upon the condition encountered in the insectivores. The inner ear preserves the lower mammalian character in the presence of an auditory bulla, a large, spherical, inflated chamber on the base of the skull within which lies the tympanic ring, which in the catarrhini assists in forming the external auditory meatus.

The lorisiforms differ from the lemuriforms in several distinctive ways. The former tend to be smaller, have larger ears, and larger eyes. In addition, they are more or less tailless, are slow-moving, and have a rudimentary or completely reduced index-finger, and a reduced second toe to which a long cleaning claw is attached. Pollex and hallux are relatively larger than in man.

The Potto (*Perodicticus*), the size of a small cat, is characterized by a unique specialization, the spines of the last cervical and the first two thoracic vertebrae project through the skin and are capped by horny spines. This curious structure constitutes a formidable defense against any attacker.

The Bush Babies (*Galagidae*) are about the size of a rat, and are characterized by the possession of long bushy tails, short muzzles, large mobile ears, and enormously elongated ankle (metatarso-tarsal) bones which make them among the most remarkable jumpers among the primates. The dwarf bush baby (*Galagoides*), for example, which nestles easily in the palm of a man's hand, can leap a dozen or more feet upwards or in any direction! The head can be turned around so that the nose is in line with the vertebral column. The digits of the hands and feet are slender and long, and the well developed pollex and hallux are widely opposed to the other digits. The pelvic limbs are much longer than the pectoral.

While the lorises are unable to leap, and climb by hand over hand motion, the galagoes progress by rapid saltation.

The number of cervical vertebrae regularly is seven, whereas the numbers of post-cervical vertebrae exhibit great generic variability (Schultz and Straus). The thoracic vertebrae range from averages of 12 (*Daubentonia, Lemur, Hapalemur, Lepilemur, Lichanotus*) to 16 (*Nycticebus*); the lumbar vertebrae from six (*Galago*) to nine (*Lepilemur*); the sacral vertebrae from three (most genera) to six (*Nycticebus, Perodicticus*); and the caudal vertebrae from five (*Loris*) to 28 (*Hapalemur*).

Compared with that of other mammals of the same body size the brain is relatively large; the olfactory parts are, however, well developed, and the cerebral hemispheres are so small that they fail to cover a considerable part of the cerebellum. The fissuration and gyri of the cerebrum are of the simplest type, and the visual area of the brain approximates in structure more nearly to that of the lower mammals than to that of the apes.

A synoptic classification of the lemurs follows

Synopsis of the Living Lemurs

SUBORDER PROSIMII

INFRAORDER LEMURIFORMES

The Lemurs of Madagascar and the Comoro Islands
The Malagasy Lemurs

I. FAMILY LEMURIDAE

SUBFAMILY LEMURINAE

Genus *Lemur*. The true lemurs (6 species, 15 subspecies)
Genus *Hapalemur*. The gentle lemurs (2 species, 3 subspecies)
Genus *Lepilemur*. The weasel and sportive lemurs (2 species, 2 subspecies)

SUBFAMILY CHEIROGALEINAE

Genus *Cheirogaleus*. The dwarf lemurs (3 species, 7 subspecies)
Genus *Microcebus*. The mouse lemurs (2 species, 3 subspecies)
Genus *Phaner*. The fork-crowned dwarf lemur (1 species, 1 subspecies)

II. FAMILY INDRIIDAE

Genus *Indris*. The endrinas (1 species, 1 subspecies)
Genus *Propithecus*. The sifakas (2 species, 10 subspecies)
Genus *Avahi*. The woolly avahi (1 species, 1 subspecies)

III. FAMILY DAUBENTONIIDAE

Genus *Daubentonia*. The "aye-aye"

Synopsis of Living Lorises

SUBORDER PROSIMII

INFRAORDER LORISIFORMES

The Lemurs of Africa and Asia
The Non-Malagasy Lemurs

I. FAMILY LORISIDAE

SUBFAMILY LORISINAE

Genus *Loris*. The slender loris (Ceylon and Southern India) (1 species, 6 subspecies)

Genus *Nycticebus*. The slow loris (Eastern India and Malaya) (1 species, 10 subspecies)

Genus *Arctocebus*. The angwantibo (West Africa) (1 species, 2 subspecies)

Genus *Perodicticus*. The potto (Sierra Leone and the Gaboon) (1 species, 5 subspecies)

II. FAMILY GALAGIDAE

SUBFAMILY GALAGINAE

Genus *Galago*. Typical bush babies (East Africa, Senegal, Zanzibar, Fernando Po) (3 species, 21 subspecies)

Genus *Euoticus*. Needle-clawed bush babies (West Africa, Fernando Po) (2 species, 2 subspecies)

Genus *Galagoides*. Dwarf bush babies (Senegal and Central Africa) (1 species, 7 subspecies)

It has already been remarked that the lemurs are almost exclusively arboreal creatures, that they are mostly nocturnal in their activities, and spend the greater part of the daylight hours in sleep. Interestingly enough, there seems to be an association between sleeping habits or waking activity, size of eyes, body size, and social habits, for the small lemurs are those which are most definitely nocturnal, have the largest eyes, and are given to living in small social units or in family groups. The larger lemurs, on the other hand, are frequently quite active by day or in twilight, have small eyes, and more often tend to live as members of a community of their own species. This suggests that increase in body size may have been a prepotent factor in releasing the early primates from their nocturnal or crepuscular habits, by enabling them to hold their own against most aggressors, and that this further led to the development of more extended social relations with animals of their own species. In practically all animals that are habitually nocturnal the eyes are large. All nocturnal prosimia are characterized by the possession of a tapetum cellulosum, an irridescent layer of cells in the choroid coat of the eye, which is responsible for vivid eyeshine in the presence of light.

The diet of lemurs is varied. Most are largely frugivorous. Many eat both animal and vegetable foods. The Indriidae are primarily leaf eaters, while the Lorisidae and the "aye-aye" are mainly insectivorous.

Lemurs do not menstruate. Pregnancy lasts about five months, and one young is usually, though two are not infrequently, born at a birth. The infant is suckled for about six months, and the young generally cling in a horizontal position across the lower abdomen of the mother. The Malagasy lemurs (and probably the galagoes) would appear to have a circumscribed breeding season falling between March and the end of June, with a peak in mid-April. The lorises probably breed throughout the year.

Since a fovea and a macula—the small pit in the yellow spot of the retina, and the yellow spot itself—are absent from the retina in all lemurs these animals are believed to be incapable of stereoscopic vision, and there is also some evidence which suggests that the lemurs are only feebly, if at all, capable of color vision.

Figure 21. Slow Loris (*Nycticebus tardigradus*). (Photo, courtesy of late Dr. Charles Hose.)

Lemurs appear to be quite incapable of facial expression.

Unquestionably the living lemurs represent a most primitive branch of the primates, but each of the existing kinds of lemurs is characterized by specializations of its own, a fact which very definitely removes the infraorder as a whole from the direct line of man's ancestry.

The Tarsiiformes

The living tarsiers are represented by possibly three species, *Tarsius spectrum*, of Salayer Island in Celebes, northeastern Celebes, and on Peleng Island of its east coast; *Tarsius bacanus*, of southern Sumatra, Borneo, Banka and Billiton Islands, and on the Natuna Islands in the South China Sea; and the Philippine tarsiers, *Tarsius syrichta*, of Samar, Leyte, Bohol, and Mindanao.

Synopsis of the Living Tarsiers

SUBORDER PROSIMII

INFRAORDER TARSIIFORMES

The Tarsiers of the Malay Archipelago, Celebes, and the Philippines

I. FAMILY TARSIIDAE

Genus *Tarsius*. The tarsier (possibly 3 species and 12 subspecies)

The adult tarsier has a body length of about 8 inches, a long tail the under portion of which is relatively bare and tufted at the tip, opposable thumbs and big toes, with nails on all digits excepting the second and third of the feet which bear claws. The leg bones, the tibia and fibula are fused together at their lower ends. The feet are very long owing to the remarkable elongation of the heel bone (calcaneus) and the bone on the inner side of the foot obliquely in front of it, the navicular, which together form part of the tarsus. This specialization of the foot is associated with the frog-like leaping mode of progression of the tarsier, and it is from this unique feature that the species takes its generic name. The palmar surfaces of the hands and the plantar surfaces of the feet are highly specialized, presenting round pads at the tips of all digits, with four interdigital pads on the hands, while on the plantar surfaces of the feet there are three large interdigital pads of highly specialized form. Since the tarsiers are completely arboreal and nocturnal creatures, these pads are of great service in the grasping activities of the animals, for they are capable of holding fast by something like a vacuum suction of these pads.

Figure 22. The Tarsier *(Tarsius syrichta)*. (Photo, Zoological Society of Philadelphia.)

The nose is quite unlike that in the lemurs; only a narrow strip of naked skin marks the opening of the widely separated nostrils, and the hairy upper lip shows a continuous smooth surface uninterrupted by a median groove. The lip is muscularized and freely mobile, not being bound to the gum as it is in the lemurs. Nevertheless, *Tarsius* drinks by lapping. The disappearance of the rhinarium proper in *Tarsius* may be regarded as the outward manifestation of the retrogression of the olfactory apparatus, the reduction in the importance of the sense of smell. This is also reflected in the marked reduction of the snout, for the face of *Tarsius* is relatively flat. On the other hand, the eyes are perfectly enormous in size, being the largest, relative to the size of the head, to be found in any of the primates. The eyes do not, however, possess a fovea or macula, and hence the tarsiers, like the lemurs, are thought to be incapable of stereoscopic vision. These animals have, however, developed a peculiar specialization of the central region of the retina, at which point the layer of rod cells is thrown into convoluting folds, and the ganglion cells are more numerous. This is very different from anything found in the higher primates, but parallels conditions found in certain bats. The retina possesses no cone cells. Possibly as a compensation for its lack of stereoscopic vision *Tarsius* has developed the ability to turn its head around so that its nose is in line with its spinal column, an excursion of 180 degrees! This accomplishment has been worthily celebrated in a limerick:

> The Tarsier, weird little beast
> Can't swivel his eyes in the least,
> But when sitting at rest
> With his tummy due west
> He can screw his head round to face east.

But as we have seen, this is an accomplishment of which the galagoes can also boast.

The brain, which is rather broader than it is long, exhibits a smooth surface. It shows a considerable reduction in its olfactory portions, and an increase in the regions associated with vision, particularly in the occipital lobe which extends over the cerebellum and covers the latter.

The palate bone forms a small part of the inner wall of the orbit, and the orbit is quite separated from the temporal fossa by a postorbital wall. The orbits are directed completely forward, more markedly so than in the lemurs. The upper opening of the tear duct (naso-lacrimal duct) lies on the face outside the orbit, as in the lemurs. The dental formula is I $\frac{2}{1}$, C $\frac{1}{1}$, PM $\frac{3}{3}$, M $\frac{3}{3}$.

The tympanic annulus or ear ring has migrated outside the auditory meatus, but the bulla or auditory chamber itself is still large and inflated.

There are seven cervical, and an average of 13 thoracic, six lumbar, three sacral, and 28 caudal vertebrae. Tarsiers exhibit a monthly estrous cycle with sexual skin swelling, and it has recently been demonstrated that vaginal bleeding of a non-menstrual kind occurs. There is no special breeding season. Tarsiers appear always to live in pairs or together with a single offspring, that is to say, in single family units, in small groups. A single offspring is produced at a birth, and this clings at first to the abdominal hair of the mother, and later rides on her back.

The diet of tarsiers appears to be insectivorous, but in captivity they will eat baby mice, meal-worms, and lizards.

Tarsiers are gentle creatures, readily tameable, though they take some time accustoming themselves to human beings.

Tarsiers are capable of a fair amount of facial expression.

In many fundamental characters, such as the morphology of the brain and skull, the reduced snout, the retrogression of the olfactory organs, in the dentition, the form of the nose and lips, the tarsiers make a much closer approach to the Anthropoidea than do any of the other Prosimii. Indeed, the Tarsioidea serve as good generalized early primates from which all the higher primates may have taken origin, that is to say, not from the existing types, but from some early tarsioid form resembling the modern tarsiers. Some students, like Wood Jones, have gone so far as to suggest that the lines which led on the one hand to the Anthropoidea and on the other to man, originated independently from some tarsioid stock. The consensus of scientific opinion is, however, against this theory. The interpretation of the evidence generally accepted at the present time supports the theory that the tarsioids gave rise to the platyrrhine and catarrhine monkeys, and possibly to the gibbons, and that it was from the catarrhine monkey stock that the early anthropoids arose, and that these, in turn, gave rise to the modern anthropoids on the one hand and to the Hominidae on the other.

ANTHROPOIDEA

SERIES PLATYRRHINI

SUPERFAMILY CEBOIDEA

The New World Monkeys comprise two distinct families, the marmosets or Callithricidae, with eight genera, some 35 species, and some 51 subspecies, and the typical South American monkeys, the Cebidae, with 11 genera, some 39 species, and about 161 subspecies. Their range is from Southern Mexico to Rio Grande do Sul on the border between Brazil and Uruguay.

Synopsis of the Living New World Monkeys

SUBORDER ANTHROPOIDEA

Series Platyrrhini

The Marmosets and Tamarins

I. SUPERFAMILY CEBOIDEA

I. FAMILY CALLITHRICIDAE

Genus *Callithrix*. The tufted marmosets (Mexico to Amazon Basin) (10 species, 11 subspecies)

Genus *Cebuella*. The pygmy marmoset (Amazon Basin to S.E. Brazil) (1 species, 2 subspecies)

Genus *Mico*. Naked-eared marmoset (Tocantins River, Brazil) (1 species, 3 subspecies)

Genus *Marikina*. The bald-headed tamarin (Northern Amazon) (2 species, 2 subspecies)

Genus *Tamarin*. The black-faced tamarin (Tropical S. America) (3 species, 6 subspecies)

Genus *Tamarinus*. The mustached tamarin (Upper Amazon Basin) (12 species, 21 subspecies)

Genus *Leontocebus*. The maned tamarin (Costa Rica to S.E. Brazil) (3 species, 3 subspecies)

Genus *Oedipomidas*. The pinché marmosets (Costa Rica to Colombia) (3 species, 3 subspecies)

The Callithricidae

The marmosets are small animals, about the size of squirrels. The long non-prehensile tail is covered with hair though rather sparsely on its under surface, and is usually tufted at the tip. The hindlimbs are considerably longer than the forelimbs, the tibia and fibula are quite separate, and all the digits bear sharp, laterally compressed claws, with the exception of the big toe which bears a flattened nail. The digital claws are doubtless associated with the squirrel-like habit of marmosets of running spirally up and down large tree trunks. The thumb is not opposable, but the big toe, which is situated rather low on the foot, is capable of a considerable degree of mobility.

The face is relatively flat, the eyes rather large, a primitive fovea and macula are present in the retina, so that marmosets are presumed to be capable of some stereoscopic vision. The brain, in proportion to size of the body, is remarkably voluminous, with well

Figure 23. Tufted Marmoset *(Callithrix jacchus)*. (Photo, New York Zoological Society.)

Figure 24. Pygmy Marmoset *(Cebuella pygmaea)*. (Photo, New York Zoological Society.)

developed frontal lobes which give the skull a very human-like appearance. The occipital lobes completely cover the cerebellum, and the olfactory parts of the brain are very markedly reduced. The surface of the brain is, however, quite free of convolutions, except for a well marked sylvian fissure, separating the temporal from the parieto-frontal portion of the brain. In the development of its frontal and parietal association areas, the marmoset brain exhibits a considerable advance upon the prosimian brain.

There is no muzzle or snout, the nose is of distinctive primate or haplorrhine type, the oval nostrils being widely separated, the tip being grooved, and the lips freely mobile. The auditory bulla is inflated, but the tympanic ring is extended outside the bulla to form an abbreviated external auditory meatus. The orbit is separated from the temporal fossa by the markedly developed zygomatic or malar bone. The latter establishes a broad contact with the parietal bone, a characteristic feature of the platyrrhine skull which, interestingly enough, is also seen in some 10 per cent of gibbon crania.

The canine teeth are well developed, and the dentition is peculiar in that most marmosets have lost the third molar tooth, hence the dental formula is I $\frac{2}{2}$, C $\frac{1}{1}$, PM $\frac{3}{3}$, M $\frac{2}{2}$.

There are seven cervical, and an average of 12 or 13 thoracic, seven or six lumbar, three sacral, and 30 to 33 caudal vertebrae.

The marmoset is the only monkey which normally produces more than a single young at a birth, the usual number being two or three. There is no restricted breeding season and pregnancy lasts five months and one week. Vaginal bleeding of a non-menstrual kind occurs, and swelling of the perineal skin, known as the "sexual skin," has been recorded. Interestingly enough, the young are generally carried by the father, to whose chest hair the infant clings, gradually shifting to the father's back as it grows older. The mother receives the infant only when sustenance is required. Quite frequently the carrying of the infant is left by the parents to the older preceding siblings.

Marmosets are diurnal and arboreal in their habits, and subsist principally upon fruit and insects. These animals are climbers and do not indulge in the flying leaps so characteristic of the Cebidae.

Marmosets are capable of a limited range of facial expression. They habitually live in pairs, or in single family groups, as part of a larger community.

The New World Monkeys

II. FAMILY CEBIDAE

SUBFAMILY CALLIMICONINAE

Genus *Callimico*. (N.W. Amazonian Brazil) (1 species, 1 subspecies)

SUBFAMILY AOTINAE

Genus *Aotes*. The douroucouli or night monkeys (Nicaragua, Peru, Amazon) (1 species, 10 subspecies)

Genus *Callicebus*. The titi monkeys (Panama to Brazil) (7 species, 33 subspecies)

SUBFAMILY PITHECIINAE

Genus *Pithecia*. The saki monkeys (British Guiana to Lower Amazon) (2 species, 6 subspecies)

Genus *Cacajao*. The ouakári or short-tailed monkeys (Amazon Basin) (3 species, 4 subspecies)

SUBFAMILY CEBINAE

Genus *Saimiri*. The squirrel monkeys (Costa Rica to Brazil and Bolivia) (3 species, 15 subspecies)

Genus *Cebus*. The capuchin monkeys (Nicaragua to Southern Brazil) (4 species, 39 subspecies)

Figure 25. Owl Monkey *(Aotes trivirgatus)*. (Photo, New York Zoological Society.)

SUBFAMILY ATELINAE

Genus *Ateles*. The spider monkeys (Mexico to Amazon Basin) (5 species, 15 subspecies)

Genus *Brachyteles*. The woolly spider monkey (South-Eastern Brazil) (1 species, 1 subspecies)

Genus *Lagothrix*. The woolly monkeys (Ecuador, Venezuela, Bolivia) (6 species, 11 subspecies)

SUBFAMILY ALOUATTINAE

Genus *Alouatta*. The howler monkeys (Eastern Guatemala to Paraguay) (6 species, 26 subspecies)

THE CEBIDAE

The 11 genera of monkeys embraced in the family Cebidae constitute a varied assortment of animals which are, however, readily distinguishable from the marmosets. The cebids are larger in size than the callithricids, but not as large, on the whole, as the monkeys of the Old World. The dental formula is I $\frac{2}{2}$, C $\frac{1}{1}$, PM $\frac{3}{3}$, M $\frac{3}{3}$. The digits all bear nails, which, with the exception of the first, are generally

Figure 26. Owl Monkey *(Aotes trivirgatus)*. (Photo, New York Zoological Society.)

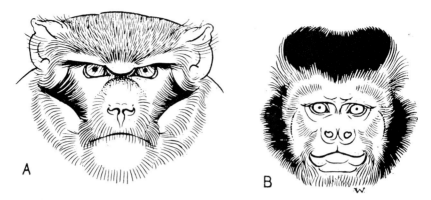

Figure 27. A, An Old World or Catarrhine Monkey *(Macaca)* and B, a New World or Platyrrhine Monkey *(Cebus)* showing the difference in the arrangement of the nostrils. (From Le Gros Clark, *History of the Primates,* 1949. Courtesy, British Museum [Natural History].)

somewhat arched or laterally compressed. Claws do not occur. The thumb is never opposable but is used as a finger, while in the spider monkeys (*Ateles* and *Brachyteles*) there are only four digits on the hand, the external thumb being absent or reduced to a mere nailless stub or tubercle, a condition which may be significantly associated with the highly developed prehensile tail in this group, a tail which has been described as a "fifth hand." The thumb is similarly reduced in the catarrhine genus *Colobus,* a group in which the tail, however, is not in the slightest degree prehensile. The big toe in the cebids is always opposable. The long tail is prehensile in only half the genera, namely, in *Cebus, Lagothrix, Ateles, Brachyteles,* and *Alouatta.* In the ouakári monkeys (*Cacajao*) the tail is very short. In the spider monkeys (*Ateles*) the forelimb exceeds the hindlimb in length. In the woolly monkeys (*Lagothrix*) fore and hindlimbs are almost equal in length, and in all other genera the hindlimb exceeds the forelimb in length.

There are seven cervical, and an average of 13 or 14 thoracic, from four to seven lumbar, and from 24 to 31 caudal vertebrae.

There is no muzzle, the projection of the jaws being appreciably less than in most Old World monkeys. The nasal cavities are also much reduced. The skull typically exhibits the articulation of the malar bone with the parietal bone. The palate is comparatively short. The auditory bulla is large and inflated, and the tympanic ring remains

Figure 28. Woolly Saki Monkey *(Pithecia monachus).* (Photo, New York
Zoological Society.)

Figure 29. Ouakári Monkey *(Cacajao calvus)*. (Photo, New York Zoological
Society.)

outside the bulla, but an external auditory meatus is not formed.
The surface of the brain is richly convoluted, the fissural pattern bearing a surprising resemblance to that of the brains of Old World monkeys, especially in the smaller forms of the latter such as occur in the
genera *Cercocebus* and *Macaca*. This resemblance has been interpreted
as due to evolutionary convergence or parallelism, that is, the process
whereby two separate stocks independently develop similar structures.
Since all the evidence indicates that the Ceboidea and Cercopithecoidea originated independently from some tarsioid stock, probably
in the Oligocene, it is most likely that convergence in this, and in

many other characters, almost certainly occurred. The fissural pattern of the brain of the larger forms such, for example, as *Ateles*, the spider monkey, and *Papio*, the baboon, show unmistakable differences.

With the exception of the night monkeys (*Aotes*), which as their name implies are nocturnal animals, all the Cebidae are possessed of a well developed fovea and macula, and are capable of stereoscopic

Figure 30. Squirrel Monkey *(Saimiri sciureus)*. (Photo, New York Zoological Society.)

Figure 31. Hooded Sapajou *(Cebus fatuellus)*. (Photo, New York Zoological Society.)

Figure 32. White-throated Sapajou *(Cebus capucinus)*. (Photo, New York Zoological Society.)

Figure 33. Spider Monkey *(Ateles ater).* (Photo, New York Zoological Society.)

vision. The few members of the Cebidae thus far investigated were found to be capable of color vision.

All the Cebidae are arboreal in their habits, and with the exception of the night monkeys (*Aotes*), all are diurnal. It is of interest to note that the night monkeys are among the smallest, in body size, of the Cebidae, that they live in pairs or in small family groups, have a limited areal range, and that they have the relatively largest eyes.

Figure 34. Woolly Monkey, Immature (*Lagothrix humboldti*). (Photo, New York Zoological Society.)

Aotes is also remarkable for the fact that this species possesses a tapetum fibrosum, an irridescent layer of cells in the choroid coat of the eye, which is said to give *Aotes* a more brilliant eyeshine than the cat.

One young is usually born at a birth, and it is normally carried by the mother on her back; in *Saimiri* and *Cebus* the father generally carries the infant on his back, the infant returning to the mother only for suckling.

The female experiences a definite estrous cycle, that is to say, a monthly period of physiological change during which the animal undergoes all those changes which lead to ovulation, to heat, and to sexual behavior. In *Ateles* and in *Cebus,* at least, a scanty menstruation occurs fairly regularly.

With the exception of the night monkeys the cebids live in communities. Diet varies from genus to genus but is mainly frugivorous; some insects are eaten, while the howler monkeys (*Alouatta*) are mainly leaf eaters.

Callimico is sometimes classed with the marmosets (Goeldi's marmoset), but its general features more closely resemble those of a cebid monkey, though in several of its characters—mane, silky pelage —it appears to be transitional between the marmosets and the monkeys. The fact that *Callimico* has 48 chromosomes whereas marmosets have 46, strengthens the view that *Callimico* is a cebid.

The Cebidae are comparatively intelligent creatures, gentle, relatively unaggressive, and capable of a very wide range of facial expression.

Anthropoidea

Series Catarrhini

The Old World Monkeys and Baboons

Superfamily Cercopithecoidea

The Old World monkeys comprise one family, the Cercopithecidae, and two subfamilies, the Cercopithecinae and the Semnopithecinae, the first with 8 genera and some 46 species and 185 subspecies, and the second with 4 genera, and some 42 species, and some 60 subspecies. All the catarrhini are African and Asiatic in their distribution, with the exception of one species which, though at home in North Africa, was introduced more than a hundred years ago to the rock of Gibraltar. The great variety of specializations exhibited by different members of the Old World monkeys is striking, but it is a question whether this exceeds the variety exhibited by other families of primates.

The Old World differ from the New World monkeys in the following characters: There are only two, instead of three, premolar teeth on each side both in the upper and lower jaws, the dental formula being I $\frac{2}{2}$, C $\frac{1}{1}$, PM $\frac{2}{2}$, M $\frac{3}{3}$; the palate is relatively long,

Figure 35. Black Guenon (*Cercopithecus nigrigenis*). Photo, New York Zoological Society.)

Figure 36. De Brazza Guenon (*Cercopithecus brazzae*). (Photo, New York Zoological Society.)

the auditory bulla is absent, and the tympanic ring is elongated to form a true external auditory meatus, the malar never articulates with the parietal bone, and the frontal bone, forming the forehead, is somewhat more depressed. The nostrils are set close together, all digits have more perfectly flattened nails, the thumb is opposable, and so is the big toe, the tail is not prehensile, the cercopitheques possess cheek pouches, and the semnopitheques, sacculated stomachs, while all species possess sitting pads of naked modified skin situated on the lower part of the buttocks, these callused pads being known as ischial callosities.

With the exception of the baboons—which are terrestrial—the Old World monkeys are arboreal in their habits, and all are completely diurnal.

Visual acuity is very highly developed, the mangabeys (*Cercocebus*), for example, having an even more highly developed retina than man.

There are seven cervical and an average of 12 thoracic, seven lumbar, three or four sacral, and from 12 to 28 caudal vertebrae.

The female experiences a regular estrous cycle, characterized by the swelling of the perineal sexual skin, in most species, and by menstruation in all. One young is born at a birth, and this clings to the hair of the mother's belly where it is carried until, in about a month, it is able to shift for itself. At a later stage, when the infant is about six months, it may be carried on the mother's back.

The Old World monkeys live in small communities. They are temperamentally aggressive creatures, and on the whole do not appear to possess as high a degree of intelligence as the New World monkeys. They are capable of a wide range of facial expression. Their diet is herbivorous and frugivorous and, in the case of the baboons especially, more or less insectivorous.

Synopsis of the Old World Monkeys and Baboons

SUBORDER ANTHROPOIDEA

SERIES CATARRHINI

The Old World Monkeys and Baboons

II. SUPERFAMILY CERCOPITHECOIDEA

I. FAMILY CERCOPITHECIDAE

SUBFAMILY CERCOPITHECINAE

Genus *Cercopithecus*. The guenons (Africa) (20 species, 99 subspecies)

Genus *Erythrocebus*. The red-haired patas or hussar monkeys (Equatorial Africa) (1 species, 3 subspecies)

Genus *Cercocebus*. The mangabeys (Equatorial Africa) (4 species, 10 subspecies

Genus *Macaca*. The macaque (Southern Asia, China, Japan, Philippines, East Indies, North Africa, Gibraltar) (12 species, 50 subspecies)

Genus *Cynopithecus*. The Celebes or black "ape" (Celebes, Philippines) (1 species, 1 subspecies)

Genus *Theropithecus*. The Gelada baboon (Southern Abyssinia) (1 species, 1 subspecies)

Genus *Papio*. The typical baboon (Abyssinia, Arabia, South Africa) (5 species, 19 subspecies)

Genus *Mandrillus*. The mandrill and drill (Senegambia to Congo) (2 species, 2 subspecies)

SUBFAMILY SEMNOPITHECINAE

Genus *Semnopithecus*. The langurs (Asia) (28 species, 15 subspecies)

Genus *Colobus*. The guerezas (Equatorial Africa) (8 species, 38 subspecies)

Genus *Rhinopithecus*. The retroussé-nosed langurs (North-western China) (5 species, 6 subspecies)

Genus *Nasalis*. The proboscis monkey (Borneo) (1 species, 1 subspecies)

CERCOPITHECINAE

With the exception of the Celebes "ape" (*Cynopithecus*), which is native to Celebes, and has been introduced into Batchian in the Moluccas and into the Philippines, all the genera of cercopitheques

Figure 37. Java Macaque or Java Monkey *(Macaca irus)*. (Photo, New York Zoological Society.)

are represented in Africa, while only one genus which occurs in Africa is represented outside that continent, namely the macaques (*Macaca*), species of which are found in Asia and Gibraltar.

The cercopitheques in contrast to the semnopitheques all possess cheek pouches. In these receptacles they are able to cram a great quantity of food which they are then able to masticate at leisure. The semnopitheques, on the other hand, are distinguished from the cercopitheques by the possession of sacculated stomachs, which are apparently well-adapted to the digestion of a diet consisting principally of leaves.

Figure 38. Barbary Ape *(Macaca sylvana).* (Photo, New York Zoological Society.)

Figure 39. Gelada Baboon *(Theropithecus gelada).* (Photo, New York Zoological Society.)

The guenons (*Cercopithecus*) are lightly built, long-tailed arboreal creatures of great agility, with short faces and rounded heads. The patas monkeys (*Erythrocebus*) are very similar in form to the guenons, but are more terrestrial in their habits. The mangabeys (*Cercocebus*) are arboreal, very long-tailed, slenderly built, white-lidded, monkeys; and the jaws project quite prominently. The macaques (*Macaca*) are at home in trees and in rocky regions, but like all monkeys are capable of getting along very well, whenever necessary, on the ground. They are stockily built creatures, the tail is usually rather short, and the muzzle projecting. The Celebes "ape" (*Cyno-pithecus*) has an extremely reduced tail, and is very baboon-like in appearance, with an elongated flattened muzzle, and a peculiar crest of hair which springs from the crown of the head. With the Gelada "baboon" (*Theropithecus*) we come to the baboons.

The baboons differ from all other Old World monkeys in being terrestrial in their habits rather than arboreal, and in having very elongate dog-like muzzles. Actually baboons live in rocky regions rather than on flat ground. The so-called Gelada baboon (*Theropithe-cus*) differs from the typical baboons (*Papio*) and the drills and mandrills (*Mandrillus*), in having the nostrils set far back instead of being situated at the most forward portion of the muzzle, and in having a deep rather than a forwardly prolonged muzzle, and in the fact that in the males the ischial callosities, the two highly callused areas situated on the lower part of the buttocks, are widely separated. The mandrill is distinguished from the drill principally by its amazing facial coloration. The top of the nose is red, the tip scarlet, the

Figure 40. Hamadryas Baboon *(Papio hamadryas)*. (Photo, New York Zoological Society.)

Figure 41. Chacma Baboon (*Papio porcarius*). (Photo, New York Zoological Society.)

elongated muzzle ridges are bright blue with purple in the intervening furrows, the lips are grayish black. The face of the drill is entirely black without other coloration. Both have extremely short tails. In the baboons the muzzle reaches its greatest length, a condition which may be associated with their pronograde posture.

SEMNOPITHECINAE

It has already been mentioned that this subfamily, which embraces the langurs and guerezas, differs from the cercopitheques in the possession of a sacculated stomach and in the absence of cheek pouches. The semnopitheques are also, as a whole, characterized by a long and often highly colored pelage. With the exception of the African genus of guerezas (*Colobus*), the semnopitheques are an Asiatic group. In addition to their geographic uniqueness, among the semnopitheques, the guerezas are also peculiar in that they alone among the catarrhini show the same extreme reduction of the thumb that characterizes the spider monkeys (*Ateles*) among the platyrrhini. All semnopitheques are lightly built, and all are arboreal and diurnal in their habits.

The true langurs (*Semnopithecus*) are slenderly built animals, with long slender tails, and short faces. The snub-nosed langurs (*Rhinopithecus*) are characterized by retroussé noses, while the proboscis monkey (*Nasalis*) is notable for the remarkable development of the nose which projects several inches beyond the face and below the level of the mouth. Interestingly enough the young proboscis monkey and the female are characterized by the possession of a retroussé nose.

The guerezas (*Colobus*) have short faces, long slender nonprehensile tails, and external thumbs reduced to a tubercle which may or may not have a rudimentary nail.

Figure 42. Mandrill (*Mandrillus sphinx*). (Photo, New York Zoological Society.)

Anthropoidea

SERIES CATARRHINI

SUPERFAMILY HOMINOIDEA

The Apes and Man

The anthropomorphous primates seem to constitute a natural unit and are therefore placed together in the single superfamily Hominoidea. The Hominoidea consists of two families, the Pongidae or anthropoid apes, and the Hominidae or men. The Pongidae consist of two sub-families, the Ponginae with three genera comprising the three great apes, the gorilla (*Gorilla*), the chimpanzee (*Pan*), and the orang-utan (*Pongo*), each with a single species. The second subfamily, the Hylobatinae, consists of two genera, the common gibbon (*Hylobates*), and the siamang (*Symphalangus*), each with several species. The Hominidae consists of a single genus *Homo*, and a single species *sapiens*.

The Hominoidea are distinguished from most other genera of primates by the absence of a tail, the presence of a vermiform appendix, a very large complex brain, arms which are longer than the legs (save in man), a laterally expanded pelvis, chest more or less flattened from front to back, ability to assume an erect posture, locomotion by brachiation or overarm swinging (except in man and the adult gorilla), the great apes being obliquely quadrupedal, while man is habitually bipedal. The thumb and big toe are opposable in the anthropomorphous apes, but in man the thumb alone is opposable.

Synopsis of the Apes and Man

SUBORDER ANTHROPOIDEA

SERIES CATARRHINI

Anthropomorpha

The Apes and Man

III. SUPERFAMILY HOMINOIDEA

I. FAMILY PONGIDAE

SUBFAMILY HYLOBATINAE

Genus *Hylobates*. The common gibbons (Asia) (5 species, 19 subspecies)
Genus *Symphalangus*. The siamang (Sumatra) (2 species, 3 subspecies)

SUBFAMILY PONGINAE

Genus *Gorilla*. The lowland and mountain gorillas (Western and Eastern Equatorial Africa) (1 species, 2 subspecies)

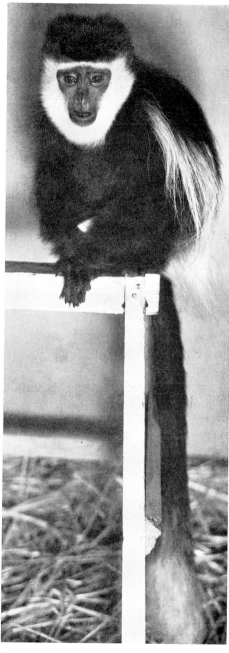

Figure 43. Guereza Monkey (*Colobus abyssinicus*). (Photo, New York Zoological Society.)

Genus *Pan.* The chimpanzee (Western and Central Equatorial Africa) (1 species, 1 subspecies)

Genus *Pongo.* The orang-utan (Borneo and Sumatra) (1 species, 2 subspecies)

II. FAMILY HOMINIDAE

Genus *Homo.* All living types of man (the habitable globe) (1 species)

We may now turn to the consideration of the Hominoidea in some detail.

HYLOBATINAE

The gibbons (including the siamangs) are the smallest of the apes, being slightly under three feet in height. The Hylobatinae comprise two genera, *Hylobates,* the common gibbon, and *Symphalangus,* the siamang, the first with 5 species and 19 subspecies, the second with 2 species and 3 subspecies. *Hylobates* is found in Assam, Burma, Siam, Indo-China, Hainan Island, the Malay Peninsula, and the British and Dutch East Indies. The siamang is found only on the island of Sumatra.

Some of the features in which the siamang differs from the common gibbon are: (1) a larger body weight (24 as against 13 pounds), and larger dimensions of nearly all bodily parts; (2) much shorter trunk and relatively broader chest; (3) shorter legs (in proportion to the trunk) and much larger arms (in proportion to the legs); (4) relatively broader hands; (5) an average cranial capacity of 124.6 c.c. as against 97.5 c.c.; (6) a longer skull; (7) the common occurrence of supernumerary molar teeth; (8) the presence of a throat pouch or vocal sac; (9) scantier body hair; and (10) frequent webbing between the second and third toes.

In the species *Symphalangus concolor* there is an interesting sexual dimorphism with respect to the throat pouch or vocal sac since only the males possess them.

The arms are of such extraordinary length in the gibbon that when the animal stands erect its finger-tips touch the ground. The length of its upper extremities is no doubt correlated with the amazing ability of the gibbon to progress through the trees by overarm swinging. The brachiating ("arming") mode of progression has reached its highest development in the gibbons, who are the true aerial acrobats among the primates. Brachiation is the mode of progression followed by the gibbon about 90 per cent of the time, walking and jumping fills in the remaining 10 per cent of the time. On the ground the gibbon normally progresses in the upright position using his long arms as balancers.

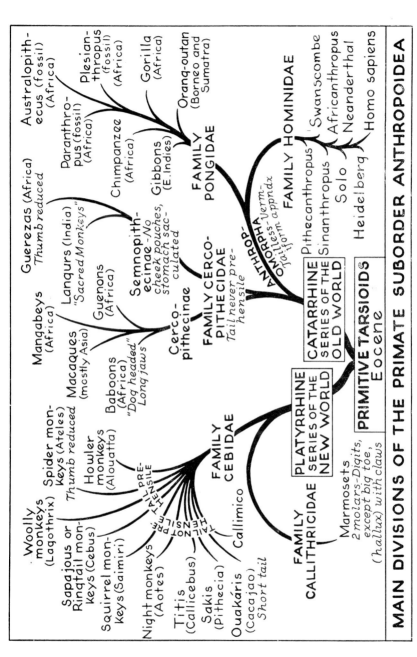

Figure 44. Main Divisions of the Primate Suborder Anthropoidea.

Figure 45. White-handed Gibbon with Baby *(Hylobates lar).* (Photo, New York Zoological Society.)

There are seven cervical, and an average of 13 thoracic, five lumbar, five sacral, and two to three coccygeal vertebrae.

Among important features which distinguish the Hylobatinae from the Ponginae are the constant presence of ischial callosities (these are occasionally present in the Ponginae), the wide flaring of the zygomatic or malar bone on the side of the skull, and its occasional contact with the parietal, the early eruption of the teeth and their smaller size, the eruption of the canine before the second deciduous molar teeth, and the great density of the body hair. Except for the external genitalia there are no perceptible external differences observable between the male and female gibbon. In many respects the gibbons stand intermediate between the Old World monkeys and the Ponginae. They are more nearly allied to the Oriental orang-utan than to the African apes, the chimpanzee and the gorilla.

Menstruation occurs at intervals of four weeks and lasts about two or three days. There are no sexual skin changes except for some slight eversion of the vaginal orifice and changes in the turgidity and color of the labia during the cycle.

There is no definite breeding season, copulation taking place

Figure 46. Gibbons on Monkey Island (*Hylobates lar*). (Photo, New York Zoological Society.)

Figure 47. Female Orang-Utan with Young from Borneo (*Pongo pygmaeus*).
(Photo, Zoological Society of Philadelphia.)

throughout the year. Pregnancy lasts about 30 weeks. One young is born at a birth, and this is devotedly nursed by the mother. From the first day the infant is able to hold on to the mother's abdominal hair, and later by encircling her waist with its long arms, while she brachiates through the trees without affording her infant any other support. The young one scarcely ever leaves its mother's protective custody until after the sixth month.

Temperamentally the gibbon is a gentle creature but very nervous and excitable and quite unpredictable. Gibbons are capable of a considerable amount of facial expression.

Gibbons live in small family groups, which are generally part of a larger territorial population.

Diet is frugivorous and insectivorous, but birds' eggs and small birds are eaten with relish.

PONGINAE

Pongo. The orang-utan is represented by a single species, *Pongo pygmaeus*, with 2 subspecies, confined to the islands of Borneo and Sumatra. The orang-utan has very long arms and short legs, and reaches a height of slightly over four feet. The average weight of the male is 165 pounds, of the female but a little over 80 pounds. Orangs are almost exclusively arboreal creatures. The coarse, shaggy, body hair is reddish-brown or "bright-foxy" red. Skin color is pale yellowish-brown. Adult males usually, and adult females, sometimes, exhibit a peculiar specialization in the form of cheek pads, great lateral out-growths on each side of the face of fat and connective tissue. With the exception of the common gibbon the apes all possess laryngeal sacs, but these reach their greatest development in the orang. These structures arise a little distance above the vocal cords and descend in the neck and chest, spreading out laterally frequently as far as the armpits, and below as far as the base of the breastbone. The function of the sac, if any, is unknown. In man the laryngeal "sac" is represented by a minute blind sinus beneath the vestibular fold just above the vocal fold. Ischial callosities occur in about five per cent of orangs. There are seven cervical, and an average of 12 thoracic, four lumbar, five sacral, and three coccygeal vertebrae.

The skull is very peculiar in form, exhibiting a short rounded brain-case, and a concave hollowed-out face. This gives the facial profile a somewhat "s"-like appearance which has been termed "sinognathism." The supraorbital ridges are not confluent with one another, and thus do not form a torus above the orbits as in the other great apes. The nasal bones are markedly reduced in breadth, and often altogether fail to develop. There is no mastoid process. The adult male generally develops a bony crest, the sagittal crest, along the middle of the top of the skull. The forehead is comparatively high and rounded. The average cranial capacity of the male is 416 c.c.

The upper extremities of the orang are so long that when the animal stands erect the finger tips reach to the ankles. The lower extremities are very short, the proportion of the upper to the lower

Figure 48. Chimpanzee Mother and Young *(Pan satyrus).* (Photo, Zoological Society of London.)

being 170 per cent. The hand is extremely long and the skeletal
opposable thumb is relatively short, about 44 per cent of the total
length of the hand.

The movements of the orang are very slow and deliberate, and
on the ground he moves on all fours in a laborious and shaky manner.

In the female menstruation occurs regularly, and in some animals
there is a definite swelling of the sexual skin during pregnancy. Pregnancy lasts 275 days, and one young is born at a birth; this is carried
by the mother in a very human-like manner.

Temperamentally the orang is very placid and sluggish, and is
facially the most expressionless of the apes, though he is not altogether incapable of a certain amount of facial expression.

Very little is known of the social life of the orang, but family
groups consisting of a male, female and young have been observed.
Little is known of the dietary habits of the orang, but they appear
to be mainly frugivorous. At nightfall the orang builds himself a

roofed nest of branches and twigs and leaves up in a tree, and there rests through the night.

Pan. The chimpanzee is an inhabitant of western and eastern equatorial Africa. There is a single species *Pan satyrus*, with one or possibly two subspecies. Two species have been described, the common chimpanzee (*Pan satyrus*), and the bald-headed chimpanzee (*Pan calvus*), but these are at most geographic races or subspecies. A pygmy chimpanzee has recently been described as a third species, *Pan paniscus*, but it is an open question whether this is not more properly to be regarded as a variant very closely related to *Pan satyrus*.

There are seven cervical, and an average of 13 thoracic, four lumbar, six sacral, and three coccygeal vertebrae.

The average weight of the male is 110 pounds, and of the female 88 pounds. The average height of the male is five feet and of the female four feet. The chimpanzees are expert climbers and brachiators, but spend much time on the ground where they walk in an obliquely quadrupedal position on the flat of their feet, supporting themselves on the middle joints of their bent fingers. The coarse, straight, body hair is black, but brown, reddish-brown, gray, and white hairs may be found more or less sparsely distributed over the body. Some chimpanzees are entirely white-skinned, others are as completely black-skinned, some are brown-skinned, still others have a mottle-brown face and a white body skin. Young animals may be white-skinned and then turn black with age. Chimpanzees kept indoors for an appreciable time may become very markedly depigmented, but regain their pigmentation in a short time when exposed to sunlight. Ischial callosities occur in about 38 per cent of animals.

The skull has a very low vault, well developed arched supraorbital ridges, a somewhat lesser projection of the jaws than the orang, and a cranial capacity, in the male, of about 400 c.c. A sagittal crest is usually absent, and there is no mastoid process. The root and bridge of the nose are depressed, and the nasal bones are relatively short and flat. The lips are extremely mobile. The upper extremities are long, the tips of the fingers reaching to the level of the knee-joint. The hand is narrow and the fingers long. The thumb is opposable, comparatively short, and its skeletal length is about 47 per cent of the total length of the hand.

In the female the first menstruation, the menarche, occurs at an average of eight years and seven months. The female experiences regular menstrual cycles with considerable swelling of the sexual skin,

Figure 49. Chimpanzee *(Pan satyrus)*. (Photo, New York Zoological Society.)

the whole estrous cycle lasting about 36 days, one week longer than in the human female. The average duration of pregnancy is 226.8 days, about 39.3 days less than in man. One young is born at a birth, and is suckled by the mother in a very human-like manner. At the Yerkes Laboratories there were 6 twin births out of 120 parturitions, a rate of 5 per cent. There is a continuous maternal safeguarding and surveillance of the activities and welfare of the infant. The young one is carried in the abdominal position for between three to six months, when it may then be changed to the mother's arm or leg, or allowed to ride upon the mother's back.

Not very much is known of the social life of chimpanzees or whether such a social unit as a paternal family exists among them, but scientific observation in the wild indicates that they live in small bands or groups, numbering, on the average, about nine individuals in summer, and somewhat more in the rainy season. The strongest male appears to be a leader of the band. The chimpanzee builds himself a nest of leaves in the trees on a foundation of skilfully intertwined branches, in which he rests for the night, but he has no permanent home, being a perfect nomad, wandering about during the day as his appetites and desires lead him. Diet is mainly frugivorous.

Chimpanzees are peaceful animals. They are capable of a wide range of facial expression.

Yerkes estimates that the life-span of the chimpanzee may be about 30 years.

Gorilla. The habitat of the gorilla is east central and western equatorial Africa. There is only one genus, *Gorilla,* and two subspecies are recognized, the western equatorial lowland or coastal gorilla, *Gorilla gorilla gorilla,* and the east central highland or mountain gorilla, *Gorilla gorilla beringei.* The western or lowland gorilla dwells in the densely forested region of the Cameroons and the Gaboon. Here, in a moist, damp, environment, the rainy season lasts for eight months. The eastern or mountain gorilla inhabits a narrow mountainous region of the eastern Congo west of Lake Edward and Lake Kivu, extending south to the northern tip of Lake Tanganyika, an area some 250 miles long by 60 miles wide. This region is also densely forested, and the mountain gorilla is found at altitudes from 7,500 to 12,000 feet. The distance separating the habitats of the lowland and mountain gorillas is about 600 miles. Hence, the two races are geographically and therefore also reproductively isolated from each other.

The differences between the lowland and mountain gorilla are many, but it takes an expert to detect them. The mountain differs

Figure 50. Male Gorilla (believed to be *Gorilla gorilla beringei*, the mountain gorilla). (Photo, Zoological Society of Philadelphia.)

from the lowland gorilla in having somewhat shorter arms, broader and short hands, usually webbed toes, narrower hips, greater length of trunk, narrower width between the eyes, greater length of neck, generally narrower skull, longer palate, thicker pelage, and in a good many other characters. It will be perceived that these are simply minor qualitative differences.

The gorilla is the largest or rather bulkiest of all the primates. The average height of the gorilla is about five feet six inches, but larger males may be a foot taller than this. Because the erect animal keeps his knees bent he usually appears somewhat shorter than he actually is. The gorilla is enormously robust with an average chest girth (below the nipples) of 56 inches, and an average weight of 450 pounds. Weights up to 670 pounds have been recorded. The number of vertebrae is the same as in the chimpanzee, seven cervical, and an average of 13 thoracic, four lumbar, six sacral, and three coccygeal. Skin color is usually black, but the writer has seen one young gorilla with a white body skin under its thick black coat of hair; in later life this may, however, have turned black.

The gorilla is the only one of the anthropoids that exhibits a slight elevation of the nasal bones, an elevation which is highest at the median ridge where the two bones fuse at an early age. Both root and bridge of nose are flat. The free margins of the nasal bones extend well below the level of the infraorbital margins. The lower portion of the nose is broader than that to be found in any other primate. The nasal wings are very thick, enclosing "V"-shaped nostrils separated by a thin septum, and pass below into the upper lip. The lips are very thin, with scarcely any exposure of mucous membrane such as gives the lip in man its characteristic appearance. The ears are small and set close to the head. Because of the presence of massive, chisel-like incisors and huge tusk-like canine teeth in the male, the upper and lower jaws are very wide in front, making the mouth-slit of great width. The female is a smaller and much less specialized animal than the male gorilla. Her canine teeth are much smaller, and in her skeletal characters she is somewhat less rugged than the male. The skull of the adult male is generally easily distinguished from that of the female by the presence of a prominent sagittal crest of bone which runs down the middle of the vault, and which is much larger than anything of the kind achieved by the male orang. To this crest are attached the temporal muscles which move the massive lower jaw. The crest is not seen in the living animal principally because the temporal muscles fill in the areas on each side of the crest, and because of the presence of a "crown pad" of connective tissue which lies above these.

Above the orbits stretches a very strongly developed bar of bone, which is internally hollowed out to form enormous frontal sinuses. Behind the bar is a depression, and from this depression the frontal bone hardly manages to raise itself into the semblance of a forehead. Externally the skull is long, but internally the cranial cavity itself is actually relatively broad, so that in the case of the gorilla we are dealing with a dolichocranial or long external skull and a brachycranial or broad internal skull. The average cranial capacity of the male is 550 c.c. and of the female 460 c.c. There is no concavity to the facial profile of the gorilla, but the face projects obliquely downwards and forwards in an almost straight line. A moderately well developed mastoid process is present. Owing to the peculiar configuration of the back of the head and the powerfully developed neck muscles there is no obvious demarcation between the back of the head and the trunk. Laryngeal sacs are present, but are not quite as well developed as in the orang.

Thumb and great toe are opposable. The gorilla spends most of his time on the ground where he progresses by walking more or less on the flat of the soles of his feet, resting his weight anteriorly on the middle joints of his fingers. The gorilla is able to stand erectly and even to take a few steps in that position, but his normal gait is obliquely quadrupedal. Since his forelimbs are considerably longer than his hindlimbs, and the latter are habitually bent at the knees, the posture thus produced is one which is best described as obliquely quadrupedal. The term "semi-erect" does not accurately describe either the posture or the habitual mode of progression of the gorilla.

The gorilla is a slow moving creature, and on the ground is easily overtaken by man. Gorillas are not entirely terrestrial in their habits, for the smaller ones occasionally climb trees, in which they progress by brachiation and by walking erectly while grasping the branches above them with their hands. At the approach of night the gorilla builds himself a comfortable nest which he uses once only, and abandons in the morning. The lowland gorilla builds nests sometimes in trees but mostly on the ground. The mountain gorilla usually builds his nest on the ground under large trees, and sometimes—interestingly enough—under ledges of rocks, but quite frequently also in trees. Diet is principally herbivorous.

The gorilla lives in small bands of from three to 10 or more families. These generally separate during the day but return before nightfall to make their nests together. Gorillas are nomadic in their habits, rarely staying longer than a month in the same locality, principally, it is supposed, because of the exhaustion of the food supply. The gorilla is a peaceable animal, and will never attack a man unless badly frightened or threatened.

Very little is known of the reproductive life of the gorilla. What is known is that the gorilla experiences a definite menstrual cycle much like that of the human female, with menstruation every 39 days, no sexual skin, and slight swelling of the labia majora prior to menstruation. Duration of pregnancy is probably about the same as in man. One young is born at a birth, and this generally clings to the mother's chest or abdomen, and is frequently carried on her arm. When the infant grows older, it rides on the mother's back.

In contrast to the chimpanzee, which may be described as a somewhat manic type temperamentally, the gorilla, in captivity at any rate, may be described as a distinctly quiet type. The latter is much less given to emotional expression of any sort than the former, and the gorilla's range of facial expression seems to be less than that of the chimpanzee.

Homo. All the living forms of man belong to the single genus *Homo*, and the single species *sapiens*. Although man is unquestionably a member of the giant anthropomorphous primates, he differs in so many respects from them as to justify his inclusion in a separate family, the Hominidae.

The following are some of the many features distinguishing man from the living anthropoid apes:

1. Fully erect posture
2. Habitual bipedal locomotion
3. Legs much longer than arms
4. Greater average relative length of lower limbs
5. Shortest average relative length of upper limbs
6. Longest thumb in relation to hand length
7. Earliest disappearance of independent *os centrale*
8. Straighter fingers and palm
9. Shorter finger bones
10. Shortest relative length of toes, excepting big toe
11. Non-opposable great toe, set in line with other toes
12. Foot arched transversely and longitudinally
13. Lowest shoulders
14. Lowest placed nipples
15. Least increase in average stoutness of trunk—more marked flattening of thorax from before backwards
16. Earlier fusion of sternebrae
17. More central position of vertebral column

18. Highest average total number of vertebrae
19. Highest average number of thoracolumbar vertebrae
20. Highest average number of coccygeal vertebrae
21. Relatively longest cervical and lumbar regions of spine
22. Marked cervical and lumbar anterior convexities of spine
23. Relatively greatest distance between thorax and pelvis
24. Sharper backward inclination of sacrum—sacro-vertebral angle
25. Large sacroiliac joints
26. Pubis much higher in relation to sacrum
27. Relatively much shorter pelvis
28. Much greater curvature of iliac blades
29. Iliac fossae of pelvis face one another
30. Relatively shortest iliac bones
31. Presence of a true inguinal ligament
32. Absence of a penis bone
33. Absence of ischial callosities
34. Fulcrum of head much nearer center of gravity
35. Forward position of occipital condyles
36. Flatter and more horizontal position of anterior cranial fossa
37. Orbits situated under anterior cranial fossa
38. Relatively greater distance between eyes
39. Shorter height of face
40. Earlier development and larger adult size of mastoid processes
41. Longer neck
42. Absence of well developed laryngeal sacs
43. Smaller musculature of back of neck (semispinalis capitis)
44. Trunk musculature (multifidus) primarily used for balancing body on lower limbs
45. Larger musculature of back
46. Great reduction in the projection of the jaws
47. Smaller and more delicate alveolar arches
48. Great reduction in size of canine teeth
49. Equality of sexes with regard to size of canine teeth
50. Much later completion of eruption of permanent dentition
51. Smaller jaw muscles
52. Attachments of neck and jaw muscles more widely separated
53. Extremely early fusion of facial maxilla with premaxilla
54. Late closure of bregmatic fontanelle
55. Late closure of metopic suture
56. Prenatal separation of nasal roof and wing cartilages
57. Very late fusion of nasal bones
58. Absence of diastemata in the upper jaw for the reception of the tip of the lower canine tooth
59. Later eruption of deciduous dentition
60. Eruption of deciduous canines before second deciduous molars
61. Second permanent molars erupt after replacement of all deciduous teeth
62. Prominent bony nose with elongated fleshy tip
63. Median furrow or philtrum of the upper lip
64. Outward rolled mucous membrane forming lips

65. A well marked chin
66. Absence of a simian mandibular shelf
67. Earlier fusion of mandibular halves
68. Much earlier development of mastoid processes
69. Great reduction in density of hair (except on scalp)
70. Reduction of tactile hairs
71. Occurrence of wavy and curly hair
72. Later appearance of pigment in skin
73. Brain more than twice as large
74. Less marked rotation of thumb
75. Less extreme reduction of caudal vertebrae
76. Earlier descent of testes
77. Greatest weight at birth in relation to body weight in adult life
78. Most retarded skeletal maturation at birth
79. Longer growth period and slower rate of development
80. Longer life span

There are numerous other morphological and particularly physiological characters in which man differs from the anthropoids, and an even larger number in which both man and the anthropoids differ from the Cercopithecidae or non-anthropomorphous catarrhines. Huxley's classic judgment of 1863 that the structural differences which separate man from the great apes are not so great as those which separate the great apes from the monkeys, has been fully confirmed by subsequent investigation. So, too, has his judgment that "the structural differences between Man and the Man-like apes certainly justify our regarding him as constituting a family apart from them."

Man may briefly be defined as a big-brained primate with the capacity of articulate speech. Walking erectly he uses his hands—freed from all locomotor activity—to make and use tools. His face and teeth are small, and his diet is omnivorous.

With respect to more qualitative features man differs from all non-human primates in the following traits or potentialities:

1. Relative freedom from constraint of biologically predetermined behavioral responses.
2. The potentialities for the development of a complex intelligence. Educability.
3. The capacity for complex symbolic thought.
4. Speech as an expression of symbolic thought.
5. The development of a complex way of life or culture.
6. The capacity for innovation.

It is in the possession of these six potentialities, and in their active realization and transmission, from generation to generation, that man

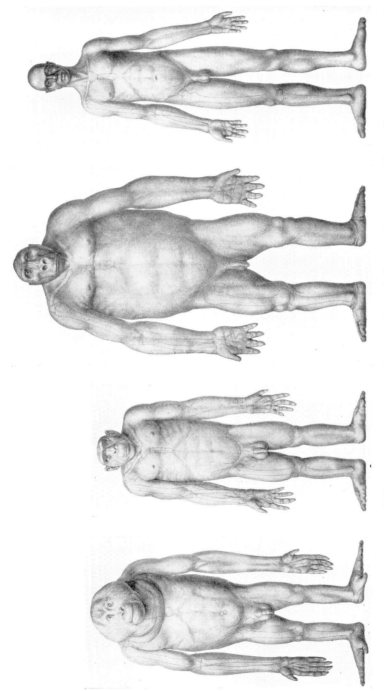

Figure 51. Body proportions in fully grown great apes and man. From left to right: Orang-Utan, Chimpanzee, Mountain Gorilla, and Man (American Negro). (From A. H. Schultz. Courtesy, *Anthropologischer Anzeiger.*)

qualitatively differs so very significantly from all other primates. It is the development of these potentialities which alone enables him to become a human being. It is probable that these peculiarly human traits are significantly associated with some of the unique features of man's anatomical structure. The size and complexity of the brain, the erect bipedal posture, and the complete freeing of the hands, are factors which are almost certainly significantly associated with man's social development, and there are doubtless others.

FOR FURTHER READING, CONSULT:

BINGHAM, H. C.: *Gorillas in a Native Habitat.* Washington, D.C., Carnegie Inst., 1932.
A study of the social life and habits of the mountain gorilla *(Gorilla gorilla beringei)* in Parc National Albert, Belgian Congo, Africa.
BOULENGER, E. G.: *Apes and Monkeys.* London, Harrap, 1936.
A popular well illustrated account.
CALMAN, W. T.: *The Classification of Animals.* New York, Wiley, 1949.
A brief excellent introduction to zoological taxonomy.
CARPENTER, C. R.: A field study of the behavior and social relations of howling monkeys. *Comparative Psychol. Monogr., 10:* Serial no. 48; 1934.
A study of the social life and habits of the howler monkey *(Alouatta palliata)* on Barro Colorado Island, Panama Canal Zone.
———: A field study in Siam of the behavior and social relations of the gibbon *(Hylobates lar). Comparative Psychol. Monogr., 16:* serial no. 84; 1940.
An invaluable study.
FYLEMAN, R.: *Monkeys.* New York, Nelson, 1936.
Intended for younger people this is a delightful book, thoroughly sound, extremely well written, and short; it may be read with advantage by all classes of readers.
HILL, W. C. OSMAN: *Primates: Comparative Anatomy and Taxonomy.*
    Vol. 1, *Strepsirhini.* Edinburgh: at the University Press, 1953.
    Vol. 2, *Haplorhini:* Tarsioidea. Edinburgh: at the University Press, 1955.
    Vol. 3, *Pithecoidea:* Pithecoidea: Platyrrhini (Families Hapalidae and Callimiconidae). Edinburgh: at the University Press, 1957.
An invaluable work to be completed in several more volumes.
HOOTON, A. E.: *Man's Poor Relations.* New York, Doubleday Doran, 1942.
One of the best available accounts of the living primates.
JONES, F. WOOD: *Man's Place Among the Mammals.* New York, Longmans, Green, 1929.
An excellent book on the primates, brilliantly written, though not always sound where factual details are brought into the discussion of controversial matters.
MAYR, E., LINSLEY, E. G., and USINGER, R. L.: *Methods and Principles of Systematic Zoology.* New York, McGraw-Hill, 1953.
The best and most practically useful treatise on the principles and methods of taxonomy.
MERFIELD, F. G.: *Gorilla Hunter.* New York, Farrar, Straus & Cudahy, 1956.
An excellent account of gorillas and chimpanzees in their native habitat.

NISSEN, H. W.: A field study of the chimpanzee. *Comparative Psychol. Monogr.*, 8: serial no. 36, 1931.
Observations of chimpanzee behavior and environment in Western French Guinea.

OAKLEY, K. P.: A definition of man. *Science News* (London), 20:69-81, 1951.
A stimulating discussion of man as a tool-making animal.

————: Skill as a human possession. In *A History of Technology*, vol. 1, (edited by C. Singer, E. J. Holmyard, and A. R. Hall), Oxford: At the Clarendon Press, 1954, pp. 1-37.
An account of the evolution of human skill in tool-making.

SANDERSON, I. T.: *The Monkey Kingdom: An Introduction to the Primates*. Garden City, New York, Hanover House, 1957.
A thoroughly delightful book introducing the primates. Highly informative, beautifully illustrated with ninety photographs and other illustrations of primates, thirty-five of them in color.

SCHENCK, E. T. and McMASTERS, J. H.: *Procedure in Taxonomy*. Stanford University Press, 1936.
A very useful presentation of the formal rules of taxonomy and zoological nomenclature.

SCHULTZ, A. H.: Characters common to higher primates and characters specific for man. *The Quart. Rev. Biol.*, 11:259-283, 425-455, 1936.
An authoritative analysis of the comparative anatomy of apes and man.

————: Ontogenetic specialization of man. *Arch. der Julius Klaus-Stiftung* (Zurich), 24:197-216, 1950.
A valuable study of the differences characterizing man at different stages of his development in comparison with other primates.

————: The physical distinctions of man. *Proc. Amer. Phil. Soc.*, 94:428-449, 1950.
An important and original study of the physical distinctions of man as compared with other primates.

SIMPSON, G. G.: The principles of classification and a classification of mammals. *Bull. Am. Museum Natur. Hist.*, 85: 1945, pp. xvi + 350.
A masterly work. Authoritatively and delightfully written, it should be obligatory reading for all students and others desiring a working knowledge of the principles of taxonomy. The author's classification of the primates is the best thus far offered, being for the first time adopted in the present volume.

SONNTAG, C. F.: *The Morphology and Evolution of the Apes and Man*. London, Bale, 1924.
Intended to serve as an introduction to anthropology, this worthy volume, illustrated somewhat primitively, gives very complete information on the anatomy and relationships of the primates with especial reference to the apes and man.

WALKER, E. P.: *The Monkey Book*. New York, Macmillan, 1954.
Admirably illustrated, the assistant director of the National Zoological Park, deals especially with the care, feeding, and housing of primates, from lemurs to gorillas.

YERKES, R. M.: *The Great Apes*. New Haven, Yale University Press, 1934.
The best and most readable account of the great apes extant.

————: *Chimpanzees*. New Haven, Yale University Press, 1943.
The most informative book on the chimpanzee as observed in the laboratory.

ZUCKERMAN, S.: *The Social Life of Monkeys and Apes.* New York, Harcourt, Brace, 1932.

The standard work on the subject. Based mostly on original observations, readably and interestingly written.

————: *Functional Affinities of Man, Monkeys, and Apes.* New York, Harcourt, Brace, 1933.

An important and very readable study of the bearings of physiology and behavior on the taxonomy and phylogeny of the primates.

Chapter III

THE ORIGIN AND EVOLUTION OF THE PRIMATES

THE FIRST KNOWN primates appeared on this earth some sixty-five million years ago, in the Middle Paleocene. In Table III will be found a systematic classification of the geologic eras, periods, and epochs, and an estimate of their duration in time, together with some of the representative forms of life which flourished therein. It is a useful thing to memorize such a time-scale, for it serves to give one a firmer grasp upon the succession of the forms of life in time than could otherwise be obtained.

During the last three decades Gidley, Jepsen, Simpson, and others, have described numerous fossil primate teeth and jaws from the Middle and Upper Paleocene of the Rocky Mountain region of North America. Before Gidley's original discovery at Fort Union, Montana, only one doubtfully recognized primate, *Plesiadapis*, was known from the (Upper) Paleocene. Today five distinct families are recognized from the Paleocene, the Anaptomorphidae, the Phenacolemuridae, the Apatemyidae, the Carpolestidae, and the Plesiadapidae. Several genera and a good number of species are distinguished in each of these families. The more important genera may be listed here.

FAMILY ANAPTOMORPHIDAE

Genus *Palenochtha*
Genus *Plesiolestes* } Middle Paleocene
Genus *Navajovius* } of North America

FAMILY PHENACOLEMURIDAE

Genus *Palaechthon*
Genus *Phenacolemur* } Middle and Upper Paleocene of
Geuns *Paromomys* } North America

FAMILY APATEMYIDAE

Genus *Jepsenella* Middle } Paleocene of
Genus *Labidolemur* Upper } North America

FAMILY CARPOLESTIDAE

Genus *Elphidotarsius* Middle }
Genus *Carpolestes* Upper } Paleocene of
Genus *Carpodaptes* Upper } North America

[94]

FAMILY PLESIADAPIDAE

Genus *Pronothedectes*	Middle Paleocene of North America
Genus *Plesiadapis*	Upper Paleocene of North America and Europe
Genus *Chiromyoides*	Upper Paleocene of France

The available remains of fossil Paleocene primates do not permit of any definite conclusions concerning the relationships of these forms to later Eocene primates. Broadly speaking the apatemyids and plesiadapids appear to be related to the primitive lemurs, while the carpolestids were possibly of proto-tarsioid origin, but do not appear to have been ancestral to any other group, whereas the carpolestids have clear genetic affinities with the tarsioids. *Palenochtha,* the most generalized type, may well be ancestral to the tarsioids. *Paromomys* has been thought to be ancestral to the European tarsioid genus *Necrolemur* but this is somewhat doubtful, while *Plesiolestes* (from Northern Wyoming) may represent a slightly modified and progressive descendant of *Palaechthon. Chiromyoides* from the Upper Paleocene of France may be related to the ancestral stock of the "aye-aye," but the similarities may be due to convergence.

Whatever the relationships may prove to be it is, in any event, clear that in the Paleocene there were already in existence several primate phyletic lines, but evidently less distinctly differentiated than those of the Lower Eocene.

The fossil teeth, jaws, and other skeletal remains of the earliest Eocene primates already display many well differentiated characters, indicating a past history extending over a very long period of time. These differences are so marked and significant that they render it necessary to recognize the existence, even at that remote period, of two separate infraorders, namely, the Lemuriformes and the Tarsiiformes. Both in size and proportions the Eocene lemuroids strongly resemble the existing lemuriform or Malagasy lemurs which inhabit Madagascar and the neighboring Comoro Islands. The latter may therefore be regarded as "living fossils," with the tree-shrews the surviving primitives among the primates. The fossil lemuroids are represented by two widespread families, the Adapidae, and the Notharctidae, each with its own subfamily, the Adapinae and the Notharctinae; the former being confined to Europe with three distinct genera, *Adapis, Anchomomys* and *Pronycticebus,* with several species; the latter, the Notharctinae, comprising the genera *Pelycodus, Notharc-*

TABLE III

GEOLOGICAL TIME-SCALE OF THE APPEARANCE OF VARIOUS REPRESENTATIVE FORMS OF LIFE

Era	Period	Epoch	Millions of Years Since the Beginning of Each Epoch	Forms of Life
CENOZOIC The Age of Mammals	Quaternary	Recent	1/40	Man, the slave and master.
		Pleistocene	1	*Pithecanthropus, Sinanthropus, Swanscombe, Homo sapiens.*
	Tertiary	Pliocene	12	Man's immediate precursors probably appeared during the latter part of this epoch. *Oreopithecus.*
		Miocene	29	Appearance of true anthropoid apes. *Dryopithecus, Sivapithecus, Proconsul.*
		Oligocene	40	Primitive anthropoid apes appear such as *Propliopithecus.*
		Eocene	60	Spread of modern mammals.
		Paleocene	75	Appearance of insectivorous preprimates and earliest primates, primitive lemuroids and tarsioids.
MESOZOIC The Age of Reptiles	Secondary	Cretaceous	135	Rise of archaic mammals and birds. Extinction of dinosaurs, pterodactyls, and toothed birds. INSECTIVORES.
		Jurassic	165	Spread of primitive mammals and pterodactyls, rise of toothed birds.
		Triassic	205	Rise of dinosaurs, pterodactyls and primitive mammals.
PALEOZOIC The Age of Ancient Life		Permian	230	Spread of amphibians and insects. Extinction of trilobites.
		Carboniferous	255	Primitive reptiles, insects, spiders. Great forests of ferns and mosses.
		Devonian	325	Rise of fishes and amphibians. Spreading of forests.
		Silurian	360	Rise of ostracoderms, sea-scorpions (Eurypterids). First land plants.
		Ordovician	425	First primitive fishes, the ostracoderms.
		Cambrian	505	Still no land-life known, trilobites, mollusks, brachiopods.
PROTEROZOIC			925	Sponges, protozoons, diatoms, and protophyta, and other commencing complex forms of life developed during this era.
ARCHEOZOIC			1 500	Probably simple unicellular sea-dwelling forms.

The estimated number of millions of years in the fourth column for the Tertiary period is based on a combination of paleontological data, with specific reference to the evolution of the horse from *Eohippus* to *Equus*, and the evidence of geology and radioactivity. The figures for the preceding periods are largely based on the uranium transformation method. When uranium and lead occur together in a fragment of rock otherwise free from these elements it may generally be safely assumed that the lead represents "decomposed" or transformed uranium. It is known that 1,000,000 grams of uranium yields 1/7600 grams of lead a year. Hence the age of such rocks can be determined from the proportions of these elements which they contain, thus:

$$\text{Age of rock} = \frac{\text{Weight of Lead}}{\text{Weight of Uranium}} \times 7600 \text{ million years}$$

tus, Smilodectes of North America, and *Protoadapis* of France. Because both tarsioids and lemuroids occur there at earlier horizons than elsewhere in the world it is possible that North America was the birthplace of the primates.

Some 20 or more genera of fossil tarsioids have been described, nearly three-fourths of which occur in America, and the remainder in Europe.

The modern lemurs may have originated from some member of the Adapidae. *Pelycodus* may well have given rise to *Notharctus*, and possibly also to *Smilodectes.*

Neither *Notharctus* nor *Smilodectes* was involved in the descent of modern lemurs. It is by some authorities thought that *Notharctus* became extinct possibly at the end of the Upper Eocene, while others consider it possible that *Notharctus* was ancestral to the Ceboidea. Others think that the long-lived stem of *Omomys*, within the Omomyidae, Middle and Upper Eocene Tarsiiformes were more likely to have been ancestral to the ceboids. With the fossil record as incomplete as it is such attempts at the reconstruction of the early history of the primates must remain largely speculative. Nevertheless, there is hardly a year that passes without some new form being discovered which helps to make that history a little more clear.

In 1953, the most ancient primate ever found in China was discovered in an Upper Eocene formation of the Yuanchu Basin of the Lower Middle Hoangho or Yellow River. The find consisted of a right mandibular fragment with M_1 and M_2, a left mandibular fragment with PM_2, M_1, and M_2, a right maxillary fragment with PM^2 and M^1, the two latter probably belonging to the same individual, and isolated M_1 was also found. This find has been named *Hoanghonius stehlini*, and on the basis of tooth structure its affinities appear to be most comparable to the American Lower Eocene tarsioid *Tetonius*. Drs.

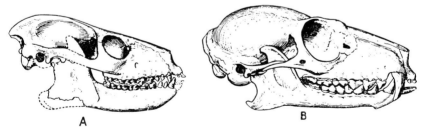

Figure 52. A, Skull of the Eocene Lemur, *Notharctus*. B, Skull of Modern Lemur. (Redrawn after W. K. Gregory.)

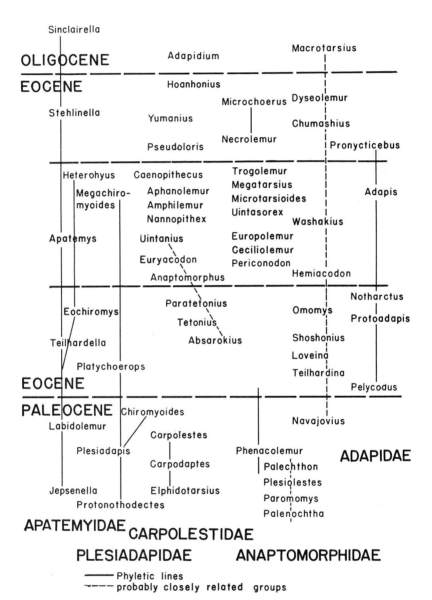

Figure 53. Relationships of early primates. (From Barth. Courtesy, *Am. J. Phys. Anthrop.*)

Woo Ju-Kang and Chow Min-Chen suggest that this specimen provides a clue to a possible relationship between the earliest primates of America and those of Asia.

The early lemuroids differ from the early tarsioids in having, on the whole, retained a greater number of primitive characters, e.g., more dependence upon smell and less upon vision, less peculiar specializations in the skeleton for leaping from branch to branch, and a less developed brain. The tarsioids, on the other hand, display many of those morphological changes which made the subsequent development of man possible. The Prosimii were, as almost all primates continue to be, tree dwellers.

But from what group of animals were the Prosimii themselves derived? We have already seen that the evidence indicates that they were derived from an Upper Cretaceous group of insectivores which very closely resembled the existing tree-shrews of the family Tupaiidae (Figure 54).

The adoption of the habit of living in the trees by some of those early shrews put a premium upon those characters which would best enable these creatures to pursue an arboreal existence. A terrestrial existence demands of the four-footed animal that in its search for a living it keep its nose, as it were, to the ground. The forefront, and greater part, of the primitive vertebrate brain was a smell-brain, a receptor for odors from the external world, and this fact determined

Figure 54. The Tree-shrew (*Tupaia ferruginea*).

the patterns of development of the brain of the earliest mammals. When, however, such a mammal takes to the trees, a nervous receptor-organ such as the brain which is dominantly olfactory, must undergo certain readjustments if the species is to make the proper adaptations and survive. In the trees the sense of smell is not as important as the sense of vision. With all four feet flat on the ground it is easy to smell out edible objects and pick them up with one's jaws. But up in the trees the problem is entirely different. It is necessary to see one's food rather than to smell it out, and when it has been seen it must often be caught on the wing by a jump to another branch and held by the forelimbs, while the supporting branch must be grasped by the hindlimbs at the same time. Insects must be caught in flight, grubs and worms picked out of the bark with finger and nail after they have been smelled or the visual signs of their presence detected. Delicate adjustments in equilibrium and in motor coördination, in the sense of hearing, in the sense of touch, and, indeed, in all the faculties of discrimination, are necessary.

Thus it came about that for orientation in space and for recognition of objects in that space the sense of vision was developed by arboreal mammals into a much finer mechanism than ever before.

In the course of several millions of years the accumulation of variations favoring animals pursuing an arboreal life resulted in the various Prosimii.

It is the development in the importance of the sense of vision which led to the birth of the primates, and it was arboreal life which provided the conditions favoring such a development. The fossil Prosimii show highly specialized divergent changes in the structures subserving the senses of smell and vision, both in the skeleton and the soft tissues as they may be interpreted from the latter, and by comparing the fossil forms with their living descendants. From the lateral position which they occupy in earlier forms the eyes now tend to assume a more frontal position, although it is only in the Lorisidae and in *Tarsius* that this position is actually achieved among prosimians. The cone cells of the retina practically entirely disappear in most forms, leaving the rod cells only. This latter specialization is associated with the nocturnal habits of the Prosimii, for they have poor vision in daylight and excellent vision at night. They spend the daylight hours in sleep and are most active at night. How this habit came into existence we do not know, though it would be easy enough to suggest that it was probably of some adaptive value.

In the Tarsiiformes the visual areas of the brain are somewhat more complex and relatively larger than in the Lemuriformes, and there is every reason to believe that this was equally true in the early tarsioids. In the latter the eyes underwent an enormous increase in size, resulting in the development of the largest eyes, in proportion to the size of the head, to be found in any mammal. This is well seen in the surviving species of the Tarsiiformes (see Figure 22). In the tarsioids vision became the dominant sense, definitely usurping the position once occupied by smell as the principal guide to the animal, thus surpassing the lemurs in whose life olfaction still plays a dominant rôle.

The gradual development of the sense of vision constitutes probably the most important single factor in the evolution of the primates. It vastly extended the "space of recognition."

It has already been pointed out that the freeing of the forelimbs for the handling of objects promotes the development of the hand and the specialization of each of the digits to perform those remarkably fine and complex adjustive movements of which the human hand is perhaps the most perfect example. Not only does the opposability of the thumb to the other digits of the hand become possible, but the ground work is fully laid for the development of the erect posture —a possibility not to be fully realized until the appearance of the first men in the Pleistocene.

The nocturnal mode of life of the Prosimii demands considerable auditory acuity, and here again, as between both groups, the sense of hearing is more highly developed in the tarsiers than in the lemurs, and was presumably so in their Eocene ancestors.

Thus, it may be perceived that because the Eocene primates learned to rely primarily on vision rather than on the sense of smell for the exploration, recognition, and apperception of their environment, there commenced a progressive development of all their senses, with the exception of that of smell which was destined to undergo a very thorough retrogression. The most important result of this revolutionary change was to produce a corresponding development of those centers of the brain which could integrate the disparate sensory stimuli into a "unity of apperception." Those centers are situated in what is termed the neopallium of the endbrain. Simultaneously a considerable involution occurred of that part of the endbrain which subserves the sense of smell, the so-called "rhinencephalon."

The neopallium contains the largest part of the "cortex" or external "gray matter" (pallium) of the brain into which lead tracts from all the non-olfactory senses. Particular areas of the neopallium receive particular kinds of stimuli. Between these cortical areas there are numerous and very intricate connections which render possible the coordination of different kinds of stimuli. There are, moreover, areas in the cortex which send out fibers relaying "motor" impulses to the lower centers of the brain and spinal cord. But that is not all, the cortex contains association areas capable not only of association but of memory. Where there is a consciousness or sense of the past, there is concern about the future. The neopallium becomes not only a regulating and coordinating organ but also a computing machine for the prediction of future events and thus for the choice of goals to be actively achieved. As it grows and develops, it more and more frees the organism from automatic and instinctive controls and determinants of behavior, and permits the development of reflection upon the basis of past experience, and conduct, adapted to meet the ends which the organism consciously seeks.

The neopallium has attained its greatest growth and highest development in man, and it is because of the special properties or potentialities of his neopallium that man is able to develop that humanity of which he is capable.

Though the brains of creatures which lived many millions of years ago are not preserved, we can, from the fossil skulls and the forms very like these animals which survive today, reconstruct something of the history of the brain. We have seen how enlightening this can be for the understanding of our own history. The progressive enlargement of the neopallium and the reduction of the olfactory areas of the brain is graphically illustrated in Figure 55, in which diagrams of the brain from insectivore to man are shown.

Eocene lemuroids did not give rise to monkeys and apes. They simply transmitted their essential lemuroid character to their lemuriform descendants, displayed to this day in the existing families and genera.

The tarsioids most probably originated from a group of insectivores similar to that which gave rise to the lemurs, but unlike the unproductive lemuroids, the tarsioids seem to have provided the material out of which all other later primates developed. A study of the living tarsiers reveals them as epitomizing in themselves, along with peculiar specializations of the teeth, skull and ankle bones, many of the potentialities for the development of all those characters which all the members of the Anthropoidea exhibit. One eminent student of the primates, the late Professor Wood Jones, believed that the evidence suggests that not the manlike apes but the tarsiers are man's closest living relations. The consensus of scientific opinion is, however, against this view. It is probable that some of the predecessors of the tarsiers stand basically in the line of development of all the monkeys, apes, and men, but the relationship is extremely distant. Most of the early tarsioids constitute highly specialized side-branches, but there were almost certainly in existence a group of Upper Paleocene tarsioids which were ancestral to the monkeys and apes of later geologic times, and these in turn to their existing descendants.

The geological record of the primates in the Oligocene is very poor, but we do know that by the beginning of that epoch the primates of North America had retreated before the advance of the cooler weather to Central and South America, where the existing New World monkeys, the platyrrhini, were evolved. Remains of several New World monkeys from the Lower Miocene are known from South America, chief among these being *Homunculus* from Santa Cruz in Patagonia.

It is most probable that at the same time another group of American Eocene primates migrated across one of the landbridges then existing between Asia and America, such as the Bering Straits, and by this route to the Eastern Hemisphere, to give rise to the Old World monkeys and apes, the catarrhini. Unfortunately the fossil record for the platyrrhini is very bare, and apart from the New World such fossil remains are quite unknown. It is in the Upper Miocene of Europe, and of the Siwalik deposits in India, that the chief representative fossil forms of the Old World monkeys are to be found.

It appears, then, that the Old World, as well as the New World, monkeys evolved in the Oligocene. Simultaneously in the Old World the stock leading to the Anthropomorpha was undergoing development.

In the Lower Oligocene of the Fayum oasis, southwest of Cairo in Egypt, the well-preserved lower jaw of an animal which is undoubtedly the most primitive known member of the catarrhini has been discovered. This has been named *Parapithecus*. Phylogenetically *Parapithecus* is conceived to stand in a position intermediate between the Eocene tarsioids and the higher apes. In this animal the premolar teeth were reduced from three to two in number, yielding for the first time the number of teeth characteristic of the catarrhine series, namely I $\frac{2}{2}$, C $\frac{1}{1}$, PM $\frac{2}{2}$, M $\frac{3}{3}$.

The ancestral placental mammalian dental formula was I $\frac{3}{3}$, C $\frac{1}{1}$, PM $\frac{4}{4}$, M $\frac{3}{3}$. The reduction in the number of premolars in *Parapithecus*, from PM $\frac{4}{4}$ of the ancestral placental mammalian dental

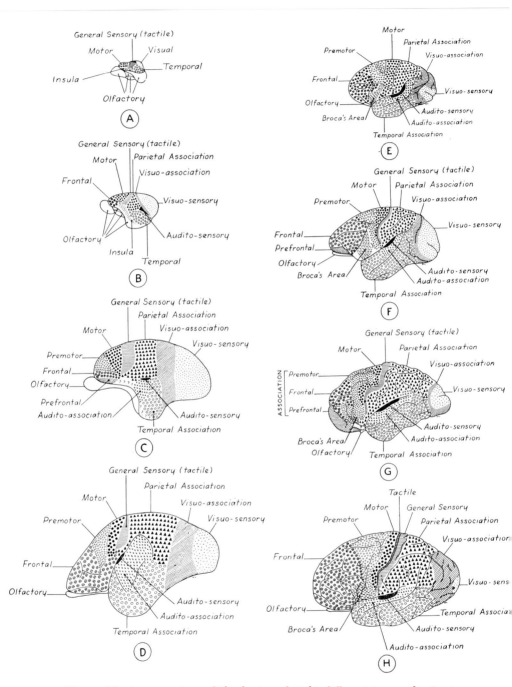

Figure 55. A comparison of the brains of eight different types of primates. A) Jumping Shrew (*Macroscelides*), B) Tree-Shrew (*Tupaia minor*), C) Tarsier (*Tarsius spectrum*), D) Marmoset (*Callithrix jacchus*), E) Spider Monkey (*Ateles vellerosus*), F) Rhesus monkey (*Macaca mulatta*), G) Gorilla (*Gorilla gorilla gorilla*), H) Man (*Homo sapiens*). The brain sizes are not in scale.

formula, suggests that already at this early period the muzzle and jaws were undergoing shortening, a trend which has reached its culmination in the reduction of these parts of the face in man. In the Eocene lemurs, the Notharctinae, the fourth premolar is still retained, while the modern lemurs are characterized by three premolars.

Parapithecus was not much larger than the modern tarsier, having actually been about the size of a big squirrel. The broad rear of the jaw suggests an expanded brain and a short face. Indeed, many morphologists believe that *Parapithecus* constitutes a possible ancestor for the apes and man.

From the same deposits has been recovered the lower jaw of an animal which is remarkably anthropoid in its characters, namely *Propliopithecus*. The latter is smaller and much more primitive than the Lower Miocene *Prohylobates*, a primitive gibbon from the Burdigalian deposits at Moghara on the northern edge of the Libyan desert, and the Upper Miocene and Lower Pliocene *Pliopithecus* of Gascony which in turn closely resembles the modern gibbons.

Propliopithecus, judging from the structure of its jaw and teeth, constitutes an even better candidate as an ancestor for the apes and man than does *Parapithecus*. *Prohylobates* is by some authorities believed to belong in the same genus with *Pliopithecus*. *Prohylobates* seems to be somewhat more primitive, but however this may be, both are so gibbon-like that they may be classed with the gibbons in the family Hylobatidae. Both are, therefore, off the main line of development leading to the great apes and man; such types gave rise to the gibbons, while a type such as *Parapithecus* was conceivably ancestral to *Propliopithecus*, from which in turn stemmed the various Miocene Anthropomorpha which led on the one hand to the existing apes and on the other to man. All these inferences are, of course, based upon the fact that, in the parts preserved, the characters are such as we would expect to find in an ancestral type.

Portions of the mandibles and teeth of two fossil apes, *Xenopithecus* and *Limnopithecus*, from the Lower Miocene of Kenya Colony, East Africa and in the case of *Limnopithecus* also from the Lower Miocene of Kapak, Northeast Uganda are of animals somewhat more than twice the height of *Propliopithecus* (which was probably not more than a foot in height), and which with *Prohylobates* and *Pliopithecus* may well represent contemporary stages in divergent lines of development from the *Propliopithecus* stock.

Among these Miocene genera of fossil Anthropomorpha one of the most important is represented by *Proconsul* from the Lower Mio-

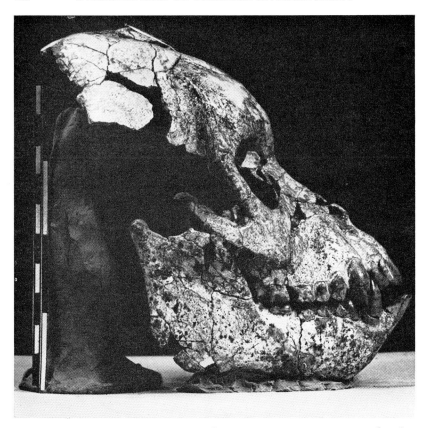

Figure 56. *Proconsul africanus.* (Photo, courtesy Dr. L. S. B. Leakey.)

cene of Kenya Colony, eastern Africa. *Proconsul* is now known from 9 localities in Kenya Colony, and from Kapak, Northeastern Uganda. Parts of the skeletons of a number of individuals are known, among these a remarkably well preserved skull. Three species have been identified. *Proconsul africanus* is represented by several individuals, the best preserved yielding a fairly complete skull, the first such ever found for any Miocene ape. This discovery, as well as most others of these Miocene apes, we owe to the labors of Dr. and Mrs. L. S. B. Leakey. An earlier find had yielded a portion of the right maxilla with upper teeth of the same species. The interesting thing about the skull, discovered in 1947, is its rather cercopithecoid appearance. The skull is that of an adult, and it is intermediate in size between that of a gibbon and a chimpanzee. The skull is delicately constructed, there is no supraorbital torus, the nasal bones are relatively broad, the incisive region of the upper jaw is narrow, and the nasal aperture is constricted, as in the cercopithecoid monkeys, at its lower extremity. The form of the intracranial cavity and the convolutional impressions on the inner aspect of the frontal and parietal bones make it clear that the sulcal pattern of the brain must have conformed closely to the cercopithecoid brain. The mandibular condyles, as in man, are somewhat outwardly rotated; the mandibular symphysis (the junction in the midline of the two sides of the jaw) is short; there is a reduction in the size, and an increase in the breadth index, of the premolars and the first molar; a simian shelf, the transverse plate of bone at the back of the lower part of the mandibular symphysis in the modern apes, is absent; the length of the premolar and molar teeth is reduced; there is a forward convergence of the tooth rows, unlike the paralleling or even divergence in the modern apes; the canine teeth are strongly developed, and the anterior lower premolars have a sectorial form.

Proconsul major is represented by the right side of a mandible with the second premolar and all the molar teeth. Discovered by the Leakeys in 1947, the body of this mandible is massively contructed, and evidently belonged to an animal closely approximating the gorilla in size.

Proconsul nyanzae, described in 1943 by MacInnes, was discovered by Leakey on Rusinga Island. This is represented by an almost complete mandible of an adult with only the right canine and four incisor teeth missing. Removed from the same deposits but not found in direct association with any of the *Proconsul* remains were two thigh bones, a humerus, part of a clavicle (all found in association), and the foot bones, the talus and calcaneus, of a single individual. In their dimensions these bones resemble those of the chimpanzee, but in many of the details of their structure these bones more closely resemble the cercopithecoid limb bones than they do those of the modern great apes. From the structure of their limb bones it would appear that the *Proconsul* group was not adapted to an arboreal brachiating mode of life. On the contrary, they seem to have been constructed on a quadrupedal plan like the cercopithecoid monkeys.

In 1958, Bishop reported the discovery of a lower second right molar tooth of *Proconsul nyanzae* from Kapak, Northeastern Uganda.

Clearly the Lower Miocene apes were extremely primitive. The form of their limbs was of a sufficiently generalized character to have allowed the evolutionary development of the locomotor specializations

Figure 57. Restoration of *Proconsul nyanzae*. (From a painting by Maurice Wilson. Courtesy, British Museum [Natural History].)

of the Pongidae on the one hand and those peculiar to the Hominidae on the other.

Evidently the derivation of man from a stock which had not passed through an arboreal stage of evolutionary development is quite compatible with the view that that stock was of anthropoid type.

From the generalized Lower Oligocene tarsioid *Parapithecus* it is possible that there emerged lines which led to the tarsiers, the New and Old World monkeys, and the anthropoid *Propliopithecus*. From *Propliopithecus* the lines leading to the later anthropoids and to man very likely took their origin. The divergent evolution of the anthropoid and hominid lines may therefore be said to have commenced in the Upper Oligocene, about 40,000,000 years ago. According to this theory an early anthropoid stage in the evolution of man is postulated, with later anthropoid types tending in the human direction.

Some authorities interpret the facts to indicate that man never passed through an anthropoid stage of development but originated from either a tarsioid or generalized catarrhine monkey either in the Eocene or early Oligocene. Still others hold the view that the separation of the anthropoid and human lines occurred in the Upper Miocene, some ten to fifteen million years ago. These authorities believe that the two genera of Middle and Upper Miocene apes, *Dryopithecus* of Europe and *Sivapithecus* of Asia, possess the characters to be expected in the common ancestors of the higher apes and man. These two genera had an extremely wide range in the eastern hemisphere from Spain in the west to India and China in the east, south to East Africa, and even to South Africa. At present more than a dozen nominal species of *Dryopithecus* are known, and about half that number of species of *Sivapithecus*. Most of these fossil apes are known from portions of their upper and lower jaws and associated teeth alone, and these parts indicate that these creatures were fairly unspecialized apes. Gregory and Hellman cite many dental characters suggesting that *Sivapithecus* may be more closely related to the orang than to man, while *Dryopithecus*, the European member of the group may be nearer to the chimpanzee-gorilla-man division.

Since these extinct apes are, for the most part, known only from their jaws and teeth, and only occasionally from other parts of the skeleton, conclusions regarding their phylogenetic relationships have had to be drawn from detailed studies principally of the teeth. For such studies the scientific world is principally indebted to the fundamental work of Professors W. K. Gregory and Milo Hellman of the

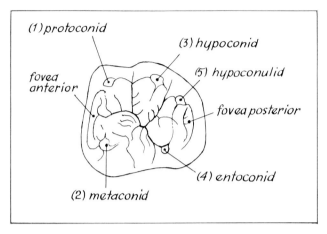

Figure 58. Third right lower molar of *Dryopithecus giganteus*, showing the Dryopithecus pattern of the tooth. (After W. K. Gregory.)

American Museum of Natural History. Such studies yield valuable indications respecting such relationships, but they are at best only indications. Each of the 32 teeth in the adult dental series, as well as each of the 20 teeth in the deciduous or milk dentition, has, as it were, its own character. Each cusp, each furrow between the cusps, and each fossa and surface, has its special significance. Studied in the light of the significance of each of these many dental characters the probable relationships of these fossil apes to one another, and of these in turn to the later apes and to the family of man, the Hominidae, are cogently suggested.

The Dryopithecus Pattern of the Molar Teeth

The upper and lower molar teeth of all members of the Hominoidea, with few exceptions, exhibit a particular pattern of cusp arrangement and other features, which in its characteristic form is known as "the Dryopithecus pattern," because it first makes it appearance in the Miocene Dryopithecine apes (Figures 58 and 60). If the reader has escaped having his lower molar pattern disturbed by the ravages of caries he may, with the aid of a mirror, determine for himself that— to take M_2 as typical—there are three main cusps on the occlusal surface nearest the cheek (buccal 1, 3, 5) and two nearest the tongue (lingual 2, 4). Each of the cusps has its own name, reading from front to back, as follows:

Lower Molars

Buccal Border	Lingual Border
1. Protoconid	2. Metaconid
3. Hypoconid	4. Entoconid
5. Hypoconulid	

In front of and between cusps 1 and 2 (protoconid and metaconid) is a crack, depression or fossa, the fovea anterior. This is a remnant of the primitive trigonid of Eocene mammals. The fossa lying between the posterior cusps 4 and 5 (entoconid and hypoconulid) is the fovea posterior.

Not infrequently a sixth cusp is present on the lower molars between the hypoconulid (5) and the entoconid (4). Sometimes in men the hypoconulid (5) is absent, but the sixth cusp is present, and sometimes both cusps (5 and 6) are absent resulting in a + or cruciate pattern of the cusps. In the evolution of man the tendency is for cusp 6 to be most frequently lost, followed somewhat less frequently by the loss of cusp 5 by reduction or fusion with cusp 3. Negroids appear to show a higher frequency of reduction of cusps 5 and 6 than do Caucasoids (Figure 59).

The upper molars show a corresponding pattern of cusps and fossae.

Each upper molar consists first of a triangle of main conical-pyramidal cusps, *protocone, paracone, metacone,* secondly of a fourth cusp, the *hypocone* situated at the antero-lingual border, and thirdly of two small crested cusps, the *protoconule* and *metaconule,* situated respectively on the anteroexternal and posteroexternal limbs of a "V." The *fovea anterior* is situated between the paracone and the protoconule, while the *fovea posterior* lies between the metacone and the posterior cingulum and the *hypocone* when the latter is present.

Upper Molars

Buccal Border	Lingual Border
Paracone	Protocone
Metacone	Hypocone
	Posterior Cingulum

Such studies enable us to perceive not so much a gradual evolution towards the hominid type of jaws and teeth, as the development of a great many variant forms. Some have manlike anterior and apelike posterior teeth or *vice versa,* still others have such specialized canine teeth that, because of their resemblance to those of the chim-

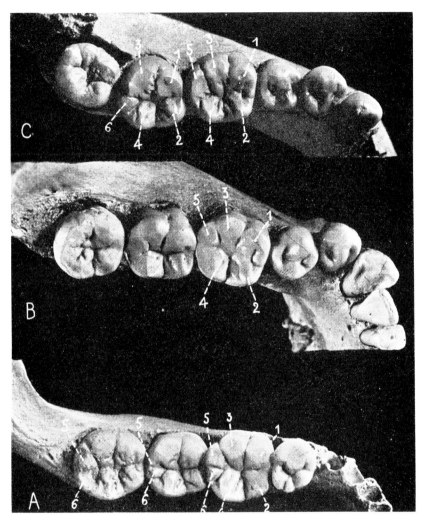

Figure 59. Human lower jaws, with the molar teeth showing the Dryopithe-
cus pattern. A, Australian aboriginal female. B, American Indian from
Tarasco, Northern Mexico. C, American Indian from same vicinity. (From
Gregory and Hellman. Courtesy, American Museum of Natural History.)

panzee and gorilla, we are led to believe that some such types must
have been ancestral to the modern African apes. On the other hand, in
certain members of the *Dryopithecus-Sivapithecus* stock, such as
Dryopithecus rhenanus and *Sivapithecus sivalensis,* the dentition has
retained many primitive features, and is of such a nature that it would

take but a few slight modifications to produce the characteristic dentition of man. Nevertheless, even these forms exhibit specializations of the canine and first premolar teeth which render improbable their being in the direct line of man's ancestry. *Dryopithecus*, for example, has sectorial premolars, while the older *Propliopithecus*, like later *Homo*, has bicuspid premolars. For some authorities this difference is alone sufficient to exclude *Dryopithecus* from the ancestry of man.

The common ancestor of man and the great apes must have been a relatively unspecialized small ape, and precisely such an ancestor is supplied by the Lower Oligocene *Propliopithecus*.

The erroneous notion is occasionally encountered that scientists believe man to be descended from one or another of the living great apes. Such a view is quite contrary to what scientists in fact believe. In *The Descent of Man* (1871) Darwin took special pains to emphasize this point, saying "We must not fall into the error of supposing that the early progenitor of the whole Simian stock, including man, was identical with, or even closely resembled, any existing ape or monkey." The accumulating evidence since Darwin's day indicates ever more clearly that man and the living great apes are collateral, and not lineal, descendants from the same stock. Since their divergence from the common ancestral stock they have pursued their evolutionary paths quite independently of one another.

Gigantopithecus blacki. Between the years 1934 and 1939 von Koenigswald found, in the drawers of Hong Kong Chinese apothe-

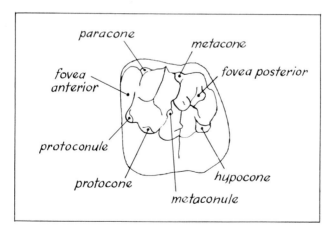

Figure 60. First left upper molar of *Dryopithecus punjabicus*. (After W. K. Gregory.)

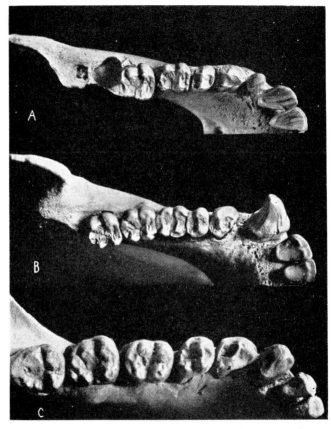

Figure 61. Anthropoid ape lower jaws showing the Dryopithecus pattern of the molars. A & B, chimpanzees, C, *Gorilla gorilla beringei*. (From Gregory and Hellman. Courtesy, American Museum of Natural History.)

cary shops, three man-like molar teeth. These consisted of right and left lower third molars belonging to different individuals, and an upper molar most probably belonging to a third individual. The size of the teeth is enormous. The volume of the crown of the lower third molar is about six times larger than the average crown of the equivalent tooth of modern man, it is almost twice as large as the corresponding tooth of the gorilla, and about one-third larger than that of *Meganthropus*. Dr. von Koenigswald considered that the first retrieved lower molar was that of a giant anthropoid, and so he named the creature to which it belonged *Gigantopithecus* (and in honor of

Davidson Black who discovered the first tooth of *Sinanthropus* under similar conditions) *blacki*. Weidenreich's study of all three teeth led him to the conclusion that they were those of an early giant form of extinct man. But on both counts, that of gigantism on the one hand and hominidity on the other, Weidenreich is probably in error.

Early in 1957 the mandible of another *Gigantopithecus* was discovered, having been unearthed from a high cliff cave by a peasant while digging for "dragon-bones" at Lucheng in Kwangsi Province, South China, in a Middle Pleistocene formation. The rami of the mandible and the body behind the second molar teeth are missing, otherwise the mandible is perfectly preserved together with all the teeth excepting the left central incisor and the third molars. The canines are massive, in man they are small, PM_1 is narrow and compressed as in apes rather than molariform as in man, which suggests a large maxillary canine. The molars are longer than they are broad, and the second molar is larger than the first, there is also a simian shelf, all traits characteristic of apes, but not of hominids. Dr. Pei stresses the fact that the mandible and teeth are more like those of a manlike ape than of a man.

Gigantopithecus was apparently a very robust ape, but there is not the least reason to believe that he was a giant of twelve or thirteen feet as some imaginative writers have suggested. Large teeth and robust jaws are quite compatible with small stature. Indeed, Garn and Lewis have quite conclusively shown that there is no correlation whatever between size of teeth and body size. Large teeth need massive jaws, but do not require long legs or large bodies. So far as the anthropological evidence goes there never were any primate giants. (See Table IV, p. 130).

Broom and Robinson consider that *Gigantopithecus* belongs with the australopithecines, a group among whom the average height of the males was about 156cm (5 feet 1 inch).

The age of *Gigantopithecus* is apparently lower Middle Pleistocene.

The Australopithecinae

It is most fortunate that in the last quarter of a century knowledge has become available of a stock which had already almost passed over into the Hominidae; this is represented by the subfamily of australopithecine apes of South Africa.

In the Pleistocene of South Africa there have been found the

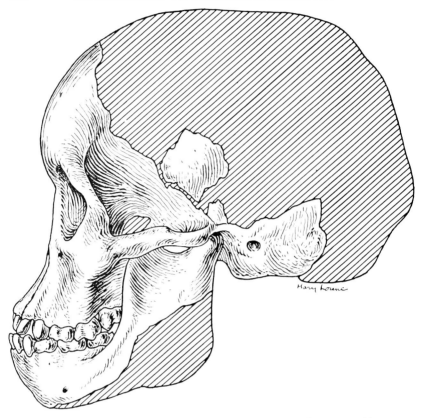

Figure 62. *Australopithecus africanus* (right side reversed).

fossil remains of several manlike apes, *Australopithecus africanus, Australopithecus prometheus, Plesianthropus transvaalensis, Paranthropus robustus, Paranthropus crassidens,* and *Telanthropus capensis.* These are extremely important finds, for they represent stages in evolution at which an ape is seen almost in the very process of merging into man.

The juvenile skull of *Australopithecus* was blasted out of a quarry at Buxton, Taungs, in Bechuanaland in 1924. The age of the formation from which it came was thought by Broom to belong to the Middle Pliocene or the lower part of the Upper Pliocene. The evidence, however, does not support an age older than the Lower Pleistocene. The almost complete skull, with the milk teeth and first permanent molars in an excellent state of preservation, is equivalent in age to a modern child of six years. The teeth are remarkably manlike though their size exceeds that of man. The premaxilla is well developed, as in anthropoids, and there is a typical anthropoid premaxillary diastema, the space in the upper jaw between the lateral incisor and canine teeth, measuring some 4.2 mm. Cranial capacity is 500 c.c., with estimated cranial capacity for the adult of 600 c.c. (Figure 62).

Plesianthropus was blasted out of a cave at Sterkfontein in the Transvaal in 1936 from a deposit of Middle Pleistocene age. At that time the remains of at least four and possibly seven individuals were

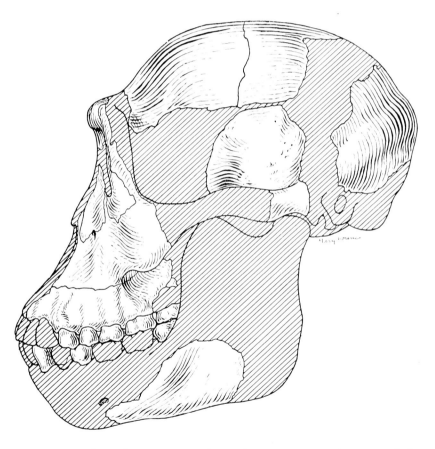

Figure 63. *Plesianthropus transvaalensis* (reconstruction using parts of the right and left sides). (Based on the reconstruction by Gregory and Hellman [1945].)

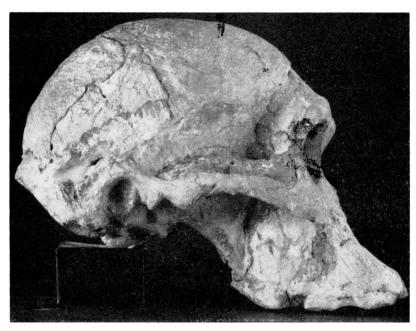

Figure 64. Skull of *Plesianthropus transvaalensis*. Found April 18, 1947. (Courtesy, Dr. R. Broom and Dr. J. T. Robinson.)

recovered. These include the nearly complete skull without mandible of a young male, the almost perfect right maxilla of a female, the crushed and fragmentary skull of an old male, and part of the mandible of a young male. Teeth were well represented, and the manlike post-cranial bones were represented by the lower end (with part of the shaft) of a femur, part of a digital bone, and one wrist bone (capitate). On the facial portion of the skull the remains of the premaxillary suture are visible, and also a small premaxillary diastema between the lateral incisor and canine. The canine teeth, judging from the preserved lower left one, are well developed and project beyond the level of the remaining teeth, but more closely resemble the human than they do the anthropoid type. The third permanent molar had fully erupted and showed signs of wear, while the coronal and sagittal sutures were still completely patent, thus suggesting a growth pattern comparable to that of man. The cranial capacity is 560 c.c. (Figure 63).

In April 1947, within a few feet of the 1936 discovery, Broom found part of the upper jaw of a young male, the upper jaw of a child of about three years, the upper canine of a male of about 30 years, the lower molar of a female of about 40 years, the complete skull, without mandible and teeth, of an elderly female, and later the manlike pelvis and upper half of a femur. All are assigned by Broom to *Plesianthropus*. The milk teeth of the child, according to Broom, are practically identical with those of the Bushman child (Figures 64 to 67).

Paranthropus robustus was found at Kromdraai, two miles east of Sterkfontein, in 1938 in a Middle Pleistocene deposit. Two individuals are represented, the greater part of the skull of an adult male together with the lower end of a right humerus, a portion of the right ulna, a left metacarpal with two phalangeal bones, two toe bones, and a talus. The remains of the second individual are represented by a much weathered mandible of a three or four year old child with the milk teeth in almost perfect condition. The mandible was found some four feet from the adult specimen. As is usual in adult anthropoids the premaxilla is united with the maxilla, and it is quite evident that the premaxilla was of the anthropoid type, with a premaxillary diastema of about 3.0 mm. In man the premaxilla is completely overgrown on the face save in a small number of infants in which the apical portion of the premaxilla is partially visible; a diastema (with the exception

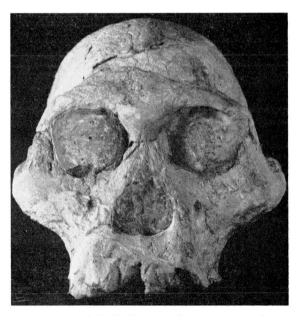

Figure 65. Frontal view of skull of *Plesianthropus transvaalensis*. (Courtesy, Dr. R. Broom and Dr. J. T. Robinson.)

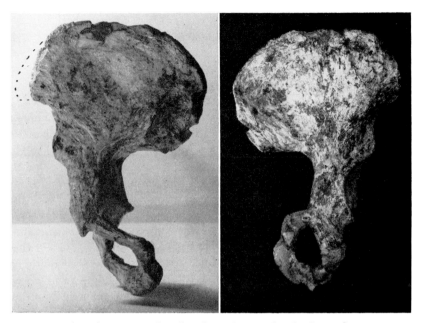

Figure 66 *(Left)*. Inner side of right pelvic arch of *Plesianthropus trans-vaalensis*. A small part of the ilium has been gnawed off. The pubis and part of the ischium have been broken and displaced. Found August 1, 1947.

Figure 67 *(Right)*. Outer side of right pelvic arch of *Plesianthropus trans-vaalensis*. Photographs of pelvis as found. (Photos, courtesy of Dr. R. Broom and Dr. J. T. Robinson.)

of *Pithecanthropus robustus*, see p. 164) is normally never present in man. The cranial capacity of *Paranthropus robustus* is 650 c.c.

The evidence provided by the limb bones of *Plesianthropus* and *Paranthropus* indicates that they habitually walked erectly or nearly erectly and that their hands were of the hominid type, being in no way adapted for the middle-knuckle obliquely quadrupedal manner of progression characteristic of the great apes. The pelvic bones of *Australopithecus* and *Plesianthropus* prove that the erect or nearly erect posture was habitual to the australopithecines. The small brain of these australopithecines, scarcely larger than that of the gorilla or chimpanzee, associated with manlike limb bones makes it quite clear that in the stage of evolution represented by these australo-pithecines the erect posture had already been attained when the brain was still of ape-like proportions. At this stage, too, the teeth were already distinctly manlike. It has been argued that these facts support the inferences which have been drawn from the evidence of comparative anatomy that many of the characters of the living anthropoid apes, such as the tusk-like canines and the large incisors accompanied by the mandibular simian shelf, the exaggerated development of the supraorbital torus, the powerful brachiating arms, and certain features of the hindlimbs, are to be regarded as aberrant specializations, and not as primitive features to be sought for in the ancestors of man.

It is, indeed, highly probable that these characters were absent in the immediate prehuman stock which gave rise to man, and it is

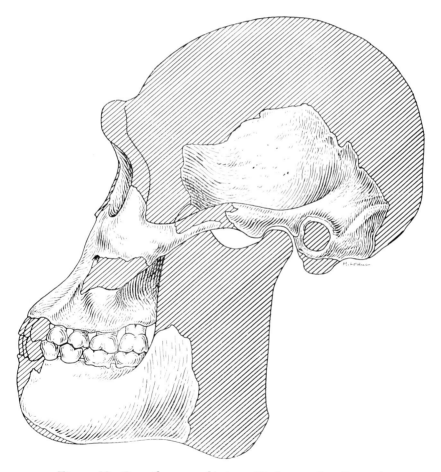

Figure 68. *Paranthropus robustus.* (Redrawn after Broom.)

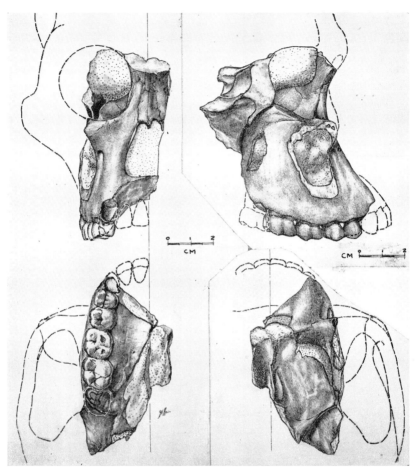

Figure 69. *Australopithecus prometheus.* The cranio-facial fragment in four views. Anterior (upper left), lateral (upper right), palatal (lower left), from above (lower right). (From Dart. Courtesy *Am. J. Phys. Anthrop.*)

agreed by almost all authorities, that the living anthropoids exhibit highly specialized characters which were developed *after* their divergence from that much earlier stock from which they originated together with the line which led to man. A distinction must be recognized between the remote anthropoid stock from which the *line* originated which led to man, and the anthropoid stock from which he immediately originated. Whether the former was a brachiating type remains to be determined, the latter was almost certainly not.

The attainment of hominid or human status is associated with the following three attributes: (1) the erect bipedal posture; (2) virtually complete emancipation of the hands; and (3) speech. The australopithecines had attained the first two; they virtually appear to have achieved the third.

In September 1947, a calvarial fragment of another australopithecid was found in a deserted limeworks dump on the farm Makapansgat some 13 miles northeast of Potieterarust in the Central Transvaal, about 200 miles to the northeast of the Taungs-Plesianthropus district of the Southern Transvaal, South Africa. The fragment consists of the major portion of the occipital bone, including most of the right

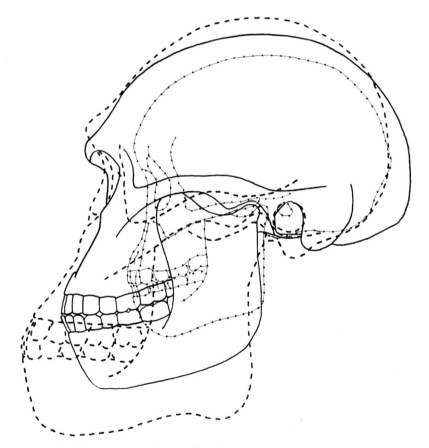

Figure 70. Craniograms of *Australopithecus africanus* (infant) —·—·—·—·—,
Australopithecus prometheus ♀——, and *Paranthropus robustus* ♂ —————
One half normal size. (From Dart. Courtesy *Am. J. Phys. Anthrop.*)

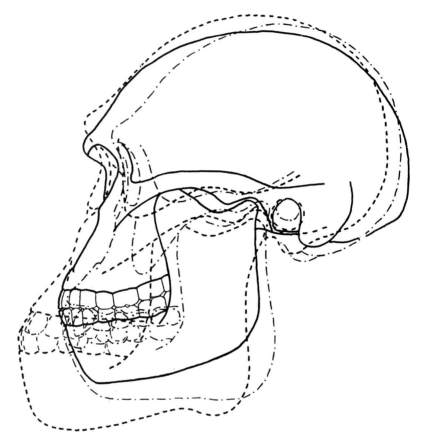

Figure 71. Craniograms of *Australopithecus prometheus* ————, *Plesian-thropus transvaalensis* ♂ —•—•—•—•—, and *Paranthropus robustus* ♂ —————•
One half natural size. (From Dart. Courtesy *Am. J. Phys. Anthrop.*)

margin of the foramen magnum and the posterior third of each of the parietal bones. It has been identified as having come from the basal gray fossiliferous stratum of the Cave of Hearths. This, together with the associated mammalian fauna, indicates a late Villafranchian or early Pleistocene age.

The bones are those of a mature adult and are extremely thick, varying between 6.0 and 13.0 mm., the base of the occiput is very broad, there is a moderately developed occipital torus, a transverse occipital suture is present, the external occipital protuberance is in-feriorly situated in relation to the point which marks the most distant one from the front of the skull (the opisthocranion), the cerebral surface of the occipital bone is 5030 mm.^{2} as compared with 864 mm.^{2} in the chimpanzee. All these features are claimed by Dart to distinguish this fragment as human, and he has assigned it to a new species of the australopithecine group, namely, *Australopithecus prometheus*.

Australopithecus prometheus was a small animal, but its cranial capacity was not less than 650 c.c.

Dart makes the startling claim that the evidence indicates *Australopithecus prometheus* was a big game hunter, who not only used bone implements, but was also acquainted with fire. Numerous smashed skulls and split bones of almost every type of big game characteristic of the eastern riverine savannah testify, Dart believes, to the hunting skill and manual dexterity of this species. That the prometheans used fire Dart believes is suggested by the chemical and microscopic analysis of glassy and ashy materials and charred bones excavated from the basal gray bone breccia.

In July 1948, some 20 feet from the site in which the occiput was found, there was discovered the almost perfect body of the mandible and dentition of an approximately 12 year old adolescent *Australopithecus prometheus*. The jaw is chinless, and a simian shelf is not pres-

Figure 72. Adult female mandible of *Australopithecus prometheus*, showing occlusal view of the teeth. (From Dart. Courtesy, *Am. J. Phys. Anthrop.*)

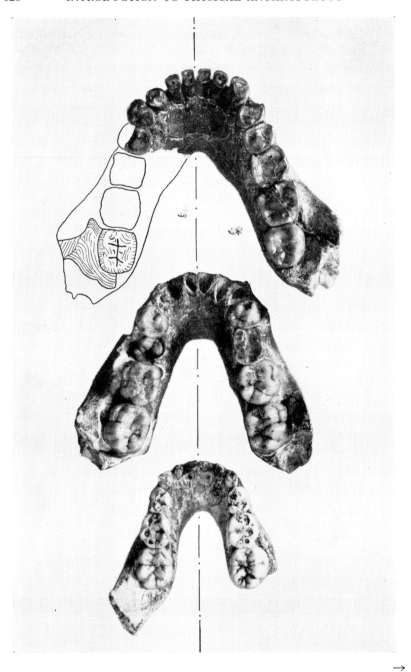

→

ent. The form and crown patterns of the teeth are even more human-like than those hitherto described in any previous australopithecine resembling most closely those of Heidelberg man and *Sinanthropus*.

In July 1953, the major portion of an undistorted adult, probably female, mandible of *Australopithecus prometheus* was recovered from the limeworks dump at Makapansgat. All the teeth are present with the exception of three molars from the missing left side of the jaw. A third molar, described in 1949 from this site, is believed to belong to this mandible, so that only the left first and second molars are wanting. The jaw appears to have been fractured behind the right third molar either a short time before death or shortly thereafter. The jaw is very robust, having a shortened body and a relatively narrow high ascending ramus. At M_1 the thickness of the mandible is 20.5 mm., which is practically the same as in the adolescent specimen which is 21 mm. The height of the mandible in the adolescent specimen is 24 mm. at this point, while in the adult it is 34 mm. In the Mauer jaw the corresponding measurements are 20 x 34, almost identical. Comparative figures are: *Paranthropus robustus* adult male 24.5 x 37. The incisors are almost vertically placed, also as in man M_3 is smaller than M_2. The attritional wear of the teeth indicates that the movement of the jaw was horizontal and grinding, and not vertical and cutting as in the living apes. The canine teeth are small, and there was clearly neither a premaxillary diastema present in the maxillae nor a post-canine one in the mandible. Dart points out the remarkable resemblances (while allowing for the differences) of this mandible to the sinanthropine mandible.

The hunting skill attributed by Dart to the australopithecines has been questioned. The accumulations of smashed skulls and split bones of other animals could well have been due to the activities of carnivores, including the bone-accumulating hyena, whose fossilized remains are found in the australopithecine deposits. Among the animals eaten by such carnivores may well have been the australopithecines, so that if they were hunters they may also have been the hunted.

As for the australopithecine use of fire, Oakley, who has studied the evidence on the spot, considers it more than doubtful, but even

---

←

Figure 73. A growth series of australopithecine lower jaws. The mandible of the six-year-old *Australopithecus africanus* (below), the adolescent male *Australopithecus prometheus* (center), and adult female *Australopithecus prometheus* (above). (From Dart. Courtesy, *Am. J. Phys. Anthrop.*)

if it were confirmed such fires could have occurred quite naturally, as such fires have been recorded to have occurred elsewhere, by a natural grass fire igniting inflammable bat-guano at the entrance to a cave.

Recently Dart published an account of four antelope cannon-bone scoops from the australopithecine breccia at Makapansgat Lime-works which bear an extraordinary resemblance to old English apple-corers. Dart surmises that these scoops were made and used by australopithecines to scoop up flesh, fat and other fluid pulps, and to serve as conveyors of them to the mouths of toothless infants and aged australopithecines. But this is an interpretation which must be held *sub judice* until further evidence becomes available.

In November 1948 Broom discovered a massive fossil manlike mandible in the deposits on the Swartkrans farm, about a mile from the main Sterkfontein quarry. Two perfectly preserved upper incisors and an upper canine were also found some 10 feet from the site of the mandible. Broom believes these teeth to belong to another individual of the same species. These teeth, according to Broom, are almost typically human, though a little larger than most human teeth. The teeth in the mandible are relatively large.

Broom believes that the Swartkrans find is related neither to *Australopithecus* nor to *Plesianthropus,* but is allied to *Paranthropus.* On the basis of its distinctive characters Broom has assinged the remains of this robust ape-man of Swartkrans to a new species of the genus *Paranthropus,* namely, *Paranthropus crassidens.*

During 1949 and 1950 Broom and Robinson discovered many more remains at Swartkrans of *Paranthropus crassidens.* Many skulls are now available, two almost complete, three perfect lower jaws, and two complete but somewhat crushed skulls of children of about seven years of age. Imperfect skulls of half a dozen other individuals and some 300 teeth, the well preserved right half of a pelvis, and various other bones of the skeleton have been recovered.

The incisor and canine teeth are typically human in form and size, the premolar and molar teeth, however, while human in form are much larger than in modern man. The lower jaw in some of the female specimens has quite a distinct human chin. The massive lower jaw is associated with a well-developed sagittal crest, to which the temporal muscles which move the lower jaw are attached. This sagittal crest on top of the skull is similar to that which is seen in the male gorilla. The orbits are overhung by a confluent supraorbital torus, and the large, flat face terminates in a prognathous upper jaw, upon which

the premaxilla is quite as evident as it is in any of the apes. A premaxillary diastema is, however, not present. This is an extremely interesting fact, for it indicates that in the evolution of man the canine
tooth first underwent reduction, that this was later followed by reduction of the premaxillary diastema, and that the early fusion of the
facial portion of the premaxilla with the maxilla occurred with the
reduction of prognathism. That this represents the probable course of
events is borne out by the fact that in *Pithecanthropus robustus* the
canine is reduced, but the premaxillary diastema remains well developed in the male, as presumably does the facial portion of the premaxilla. The inference from this would be that prognathism was more
marked in *Pithecanthropus robustus* than in *Pithecanthropus erectus*
in whom the canine teeth and the premaxillary diastema were reduced.

Broom estimated the cranial capacity of *Paranthropus crassidens*
to be well over 900 cc., in the males possibly as high as 1050 cc., thus
falling within the range of man. But these estimates appear to be
excessive.

The whole right side of the pelvis of *Paranthropus crassidens* has
been recovered. This is entirely manlike, except for the form of the
ischium which is more like that of an ape. From the form of the pelvis
as a whole it may be concluded that *Paranthropus crassidens* habitually walked more or less erectly.

We have, then, in *Paranthropus crassidens* a being with a brain
approaching that of man, a lower jaw with a manlike chin in several
instances, manlike teeth in both jaws, and a manlike pelvis, but with
a skull retaining many apelike features such as the sagittal crest, the
supraorbital torus, the facial premaxilla, and an apelike nose. Is it
ape, ape-man, man-ape or man? Whatever we decide to call *Paranthropus crassidens* this form represents one very like that from which
man himself may have originated.

In the summer of 1949 Robinson and Broom discovered at Swartkrans the crushed complete skull of a young male of about 7 years
of age, the very robust, almost perfect, lower jaw of a male together
with the lower part of the face, and the upper jaw and palate with
the premolar-molar teeth *in situ*, all referred to *Paranthropus crassidens*.

That robust manlike forms lived in South Africa during the Pleistocene, and probably earlier, need not surprise us. We know such forms
from Java and North Africa, namely *Meganthropus* and *Atlanthropus*.

What is the meaning to be attached to these robust-jawed forms?
Were they giants? As we have already observed robust jaws do not

TABLE IV

Tooth Size and Stature

Form	Place-Name or Group	Mesio-distal Diameter of M_1 Mm.	Male Stature Cm.
Paranthropus crassidens	Swartkrans	15.0	160
Plesianthropus transvaalensis	Sterkfontein	13.2	152
Paranthropus robustus	Kromdrai	14.5	156
Sinanthropus pekinensis	Choukoutien	12.6	156
Pithecanthropus erectus	Sangiran	12.5	170–175
Homo sapiens	Australian aborigines	12.3	164
Homo sapiens	Ohio whites	11.0	176

Source: After Garn & Lewis: "*Tooth-Size, Body-Size and 'Giant' Fossil Man.*"

in the least mean that the rest of the body must have been robust. It must be repeated that there is not the slightest reason to believe that any giant primate ever existed. All the evidence we have indicates that throughout the history of man his stature has never exceeded, nor fallen below, the range of variation for stature that characterizes the human species today. As may be seen from Table IV, if anything there is a negative correlation between size of teeth and stature—the larger the teeth the shorter the stature and *vice versa*. The truth, however, is that stature is not determined by the size of the jaws or teeth, nor is it correlated with them.

In the cave at Swartkrans which yielded the jaws and skulls of the robust-jawed *Paranthropus crassidens*, on April 29, 1949, Dr. J. T. Robinson found the lower jaw of a new manlike form. This has been named *Telanthropus capensis*. The jaw is nearly perfect except for the loss of most of the left condyle and the whole of the right. A very small part of the lower symphyseal region is lost. The general appearance is not unlike that of the Heidelberg jaw, according to Robinson and Broom. The ramus is broad but short, and so is the cranio-caudal extent of the body. The height of the jaw from base to condyle is 55.0 mm. There is no simian shelf, and the mylohyoid groove runs up to the mandibular foramen, as in human skulls. The teeth are slightly larger than human. The third molar is the largest of the series, unlike man. The incisors and canines, so far as can be judged from the sockets, are human in form. In *Plesianthropus transvaalensis* the three molars measure in the male about 43.0 mm.; in *Paranthropus robustus* about 45.0 mm. In *Paranthropus crassidens* about 51.0 mm., while in *Telanthropus capensis* they measure 38.4 mm. In South African native the molars measure 35.0 mm.

Robinson and Broom regard *Telanthropus capensis* as possibly allied to Heidelberg man, and as intermediate between ape-man and true man.

In August 1959, Robinson reported the discovery of some 228 stone artifacts in the Sterkfontein red-brown breccia not far from the original site of the australopithecines. All but one of the artifacts are composed of materials which are not native to the site or the immediate vicinity of the find. The industry is not of the most primitive type. Some of the more advanced artifacts represent a late Oldoway or very early Chelles-Acheul stage in the South African Stone Age sequence. These artifacts could not have been made by australopithecines, and Robinson suggests that they were made by a "euhominid" (true man) like *Telanthropus*. This is quite possible. However, it is also quite possible that the australopithecines were living contemporaneously with hominids who were responsible for making these tools. Even more interesting was the recovery of a bone implement from this site in June 1958. This consists of a long bone which had been split longitudinally. One-half was then broken in a manner which produced a pointed end. The broken surfaces leading to the point have become polished completely smooth. Length is 9¾ cm., width 3 cm., and

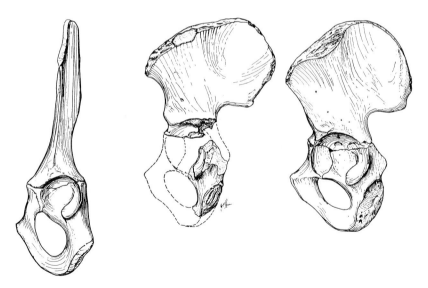

Figure 74. Left lateral views of innominate bones in chimpanzee (left), *Australopithecus prometheus* (center) and Bushman (right). Male adolescents taken from dioptographic tracings of the assembled pelves. (From Dart. Courtesy *Am. J. Phys. Anthrop.*)

thickness 1½ cm. The implement was originally longer than its present length, having been broken and lost in excavation at its butt-end. Robinson believes that this implement may have been made by *Telanthropus*, but acknowledges that it may be of australopithecine origin.

In June 1949 Dart published a description of the craniofacial fragment of an adult, probably female, australopithecine skull from the Makapansgat Limeworks dump. By ingenious casting it was possible to restore this fragment sufficiently well to obtain a good idea of the form of the face, palate, and teeth, as shown in Figure 69. The fragment probably belonged to the same individual whose occiput formed the holotype of *Australopithecus prometheus*. The maxillary premolars and the first and second molars were preserved *in situ*. The craniograms shown in Figures 70 and 71 indicate how closely *Australopithecus prometheus* resembles *Australopithecus africanus*.

In the same month, June 1949, Dart announced the discovery, at Makapansgat, of an almost complete left ilium and the major portion of a right ischium of an australopithecine adolescent, which may have belonged to the same adolescent individual whose mandible was found in the same dump of breccia, and which was referred to *Australopithecus prometheus*. As may be seen from the dioptographic drawings shown in Figure 74 the pelvic bones of this australopithecine are strikingly manlike, closely resembling those of the living Bushman and differing markedly from the anthropoid chimpanzee pelvis. The pelvis of *Australopithecus prometheus* is more manlike than that of *Plesianthropus* discovered at Sterkfontein, some 200 miles southward in the Transvaal. Dart points out that the external iliac surface is anteriorly and medially rotated in *Australopithecus prometheus,* a fact which shows that the gluteal muscles necessary for the maintenance of the erect posture were disposed on the lateral aspect of pelvis and thigh essentially as in man. The indications are, therefore, that *Australopithecus* was capable of standing and walking erectly in approximately human fashion.

In June 1950 Broom and Robinson announced yet another discovery in the main deposit of the cave at Swartkrans, the very same deposit from which the remains of at least 10 individuals of *Paranthropus crassidens* have thus far been recovered. The discovery represents a considerable portion of the right side of a lower jaw with the first and second much-worn molars *in situ*. Broom and Robinson believe the jaw to be the relict of an early man, and they are certain that it is contemporaneous with *Paranthropus crassidens*, though manifestly

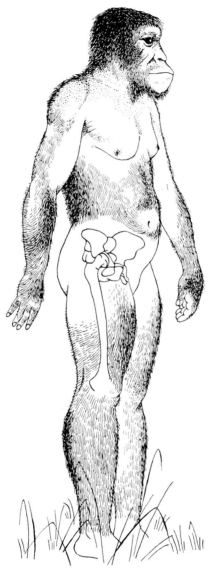

Figure 75. Reconstruction of an Australopithecine. (Modified after Oakley. Courtesy, World Publishing Co.)

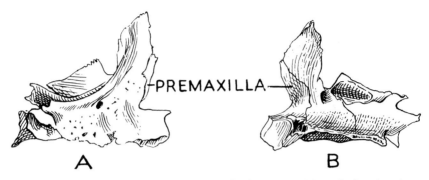

Figure 76. Upper jaw of a newborn male (American Negro) showing A, a portion of the premaxilla upon the facial aspect of the skull, and B, the whole of the ascending process of the premaxilla within the nasal fossa. (Author's specimen now in the Anatomical Museum, Oxford University.)

differing from that form both in size and in other characters. The new jaw does not differ very much in size from that of *Telanthropus capensis*, and the discoverers are uncertain as to whether it may belong to the latter species or not. There is no simian shelf, and the front of the symphysis was probably rounded. The jaw is rather deep towards the front of the body, but is not more massive than in most modern jaws. The first molar measures about 12.3 mm. in length, and the second 12.0 mm. in length and 12.3 mm. in greatest breadth.

In the Australopithecines it seems fairly evident that we are dealing with a single genus represented by several polytypic species.

Gregory and Hellman believe that the australopithecine group were derived from the *Dryopithecus-Sivapithecus* stock of the late Tertiary, and that they represent the conservative cousins of the contemporary human branch. On the other hand, Weidenreich, and also Broom and Schepers believe that the australopithecines separated from the typical anthropoids at a pre-dryopithecid stage probably as early as the Lower Oligocene and that the earliest hominids, possibly the pithecanthropoids, arose from a form very near to *Australopithecus* in the Pliocene.

It has already been mentioned that the size of the teeth in the australopithecines is somewhat larger than are the teeth of any known form of man, with the exception of *Meganthropus palaeojavanicus* (see p. 160), otherwise they are remarkably manlike in character. This difference in size is regarded by von Koenigswald as significant, for the larger teeth of the australopithecines, according to him, must be regarded as a specialization which precludes these forms from being ancestral to man; the size of the teeth in relation to the size of the brain indicating an animal too large to be an ancestor of man.

The fact, however, is that during the process of evolution teeth do undergo a reduction in size, and as for bodily size Broom has estimated that the australopithecines were small animals weighing between 80 and 100 pounds.

It is quite possible that the australopithecines pursued a parallel evolution with early men since Lower Pleistocene times, and may even have originated from a common Pliocene ancestor. In the latter case they would best be regarded as a side branch stemming from the main line which led to man.

Wood Jones (1947) has argued that since the premaxilla is of anthropoid type in the australopithecines man could not have originated from such a stock. This argument is of doubtful cogency, for only the very slightest genetic changes would be required to transform the australopithecine into the hominid type of upper jaw. In the evolutionary series immediately leading to man it would appear that so far as the upper jaw is concerned there was first, a reduction in the size of the canine teeth (e.g., *Australopithecus*), followed second, by early fusion of the premaxilla with the maxilla with retention of the premaxillary diastema (*Pithecanthropus robustus*), and third, complete reduction of the premaxillary diastema (*Pithecanthropus*

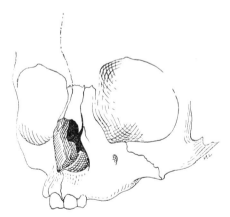

Figure 77a. Cranio-facial aspect of the skull of a white infant aged about 11 months showing the apical portion of the premaxilla separated from the maxilla. Within the nasal cavity the premaxilla and its suture (indicated here by a white line) are clearly visible in their entirety. (Author's specimen.)

Figure 77b. Right lateral view of the *Plesianthropus* and *Zinjanthropus* skulls. (From Leakey, Courtesy, *Illustrated London News*.)

erectus or *Sinanthropus*). Furthermore, to judge from the characters of the mandible of *Australopithecus prometheus* it is quite likely that the premaxillary diastema had disappeared in, at least, some of the members of that group.

It is probable that the hominid type of upper jaw has been derived from an anthropoid type of upper jaw in which the premaxilla was suturally separated upon the face from the maxilla. When in early fetal life the fusion of premaxilla with maxilla has been retarded the relationship between these bones are seen to be exactly as in the anthropoids, and differing substantially from the condition seen in other primates, at least, as far as the form of the suture separating the two bones is concerned (see Figure 73). Furthermore, portions of the premaxilla may occasionally be seen on the facial aspect of human crania as late as the fifth year (Figure 74).

Zinjanthropus boisei: An East African Australopithecine Tool-Maker. On 17 July 1959 Mrs. and Dr. L. S. B. Leakey discovered the skull and shin-bone of the earliest known tool-making hominid. The find was made in a Lower Pleistocene deposit in Olduvai Gorge, Tanganyika Territory, East Africa. The skull, which is almost complete, was dug out of a living floor associated with primitive stone artifacts, of a type which have been found in the lowermost bed of Olduvai Gorge on and off for thirty years by Dr. Leakey and others.

Zinjanthropus boisei ("Zinj" after the classical Arabic name for East Africa, and the specific name after an English benefactor) is represented by an almost complete skull without mandible, and the larger part of the tibia. Leakey's approximate measurements indicate the proportions of the skull:

Length from inion to glabella	174 mm.
Greatest breadth at supra-mastoid torus	138 mm.
Greatest breadth of braincase on squamosal element	118 mm.
Height from basion in Frankfurt plane	98 mm.
External orbital angle width	122 mm.
Interorbital width	32.5 mm.
Postorbital width	88 mm.
Palate length from incisors to retromolar plane	84 mm.
Palate width at second molars	82 mm.
Palate width at first premolars	62 mm.

Figure 77c. Frontal views of the *Plesianthropus* and *Zinjanthropus* skulls. (From Leakey, Courtesy, *Illustrated London News*.)

Figure 77d. Gorilla and *Zinjanthropus* skulls compared. (From Leakey, Courtesy, *Illustrated London News*.)

Length of premolar-molar series   72 mm.
Teeth in mm.: I^1: 10 x 8, I^2: 7 x 7, C: 9.5 x 9, PM^1:
    17 x 11.5, PM^2: 18 x 12, M^1: 18 x 15.5, M^2: 21 x 17,
    M^3: 21 x 16.

The skull is that of a youth between 16 and 18 years of age. The sutures are all patent, and the cranial capacity, which at the time of writing has not yet been firmly determined, is estimated at somewhat over 600 cc. Stature is estimated at not more than 4 feet 9 inches. The skull is strikingly constricted postorbitally (stenocrotaphy), thus making the temporal fossae very large indeed, an arrangement in perfect harmony with the large temporal muscles which filled them, as indicated by the presence of the sagittal crest to which they were attached. The sagittal crest is well developed as in *Paranthropus crassidens* and in the living gorilla. There is practically no brow, the supraorbital torus is massive, the interorbital width is enormous, 32.5 mm., and exceeds that of the pyriform (nasal) aperture. The nasal bones are long and narrow, and are broader superiorly than they are inferiorly, and are only slightly elevated at the median ridge. The face is long and wide, the frontal processes of the maxilla are quite wide, contributing most to the great interorbital width. The facial and zygomatic portions of the maxilla are enormous, as is the depth of the body of the maxilla. The palate is exceedingly high. It is surprising to find a strongly developed anterior nasal spine in so prognathous a jaw, and with so unsharp an inferior nasal margin. The canines and incisors are as small as they are in contemporary man, and there is no premaxillary diastema. The premolars and molars are, however, very large. All the teeth are in situ, perfectly preserved, and show evidences of wear such as is seen among food gatherers who take in a great deal of grit with their vegetable foods. The third molars, which are smaller than the second molars—as in man—had not yet erupted beyond the gum level, and are particularly interesting because they show a crinkling of the occlusal surface similar to that seen in the orang. It is of great interest to note that the right lateral incisor is somewhat smaller than the left, a condition which is occasionally seen in contemporary man, but seldom occurring among anthropoids. The canines are no larger than those of contemporary man, while the incisors are, if anything, smaller than those of modern man. This is somewhat surprising in view of the large size of the premolars and molars, but what it, in fact, may indicate is that in the

Figure 77e. Right lateral view of gorilla and *Zinjanthropus* skulls. (From Leakey, Courtesy, *Illustrated London News*.)

Figure 77f. Occipital view of modern human and *Zinjanthropus* skulls. (From Leakey, Courtesy, *Illustrated London News*.)

evolution of the hominid dentition the incisor-canine series underwent reduction first, only to be followed by a reduction of the premolar-molar series later. This interpretation is, in fact, suggested by the conditions seen in the pithecanthropines. In view of the small size of the incisor-canine series it is somewhat of a puzzle to understand what the function of so massive a maxilla could have been.

Another well-developed hominid trait is the presence of large mastoid processes which appear to be slung from an enormous laterally projecting supramastoid shelf. It was a bit of the projecting left mastoid first seen by Mrs. Leakey that led to the uncovering of the skull.

The nuchal crest is very strongly developed, but is typically hominid in its low situation and form, and quite unlike the condition in the anthropoids. The foramen magnum is situated even more toward the frontal plane than it is in the skull of contemporary man—a really quite extraordinary finding, and one which leaves no doubt that *Zinjanthropus* habitually walked erectly.

The skull was found on a living floor containing pre-Chelles-Acheul tools in Bed I of Olduvai Gorge. These tools are characterized by the fact that only a few flakes have been removed from the stone in either one or two directions on both faces to make a simple chopping tool with a sharp but irregular cutting edge on either the side or the edge of the stone (Figure 77h). These are regarded as

Figure 77g. The palate and teeth of *Zinjanthropus* compared with those of a modern human adult. (From Leakey, Courtesy, *Illustrated London News.*)

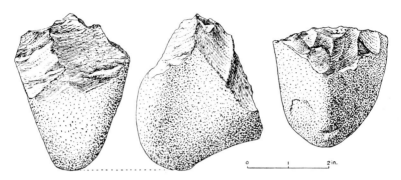

Figure 77h. Oldowan pebble-tools (lava), Bed I, Olduvai Gorge, Tanganyika Territory, East Africa. (From Oakley, *Man The Tool Maker*. Courtesy, British Museum [Natural History].)

the type tools of Oldowan industry or Developed Kafuan. The most primitive tools, known as Kafuan, are pebbles from which flakes have been removed from one side only. Specimens are found in Bed I at Olduvai as elsewhere in Africa. Since there is no stone in Olduvai Gorge at this level, but clay only, the materials from which the tools were made, quartzite and lava, must have been brought from elsewhere. There were found on the living floor associated with the skull 9 Oldoway choppers, 1 hammerstone, 5 natural stones, and 176 flakes, indicating that the tools were manufactured on the spot.

Zinjanthropus, then, was a tool-maker. There is no evidence that he made fire or bone tools in addition to stone ones. In fact, at the handaxe level of development there is no evidence of fire-making anywhere in Africa.

Zinjanthropus was found at a depth approximately 22 feet below the upper limit of Bed I. Since the Olduvai I beds belong to the upper part of the Lower Pleistocene (the same age as the Taungs beds in which *Australopithecus africanus* was found), *Zinjanthropus* dates back some 600,000 years, and thus becomes the earliest established hominid tool-maker. The making of a tool implies the altering of an object to serve a specific purpose by cutting, striking, scraping, rubbing or other process. Once the tool has been used it need not be used again, but when the need arises another is made according to a specifically established pattern. A creature who makes tools in such a manner is one capable of using ideas, symbols, in a fashion characteristically human. This fact makes *Zinjanthropus* unquestionably a man—the earliest known man.

Zinjanthropus demonstrates that it is not the morphological appearance of the brainbox and its appendages which so much matter in differentiating man from ape, as the quality of the brain that is contained in the brainbox, however apelike the latter may appear. The distinction between a man and an ape rests not so much on a morphological as on a functional difference, and that is the mental capacity which enables the creature to *make* tools. And not only to make tools, but to make them with a future or deferred use in mind. As Oakley has pointed out, the power of abstraction, of conceptual thought, is basic for the regular manufacture of tools. Such a regular *tool-maker*, even though he use his tools intermittently, is a man— no matter what his skull looks like.

With the discovery of *Zinjanthropus* two entrenched beliefs among morphologists are forever toppled. The first is the traditional morphological criterion of hominid status, as requiring a skull that is rather more manlike than apelike. The second is that the "Cerebral Rubicon," that is the brain size that would constitute the lowest limit of hominid status is 750 cc.

The belief in the necessity of some arbitrary standard of morphological likeness, especially in the skull, has led more than one distinguished student astray in claiming that for this reason the australopithecines could not be hominids. The emphasis has been too much upon morphology and not enough upon functional traits. The presence of pebble-tools in Olduvai I beds, and the association of *Zinjanthropus* with these, makes the Oldowan pebble-tools found together with three australopithecine teeth in the breccia at Sterkfontein quite possibly the handiwork of australopithecines who, if this is proven to be the case, will also have to be regarded as hominids. *Zinjanthropus*, in spite of about twenty major morphological characters in which it differs from all known australopithecines, may be placed, tentatively at least, in the sub-family Australopithecinae.

The belief that the "Cerebral Rubicon" is irreversibly established at 750 cc. must now also be dropped in view of the lesser cranial capacity of *Zinjanthropus*. We do not know what the variability in cranial capacity among adults may have been, but on the basis of the known adolescent skull, almost certainly that of a male, it is unlikely to have exceeded, if it ever reached, 700 cc. in its upper reaches. If either the bone tool discovered by Robinson in 1958, or the Oldowan pebble tools discovered by Brain in 1957 in the breccia at the western end of the cave at Sterkfontein which yielded the adult *Plesianthropus transvaalensis* with a cranial capacity of 560 cc., turn out to have been made by this form it is probable that the "Cerebral Rubicon" will have to be yet further contracted.

The discovery of *Zinjanthropus* throws much additional light upon the early history of man. One question, however, must be dealt with here before passing on to these other matters. It is a question that is bound to be raised. That question is: Was *Zinjanthropus* capable of speech? The answer is that we do not know, but that anatomically there was certainly nothing to prevent him from speaking, and that as a hominid capable of making tools he may very well have been capable of expressing and communicating simple ideas in sound.

The living floor of *Zinjanthropus* was situated at the edge of a lake. Associated with the skull and tibia of *Zinjanthropus* were found the remains of his larder, baby pigs and baby antelopes, whose bones he had split open for their marrow, rats, mice, frogs, lizards, snake, tortoise, and birds. It is to be noted that these are all small animals that could be collected with one's bare hands. At this stage man was not yet a hunter of large animals, and his diet was still largely vegetarian, as evidenced by the wear of the teeth in *Zinjanthropus.*

Surrounded on all sides by giant animals, by pigs as large as rhinos, sheep that stood seven feet high at the shoulder, giant hippos, antelope, cattle, and baboons, *Zinjanthropus,* in fact, was not yet a hunter. He was a food-gatherer. In gathering his vegetable foods he would encounter small animals and the infants of large ones, and these he would gather into his larder just as he gathered his vegetables. This is not hunting. It is still food-gathering. An advance upon the strictly food-gathering activities of anthropoids, but still a food-gathering, and not a hunting economy.

The Relationships of the Australopithecinae

With the exception of *Zinjanthropus* and *Telanthropus*, the variability presented by the australopithecines is such as to render it unlikely that more than one genus, *Australopithecus,* is involved. The differences between the various australopithecines, with the two exceptions noted, are at most specific, and in several cases are no more than subspecific. It has been suggested that in order to avoid confusion it would be preferable to refer to the various australopithecines by the place-names of the sites at which they were discovered, rather than by the names first given them by their discoverers. Thus, one would refer to the Kromdraai skull rather than to *Paranthropus,* or to the Sterkfontein skull instead of *Plesianthropus,* until there is common agreement as to exactly where the forms represented by these fossil remains are to be situated.

Oreopithecus. During the years commencing in 1949 Dr. Johannes Hürzeler of the Museum of Natural History at Basle has been claiming that the fossil form *Oreopithecus bambolii*, discovered in the late 1860's in the lignite of Montebamboli, in the Province of Grosseto in Northern Italy, is a hominid and not a cercopithecoid monkey as most authorities have claimed. Since the geological age of *Oreopithecus* is Lower Pliocene, *i.e.*, about 10,000,000 years ago, Dr. Hürzeler's claims have created quite a fluttering in paleoanthropological dovecotes—the more so since Dr. Hürzeler has presented the case for *Oreopithecus* with great cogency. Summarized the case for the hominid status, according to Dr. Hürzeler rests on the following nine points: (1) the smallness of the teeth, (2) the mandibular premolars are

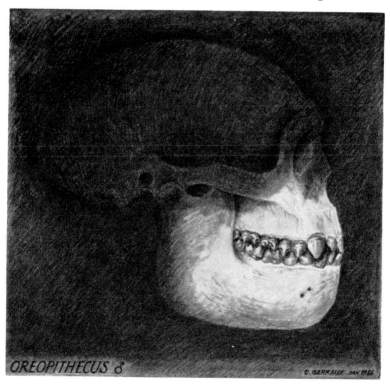

OREOPITHECUS ♂

Figure 78. Reconstruction of the skull of *Oreopithecus bambolii*. (Courtesy, Dr. J. Hürzeler.)

homomorphic, *i.e.*, they resemble each other, rather than resembling the heteromorphic premolars of the apes in which PM_1 will be unicuspidate and PM_2 is molarized, (3) the simian gap or premaxillary diastema is absent, (4) the canine teeth are small, (5) the fovea anterior of the upper molars closely resembles that in the same teeth in man but is unlike that of any of the apes, (6) the upper and lower incisors are implanted steeply in the jaws, unlike the rather more forward slantwise projection of these teeth in apes, (7) the face is short, more orthognathic than in apes, (8) the mandibular symphysis is steep and not slanted as in apes, and (9) the mental foramina are high in position as in man, but not as in the apes. To these points may be added the fact that the lumbar vertebrae are relatively large and robust, suggesting that *Oreopithecus* may have walked erectly.

In remarking upon these resemblances the point may be made that all these characters are, indeed, impressive and while they may cause *Oreopithecus* in respect of them more closely to resemble a hominid than an ape, it is the totality of structural and functional characters that must be considered before a definitive judgment can be arrived at.

Drs. P. M. Butler and J. R. E. Miles have studied the dentition of *Oreopithecus* and conclude that it does not fall within the range of variation of the living cercopithecids, pongids, or hominids, and that its combination of primitive and specialized dental characters suggests that it is a terminal form of a separate hominoid stock probably extending back to the Oligocene. Upon this view, then, *Oreopithecus*, is a hominoid but not a hominid.

On August 2, 1958 the almost complete skeleton of *Oreopithecus* was discovered by Drs. Hürzeler and Helmut de Terra in the coal face of the Baccinello mine some 600 feet underground in the area between Pisa and Grosseto. This specimen apparently stood between 52 and 56 inches in height. It will be wisest to await the studies of this specimen before any judgment is ventured upon its probable zoological status.

It has been suggested that the rediscovery of *Oreopithecus* challenges the Darwinian theory of man's descent from an apelike stock for if, it is argued, a form like *Oreopithecus* was already in existence in the Lower Pliocene, without exhibiting any pongid traits, it may well have evolved independently of the apes, and given rise to a line which eventually led to man. This is, of course, a possibility, but the truth is that *Oreopithecus* exhibits a great many both cercopithecoid and ape-like traits, for example in the pattern of the molar teeth and in the size of the skull and cranial cavity.

The absence of any later Pliocene hominids of any kind suggests that *Oreopithecus, if* he was a hominid left no descendants and became extinct. On the other hand, such an absence of Pliocene hominids may simply be due to the fact that they still remain undisturbed in the rocks.

Whether or not *Oreopithecus* is a hominid future research will determine, meanwhile he remains an extremely interesting fossil primate, who has already been accepted by some paleoanthropologists, like Hürzeler, de Terra, Heberer, and Straus, as a hominid, while others like Remane, von Koenigswald, and Robinson insist that he is a cercopithecoid on his way to apedom rather than to hominidity.

Among the widely dispersed and variegated Tertiary apes it is quite impossible to point with any certainty to any one form and say: This is the animal which, without any intermediate stages of development, gave rise to the earliest men.

In the present state of our knowledge one can only point to the australopithecines and say, that while no one of them may have been directly ancestral to man, a type very like them must have been; which is to say that the manlike apes from South Africa are man's nearest present known relatives, and that there may have been one or more stages of development between a form like them and the appearance of the first man. There cannot have been, however, more than a few such intermediate stages for the australopithecines have themselves almost made the passage into the family of man, the Hominidae, to the rise of which we shall give our attention in the next chapter.

Darwin's conclusion, in *The Descent of Man* (1871), that mankind originated from an early unspecialized anthropoid ape has to-day been so strengthened by the investigations of innumerable workers that it has come to be generally, though by no means universally, accepted by scientists.

The facts indicate that man and the anthropoid apes constitute a natural group, the superfamily Hominoidea, characterized by the common possession of hundreds of known diagnostic characters which separate them as a group from the remainder of the primates.

FOR FURTHER READING, CONSULT:

ASHTON, E. H.: The endocranial capacities of the Australopithecinae. *Proc. Zool. Soc.* London, *120*:715-721, 1950.
A statistical study of the cranial capacities of the australopithecines as compared with the anthropoids.

BROOM, R. and SCHEPERS, G. W. H.: *The South African Fossil Ape-Men, the Australopithecinae.* Pretoria, Transvaal Museum Memoir No. 2, 1946.
The official account of the australopithecines.

CHRONOLOGICAL-CULTURAL TABLE OF THE DIVISIONS OF PREHISTORY AND OF THE HISTORIC PERIOD

Age	Alpine and Scandinavian glacial oscillations with corresponding changes of sea level and climate	Approximate dates	Principal Culture Stages of Europe, Egypt, and the Near East			
			Northwestern Continental Europe	West Central Europe	Egypt and the Near East	Human Types
Power Tools	Present conditions of Mya Period in Baltic Area	A.D. 1900	Rise of the Age of Power Tools			
Steel — New		A.D. 1850	Steel Age Develops			
Steel — Old		A.D. 1700	Steel (carbonized iron)			
Iron — Late		A.D. 1000	Viking Age			
Iron — Middle		A.D. 500	Roman Period of Iron Age	Historic Times		
Iron — Early		0	Iron Age Introduced			
Iron — Early		500 B.C.		Iron Age Introduced		
Bronze	Final land rise in Baltic area or Late Tapes Period	1000 B.C.	Bronze Age Introduced			
Bronze		1500 B.C.		Bronze Age Introduced	Iron Age Begins	
Bronze		2000 B.C.	Traces of Copper		Bronze Age Begins	
Copper		2500 B.C.	Late Neolithic with thick poll axe	Copper Age Introduced	Alloys in use	
Neolithic — Late		3000 B.C.			History Begins Writing Invented	
Neolithic — Late		3500 B.C.	Middle Neolithic with thin poll axe	Late Neolithic		
Neolithic — Middle	Sea rising, Ragunda retreat, with Littorina Sea (Early Tapes Period) preceded by late Ancylus Lake	4000 B.C.			Use of Iron Begins Agriculture and the Domestication Animals	
Neolithic — Middle		4500 B.C.	Early Neolithic: Shell mound or Campignian industry Ertebølle industries	Middle Neolithic or Robenhausian industry		
Neolithic — Early		5000 B.C.	Norse industry with petroglyphs	Early Neolithic or Campignian and Asturian industries	Use of Copper Begins	
Neolithic — Early		5500 B.C.			Amratian industry	
Mesolithic		6000 B.C.	Maglemose industry		Badarian industry	
Mesolithic	Ragunda pause with Ancylus Lake	6500 B.C.	Lyngby industry	Azilian, Tardenoisian, and Capsian Industries		
Upper	Fini-Glacial pause with Baltic ice-lake	7800 B.C.		Late Magdalenian	Tasian industry	Chancelade
Upper	Fini-Glacial pause with Baltic ice-lake	8500 B.C.		Early Magdalenian and Capsian industries	Probable beginning of Neolithic culture in Nile Valley floor silts	
Upper	Gothi-Glacial retreat with Baltic ice-lake	13,500 B.C.		Solutrean industry. Late Aurignacian industry		Predmost Baker's Hole Rhodesian Cro-Magnon

Period	Glacial / Geological	Date	Cave and Somme Industries	Nile Terrace Industries	Fossils
PALEOLITHIC — MIDDLE	Gothi-Glacial pause with Baltic ice-lake	18,500 B.C.	Early Aurignacian or Châtelperronian and Capsian industries	Sebilian industry of Nile valley terrace silts	Châtelperron, Grimaldi, Cro-Magnon, Africanthropus, Solo
	Würm or Aachen and Dani-Glacial retreats with Frankfort and Pomeranian pause. Flandrian terrace	50,000 B.C.	Final Mousterian of the caves	Late Mousterian of the 10 ft. Nile terrace	Boskop
	Würm and Brandenburg or Dani-Glacial advances, 4th glacial		Mousterian of the caves		Florisbad, Skhūl, Gibraltar II, Wadjak, Rhodesian
	Riss retreat with Monastirian terrace, 3rd Interglacial. Hot summer	75,000 B.C.	Contemporary Acheulian, Early Mousterian, Tayacian, Micoquian, Levalloisian, and Clactonian industries from Somme terrace, etc.	Early Mousterian of the 30 ft. Nile terrace	Tabun, Neanderthal, Ehringsdorf, Fontéchevade, Saldhana, Montmaurin
	Riss and Polonian Advances, 3rd Glacial	150,000 B.C.	Derived implements		*Rabat*, *Sidi Abderrahman*
PALEOLITHIC — LOWER	Mindel retreat with Tyrrhenian terrace. 2nd Interglacial	250,000 B.C.	Acheulian and contemporary Abbevillian and Clactonian industries from 2nd Somme terrace. Clacton-on-Sea, Mesvin, etc.	Acheulian industry of the 50 ft. Nile terrace	*Steinheim*, Swanscombe, Heidelberg, Atlanthropus, Sinanthropus, Pithecanthropus erectus
	Mindel advance. 2nd Glacial	450,000 B.C.	Derived implements		Pithecanthropus robustus
	Gunz retreat with Milazzian terrace. 1st Interglacial	550,000 B.C.	Proto-Abbevillian industry from below the Cromer forest beds and 3rd Somme terrace	Abbevillian and Early Abbevillian industries of the 100 ft. Nile terrace	Pithecanthropus (Modjokerto), *Meganthropus*
ARCHAEO-LITHIC	Gunz Advance. 1st Glacial — PLEISTOCENE	600,000 B.C.	Pre-Abbevillian or Ipswichian flake industry of East Anglian Crag formations	?	Zinjanthropus
	PLIOCENE — Donau with Sicilian terrace	1,000,000 yrs.	Pre-Abbevillian or Ipswichian flake industry of subcrag formations		

In using this table it should be understood that the approximate dates assigned to the different "Ages" refers only in a general way to the areas mentioned. As the table indicates these "Ages" were not everywhere contemporaneous. The different "Ages" do not afford a measure of time, for they varied in different parts of the world both in the time of their appearance and in their duration, while some of the cultural stages they embrace never appeared at all, but were completely skipped in the progress from one cultural stage to another. These ages are therefore to be regarded as *cultural or technological* rather than as chronological periods. It is extremely important to grasp this fact. There was no world-wide evolution from one stage to another, each stage represents an industrial revolution in the manufacture of tools which occurred in different places at different times, nor did the several stages begin and end simultaneously all over the world. Thus, to give a simple example, the Early Iron Age began in Asia Minor about 1200 B.C., in Italy about 1000 B.C., in central Europe about 900 B.C., in China about 700 B.C., in southern England about 600 B.C., in Japan about A.D., 200, and in Fiji about 1872. Compare this table with Table VIII p. 270, and note the difference in dating. In the last column names in *italics* refer to types which are uncertainly dated.

————: *Commemorative Volume.* Cape Town, Special Publication of the Roy. Soc. South Africa, 1948.
Contains a series of excellent papers on South African anthropology, and Broom's ideas and contributions.

————: The genera and species of the South African fossil ape-men. *Am. J. Phys. Anthropol.*, n.s. 8:1-13, 1950.
A generic analysis.

————: *Finding the Missing Link.* London, Watts, 1950.
Broom's personal very lively account of the discovery of the South African ape-man.

———— ROBINSON, J. T., and SCHEPERS, G. W. H.: *Sterkfontein Ape-Man Plesianthropus.* Pretoria, Transvaal Museum Memoir No. 4, 1950.
A first-hand account of the remains of *Plesianthropus.*

———— and ROBINSON, J. T.: One of the earliest types of man. *South African J. Sc.,* 47:55-57, 1950.
A short account and restoration of *Paranthropus crassidens.*

———— and ROBINSON, J. T.: Notes on the pelves of the fossil ape-men. *Am. J. Phys. Anthropol.,* n.s. 8:489-494, 1950.
A description of the right pelvis of *Paranthropus crassidens* with a discussion of the pelves of the other australopithecinae.

———— and ROBINSON, J. T.: *Swartkrans Ape-Man: Paranthropus crassidens.* Pretoria, Transvaal Museum Memoir No. 6, 1952.
A full and excellently illustrated account.

CLARK, W. E. LE GROS: *Early Forerunners of Man.* Baltimore, Wood, 1934.
A morphological study of the evolutionary origin of the primates.

————: *History of the Primates: An Introduction to the Study of Fossil Man.* 6th ed. London, British Museum (Natural History), 1958.
A most excellent and readable introduction.

————: New palaeontological evidence bearing on the evolution of the Hominoidea. *J. Geol. Soc.,* (London), 105:225-264, 1949.
A brilliant account and discussion of *Proconsul* and the australopithecines.

———— and L. S. B. LEAKEY: The Miocene Hominoidea of East Africa. *Fossil Mammals of Africa,* No. 1, British Museum (Natural History), 1951.
A thorough description of the East African primates discovered by Leakey, *Proconsul, Sivapithecus,* and *Limnopithecus.*

DART, R. A., and CRAIG, D.: *Adventures with the Missing Link.* New York, Harper, 1959.
Dart's interesting account of his many years of work on the australopithecines.

DARWIN, C.: *The Descent of Man.* London, 1871 and later editions.
The classic work on the probable manner of origin and evolution of man.

ELLIOT, D. G.: *A Review of the Primates,* 3 vols., New York, American Museum of Natural History, 1913.
A monumental, much used, but not entirely reliable, work on the characters and classification of the primates. To be used with caution.

FORBES, H. O.: *Monkeys,* 2 vols. London, Shaw, 1894.
On the characters and classification of the primates, in many ways more attractive and reliable than Elliot's work, though lacking the latter's invaluable plates of crania.

GARN, S. M., and LEWIS, A. B.: Tooth-size, body-size and "giant" fossil man. *Am. Anthropol.*, n.s. *60*:874-880, 1958.
A valuable discussion of the relation of tooth, jaw, and body size.

GAZIN, C. L.: A Review of the Upper and Middle Eocene Primates of North America. *Smithson. Miscell. Collections, 136*:iii + 112, 1958.
An admirable review and discussion of relationships, with fine illustrations.

GREGORY, W. K.: Studies on the evolution of the primates. *Bull. Am. Museum Natur. Hist.*, *35*:239-355, 1916.
A classic work on the evolution of the primates, abundantly illustrated.

——— and HELLMAN, M.: The dentition of the extinct South African Man-Ape *Australopithecus (Plesianthropus) transvaalensis* Broom. A comparative and phylogenetic study. *Ann. Transvaal Museum, 19*:339-373, 1939.
A study of the dentition and phylogenetic relationships of the australopithecines.

———: *The Origin and Evolution of the Human Dentition.* Baltimore, Williams & Wilkins, 1922.
The best book on the subject, containing far more general material than the title suggests.

———: *Man's Place Among the Anthropoids.* New York, Oxford, 1934.
A good account and discussion of the morphological relationships of the anthropoid apes, fossil and living, to man. Valuable also as an example of the manner in which controversial points are handled. The theories and claims particularly criticized are those of Wood Jones.

———: The bearing of the Australopithecinae upon the problem of man's place in nature. *Am. J. Phys. Anthropol.*, *7*:485-512, 1949.
A most important study.

HOOTON, E. A.: *Up From the Ape*, revised edition. New York, Macmillan, 1946.
An amusingly written account of man's evolutionary and morphological relationships to the primates.

———: *Man's Poor Relations.* New York, Doubleday, Doran, 1943.
A sound popular account of the lemurs, tarsiers, monkeys, and apes.

HOPWOOD, A. T.: Miocene primates from Kenya. *J. Linnaean Soc., London* (Zoology), *37*:437-464, 1933.
A description of the first find of *Proconsul africanus* and other primates found at Koru in East Africa.

HÜRZELER, J.: *Oreopithecus bambolii* Gervais. *Verh. Naturf. Ges. Basel, 69*:1-48, 1958.
A valuable account of *Oreopithecus*.

JONES, F. WOOD: *Man's Place Among the Mammals.* New York, Longman's, 1929.
A brilliant and original work in which an attempt is made to sustain the hypothesis that man is derived from a tarsioid stock. Discusses the primates fully but not always accurately. For a critical examination of Wood Jones' theories and claims, see M. F. Ashley Montagu's "The Tarsian Hypothesis and the descent of man," *J. Roy. Anthropol. Inst.*, *60*:335-362, 1930.

KOENIGSWALD, G. H. R. VON: *The South African Man-Apes and Pithecanthropus.* Washington, D.C., Carnegie Inst., 1942, publication, 530, pp. 205-222.
An important study.

KURTÉN, B.: Mammal migrations, cenozoic stratigraphy, and the age of Peking Man and the Australopithecines. *J. Paleontology*, *31*:215-227, 1957.

————: A case of Darwinian selection in bears. *Evolution, 11:*412-416, 1957.

————: A differentiation index, and a new measure of evolutionary rates. *Evolution, 12:*146-157, 1957.

————: Life and Death of the Pleistocene Cave Bear. *Acta Zoologica Fennica* 95, Helsinki-Helsingfors, pp. 1-59, 1958.

Four excellent studies in paleoecology and evolutionary rates, as well as their significance for dating extinct populations.

LEAKEY, L. S. B.: A new fossil skull from Olduvai. *Nature, 184:*491-493, 1959. Also *The Illustrated London News,* 12th & 19th September 1959.

Zinjanthropus boisei described and illustrated.

————: *Olduvai Gorge.* London & New York, Cambridge University Press, 1951. A report on the evolution of the hand-axe culture in Beds I-IV.

MacINNES, D. G.: Notes on the East African Miocene Primates. *J. East African and Uganda Natur. Hist. Soc.,* 17:141-181, 1943.

A description of the four specimens of *Proconsul africanus* and other fossil primates found in East Africa. An invaluable study.

ROBINSON, J. T.: *The Dentition of the Australopithecinae.* Pretoria Transvaal Museum Memoir No. 9, 1956.

A definitive monograph on the teeth of the australopithecines demonstrating how much more manlike they are than apelike.

———— and MASON, R. J.: Occurrence of stone artefacts with *Australopithecus* at Sterkfontein. *Nature, 180:*521-524, 1957.

An interesting report on artifacts at Sterkfontein probably not made by australopithecines.

ROMER, A. S.: *Man and the Vertebrates,* 4th edition. Baltimore, Penguin Books, 1958.

A most excellent and attractively written book on the origin and evolution of the vertebrates, including the primates, abundantly illustrated.

RUCH, T. C.: *Bibliographia Primatologica.* Springfield, Illinois, Thomas, 1941. The best and most exhaustive classified bibliography on studies of every kind relating to the primates.

————: *Diseases of Laboratory Primates.* Philadelphia, Saunders, 1959. Covering not only laboratory animals, but also those in captivity. An invaluable work.

STRAUS, JR., W. L.: The riddle of man's ancestry. *Quart. Rev. Biol.,* 24:200-223. 1949.

A most interesting criticism of the "anthropoid-ape" theory of man's origin. The author cites some of the evidence which suggests man's derivation from un-specialized, monkey-like quadrupeds.

WASHBURN, S. L.: Australopithecines: the hunters or the hunted? *Am. Anthropol.,* n.s. 59:612-614, 1957.

On the basis of the eating habits of carnivores in Africa and their disposal of the bones, it is questioned whether the australopithecines may not have been the hunted rather than the hunters.

WILDER, H. H.: *The Pedigree of the Human Race.* New York, Holt, 1926. Though somewhat out of date this is still a most readable book.

VOSS, H.: *Bibliographie des Menschenaffen (Schimpanse, Orang, Gorilla).* Jena, Fischer Verlag, 1955.

An incomplete bibliography on the great apes, but not unuseful.

ZUCKERMAN, S.: *Functional Affinities of Man, Monkeys and Apes.* New York, Harcourt, 1933.

A study of the bearings of physiology and behavior on the origin, relationships, and the classification of the lemurs, monkeys, apes, and man.

Chapter IV

THE ORIGIN AND EVOLUTION OF MAN

IF THE theory is sound that man originated from an anthropoid stock, it would follow as a necessary inference that the earliest men ought more closely to resemble such a stock than do the later evolved types. And this, at least in the earliest types, is precisely what we find.

The question may well be asked: If such early men so much resembled apes, how is it possible to determine at what point an animal ceases to be an ape and becomes a man? This is always a good question to ask, and it is an important one. Let us try to answer it.

Whether the skeletal remains of an animal represent those of an ape or of a man is a matter which is determined in much the same way as we determine the status of any living animal, namely, by its resemblance to other known forms. If it is unique, then we ask the obvious question: Does it more closely resemble the one group, say the ape, or the other, say man? Or does it, perhaps, resemble them both equally? Is it then, an intermediate type?

These are the kinds of questions that the physical anthropologist or paleoanthropologist asks, and the answer he returns depends primarily upon the weighing of the results of his analysis of the structural characters of a given specimen. It is not necessarily the number of the resemblances involved which matters, though this is important, so much as the quality of those resemblances. Thus, for example, ape-like canine teeth and the absence of a chin are characters found together only among the apes. When one or both of these characters is found in any mandible the suggestion is that we are dealing with an ape, but when in the same skull we find a cranial capacity very substantially exceeding that of an ape and falling within the range of that of man, such a single fact would alone qualitatively outweigh any quantity of ape-like characters. Such an aggregation of characters has actually occurred in more than one example of fossil man. Usually the form of the vault of the head and of the jaws, and the size and form of the teeth are alone sufficient to make the differentiation between ape and man clear.

[154]

Apes do not habitually walk erectly. When, therefore, we find evidences of the habitual assumption of the erect posture, we have a pretty definite indication of the attainment of hominid or near-hominid status.

To the question how is it possible to tell at what point an animal ceases to be an ape and becomes a man, the answer is that it is, in fact, not possible to make such a distinction on purely morphological grounds. The distinction between man and ape rests principally on functional grounds. *Zinjanthropus boisei* provides a good example of this fact. Even though *Zinjanthropus* walked erectly he possessed a brain of ape-like size and a skull of ape-like appearance. Nevertheless, *Zinjanthropus* was a man because he was capable of a unique kind of conceptual thought of which man alone is capable. This is evidenced by the fact that he was a tool maker, an innovator. On morphological grounds alone it would not have been possible to say that *Zinjanthropus* was a man. On the evidence of his tools it is clear that he was—and that fact makes his morphological traits all the more interesting.

In the following pages a description is given of the most significant fossil forms of man. Insofar as it is possible to do so this will be followed by a discussion of their general relationships. Before proceeding further, however, a few words are necessary on the subject of the nomenclature used with respect to fossil man. In its present form this nomenclature is most misleading.

When the first fossil manlike remains were discovered the differences presented by these from any other known form of man led students to place them in distinct genera. Thus, Java man was named *Pithecanthropus erectus,* and continuing this trend Peking man was distinguished as *Sinanthropus pekinensis* even though this form clearly represents no more than a geographic race of *Pithecanthropus.* As more and more fossil remains were discovered the gaps between the already known fossil types were narrowed, and the earlier known types at once lost the appearance of extremes. The tendency was now to regard most types of fossil man as representing different species. Today it is slowly beginning to be recognized among anthropologists that with the possible exception of the fossil giant ape-man *Meganthropus,* all fossil and living forms of man probably belong to the same polytypic species, the different types representing geographic or temporal races or subspecies. If and when this viewpoint becomes generally accepted an entire revision will become necessary of the names which fossil men have hitherto been given. Such a revision can be satisfactorily achieved only by an international commission. Man is a zoological species and the taxonomic rules of nomenclature should be applied to him just as they are to any other animal.*

If all forms of man, fossil and living, belong to a single species, then the generic and specific names which have priority are the names originally bestowed by Linnaeus upon man, *Homo sapiens.* The distinctive types of man, fossil and living, would then be distinguished as subspecies or races of *Homo sapiens.* Without the common agreement of a commission of experts on the names which should be substituted for those now in use it would perhaps be confusing to attempt any change at this time. However, without the necessary cautions it is misleading to continue to use the old names, for these names have a way of distorting the facts and of forcing thought concerning the evolution of man in a direction which does not correspond with the facts. Names that correspond more closely to the facts, and that lead one to think more accurately are to be preferred. As Julian Huxley has pointed out, the basic theoretical aim of taxonomy is the accurate description of organic diversification in nature. With these cautions, then, we may proceed.

The order of the descriptions followed in these pages is morphological. That is to say, each type is described in the order, roughly, of its decreasing physical resemblance to some imagined anthropoid ancestral type. Such an order of description has the effect of producing a linear view of the relationship of these types to one another against which the reader must be cautioned. The reason for preserving the morphological order of description here is that it does effectively serve to convey some idea of the kind of changes that occurred during the evolution of the various types of man. The important point to remember is that many of these changes probably occurred at the same time level, that is, horizontally while others occurred vertically, in geographically separated groups of the species, and hence that many of these forms were contemporary potentially or actually inter-breeding groups.

We have already seen in the discussion of the non-human primates (Chapter II) that most groups of such primates that have been described as species are probably nothing but geographic races of a single polytypic species. The evidence clearly shows that the same holds true for man. It will be recalled that a species was defined as a group of actually or potentially interbreeding natural populations, which is reproductively isolated from other such groups. The actual

---

* For such a suggested revision see pp. 287-288.

or potentially interbreeding populations may be recognized as sub-species or geographic races, the subspecies or races being defined as populations which differ from one another in the incidence of one or more genes. Such populations comprise a single polytypic species, that is to say, a species is made up of a number of populations, each of which is a more or less self-contained breeding unit, which differs from other such breeding units in the incidence of certain genes.

All forms of fossil and living man fall within the limits of this conception of a species.

Morphologically the variation presented by the Hominidae is of the continuous kind; there are very few striking discontinuities or gaps between one group and another, and this is true even when early types such as the Java men are compared with modern man. As Dobzhansky and Weidenreich have independently pointed out, the available evidence indicates that no more than a single hominid species has existed at any time level during the Pleistocene. What-ever races existed within the species either interbred or were capable of doing so.

These views mirror the biological facts, and are supported by modern genetics and the findings of the new systematics. We shall return to their discussion a little later in this chapter.

As we shall see, types very like modern man almost certainly lived contemporaneously with pithecanthropoid types; and it is now fairly clear that such types lived prior to the advent of Neanderthal types and subsequently absorbed them.

Several further methodological considerations are in order here. Since the orthogenetic or straight-line conception of the evolution of man from a "primitive" to a more "advanced" stage of man was a basic tenet of most anthropologists' faith, up to very recent times, it was considered that the earliest types of men must have been morpho-logically "primitive" (nearer to the ancestral form), while the later types were less so, becoming morphologically more "advanced" as time progressed (further removed from the ancestral form). It was in this way that morphological evolution and Time became associated, according to the formula: the more "primitive" the form the earlier in time, the more "advanced" in form the later in time.

Since it was believed that the original ancestral stock of the earliest men was an anthropoid group not unlike an "unspecialized" group of chimpanzees or gorillas, it followed that the   forms of man most closely resembling the postulated ancestor would be more "primitive" than those forms of man that showed more resemblance to modern man,—modern man being conceived to be the latest product of the primate evolutionary process. This seemed to be a reasonable enough theory. It was, however, based on several assumptions, and reasonable as they seemed, there is now very good reason to believe that those assumptions were unsound.

The first of these assumptions was a covert one which was for the most part unconsciously injected into the conception of man's descent from an "unspecialized" anthropoid. The theory of man's descent from an "unspecialized" anthropoid seems to be sound enough, but what is unsound is the meaning which that idea appears to have had for many students. That meaning seems unavoidably to creep into their thinking, and that is the habit of thinking of the ancestral stock of man as resembling a chimpanzee or gorilla. This habit of thought is evident in the practice of those innumerable studies which are undertaken in order to point out the likenesses and differences between these apes and man. A consequence of this habit of thought is that any manlike form which in some of its characters strongly resembles these apes is regarded as clearly more primitive than any form which shows fewer resemblances to them. The image of a living ape or even its skeleton makes much more of an impression upon the mind than the scrambled mess of fragments of a hundred fossil jaws and teeth. But in fact we have good reason to believe that the existing great apes are highly divergent and specialized forms that in many respects probably bear considerably less resemblance to the common stock from which they and man originated than does modern man! Hence, it is suggested that it is a mistake to evaluate the degree of primitiveness or advancement of a character by reference to the standard of an animal resembling the living great apes. The great apes have almost certainly departed very much more considerably from that common ancestral stock than has modern man. It would, almost, be more in keeping with the evidence today to utilize modern man as a standard by which to measure the primitiveness or development not only of any other form of man, but even of the anthropoid apes!

Contemporary man possesses a large number of morphological and functional traits of a highly unspecialized, rather primitive, creature. As we shall see, in subsequent pages of this book, taken altogether the evidence today very strongly suggests that contemporary man represents the persisting form of an early unspecialized type, whereas other forms of man, such as the Pithecanthropoids and Neanderthaloids, represent specializations away from a type closely resembling contemporary man.

The second erroneous assumption was to equate "primitiveness" with morphologically "brutal" traits, and "advancement" with morphologically gracile traits. The third erroneous assumption has already been touched upon, namely, the equation of "primitiveness" in the brutal sense with early appearance in time, and the equation of "advancement" in the sense of the less brutal, more gracile form with later development in time.

Unfortunately, some of the terms we shall have to use in this book enshrine some of these errors of thought. For example, the term "neanthropic" refers to "new or recent man," meaning what it suggests, namely, that the latest type of man is the newest type of man. This, it has already been suggested, there is good reason to believe, is untrue. Yet the term (coined by Elliot Smith in 1916) is now widely used to refer to the modern type of man. It will do no harm if we realize what is the matter with it, particularly if it is strictly used—as we intend—throughout this book, to refer to *the morphological type of man persisting into the contemporary period, wherever, and in relation to whatever time, he is found upon this earth.*

The term "palanthropic man" ("old or ancient man") was used in connection with the phase of man which was believed immediately to have preceded the appearance of neanthropic man, namely, Neanderthal man. The idea behind the original coinage of the term is unsound. We shall, however, retain the term in the sense of *a morphological type of prehistoric man, ranging from Pithecanthropus to Neanderthal man, which has become extinct.*

The sense in which these terms have been used by other students may be exemplified in the practice of Weidenreich and of Kroeber.

The Pithecanthropine types are called Archanthropinae by Weidenreich, and Protoanthropic types by Kroeber. The Neanderthaloids, Solo, Heidelberg, Rhodesian, and Mount Carmel men, are called Paleoanthropinae by Weidenreich, and Paleoanthropic types by Kroeber. The Neanthropinae are, according to Weidenreich's usage, recognized as presenting two phases: the Upper Paleolithic phase, and modern man. In Kroeber's usage the term Neanthropic refers to the men of the Upper Paleolithic, who "differed from us only as a subspecies or race."

If these terms are to be used at all it might be wiser to restrict the term "Protoanthropic" man to such forms as the Australopithecines, and to *Meganthropus.*

Since neither the term palanthropic nor neanthropic should carry temporal implications, one may speak of late or early palanthropic types, and similarly of early or late neanthropic types. In general, it may be said that early neanthropic man closely resembles contemporary man in every way except for the characteristic possession of somewhat thicker cranial bones. Examples, are Swanscombe, and Fontéchevade man. The development of thinner cranial bones appears to have occurred during the Upper Pleistocene.

It is important to remember that the greater part of man's evolutionary development falls within the Ice Age or Pleistocene, a period from which the earth has only just emerged. During the Pleistocene ice-caps were formed at varying intervals in the polar and temperate regions of the earth with appreciable effects upon the climate everywhere. The intervals between the periods of glaciation were characterized by climates very different from those of the present day. Pleistocene man was forced to adapt himself to these climatic changes, but since they occurred at a very gradual rate the processes of his cultural adjustment were correspondingly extended over considerable periods of time.

Let us now proceed with the description of the more important types of fossil man.

Meganthropus palaeojavanicus. In the year 1941 Dr. G. H. R. von Koenigswald, a Dutch geologist, discovered the fragments of two lower jaws in the Lower Pleistocene beds of Sangiran in Central Java. These probably belonged to a very early form of man. The jaw is considerably larger in size, and particularly in thickness, than the jawbone of any hitherto known form of man. For this reason, and with reference to the region in which it was found it has been named *Meganthropus palaeojavanicus*. Weidenreich, comparing this jaw fragment with the same parts in the great apes, estimates that *Meganthropus* reached the size, stoutness and strength of a big gorilla. The only other known hominid jaw which approaches this in size, is the Swartkrans jaw discovered by Broom at Sterkfontein in South Africa in November 1948 (see p. 128).

The existence of such a robust skulled form of early man as *Meganthropus* may serve to explain the thickness especially of the cranial bones in subsequent forms of early man—the persistence of an inherited tendency rather than the development of a novel feature. All the evidence certainly points in such a direction. From this it would appear to follow fairly clearly that in the evolution of man there has been a progressive tendency toward reduction in massiveness or, to put it positively, toward the development of a greater gracility in most features of the skull.

Pithecanthropus erectus, Skulls I, II, and III. When the remains of the first so-called "ape-man" were found at Trinil, in Central Java, in 1890-97, the problem of its status at once arose. The find consisted of a skull vault, a fragment of the lower jaw, three teeth, and a complete left thigh bone. Each of these remains were discovered at different times, and at varying distances from one another. The fragment of jaw was found at Kedung Brubus, 22 miles from Trinil, the skull and the femur were found within fifty feet of each other. The three teeth were found at different times near the site of the discovery of the skull-cap. For these reasons there was some doubt whether all these parts belonged to a single individual. The probabilities were that they belonged to more than one individual of the same species. Today there is some question whether the teeth did not belong to an extinct orang-utan.

The contemporaneity and antiquity of the skull and thigh-bones (as well as of five other thigh-bones attributed to *Pithecanthropus erectus*) have been confirmed by the fluorine method (see pp. 240-241). The fluorine content being 1.22 per cent for the skull-cap and 1.05 to 1.12 per cent for the thigh-bone. For the additional five thigh-bones the range is from 1.01 to 1.50 per cent. For the associated Trinil fauna the range is from 1.17 to 1.72 per cent.

All the remains were discovered in an horizon which is now generally agreed to be of Middle Pleistocene age, a fact which would endow the creature or creatures to which they belonged with an antiquity of something like half a million years. From the rather ape-like vault of the skull, Dr. Eugene Dubois, the discoverer of the remains, was able to determine that the animal to which it belonged had a cranial capacity of between 900 and 1,000 cubic centimeters; later this was re-calculated at somewhat more than 1,000 c.c. At the present time the most generally accepted estimate is 940 c.c.

The cranial capacity of the anthropoid apes varies between a range of 290 to 655 c.c., the gorilla possessing the largest brain, with an average of 550 c.c. Mean cranial capacities for modern men vary between 1,200 c.c.,—with an average of about 1,350 c.c.—to 1,500 c.c. In its lowest range a brain volume of 900 c.c. occasionally occurs in contemporary man. Clearly, then, in the matter of cranial capacity, the Trinil skull falls within the range of human brain volume. It may be recalled here, by way of comparison, that the estimated adult cranial capacity of the Taungs ape, *Australopithecus transvaalensis*, is about 600 c.c., while the cranial capacity of *Paranthropus crassidens* has been estimated at 850 to 1,100 c.c.

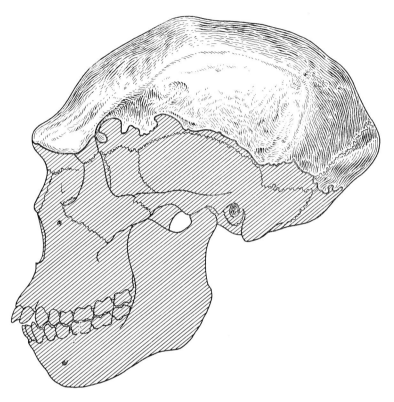

Figure 79. A reconstruction of the skull of *Pithecanthropus erectus I.*

Brain volume then, puts *Pithecanthropus erectus* among the Hominidae rather than among the apes. An endocranial cast, that is, a cast of the interior of the cranium, reveals the presence of an interesting bulge of the inferior or third frontal convolution. This region of the brain is, in man, believed to be associated with the faculty of speech. It is quite impossible to say, but it may be that *Pithecanthropus* may have used some form of language.

The character of the femur or thigh bone is entirely manlike and proves that its owner habitually walked erectly, hence the specific name *erectus* was added to the generic name *Pithecanthropus*, which means "ape-man." From the femur the height of *Pithecanthropus* has been calculated to have been about five feet eight inches and his weight about 150 pounds. In point-of-fact there is some doubt whether the femur is not that of a modern type of fossil man, a doubt, however,

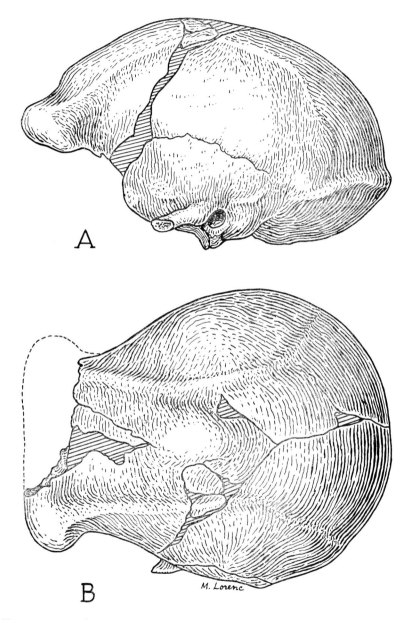

Figure 80. A, lateral, B, vertical views of the cranium of *Pithecanthropus erectus II* (after von Koenigswald). (Courtesy, Carnegie Institution of Washington.)

which has been considerably reduced by the surprisingly manlike limb bones of the australopithecine apes.

Pithecanthropus erectus II was discovered early in 1937 by Dr. G. H. R. von Koenigswald at Sangiran in Central Java. This represents an adult specimen in which only the facial bones and lower jaw are missing (see Figure 80). The resemblance between this and the skull discovered by Dubois in 1891 is very striking, except that the cranial capacity in this second skull was only 775 c.c., the smallest cranial capacity thus far recorded in any hominid. From the same district there had been recovered, in 1936, the fragment of a lower jaw with four teeth, undoubtedly of *Pithecanthropus,* and in 1938 the fragment of the skull of a juvenile *Pithecanthropus,* now known as Skull III. The fragment of the lower jaw, with three molars increasing in size from the first to the third, unlike the usual sequence in man, and one premolar *in situ,* is massive, and a chin is not developed. All are Middle Pleistocene.

Pithecanthropus robustus. Skull IV. By far the most important find was made by Dr. von Koenigswald in a Lower Pleistocene bed in the Sangiran district in January 1939. This consisted of the posterior three-quarters of the brain-case including the base, and the upper jaw with the teeth *in situ* with the exception of the incisors and the second and third molars of the left side. The teeth are essentially hominid in form. The canine tooth projects somewhat beyond the level of the other teeth and is larger than that of any recent or fossil hominid. As is the case in all hominids the breadth of the molars exceeds their length. What is unique for any hominid form, is the presence of a bony diastema or space, the premaxillary diastema or simian gap, measuring 6.2 mm. on the left and 5.0 mm. on the right side, separating the canine from the lateral incisor tooth. In a later find of what is believed to be a portion of the upper jaw of the female of this type a similar, though reduced, premaxillary diastema is present.

The canine tooth of *Pithecanthropus robustus* is, in fact, very small compared with that of the anthropoids, but not smaller than the same tooth in *Sinanthropus,* thus suggesting the presence of a similar small canine in the lower jaw. There is no precanine diastema in the lower jaw corresponding to the premaxillary diastema of the upper jaw. The presence of the premaxillary diastema in the upper jaw, which in the anthropoids affords room for the upper part of the large lower canine, suggests that in the evolution of man the canine tooth underwent reduction first, and that it took another separate evolutionary change to bring about the reduction of the diastema, and thus to produce a further shortening of the jaws.

The upper jaw in *Pithecanthropus robustus* is wider and longer and projects farther beyond the face than in any other known form of man. The palate exhibits certain unique features, such as the complete absence of a median torus or ridges and furrows of any kind, and the presence of posterior palatine hillocks. The bones are more massive than in any other known form of *Pithecanthropus*, and while the skull is longer than that of any of these forms it is actually appreciably lower, the length being 158 mm. as compared with 135 mm. in Skull II, while the corresponding heights are 102 mm. in the former and 105 mm. in the latter. The cranial capacity was about 900 cc. The basal breadth of the skull exceeds the greatest parietal breadth very much more markedly than in any other known hominid skull; the shape of

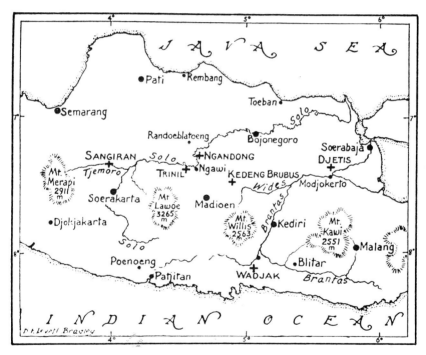

Figure 81. Map of central and East Java, showing the chain of volcanoes and the valleys of the Bengawan (Solo) River, with the sites of the human finds marked by a cross. (From Weidenreich. Courtesy, University of Chicago Press.)

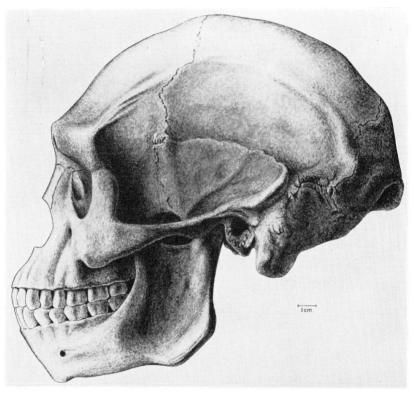

Figure 82. Reconstruction of the skull of Solo Man. (From Weidenreich. Courtesy, American Museum of Natural History.)

the skull as seen from behind or in a coronal section is distinctly triangular. A unique keel-like elevation or sagittal crest runs over the top of the skull in the mid-line from top to back, and there is an enormous bulging of the occipital torus. All these are features unique to Skull IV, and in recognition of its difference from other forms of *Pithecanthropus* it has been named *Pithecanthropus robustus*.

Homo modjokertensis. In 1936 one of Dr. von Koenigswald's native collectors found a fossil human skull in a Lower Pleistocene bed in the Djetis zone near Modjokerto, west of Soerabaja in east Java. The skull, with facial parts and teeth missing, proved to be that of a child of about three years of age. The incipient temporal narrowness, the depressed parietal, the peculiar form of the occiput, the low frontal region and the well marked supraorbital torus, all bespeak a primitive type. The skull of this child of Lower Pleistocene age is almost certainly a member of the Pithecanthropoid group. It is very likely a juvenile member of the *robustus* type.

It should be noted that the *robustus* skulls were discovered in a Lower Pleistocene horizon older than the Trinil beds from which *Pithecanthropus erectus* was recovered.

Homo soloensis. In 1931 in the region of the Solo river near Ngandong, in Central Java, a fossil human skull of Upper Pleistocene age was discovered which led to the subsequent finding of portions of ten others. Faces and teeth were missing, but the characters of the remainder of the skulls showed an extraordinarily thick-skulled primitive type having the clearest immediate affinities with *Pithecanthropus* and Modjokerto man on the one hand, and Rhodesian and Neanderthal man (see pp. 184 and 194) on the other. There is, how-

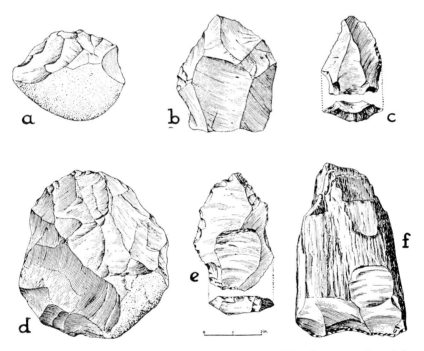

Figure 83. Artifacts of Soan culture group. *a*. Pebble chopper-tool, and *b*, flake tool, probably of quartzite, Early Soan, N.W. Indian. After de Terra and Paterson. *c*. Late Choukoutien flake-tool of chert (resembling Mousterian point), Choukoutien, China. After Pei. *d*. Chopper-tool, and *e* flake-tool of silicified tuff, Patjitanian, Java. After Movius. *f*. Chopper-tool (hand-adze) of fossil wood, Anyathian, Upper Burma. After Movius. (From Oakley, *Man The Tool-Maker*. Courtesy, British Museum [Natural History].)

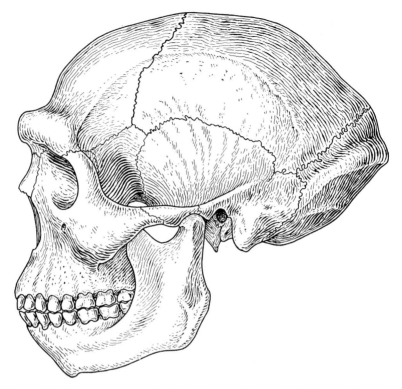

Figure 84. Reconstruction of a female *Sinanthropus* skull (somewhat modified after Weidenreich).

ever, not the slightest doubt that Solo man, with an average cranial
capacity of 1,100 c.c. (range 1,035-1,225 c.c.) represents a Neanderthaloid advanced member of the Pithecanthropus group.

In association with Solo man were found several beautifully worked
bone implements, an axe made of deer antlers, a barbed spearhead,
and a number of crude stone tools. Culturally, then, Solo man appears to have been a fairly advanced type, belonging in the upper
reaches of the Paleolithic or Old Stone Age.

In the Trinil level of Central Java primitive stone implements
have been discovered which may have been used by Pithecanthropoid
forms. These consist of flakes, points, scrapers, and cores made of
different silicified rocks (quartz, lydian stone, etc.).

On the south coast of Central Java near Patjitan similar implements
have been found including a variety of chopping tools.

All these artifacts correspond to those which have been discovered in almost every part of the world, though they belong to an entirely different tradition, and in Java they are of particular interest because they strongly suggest that physical and cultural evolution was proceeding there contemporaneously with, and to some extent independently of, similar stages of evolution occurring elsewhere in the world. *Sinanthropus* or Peking man and his culture represent such contemporary stages.

Sinanthropus pekinensis. Discovered at Chou k'ou tien near Peking in China in 1929, "China Man" or *Sinanthropus* is now known from the remains of some fifty-nine individuals forty of which were found in the same Chou k'ou tien caves in subsequent years. Five more or less complete skulls and fourteen mandibles, and 152 isolated teeth were discovered in these caves in 1957. Like *Pithecanthropus erectus* Peking man is of Middle Pleistocene age, and morphologically so closely resembles the former that there can be little doubt of their genetic relationship.

The cranial capacity of the Sinanthropus group varies from 915

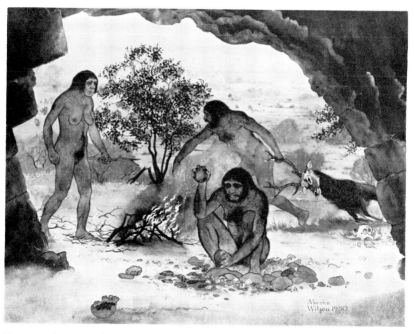

Figure 85. *Sinanthropus pekinensis* at home. From a painting by Maurice Wilson. (Courtesy, British Museum [Natural History].)

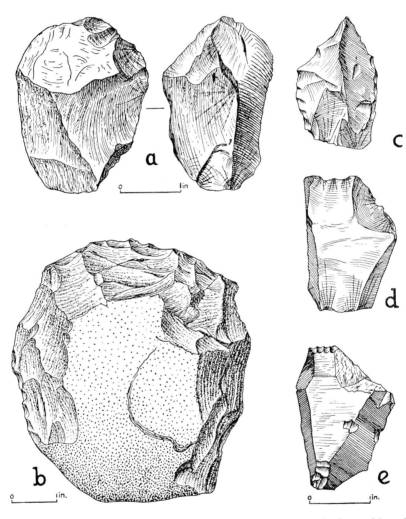

Figure 86. Stone tools of Pekin Man. *a.* Quartz chopper-tool. *b.* Boulder of greenstone flaked into chopper form. *c.* Pointed flake of quartz. *d.* Bi-polar flake of quartz. *e.* Bi-pyramidal crystal of quartz utilized as tool. After Pei and Black. (From Oakley, *Man The Tool-Maker.* Courtesy, British Museum [Natural History].)

c.c. to 1,225 c.c., with an average of 1,043 c.c. The average brain size of *Sinanthropus* is about 20 per cent greater than that of *Pithecanthropus*. The frontal region of the skull shows a bump-like development, a more globular form, than is the case in *Pithecanthropus* in which the same region is relatively flat, while the frontal sinus is less expanded in the former than in the latter. The occipital region is comparatively narrow and elongated in *Sinanthropus* and broad and rounded in *Pithecanthropus*, and the mandible is considerably more robust in the latter than in the former. There is no diastema between the maxillary canine and the lateral incisor in *Sinanthropus*, whereas in one form at least of *Pithecanthropus* an appreciable diastema is present. Apart from these there are no really significant differences between the skulls of *Sinanthropus* and *Pithecanthropus*, and it is generally agreed that they ought both to be included in the single group *Pithecanthropus* of the genus *Homo*. Next to *Zinjanthropus* and *Meganthropus* these Sino-Malayan forms are the most primitive morphological types of man known.

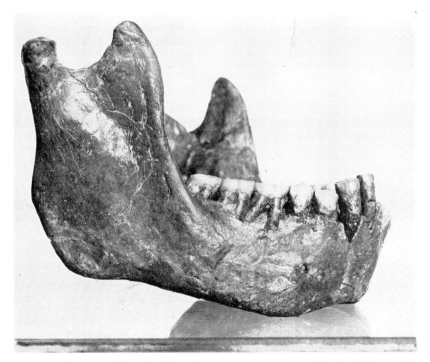

Figure 87.   Mandible of *Atlanthropus mauritanicus III*.   Probably male.
(Courtesy, Dr. C. Arambourg.)

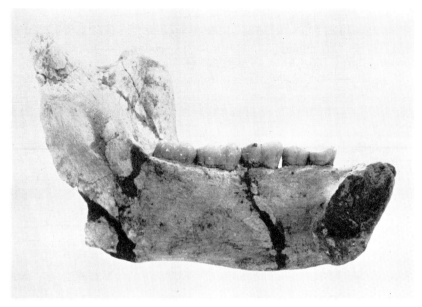

Figure 88. Inner aspect of left side of mandible of *Atlanthropus mauritani-cus II*. Probably female. (Courtesy, Dr. C. Arambourg.)

Taken all in all there can be little question that *Sinanthropus* represents a slightly more advanced stage in the evolution of man than *Pithecanthropus*, the difference in brain size and the absence of a premaxillary diastema would alone be sufficient indication of that. The resemblances, however, between the two forms are such as to suggest that *Sinanthropus* merely represents a geographic race of the Javanese Pithecanthropoid stock.

The flakes, points, scrapers, choppers and cores, of the Trinil beds, presumed to be the handiwork of *Pithecanthropus,* are very similar to the artifacts which were found associated with *Sinanthropus.*

All of these forms are very closely related. As a group the Pithe-canthropoids *robustus, modjokertensis, erectus, pekinensis,* and *solo-ensis,* exhibit the kinds of differences which (save in the case of *modjokertensis* which probably belongs with *robustus*) render it clear that each type represents a geographic race or subspecies of a closely allied group of the same species.

The Pithecanthropoids in every sense of the word are men, and they properly belong in the genus *Homo,* with the single species *erectus,* and the subspecies *erectus, pekinensis,* and *soloensis.*

It has already been pointed out that in view of certain morphological resemblances of Solo man to the skeletal remains found at Broken Hill in Northern Rhodesia, South Africa, and to Neanderthal man, a possible relationship between Solo man and these two types has been suggested.

Atlanthropus mauritanicus. In June 1954 Dr. Camille Arambourg, of the National Museum of Natural History, Paris, discovered two human mandibles associated with an abundant Chelleo-Acheulian industry in a sand pit at Ternifine, near Mascara in Algeria. The associated remains of extinct mammals, among them a giant baboon, a *Machairodes*, and a giant wart hog of the *Notochoerus* group would alone be sufficient to assign these remains to the base of the Middle Pleistocene or Kamasian.

One of the jaws, thought to be that of a male (Figure 87) is al-

Figure 89. Bifaces in quartzite found associated with *Atlanthropus mauritanicus.* (Courtesy, Dr. C. Arambourg.)

Figure 90. Hatchets found associated with *Atlanthropus mauritanicus*.
(Courtesy, Dr. C. Arambourg.)

most complete with all but the canines and three incisors in place.
The smaller jaw, believed to be female, is represented only by its left
half with only the canines and incisors lacking (Figure 88). The two
jaws are remarkably robust. There is no chin, and there is no simian
shelf. The ramus is low and broad as in *Sinanthropus* but somewhat
more gracile than that of the Mauer jaw. The molars are low, broad,
large, with large pulp cavities. The occlusal surfaces of the teeth bear
secondary crenulations as in some specimens of *Sinanthropus*. Arambourg concludes that *Atlanthropus*, as the form of man represented
by these two jaws has been named, is very closely related to *Pithecanthropus* and *Sinanthropus*. In its robustness and the form of the di-
gastric fossae which extend along the ventral border of the symphysis
and a portion of the lingual surface, *Atlanthropus* more closely resembles *Meganthropus* of Java.

As Straus has pointed out, the *Meganthropus* fragment emanated
from the same deposits as *Pithecanthropus*, and only its enormous
size has excluded it from jointure with the pithecanthropines. The
Atlanthropus mandibles, in respect of size, would go far toward
bridging the gap between *Meganthropus* and *Pithecanthropus*, and

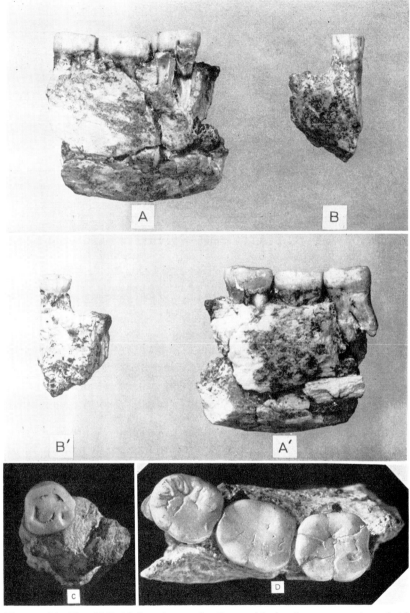

Figure 91. The Sidi Abderrahman fossil mandibular fragments. A and A′ Outer and inner aspects of right posterior fragment. D Occlusal view of the three molars. B and B′ Outer and inner aspects of left postsymphyseal fragment. C Occlusal view of the first premolar in the postsymphyseal fragment. (Courtesy, Dr. C. Arambourg and Mons. P. Biberson.)

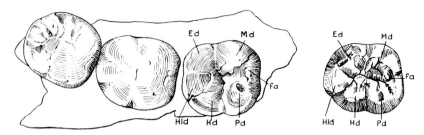

Figure 92. The Sidi Abderrahman molar series clearly showing the dryopithecus pattern on the first molar compared with a second molar of *Sinanthropus*. (Courtesy, Dr. C. Arambourg and Mons. P. Biberson.)

would simply indicate the great variability of jaw size in early forms
of man.

In 1955, a third jaw together with a parietal bone of *Atlanthropus*
were discovered. The parietal is remarkable for its thickness, and for
the slightness of its curvature, suggesting a low cranial vault, and for
the presence on its inner surface of a sylvian crest as in *Sinanthropus*.
The sylvian crest is a thickened bony relief extending into the parietal
bone as if it were a continuation of the lesser wing of the sphenoid,
and generally situated above the impressions for the middle meningeal
artery. The crest is present in *Pithecanthropus, Sinanthropus* and in
Neanderthal man, but is never present in anything like a similar degree of development in contemporary man. With the exception of
the orang the crest is absent in the apes. Thus, the presence of a
well developed sylvian crest in the *Atlanthropus* parietal together
with the form of the brain itself adds further strong testimony to the
probability that *Atlanthropus* belongs with the Pithecanthropine
group.

The artifacts found in association with *Atlanthropus* comprised
more than a hundred tools of roughly worked quartzite, silcrete or
limestone, with very rare flint. There are primitive rostroid (high-
backed) bifaces, cleavers, and large flakes of Clactonian type (Figures
89 and 90). The industry is characteristic of the Chello-Acheulian,
and belongs to the beginning of the Middle Pleistocene.

Sidi Abderrahman. In 1954, P. Biberson discovered in Littorina
Cave, a commercially worked pit at Sidi Abderrahman, about 6 miles
southwest of Casablanca, French Morocco, an incomplete mandible
associated with a Middle Acheulian industry. The stratum in which
the mandible was found was dated with great accuracy as correspond-

ing to the end of the maximum transgression of Tyrrhenian I, or the North African Third Pluvial, that is, at the end of the Second Interglacial and the beginning of the Third Glacial.

The portions of the mandible recovered consist of the posterior part of the right body with the three molars in place; this piece is broken just behind M_3, of which the roots are visible, and at the middle of the alveolus of PM_2; the inferior border is intact. The second fragment of this mandible is a part of the postsymphysial region, with PM_1 in place, and is broken just behind this tooth, as well as at the level of the mesial border of the alveolus of I_2; the latter tooth and the canine are missing.

In virtually every respect the characters of the teeth and mandible closely resemble those of *Atlanthropus* and the pithecanthropines. The jaw is robust, the teeth large, the molars low-crowned and long, and there is a predominance of the protoconid over the metaconid on the

Figure 93. Two bifaces of Middle Acheulian II. Littorina Cave, Level D_0 of the cave entrance in continuity with the sandy lens F containing the Sidi Abderrahman human fossil bones. Half natural size. (Courtesy, Dr. C. Arambourg and Mons. P. Biberson.)

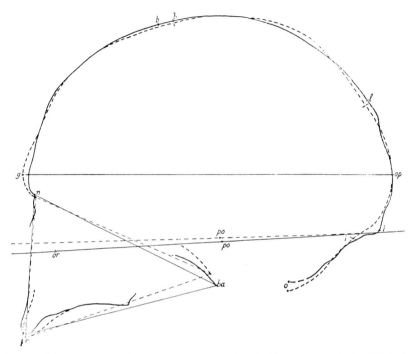

Figure 94. Mid-sagittal craniograms of Keilor skull ——————, and the Wadjak
skull II   – – – , both superimposed on the glabella-opisthocranion line
(g-op) and the opisthocranion. Half natural size. (From Weidenreich.
Courtesy, *Am. J. Phys. Anthrop.*)

molars. Arambourg concludes that the Sidi Abderrahman mandible
falls within the range of possible variation of *Atlanthropus*.

The associated artifacts belong to the Middle Acheulian industry,
corresponding very closely to the Chelles-Acheul stage 8 at Olduvai
Gorge described by Leakey. Sidi Abderrahman man, therefore, is
of somewhat later age than the men of Ternifine.

Rabat. A short distance to the north of Casablanca there was discovered, in February 1933, in the Rabat sandstone, the cranial fragments, part of the maxilla of the left side with palate and teeth, and
the major part of the body of the mandible with three incisors, the
canine, and the first molar *in situ*. Apparently a complete skull was
present which was destroyed by a mine explosion. There was no
associated industry, but the geological evidence suggests a Middle
Pleistocene age. The remains are those of an adolescent, probably
male. The mandible is very robust and the teeth correspondingly

large. Rabat man would appear to belong to the *Atlanthropus* group.

Wadjak Man. In 1889-90, before his discovery of the original *Pithecanthropus* remains in 1890-97, Dr. Eugene Dubois had discovered two extremely interesting fossil crania at Wadjak, some 60 miles southeast of Trinil, in Java. The discovery of these skulls was not announced until thirty years later, in 1920. In Wadjak I, possibly a female, the cranial capacity is 1,550 c.c., in Wadjak II 1,650 c.c. These skulls, for which Dubois claimed a Pleistocene age, bear a striking resemblance to the Australian aboriginal skull, except that the skull of Wadjak man is appreciably larger in all its dimensions than the Australian. This resemblance has recently assumed considerable significance for in 1940 there was discovered, in a sand-pit one mile north of the village of Keilor, 10 miles northwest of Melbourne, Australia, a fossil skull which is almost identical in form with that of Wadjak man. The Keilor skull was found some 18 feet below the surface of the Maribyrnong River terrace. The deposit, at first

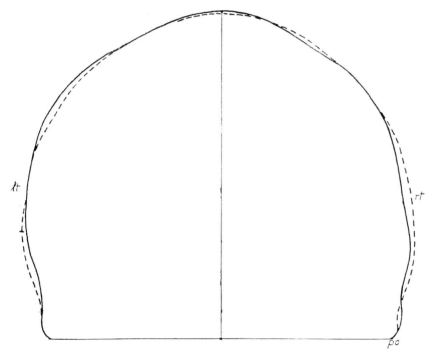

Figure 95. Transverse diagram of the Keilor skull ————, and the Wadjak skull I, — — — — ,   both superimposed on the interporion line (po). Two-thirds natural size. (From Weidenreich. Courtesy, *Am. J. Phys. Anthrop.*)

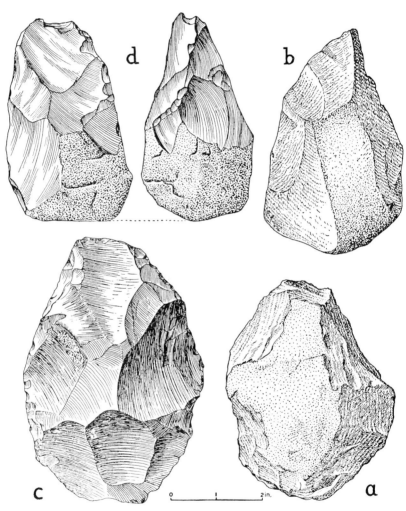

Figure 96. Abbevillian (Chellean) tools. *a.* Lava hand-axe, Bed II, Oldo-way Gorge, Tanganyika. *b.* Quartzite hand-axe 90 metre beach, Morocco. After Neuville and Ruhlmann. *c.* Hand-axe, derived, Chelles-sur-Marne. After Breuil. *d.* Hand-axe, 150 ft. terrace of Thames, near Caversham, Berks. Oxford University Museum. (From Oakley, *Man the Tool-Maker*. Courtesy, British Museum [Natural History].)

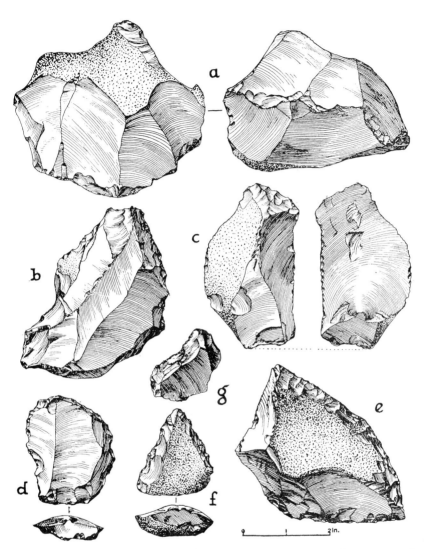

Figure 97. Clactonian and Tayacian artifacts. *a*. Clactonion flint core, and *b,c*, flake-tools, Lower Gravel, 100 ft. terrace, Swanscombe, Kent. *d*. Flake-tool, *Elephas antiquus* gravel, Clacton-on-Sea, Essex. *e*. Acheulo-Clactonian scraper, High Lodge, Mildenhall, Suffolk. *f*. Pre-Mousterian flake-tool, Combe-Capelle, Montferrand (Dordogne). *g*. Tayacian flake (utilized), interglacial river gravel, La Micoque, Tayac (Dordogne). (From Oakley, *Man the Tool-Maker*. Courtesy, British Museum [Natural History].)

believed to be of Riss-Würm Interglacial age, is now known to be of more recent age. Charcoal from hearths within the Keilor site yield a radiocarbon date of 6,546 ± 25 years. The fluorine content of Wadjak I is 0.25 and of Wadjak II 0.63 per cent. Bergman and Karsten suggest that the Wadjak skulls are of Upper Pleistocene age. It is of interest to note that the fluorine content of the Keilor skull is 0.30 per cent (Gill). On morphological grounds there is a strong indication of a relationship between the Javanese Wadjak people and the Australian aborigines, *via* Keilor, an apparent Wadjak type. The Keilor skull, like Wadjak, is much larger than the Australian skull, Keilor having a cranial capacity of 1,593 c.c., well within the range of Wadjak, whereas the cranial capacity of the aboriginal Australian skull of the Melbourne region averages 1,338 c.c. Interestingly enough this is the largest average cranial capacity for the Australian group in the whole continent, and it is significant that the Australian cranial type most resembling the Keilor skull is found in the same general region.

It is possible that the Wadjak people reached Australia in late Pleistocene or even in more recent times and possibly by admixture with some Negroid type gave rise to the modern Australian aboriginal. The general resemblance of the Australian skull to the Pithecanthropoid type, the presence of Wadjak man in Java, and the discovery of the Australian Wadjak type, Keilor, in the extreme southeast of the continent, rather than in the extreme northwest, are the sort of loose pieces in the jigsaw puzzle of the evolution of man which the anthropologist delights to fit together. Weidenreich has suggested that we have now an almost continuous phylogenetic line leading from the Pithecanthropus group through Solo man to Wadjak man and thence to the Australian aboriginal. This suggestion, however, very likely errs on the side of over-simplification.

Homo heidelbergensis. In 1907 at Mauer, some six miles southeast of Heidelberg, in Germany, a massive human lower jaw, together with all the teeth *in situ*, was discovered in a Lower Pleistocene deposit of Abbevillian (Chellean) age. No implements were found associated with the jaw, and indeed, records of Abbevillian industry have never been found in Germany. It is, however, possible by comparison of the geological strata of the Mauer sand-pit in which the jaw was found, with similar strata elsewhere in Europe, notably in Belgium, to state that the owner of the Mauer jaw probably flourished during the Abbevillian period, probably during the first, and certainly not later than the second, interglacial period.

The massive character of the Mauer mandible, the great breadth of the ramus, the absence of a chin, and the shallowness of the sigmoid notch, all suggest a primitive type. The teeth are remarkably like those of modern man in every respect, save that the pulp cavities are slightly larger, and the crowns and bodies of the molar teeth are somewhat more "swollen" than in modern man. Nevertheless, all these characters fall within the range of variation encountered in the living varieties of man. Weidenreich suggests that the greater length of the roots of the front teeth is associated with the fact that the tooth-bearing portion of the jaw fails to undergo recession and thus, as in modern man, leaves the lower portion of the jaw to jut out as a chin. Dr. Ronald Singer has pointed out that the fragment of the ramus of Saldanha man, found near Hopefield, South Africa (see p. 187), though less robust, fits the same region of the Heidelberg jaw perfectly, so that there may be some connection between these forms.

In view of the characters of the jaw of Heidelberg man it is generally considered that he was probably ancestral to Neanderthal man, and that he himself was in fact, an early variety of Neanderthal man.

As a Lower Pleistocene form it is quite possible, even probable,

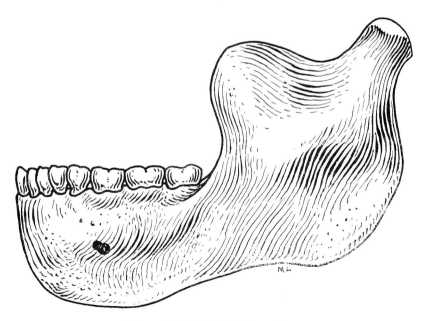

Figure 98. The Heidelberg Jaw.

that Heidelberg man intermingled with other forms of man, and that one of the varieties subsequently resulting from such intermingling was Neanderthal man. Who, and how many, the actual ancestors of Neanderthal man were, it is at present impossible to say; *Homo soloensis* has already been suggested as a possible one, *Sinanthropus* may be another, and a recently discovered type, *Africanthropus njarasensis*, described below, may represent still another. As our discoveries increase in number and importance the probability increases that we shall some day be able to name the actual groups from which Neanderthal, and other types of man, may have originated.

Homo rhodesiensis. In 1921 a complete skull, lacking the lower jaw, and portions of the remainder of the skeleton were found together with more fragmentary remains of a second individual. Associated artifacts found in the black cave earth consisted of flake tools mainly in quartz, stone balls possibly used as bolas, bone awls, and bone gouges—an industry in the Levalloisian tradition, putting Rhodesian man into a period contemporaneous with the Upper Paleolithic of Europe. The artifacts are considered to belong to the African Middle Stone Age (Developed Levallois or Proto-Stillbay). The cave at Broken Hill in which the remains were found is of Upper Pleistocene age. Until the recent discoveries in China and Java, Rhodesian man constituted even more of a puzzle than he does today. Combining Pithecanthropoid, even gorilloid, and Neanderthaloid characters with a goodly number which might be said to be of early neanthropic type, Rhodesian man had a rather primitively formed brain with a cranial capacity of about 1,250 c.c., enormous brow-ridges, a projecting large gorilla-like upper jaw, an unusually broad palate, and a face very large in all its dimensions, the cranial vault seems even more depressed, though it is actually not, than it is in the typical Neanderthaloid; the teeth, on the other hand, are far less specialized than in Neanderthal man, and closely resemble those of modern man. The resemblance between Solo man and Rhodesian man may be accidental, a close genetic relationship between the two types is, however, a possibility. It is interesting to note that both Rhodesian and Solo man appear to have been familiar with bone-working techniques and with the manufacture and use of spherical "bolas" stones.

The presence of Neanderthaloid and early neanthropic features conspire to lend Rhodesian man an unusual degree of interest.

Rhodesian man together with Solo man are regarded by some students as early sapiens types which bear no relationship to Neanderthal man at all, but which may possibly be closely related to the Australoid type. Keith regards Rhodesian man as a type which appears in the line leading to the neanthropic type soon after this line "had broken away from the Neanderthal line." A third view would regard Rhodesian man as a possible descendant of Solo man and as a collateral relative of the stock leading to later types of *Homo sapiens* on the one hand and to Neanderthal man on the other. A fourth, but rather unlikely, view regards Rhodesian man as a variant of Neanderthal man, with Negroid traits, which may serve to make him the prototype of modern Negroids.

These views are not necessarily in conflict with each other, but obviously it is for the present best to leave the question of the relationships of Rhodesian man open.

An interesting feature of the Rhodesian skull is the fact that nearly every one of its teeth was badly decayed, thus proving that caries is not altogether a disease of civilization. The fact remains, however,

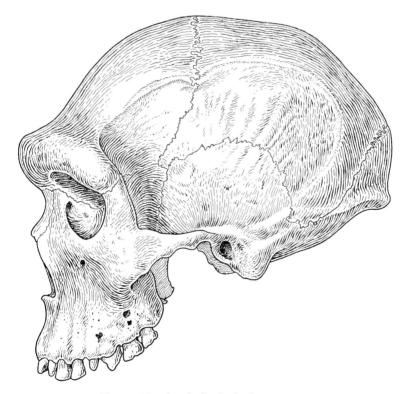

Figure 99. The skull of Rhodesian Man.

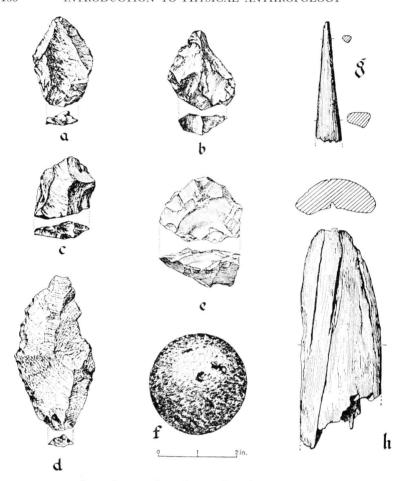

Figure 100. The industry of Broken Hill (Rhodesian) Man. *a-c*. Quartz flakes with faceted striking-platforms. *d*. Flake-blade of quartz. *e*. Disc-core (chert). *f*. Spherical "bolas-stone" (granite). *g*. Bone point or awl. *h*. Bone gouge. (From Oakley, *Man the Tool-Maker*. Courtesy, British Museum [Natural History].)

that fossil men almost always have teeth completely free from decay. Evidence of suppuration in the mastoid region of the skull indicates that this individual suffered from severe mastoiditis. A peculiar lipping at the articular end of the leg-bone, the tibia, suggests the effects of arthritis. A broken humerus and a fragment of a parietal bone recovered among the animal bones are regarded as probably belonging to neanthropic man.

Saldanha Man. In 1953, Mr. Keith Jolly and Dr. Ronald Singer of the University of Cape Town discovered a fossil hominid skullcap and fragment of a lower jaw, associated with an abundance of fossil vertebrates and stone artifacts. The discovery was made in a village near Saldanha Bay, 10 miles from Hopefield, and some 90 miles north of Cape Town.

The Saldanha skullcap strongly resembles that of the Rhodesian skull, and there can be little doubt that both belong to the same form of man. The contours and form of the skullcap, brow ridges and frontal bone are very similar to those of Rhodesian man, while the fragment of the mandible consisting of part of the ramus together with its coronoid process, found some 500 yards from the skullcap together with a small piece of parietal bone, is remarkable in that it is almost identical in shape and dimensions with the sample portions of the

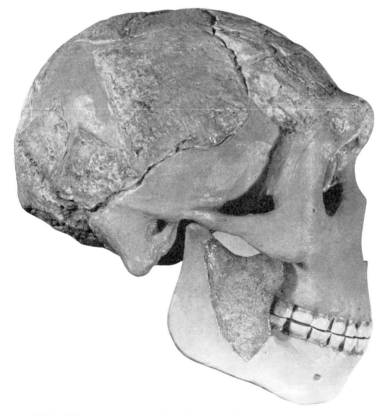

Figure 101. The reconstructed Saldanha Skull. (Courtesy, Dr. Ronald Singer.)

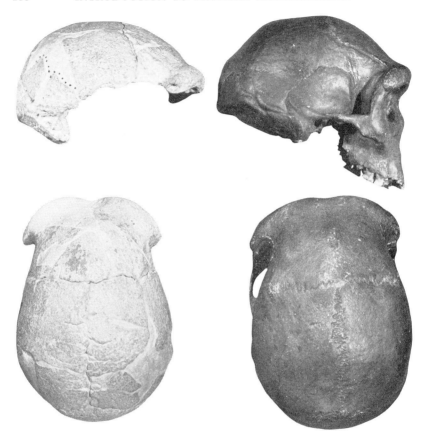

Figure 102. The Saldanha skullcap compared with the Rhodesian Skull. Right lateral, and vertical views. (Courtesy, Dr. Ronald Singer.)

Heidelberg jaw. This is not surprising, for the large size and width of the masticatory apparatus of the Rhodesian skull suggested that it would have had to have a jaw which corresponded to that of the Heidelberg jaw. The Saldanha ramus is, however, less robust than the corresponding part of the Heidelberg jaw. The small fragment of parietal, it is of interest to note, fitted exactly into the Saldanha skullcap.

Handaxes and other stone implements of Acheulian types were found in association with the Saldanha remains. Some equid tarsal bones at first thought to be bone chisels have been shown to be due to the combined effects of gnawing by carnivores and the ravages of the weather. The combined archeologic, paleontologic, and geologic

Figure 103. Large and small cleavers. Cape Coastal Fauresmith. From the same horizon as the Saldanha Skull. (Courtesy, Dr. Ronald Singer.)

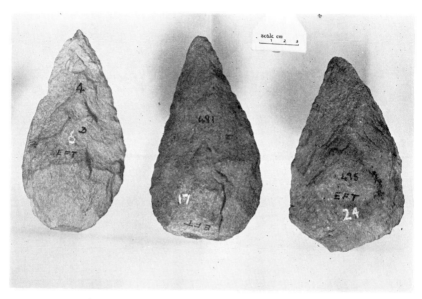

Figure 104. Three typical almond-shaped hand-axes. Cape Coastal Faure-smith. From the same horizon as the Saldanha Skull. (Courtesy, Dr. Ronald Singer.)

evidence, as well as fluorine dating, makes it possible to assign Saldanha man to the early part of the Upper Pleistocene, probably corresponding to the time prior to the last glaciation of Europe. These facts would render Saldanha man somewhat older than Rhodesian man.

Africanthropus njarasensis. In 1934 an important find of the badly crushed and weathered fragments of three skulls was made by Kohl-Larsen in the northern part of what was formerly German East Africa and is now Tanganyika Territory. The most complete of these skulls, probably that of a male, has been cursorily described by Reck and Kohl-Larsen, by Leakey, and by Weinert. The skulls were recovered from a deposit believed to be of Upper Pleistocene age north-west of Lake Eyasi (Njarasa). They exhibit a number of characters which bear a striking resemblance to those characterizing the *Pithecanthropus-Sinanthropus* group. Kohl-Larsen, the discoverer, and Hans Reck, a German geologist, in a joint paper published in 1936, described this new form of man as *Palaeoanthropus njarasensis*, but Weinert considered the name unsuitable and renamed the find *Africanthropus njarasensis.* The former name has priority, but the latter is the name most frequently used in the literature.

The bones recovered consisted of the greater part of the occipital, left parietal, and left temporal including the mastoid and petrous portions. These parts articulate perfectly with one another at their sutural junctions. Several parts of the frontal bone were also recovered, including a portion of the glabella, and the right supraorbital torus and external orbital angle. In addition there was recovered a fragment of the maxilla containing the broken sockets of the two incisor teeth, the left canine, the first premolar, and the broken socket of the second premolar, and a loose first molar. The canine tooth is of human form, and there was no space between the upper lateral incisor and canine teeth (premaxillary diastema). The right tympanic plate, which was also recovered, is, according to Leakey, very chimpanzee-like in form.

The foramen magnum, part of which is preserved, is inclined backwards at an angle comparable to that found in the anthropoid apes and in Solo man. The greatest width of the skull is in the region of the mastoid processes. The bones of the skull in *Africanthropus* are very thick, and the supraorbital torus, which is very strongly developed, bears a close resemblance to the same structure in *Pithecanthropus* and *Sinanthropus*. The form of the forehead is also much the same as in these two types, the angle of slope (glabello-bregmatic angle) of the forehead, for example, being 36 to 37° in *Africanthropus* as compared with 38° in *Pithecanthropus*. On the other hand, the form of the occiput approaches that of neanthropic man, but actually most closely resembling that of Steinheim man of the early Neanderthaloid type (see p. 201); the occipital torus, for the attachment of some of the muscles of the back of the neck is, however, very strongly developed.

Unfortunately, a thorough description of the skull and teeth of *Africanthropus* has not yet been made available, so that we are not, at the present time, in a position to draw any sound inferences as to its exact characters and relationships. In Figure 115 is shown an outline of the sagittal section of *Africanthropus* compared with similar outlines of *Sinanthropus I* and *II* and *Homo neanderthalensis*, the latter represented by the La Chapelle-aux-Saints skull. It will be seen that there is a striking resemblance in the outline of all these forms. The same holds true for many of their physical characters, but the resemblance of *Africanthropus* is obviously closest to the *Pithecanthropus-Sinanthropus* group.

Weinert believes that *Africanthropus* belongs with the *Pithecan-*

thropus-Sinanthropus group, and that the former undoubtedly bears some relationship to the Neanderthaloid group. The two geologists, Reck and Kohl-Larsen, believe that *Africanthropus* represents the earliest or most primitive member of the Neanderthaloid group, a proto-Neanderthaloid rather than a fully developed member of that group. Dart and Weidenreich believe that *Africanthropus* is most closely related to the Rhodesian Neanderthaloids. Leakey, who studied the skull in 1936, is convinced that it belongs with the *Pithecanthropus-Sinanthropus* group. Wells, who examined a cast of the skull fragments in 1950 is convinced that they are definitely not pithecanthropine.

Reck and Kohl-Larsen stated that with the remains of *Africanthropus* were found associated artifacts of early Levalloisian industry. Weinert, however, stated that the associated artifacts range all the way from Abbevillian to Neolithic. To settle this question Leakey and Mr. G. H. Reeve, a geologist, restudied the site in 1937, and fully confirmed Reck and Kohl-Larsen's statements. The deposit is, without doubt, Upper Pleistocene (Gamblian). The stone culture is developed Levalloisian, which in Kenya has been proven to be contemporary with the Upper Kenya Capsian (Aurignacian).

It is an interesting fact that the types of man associated with the Kenya Capsian culture, Oldoway (1913), Gambles Cave, Elmenteita (1924), and Naivasha (1940), all are neanthropic types, while the contemporary Levalloisian culture is associated with *Africanthropus*. This latter association fits the European evidence, for in Europe the Mousterian-Levalloisian industries are invariably associated with men of Neanderthal type.

The exact status of *Africanthropus* is uncertain. If he is a pithecanthropoid then he was a contemporary of neanthropic man, as represented by Leakey's Kenya group of Upper Pleistocene types. However, it is possible that *Africanthropus* is a proto-Neanderthaloid with closer affinities to the Rhodesian Neanderthaloids than to the Pithecanthropoid-Sinanthropoid group. Whatever the truth may be, it is well to remember, as Kroeber has said in this connection, that no judgment on a fossil human form is wholly reliable until it reflects the consensus of several experts, and even then, it should be added such "wholly reliable" judgments in many cases may, with the progress of knowledge, prove susbtantially modifiable.

Montmaurin Man. In 1949 Mons. R. Cammas discovered a fossil human mandible in a cave of Montmaurin in the Haute-Garonne in France. Associated with a pre-Mousterian industry and with a bone layer of extinct fauna, there can be little doubt that this mandible is of Riss-Würm interglacial age and represents the remains of the oldest fossil man thus far found in France.

The Montmaurin mandible is in an excellent state of preservation, and though smaller somewhat resembles the Heidelberg jaw. It is extremely robust, the index of robustness being the same as that of the Heidelberg jaw, namely 58.6. It is, thus, thicker than the mandible of nearly all known Neanderthals, being strongly re-enforced in the region anterior to the mental foramen. The mental foramen is doubled. There is no chin (see Figure 105).

The anterior symphyseal angle (anterior symphysis with plane of inferior border of mandible) is 105°, the angle of the symphysial axis with the same plane is 101°, almost the same as in the Heidelberg jaw and greater than in the majority of Neanderthals. The rami are not as broad as those of the Heidelberg jaw, but are larger than those of the Neanderthal, and their index, 64.7, exceeds that of neanthropic man. The mandibular angle is typically that of fossil man, 110°, not sharp but regularly curved and rounded. The medial and lateral aspects of the rami exhibit strong tori, a lateral oblique torus, and a medial triangular torus which is inferiorly continuous with the alveolar "bourrelet." The mylohyoid groove is partly transformed into a

Figure 105. The Montmaurin Jaw. (Courtesy, Prof. Henri Vallois.)

Fr. **N.** **M.** **H.**

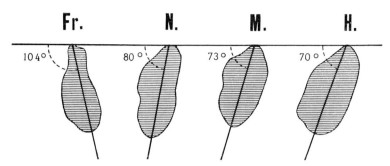

Figure 106. Inclination angles of the chin region of Frenchman, Neanderthal Man, Montmaurin Jaw, and Heidelberg Jaw. The sections are in the midline of the chin, with the anterior surface to the reader's right. (Courtesy, Prof. Henri Vallois.)

canal. All these features recall Neanderthal characters. The condyles are broader and longer than those of neanthropic man, and their axial angle with the frontal plane is 16.5°. The condylar articular surfaces are more oval, as in the Heidelberg jaw, than flattish as in the Neanderthals. The condyles project markedly outwards. The sigmoid notch is deeper than that of the Heidelberg jaw, but not as deep as in the Neanderthal.

The alveolar arcades are markedly divergent. The only teeth present, the molars, exhibit a remarkable ensemble of primitive features. M_2 is a little smaller than M_1, and M_3 is the largest of all, its module (length x breadth x height) attaining the exceptional figure of 106. The mesio-distal diameter of each of the teeth is plainly greater than their bucco-lingual diameter. The Dryopithecus pattern is present on all the molars, there is no cingulum, the hypoconulid and sixth cusp are present. The pulp cavities exhibit some taurodontism.

The Montmaurin mandible presents features which give it a position intermediate between Heidelberg and Neanderthal man.

Neanderthal Man. Neanderthal man is, perhaps, the best known of our fossil relatives, the remains of more than one hundred individuals, in addition to a good many variant types, having been discovered and described. Neanderthal man is essentially an Upper Pleistocene, late Early, and early Middle Paleolithic form of man, one whose physical characters and mental potentialities have most probably gone into the making of ourselves, and who ends the long line of palanthropic types as distinguished from the early and late neanthropic types.

The cranial capacity of Neanderthal man had reached, and even exceeded that of modern man, varying between 1,425 cc. and 1,641 cc. in males, with an average of about 1,553 cc. In females the range is from 1,200 cc. to 1,480 cc., with an average of 1,327 cc. The average cranial capacity of contemporary Europeans is between 1,350 and 1,400 cc. The skull of the Neanderthal child found in 1938 in the Teshik-Tash cave in Southern Uzbekistan—the first Neanderthaloid to be discovered in Central Asia—had a cranial capacity of 1,490 cc. Its estimated age is nine years, sex is surmised as male. At the same age the average modern European boy has a cranial capacity of 1,325 cc. The cranial capacity of the Neanderthal boy, discovered on the Rock of Gilbraltar in 1927, was 1,400 cc. The age of this boy at death, judging from the state of eruption of his teeth and other characters was about 6 years. At this age a modern child has about 250 cc. to go before he attains final brain volume, which would yield 1,650 cc. for the

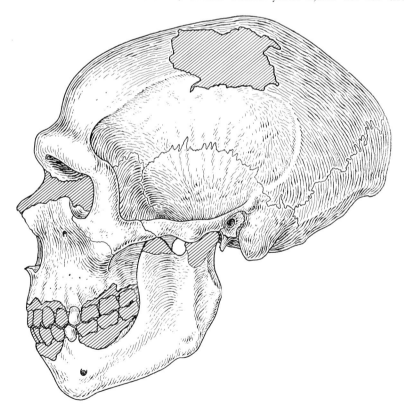

Figure 107. One type of Neanderthal. "The Old Man" of La Chapelle-aux-Saints.

Gibraltar boy's cranial capacity at its adult volume. The important point emerges that the average cranial capacity of Neanderthal man— even though the frontal lobes were of lesser volume—probably exceeded that of modern man, and the size of his brain suggests that as far as potentialities for intelligence and humanity were concerned he was probably not less well endowed than modern man.

Compared with modern man Neanderthal man is distinguished by a forehead which is much less sloping than it appears to be, the apparent sloping is an illusion created by the presence of markedly developed eyebrow ridges, the supraorbital torus. The lower jaw is heavy and chinless, and the occiput is broad and projecting. All these characters occasionally occur in individuals of every living variety of man. In spite of the fact that conclusions relating to mentality drawn from the shape of the normal head have long ago been demonstrated to be utterly valueless, there are still some students who forget themselves so far as to assert that Neanderthal man must have had a poor mind because he had a rather more beetling brow than their own. The fact is that, within a certain range of variation, neither the volume, shape, nor the size of the brain in the Hominidae bears any relation whatsoever to intelligence. Individuals whose brain did not exceed 750 cc. have been recorded who were of perfectly normal intelligence. Persons with low foreheads are known to be not one bit better or worse mentally than those with high ones. Patronizing "highbrow" remarks on the low brain development of our early "lowbrow" relatives are therefore strictly out of order. This is an important point, and we shall have something more to say about it in Chapter VI. But before leaving this subject here a few words must be said concerning the reconstructions of the facial appearance and expression of Neanderthal and other early types of man. Such reconstructions have engaged the attention of several anthropologists and their reconstructions have, quite unconsciously no doubt, been determined by their belief that these presumed earlier types of men were nearer to the apes than we are. Hence they have been given a somewhat apelike appearance. On the other hand, early neanthropic man is always made to look very noble indeed. But the real truth is that we know nothing about the soft parts of extinct man, and less than nothing concerning the expression of his features, which were probably not less benign than our own.* The facts, as we know them, do not lend any support to the

---

* Experiments and experience have led most anatomists to believe that it is impossible to reconstruct the facial appearance and expression of a person, from

--→

notion of a beast-like early man. Straus and Cave opine that if Neanderthal man "could be reincarnated and placed in a New York subway —provided that he were bathed, shaved, and dressed in modern clothing—it is doubtful whether he would attract any more attention than some of its other denizens."

Owing largely to preconceived notions as to what Neanderthal man should have looked like he was reconstructed by Boule on the basis of the Chapelle-aux-Saints skeleton as having been characterized by a bull-like neck, knock-knees, and as having walked with a stoop, that is, not fully erectly. A restudy of the skeleton by Straus and Cave has led them to the conclusion that Boule's inferences were quite wrong, and that "there is no valid reason for the assumption that the posture of Neanderthal man of the fourth glacial differed significantly from that of present-day man."

The handicrafts of Neanderthal man are known from the stone artifacts he left behind him. These characterize a specific culture associated with, but not necessarily peculiar to, Neanderthal man wherever found. Such artifacts are known as Mousterian after Le Moustier in France, the type locality where they were first found, though some belong to the still earlier Acheulian culture. The flint ball, which may have been used as a sling stone, is typically associated with Neanderthal man. In addition to the manufacture of perforators, points, discs, scrapers, and stone knives, he introduced the use of mineral pigments into human culture, and practiced ceremonial interment of the dead, thus suggesting the existence of a religious system. To the spiritual life of Neanderthal man we may possibly owe more than we at present remotely suspect.

The designation "Neanderthal man" actually refers to a variety of man who, far from being the homogeneous "type" he is generally represented as, consists of a variety of forms which are morphologically distinguishable as (1) Early Neanderthals, and (2) Later Neanderthals (or so-called "Classic" Neanderthals).

←

the skull, with any degree of exactness. See, for example, K. F. Lander, The Examination of a Skeleton of Known Age, Race and Sex. *J. Anat. Physiol.*, 52: 282-291, 1918. See also, Jones, F. Wood: *Man's Place Among the Mammals,* p. 362-365, and Glaister, J. and Brash, J. C.: *Medico-Legal Aspects of the Ruxton Case,* p. 244-248. For a claimed successful reconstruction see W. M. Krogman, The Reconstruction of the Living Head from the Skull. *FBI Law Enforcement Bulletin.* July, 1946. M. M. Gerosimov, *Vosstanovlenie litsa po cherepu.* Moscow, Izdatel'stvo akademii nauk SSSR, 1950.

Figure 108. Neanderthal Man. Domestic scene. From a painting by Maurice Wilson. (Courtesy, British Museum [Natural History].)

The Early Neanderthals are associated with the Third or Riss-Würm Interglacial, and are represented by such specimens as Ehringsdorf, Saccopastore, Krapina, Mount Carmel, Galilee, while the *Later Neanderthals,* associated with the Fourth Glacial or Würm I, are represented by such forms as Gibraltar, La Ferrassie, La Chapelle-aux-Saints, Le Moustier, Monte Circeo, Spy I and II, Neanderthal, La Naulette, Engis, La Quina, La Chaise.

Early Neanderthals. The Third Interglacial (Riss-Würm) Neanderthals differ from the Later Neanderthals in the following features of cranial morphology: The skull is slightly shorter, narrower, and higher, the supraorbital tori are slightly heavier, the parietals and occipital are slightly more expanded, the vault more arched, the cranial base more flexed, the external auditory meatus tends to be vertically elliptical rather than horizontally so, the tympanic plate tends to be vertically or obliquely oriented, the facial skeleton tends to be smaller, there is a tendency to separation of ciliary and orbital portions of the supraorbital torus, the malar is large with sharp demarcation between it and the maxilla, and there is a tendency to formation of a canine fossa. In most of these traits the Early Neanderthals more closely resemble modern man than do the later Neanderthals.

Later Neanderthals. The Fourth Glacial (Würm) Neanderthal's principal area of distribution was Southwestern Europe. Sites which have yieled Later Neanderthal remains are, *Germany:* Neanderthal, *Belgium:* Bay-Bonnet, Engis, La Naulette, Spy, *Channel Islands:* St. Brelade, Jersey, *France:* Malarnaud (Ariège), La Chaise, La Quina, Petit-Puymoyen (Charente), La Chapelle-aux-Saints (Corrèze), Genay (Côte d'Or), Combe Grenal, La Ferrassie, Le Moustier, Pech de l'Azé (Dordogne), Monsempron (Lot-et-Garonne), Hyena and Wolf Caves, Arcy-sur-Cure (Yonne), *Spain:* Bañolas, Cova Negra, Gibraltar (Forbes Quarry), Devil's Tower, Piñar, *Italy:* Fosselone and Guattari Caves (Monte Circeo), Santa Croce di Bisceglie.

The Later Neanderthals differ from the Early Neanderthals in the following cranial features: Larger, lower, and wider cranial vault, with frequent postlambdoidal flattening (resulting from peculiar pattern of growth and closure of lambdoid suture), less flexed cranial base, more sharply angulated occipital bone with relatively heavier occipital tori, more horizontal orientation of tympanic plate, with heavier anterior and posterior portions, larger facial skeleton, large round orbits, large nasal aperture, large interorbital spaces, semicircular supraorbital tori with fused medial and lateral elements, with no

TABLE V

CRANIAL CAPACITIES OF NEANDERTHAL MAN IN CUBIC CENTIMETERS

Early			*Later*		
Europe			*Europe*		
Ehringsdorf	♀	1,480	Gibraltar boy*	♂	1,650
Saccopastore	♀	1,200	La Ferrassie	♂	1,641
Krapina		?	La Chapelle-aux-Saints	♂	1,625
Southwest Asia			Le Moustier	♂	1,564
			Monte Circeo	♂	1,550
Mt. Carmel, Skhul 4	♂	1,550	Spy I	♂	1,525
Mt. Carmel, Skhul 5	♂	1,520	Neanderthal	♂	1,450
Mt. Carmel, Skhul 9	♂	1,590	Spy II	♂	1,425
Mt. Carmel, Skhul 2	♀	1,300	La Naulette		?
Mt. Carmel, Tabun 1	♀	1,270	Engis		?
Galilee, Israel	♀	1,400	Gibraltar	♀	1,333
Shukbah, Israel		?	La Quina	♀	1,307
Shanidar, Kurdistan		?			
Bisitum, Iran		?			
Average Male		*1,553*	*Average Male*		*1,553*
Average Female		*1,330*	*Average Female*		*1,320*

* Six year-old with capacity of 1,400 cc., corrected to probable adult capacity.

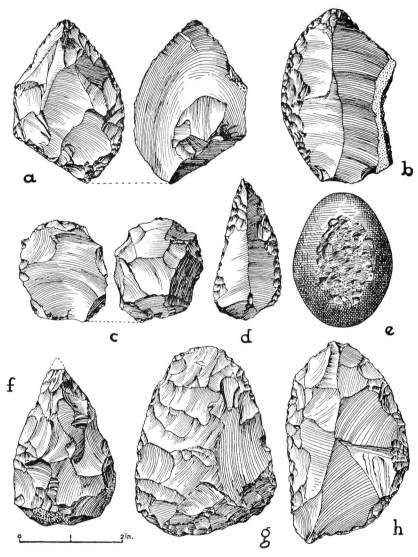

Figure 109. Mousterian industries. a, b, Side-scrapers (racloirs), c, disc-core, and d, point, from rock-shelter at Le Moustier near Peyzac (Dordogne). e, Small anvil- or hammerstone (pebble of ferruginous grit), Gibraltar caves. f. Hand-axe from Le Moustier. g. Hand-axe (chert), and h, oval flake-tool (flint), from Kent's Cavern, Torquay. a-d. Typical Mousterian; f. Mousterian of Acheulian tradition; g, h, of Acheulo-Levalloisian tradition. (From Oakley, *Man The Tool-Maker*. (Courtesy, British Museum [Natural History].)

concavity of maxilla from body to malar, there is a convergence of maxillary walls and absence of the canine fossa.

The Later Neanderthals were robustly built and of fairly short stature, about 1.65 m (5 feet 5 inches).

As will be seen from Table V there appears to have been no difference in the size of the brain between Early and Later Neanderthal man.

It was until recently believed that Neanderthal man was exterminated by some other type of man, possibly Cro-Magnon man, but there is now some reason to believe that this was not the case. Discoveries of many varying forms within the Neanderthal group show that there were markedly different types ranging from a heavy supra-orbitally-ridged low-browed group to a type very closely resembling neanthropic man. Three of the many types of Neanderthaloids now known may be briefly mentioned.

The earliest representative of the Neanderthaloid type so far discovered in Europe, so-called Steinheim man, exhibits a curious blend

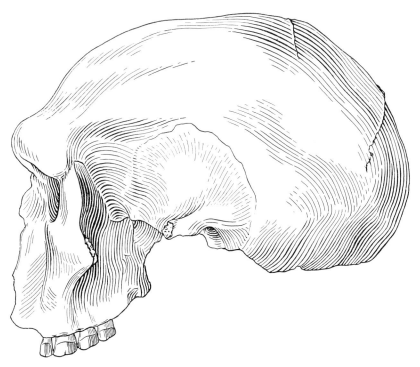

Figure 110. The Steinheim skull. Right lateral view reversed. (From a cast.)

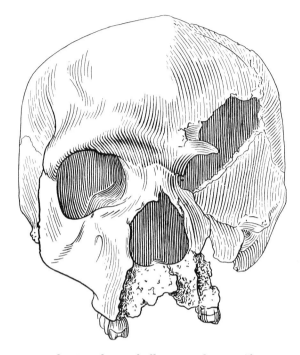

Figure 111. The Steinheim skull. Frontal view (from a cast.)

of Neanderthal and neanthropic traits. Found at Steinheim-am-Murr in 1933, the Steinheim skull (probably that of a female) was associated with artifacts of Acheulian age, in a deposit of the Mindel-Riss interglacial period of the Middle Pleistocene.

The cranial capacity was 1,070 c.c., rather small for a Neanderthaloid, the facial and occipital parts of the skull display a number of features common to neanthropic rather than to Neanderthal man, though, interestingly enough, the form of the forehead region is reminiscent of *Pithecanthropus*. There can, however, be little doubt of the essential Neanderthaloid character of Steinheim man. It is not unlikely that he was a descendant of Heidelberg man.

Another type was found at Krapina near Zagreb in Northern Croatia in 1899. Krapina man is represented by the skeletal remains of some twenty individuals—all in fragmentary condition—all clearly of a Neanderthaloid character, and associated with a typical Mousterian industry. The typical supraorbital torus, and massive lateral orbital processes are present, but there is also a strong tendency towards a neanthropic type of forehead and round-headedness. Brachycephaly, or broad-headedness, occurred in most of the individuals whose skulls could be reconstructed, the best skull yielding an index of 83.7. It is in the Krapina Neanderthaloids that brachycephaly occurs for the first time in the Hominidae.

Discoveries made at Ehringsdorf, a village near Weimar, in Germany, during the years 1914, 1916, and particularly 1925, yielded respectively the greater part of a human jaw, the fragmented skeleton of a child, and the vault and sides of the skull of an adult thought to be female. Associated with the skull were implements of Pre-Mousterian late Acheulian type. The skull, which was clearly of Neanderthaloid type, was found in a deposit which belongs to the Riss-Würm or third interglacial period, and is therefore somewhat later in age than Steinheim man.

The Ehringsdorf woman had a cranial capacity of 1,480 c.c. In important features of the skull such as the form of the supraorbital ridges, the position of the ear-hole, the form of the occiput, the jaws and the teeth, the Ehringsdorf skull is frankly Neanderthaloid, but in almost all other characters this early Neanderthaloid makes a closer approach to the character of the neanthropic skull than do the later and more typical crania of Neanderthal man. The forehead, for example, is remarkably high in spite of massive supraorbital ridges— quite like that of neanthropic man, and the head, in spite of its length, is quite high.

Such other variant types of Neanderthal man as Spy II (1886), and Galilee (1925), Gibraltar II (1926), all exhibit an approach towards neanthropic man in various important cranial features. It is difficult to believe that so many like mutations can have been responsible for the appearance of these characters, the more likely explanation would seem to lie in a combination of factors in which hybridization probably played an important rôle.

Clear evidence of such mixture or hybridization is to be found in the assemblage of neanderthaloids discovered in 1931-1932 in caves on the slopes of Mount Carmel in Palestine. These consisted of a frankly Neanderthal type, the Tabūn group, and another which had closely approached the neanthropic type in its physical characters, the Skhūl group (see Figures 112, 113 and 114). Based on a matrix of fundamental likeness, the differences exhibited by these types are of such a nature as to render it improbable that they could have arisen spontaneously by mutation. They must be regarded as representing the expression of fairly recent mixture between neanderthaloids and neanthropic types or a form closely resembling the latter. This theory

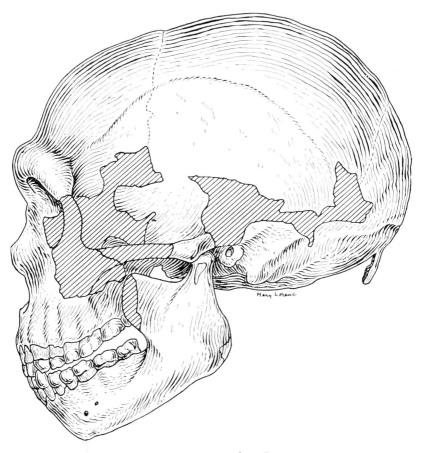

Figure 112. Tabūn I.

is supported by the presence of a remarkable variety of intergrading types between the Tabūn and Skhūl groups. Any other theory would have to assume the spontaneous mutation of far too many genes or far too great a change in gene variability to explain the kind of differences exhibited by these two types.

Left to themselves small breeding groups rapidly tend to produce a phenotypic similarity in their members without in any way affecting their genetic heterozygosity. There is a scattering of phenotypic variability, and the group tends to become temporarily phenotypically distinguishable, as a group, from other groups or populations. In man any radical change in the phenotypical character of the group is generally produced by the introduction of new genes into the breeding population. The result may be a temporary increase in phenotypic variability, until there is again a synthesizing of the new phenotypic combinations and the group is once more relatively stabilized in its phenotypic character. The evidence appears to indicate very strongly that the neanderthaloids of Mount Carmel represented a group which, not too many generations in their past, had received a new infusion of genes from some neanthropic source. In a recent exhaustive study of the evidence Thoma has thoroughly substantiated this conclusion. "En definitive," he writes, "on voit que la transformation des Neander-taliens de Palestine ne peut être expliquée par les mécanismes connus

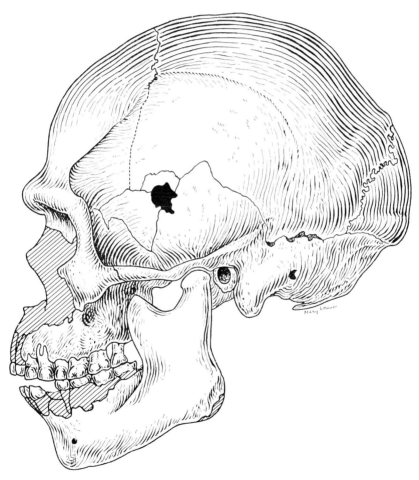

Figure 113. Skhūl V (right side reversed.)

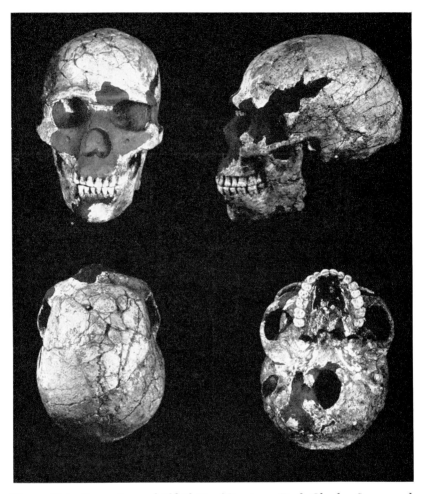

Figure 114. Four views of Skhūl V. (Courtesy, Prof. Charles Snow, and
The Peabody Museum, Harvard University.)

de l'evolution. L'analyse des materiaux fossiles vérifie tout au contraire l'hypothèse du metissage."

While man of the neanthropic type has not yet been found in Israel, there is a high probability that he will be. At any rate, during the Neanderthal phase of development, and even during the earlier late pithecanthropoid phase, there were several forms of man living, such as Swanscombe, and possibly Rhodesian man, who were of an early neanthropic type. It has even been claimed, by Leakey, that during the pithecanthropoid phase of development there were already in existence several types of man in East Africa who had attained the full status of neanthropic man but the evidence upon which this claim is based, has not yet been fully substantiated (see p. 256). These are facts of the first importance for our understanding of the evolution of man, and they are facts which have become available only during the last two decades. In the light of the discoveries made during the last twenty years the older view that man developed or evolved to his present high estate by a series of jumps from ape to man, has been forced to make way for a more comprehensive view. The notion that a more primitive type simply produced, by spontaneous generation as it were, a more advanced type, and so on in linear succession until modern man was reached, no longer agrees with the facts.

This type of reasoning seems also to have conditioned our conception of the manner in which the existing varieties of man were produced, so that there are some who still tend—incorrectly—to speak of "higher and lower races." It is tacitly assumed that both morphologically and temporarily the "higher" types were evolved later than the "lower" ones.

The facts now available suggest that this is an unsound view, and

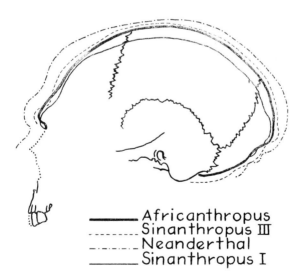

Africanthropus
Sinanthropus III
Neanderthal
Sinanthropus I

Figure 115. Left lateral craniograms of four types of fossil skull. (After Weinert.)

that while in the phylogeny of man there exist undoubted linear genetic relationships between some primitive and some types more advanced toward the status of modern man, hybridization between different types, differing more or less from each other, was an important agency responsible for the emergence of new types of men. The emergence of new types through hybridization, of course, presupposes the existence of earlier hybridizing parental types which are generally more primitive than their descendants. Since the new types thus produced will be possessed of some qualitatively different characters these have generally been considered as an advance upon the more primitive characters of their ancestors, immediate and remote. In the conception of a "scale" or "ladder" of development such differences were spoken of as "higher" and "lower," but evolution is inadequately envisaged as either a scale or a ladder. It is more akin to a reticulum in which many different strands are interwoven in a variety of different ways and in different patterns. Conceptually the terms "higher" and "lower" tend to inject undesirable meanings into the proper understanding of these matters. The terms "advanced" and "primitive" are scarcely less objectionable.

An earlier form of man need not necessarily be less morphologically developed than a later form of man, and, indeed, may be more so. A skull like that of the Later Neanderthals was not necessarily less adaptively efficient than that of neanthropic man. The skull of neanthropic man has become less massive than that of palanthropic man. This does not necessarily make it superior to the palanthropic skull, as is often implied when the words "more advanced than" or "more evolved than" are used in this and in similar connections. Difference does not imply superiority. Some differences may reflect superior adaptive values, but not all do so. The more robust skulls and larger supraorbital tori of palanthropic man may have been of superior adaptive value to the less robust skulls and comparatively smooth supraorbital regions of neanthropic man—or they may not. We really don't know. Robusticity of the skull endured in palanthropic man as a legacy from his apelike ancestors for the greater part of his history, and certainly must have had considerable adaptive value. That this robustness of the skull disappeared in neanthropic man may have some connection with his increasing fetalization—a matter with which we shall deal in the next chapter.

No examples of Neanderthal man have ever been found in England, but remains (principally teeth) of undisputed Neanderthal man have been found in the Channel Island of Jersey not many miles away, while in England itself several Mousterian sites have been discovered, affording strong inferential evidence of the presence of Neanderthal man in that country. As we shall see, the evidence is now beyond dispute that neanthropic types were not only in existence contemporaneously with Neanderthal man, but that they were already flourishing even before the latter's appearance upon the scene at all.

Neanderthal man may be interpreted as bearing many of the earmarks of a hybrid type, with a large brain as the primary novel emergent, and a perfectly harmonious mixture of primitive and more advanced morphologic traits, almost as if some pithecanthropoid and some neanthropic type had been the hybridizing stocks from which he had emerged. Solo man would be an excellent possible ancestor of the first kind and some early neanthropic type, like Swanscombe or Fontéchevade, of the second. On the other hand, it is quite possible to envisage Neanderthal man as a larger-brained descendant of *Sinanthropus* or *Africanthropus*.

That there were quite a number of early neanthropic types already in existence in the Middle Pleistocene is a possibility which we have to consider in the pages which follow.

Meanwhile, it must continually be borne in mind that though many discoveries of different types of men have been made during the last few decades, these discoveries are probably as nothing compared to those which yet remain to be made. It is more than likely that we shall eventually find that in the Upper Pliocene and the Lower and Middle Pleistocene there were a fairly large number of different types of men, much greater in variety and morphologic character than is to be found among the varieties of man living at the present day.

Whether some of these types of men originated from independent proto-hominid lines (polygenesis) or from a single such line (monogenesis) and subsequently underwent differentiation are questions to which there is at present no answer. It is quite possible that some early types of men did originate from different proto-hominid lines and that from the mixture of such different early men new types were produced, but the evidence is inconclusive. The majority of students are, however, agreed that the living varieties of man belong to the same single species and that they originated from a common ancestral group. But this is a matter with which we shall deal in a subsequent chapter.

The Châtelperron Skull. During the latter third of the nineteenth century Dr. Joseph Bailleau, a French physician and enthusiastic archeologist, apparently discovered a human calvarium in the multiple

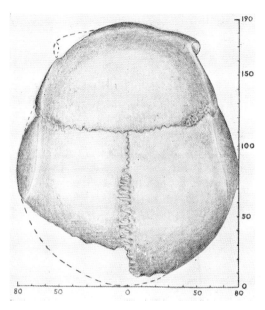

Figure 116. The Châtelperron Skull. (From Cave. Courtesy of *Archaeologia*.) See opposite page.

cave of La Grotte des Fées, in the commune of Châtelperron (Allier) in Central France. Stone and bone artifacts from this cave have long been held to typify the first stage of French Upper Paleolithic culture. This culture was already foreshadowed in Acheulian times. It seems to have originated in south-western Asia and spread to western Europe before the end of Mousterian times. The characteristic tool of Châtelperron is a flint blade knife with one edge straight and razor-like, and the other edge curved over to a point and blunted by trimming. This earliest Upper Paleolithic culture was formerly called Lower Aurignacian, but is now known as Châtelperronian (see Figure 118).

The Châtelperron calvarium, which almost certainly came from the cave of La Grotte des Fées, is highly mineralized and extremely heavy. The character of the bones is identical in degree of mineralization and hue with most of the animal bones from Châtelperron. The industry of La Grotte des Fées is characteristic, and there can be little doubt that the calvarium came from the same horizon.

The Châtelperron skull consists of an incomplete skull-cap, comprising the entire right and the greater part of the left parietal, the whole of the right and the greater part of the left frontal. The skull is probably that of a male who died within his fourth decade. The

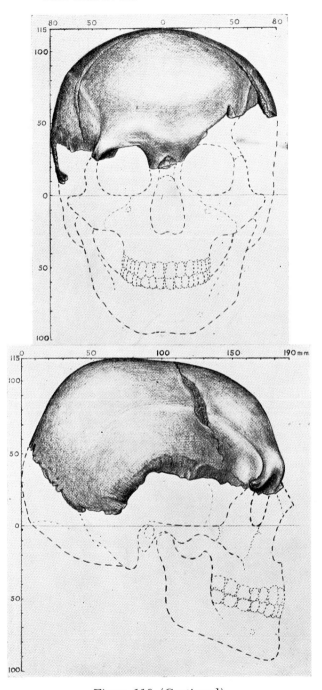

Figure 116 (Continued)

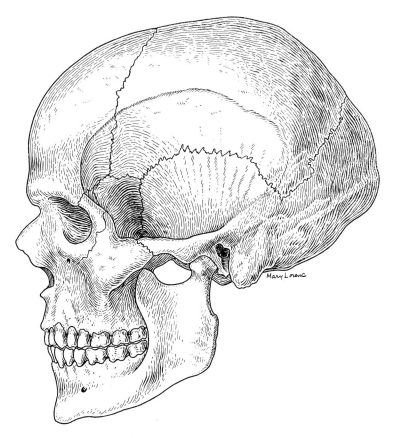

Figure 117. The skull of a Cro-Magnon male.

bones are extremely thick, varying between 6.0 to 10.0 in the medio-frontal region, being 7.5 mm. at the right parietal eminence (euryon), and 11.0 mm. at the thickest parts of the parietals. The merest remnant of the bony nose indicates that the nasal skeleton was prominent. The (right) superior orbital margin is sharp and gracile, and terminates laterally in a strikingly developed external angular process.

Perhaps the most striking feature of the skull is its extreme brachycephaly. The maximum length is 186.0 mm. and its maximum breadth 158.0 mm., the cranial index is therefore 85.5, being in fact a little over an inch short of being as broad as it is long. The top and the lower sides of the skull exhibit a markedly flattened (platycranial) contour.

When compared with crania of later, Aurignacian culture, such as

the Solutrean, Prĕdmost, and Obercassel skulls, the Châtelperron skull
is somewhat broader and flatter in the vault, but otherwise very similar in its contours. The cranial capacity of the Châtelperron skull is
about 1,425 c.c.

Cro-Magnon Man. It was formerly believed, principally, because
it was the most convenient theory at the time, that Cro-Magnon man
had exterminated Neanderthal man. This would have constituted quite
a feat, since Neanderthal man is known to have inhabited almost
every part of the Old World! On the other hand, there seems good
reason to believe that far from exterminating Neanderthal man, Cro-
Magnon man, a true neanthropic type, was at least a late contemporary
of Neanderthal man and that intermixture between them probably
occurred in Europe, if not elsewhere in the world, upon a fairly appreciable scale.

The Cro-Magnons were originally discovered in 1868 in a rock
shelter in the limestone cliffs of the little village of Cro-Magnon in
southern central France. Between 1872 and 1902 the remains of
thirteen other Cro-Magnon individuals were discovered in the caves
of the Red Rocks of the Côte d'Azur, some forty minutes walk from
Mentone on the Italian Riviera. Since these discoveries were made
a headless incomplete skeleton found in Paviland Cave in Southwestern
Wales in 1823 has been identified as almost certainly a member of
the Cro-Magnon variety of man.

The Cro-Magnons were a remarkable people in many ways. Physically they were a very variable group, some of them reaching a height
of five feet eleven inches, and a cranial capacity of 1,660 c.c. The size
of the brain-case compared to the size of the face, which is very
short, is large. Culturally the Cro-Magnons were the makers of those
masterfully worked stone and bone implements which are typically
associated with the Aurignacian period. The Cro-Magnons are also
thought to be the people responsible for the masterly cave paintings
and realistic sculptures of animals which have been discovered in many
different parts of Europe.

Where the Cro-Magnons originated remains at present a mystery,
but it would appear likely from the nature of their physical characters
that they must have had quite an interesting biological history behind
them.

Grimaldi Man. In one of the caves of the Red Rocks called the
Grotte des Enfants, below the village of Grimaldi, there was found
intruded, by burial, into a Mousterian hearth, the skeletal remains of
a female of about 30 years of age and of a boy of about 15. The skele-

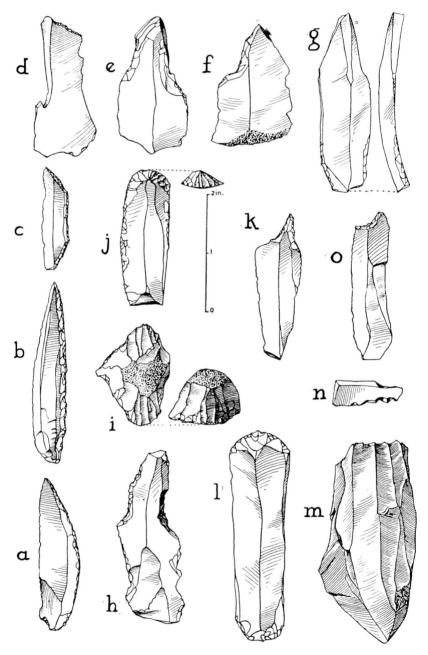

Figure 118. See legend opposite page.

ton of the boy was stained with red orchre. Associated artifacts prove the remains to belong to the early Aurignacian period.

Immediately above these remains, at various levels up to the floor level of the cave, were found the remains of four other Cro-Magnon individuals.

The Grimaldi remains are assumed to be those of mother and son since they closely resemble one another. Especially in their cranial characters, which are best seen in the boy, the Grimaldis exhibit certain significant differences from the Cro-Magnons. Thus, the teeth of the boy are large, and are associated with projecting upper and lower jaws. The chin is somewhat receding. The nose is broad, and the lower margin of the nasal opening instead of terminating in a sharp edge, ends in gutters which continue on the outer surface of the upper jaw. The palate is distinguished by the median bony elevation known as the *torus palatinus*. The face is short and broad, but very narrow below the cheekbones, with low broad orbits, as is the case in Bushmen-Hottentots. Cranial capacity was 1,265 c.c. for the female, and 1,454 c.c. for the boy.

The long forearm in proportion to the upper arm, the long lower leg in proportion to the length of the thigh, the flatness of the iliac blades of the pelvis, and the projection of the heel-bone (calcaneus) behind the ankle-joint (astragalo-tibial joint), have been interpreted as Negroid characters, the suggestion being that it would be difficult to account for them upon any other hypothesis than that their bearers were at least partially of Negroid origin.

←

Figure 118. Upper Paleolithic flint tools. a. Châtelperronian knife-point, Châtelperron (Allier). b. Gravettian knife-point Laussel (Dordogne). c. Trapezoid blade, Creswellian, Kent's Cavern, Torquay. d. Perigordian (Gravettian) graver or *burin*, Laugerie Haute (Dordogne). e. Aurignacian nosed graver *(burin busqué)*, Ffynnon Bueno, Vale of Clwyd. f. Aurignacian *burin busqué*, Cro-Magnon, Les Eyzies (Dordogne). g. Magdalenian graver *(burin bec-de-flûte)*, La Madeleine rock-shelter, Tursac (Dordogne). h. Strangulated blade, or double "spokeshave," Aurignacian, Laugerie Haute. i. Nosed scraper, or "push-plane," Aurignacian, Laugerie Haute. j. End-scraper *(grattoir)*, Cae Gwyn, Vale of Clwyd. k. Solutrean piercer, or "hand-drill," Laugerie Haute. l. Double-ended grattoir, Magdalenian, Grotte des Eyzies (Dordogne). m. Magdalenian blade-core, Grotte des Eyzies. n. Fragment of saw-blade, Magdalenian, Laugerie Haute. o. Magdalenian concave end-scraper or "spoke-shave," Limeuil (Dordogne). (From Oakley *Man the Tool-Maker*. Courtesy, British Museum [Natural History].)

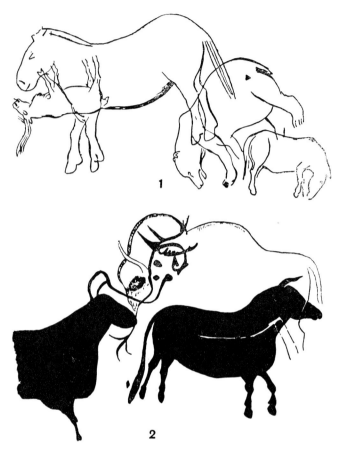

Figure 119. Superpositions. 1, At Teyjat, superpositions of engravings of the same phase (phase 3) and style. 2, At Font-de-Gaume, superpositions of paintings of different phases—the head of a rhinocerus in red outline (phase I), covered by a shapeless figure in black, covered by oxen in black flat wash (phase 3), covered by a feebly polychrome bison (phase 4). Upper Paleolithic. (From Burkitt. Courtesy, Cambridge University Press.)

Some of these Negroid characters, such as the limb-proportions, the projecting heel-bone, and the general characters of the face are retained by the Cro-Magnons, but in all other respects the latter are predominantly Caucasoid in type. In point of fact the Grimaldi skulls exhibit traits which are far more reminiscent of the Archaic Caucasoid than they are of the Negroid type, that is to say they resemble those of Australians or Pre-Dravidians of India and Ceylon more closely than they do those of Negroids. Whatever the truth may be, the relationship between Grimaldi and Cro-Magnon man is a very close one indeed, and the skeletal remains of both these forms of neanthropic man suggest the possibility that a North African Negroid or Asiatic Archaic Caucasoid or Australoid (see pp. 447-448) component played a part in the development of the early populations of Europe. Indeed, it would be difficult to conceive of such a component or components not entering into the formation of any of the peoples living along the fringes of the Mediterranean basin on the one hand, and in northern Europe on the other.

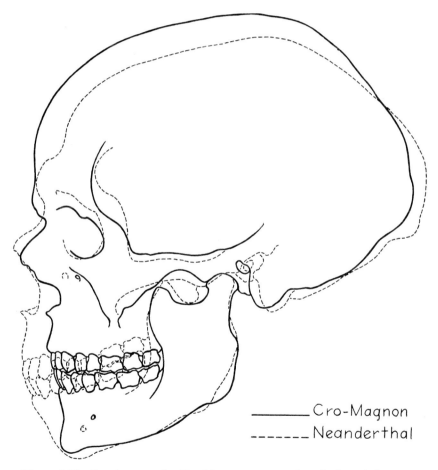

Figure 120. Craniogram of a Cro-Magnon compared with that of the Neanderthal skull of La Chapelle-aux-Saints.

Thus we see that Neanderthal man had two variable types of neanthropic man as possible contemporaries with whom intermixture may have occurred to produce new types of men. There is even a possibility that there were quite a number of additional neanthropic types with whom such mixture may have occurred. These are the men of Engis, Aurignac, and Combe Capelle, all associated with early Aurignacian cultures. The latter have, at one time or another, been cited as possible resultant examples of hybridization of other forms with Neanderthal man. None of them are definitely known to have been contemporary with Neanderthal man.

A group of neanthropic men who may be the descendants of crossing between Neanderthal man and Cro-Magnon man or simply a local variety of the latter are the people of Brünn and Předmost in Moravia or Czecho-Slovakia, these are generally known as the Předmost people.

The Předmost People. At Brünn in 1888 a skeleton was found, in 1891 a skull, and in 1927 another skeleton, of a neanthropic type associated with artifacts belonging to the late Aurignacian and the early Solutrean period. At Předmost, some fifty miles to the east of Brünn, there were found between 1890 and 1928 the skeletal remains of over 40 individuals of the same type and of the same culture.

The Předmost people exhibit a number of characters which suggest Neanderthal-Cro-Magnon ancestry, with the latter predominating. For example, in the development of the supraorbital ridges, in the preauricular length of the skull, in the retention of some degree of prognathism the Neanderthaloid ancestry of the group is believed to be reflected.

While it is true that the supraorbital ridges are very different in character from those of Neanderthal man, they are nevertheless such as would be expected in the descendants of a Neanderthal-Cro-Magnon cross, an expectation based on the fact that in Australian-Caucasoid crosses, where the Australian has marked supraorbital ridges and a low forehead, while the white has slight supraorbital ridges and a moderately high forehead, the latter conditions are dominant in the hybrids and in their descendants.

The mean cranial capacity of Předmost man is 1,590 c.c., height was about five feet and seven inches, figures which agree with expectation on the Neanderthal-Cro-Magnon theory of their ancestry. Further evidence in support of this theory is to be found in the presence of several Negroid or Australoid traits in the skull of Předmost man, such as its narrow, flat-sided, long and high form, together with an appreciable degree of prognathism, characters also found in the male skull of Combe Capelle. It is practically certain that, at least in one period of his existence, Předmost man was a contemporary of Neanderthal man. However this may be, we now have clear evidence of the existence of the neanthropic type *before* the appearance of

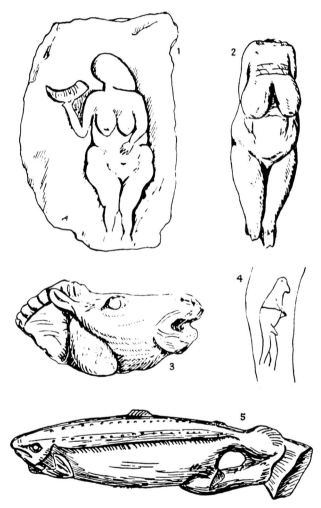

Figure 121. Upper Paleolithic home art. 1, Venus of Laussel. 2, Venus of Kostenki. 3, Horse's head from Mas d'Azil. 4, Engraving on bone from Cresswell Crags. 5, Fish palette from Grotte de Rey. (From Burkitt. Courtesy, Cambridge University Press.)

Neanderthal man. We may now turn to a consideration of this evidence—with a brief side-excursion before quite doing so.

The Piltdown Hoax. The Piltdown remains are discussed here for several reasons. Firstly, because they have played a leading role for over forty years in discussions concerning the evolution of man, and secondly because they provide something of an illustration of the difficulties besetting the student of the fragmentary remains of hominoids —whether early or late. Finally, the whole story provides something of a cautionary lesson for those engaged in the evaluation of such remains.

"Discovered" between the years 1909-1915, by Mr. Charles Dawson, an amateur English archeologist, at Piltdown, near Lewes, in Sussex, England, Piltdown man's discovery was announced to the world in December 1912, and named the Dawn Man of Dawson, *Eoanthropus dawsoni.* A subsequent series of finds brought the alleged number of the type up to two. The remains consisted of the right half of a lower jaw with two molar teeth *in situ,* the left temporal, parietal, and nasal bones, a turbinate bone, and a good part of the frontal and occipital bones. The second find, stated to have been made at a distance of two miles from the first, consisted of a molar tooth and parts of the frontal and occipital bones. Part of a third skull, found at Barcombe Mills near Piltdown remained undescribed until 1951. The Barcombe Mills skull is in every respect modern, but from the character of its artificial staining it is probable that it was used for experimental purposes in preparing the forger's *chef d'oeuvre.* The Barcombe Mills skull consists of a large part of the frontal bone, a fragment of what may have been part of a right parietal, a pair of zygomatic bones which do not in any way fit the frontal, and a mandibular right second molar tooth. A canine tooth, allegedly found in 1915 in the same Pleistocene gravels from which the original bones were said to have been removed, is very chimpanzee-like in form.

The Piltdown remains immediately became bones of contention. It was questioned whether the jaw and teeth could possibly belong with the hominid cranial bones. The former were apelike, the latter were unquestionably human. It was asking a great deal of anyone critically considering the evidence to believe that a chimpanzee-like mandible and canine tooth could possibly have belonged to a skull so like that of modern man. Morphologically, the association seemed to be so improbable that most students refused to accept the jaw and canine tooth as belonging to anything but an ape. On the other hand, Broom, who re-examined the Piltdown remains in 1949, had very little doubt that the Piltdown mandible belonged to the same individual as the brain-case. He considered that Piltdown was a big-brained type of man that evolved on a quite different line from true *Homo*. As for the simian shelf (a sort of internal chin) in the Piltdown mandible, this he reasoned is probably not an indication of close affinity with the anthropoids, but a specialization due to evolution parallel with that of modern apes, just as the large brain of this type may have been a parallel development to what is found in the line of *Homo*.

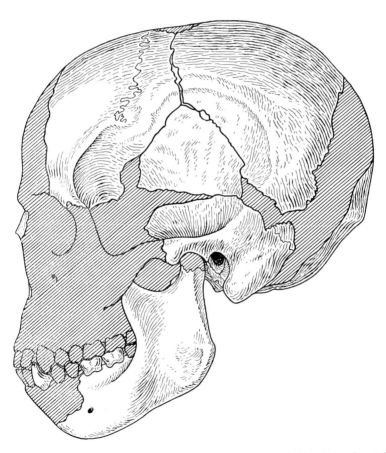

Figure 122. Reconstruction of the spurious Piltdown skull. Only the *right* side of the mandible, the first two molars *in situ* in the orang jaw, and the probable chimpanzee canine are shown in this manufactured specimen. These structures are here drawn as of the left side to match the cranial bones.

There is not the slightest evidence that anthropoid apes ever existed in England. But even if they had it is extremely improbable that an anthropoid ape's mandible would be deposited in the same gravels with a human brain-case. It was pointed out, in opposition to this argument, that when the thigh-bone of *Pithecanthropus erectus* was described many students refused to accept it as belonging with the skull cap because they felt it was too human-like for so primitive a skull. Today no one hesitates to accept the two bones as having belonged to the same type, if not the same individual. Evolution, insofar as it affects the various parts of the body, has been asymmetrical. The lower extremities attained their manlike form before the skull. Similarly, the skull in its various parts exhibits evidences of asymmetric evolution. In all early forms of man the mandible seems to lag behind the brain-case in its development. The lack of a developed chin in most early forms of man is a good example. In the case of the Piltdown mandible, it was argued, we may be dealing with an example of asymmetric evolution in much the terms suggested by Broom. The simian shelf is not a primitive character in the Anthropomorpha. It is not present in any of the early anthropoid fossil types, but is obviously a late specialization. If it developed in the great apes, why not in an aberrant branch of man as well? Despite these arguments, many students remained unconvinced. The mystery to many scientists will always remain how anyone with the slightest knowledge of osteology, the comparative osteology of the primates, could have failed to recognize that the mandible under no circumstances could be morphologically harmonized with the cranial bones. That, it in fact belonged to an anthropoid ape. The great thickness of the cranial bones compared with the slightness of the mandible presents a striking disharmony such as is never seen in any normal skull. The canine tooth perfectly matched the anthropoid character of the jaw, and no known form of man was known to possess such a tooth. The openmindedness of the experts, however, was such that they were willing to grant the possibility that both mandible and canine belonged with the cranial bones.

If there was any doubt about the hominid character of the mandible and canine there was none whatever concerning the brain-case, for in its reconstructed form this revealed an obvious member of the genus *Homo* of an early neanthropic type with skull bones almost twice as thick as those of modern man. The cranial capacity was computed to be between 1,200 and 1,400 cc., McGregor estimating it to be about 1,240 cc.

In association with the Piltdown fragments there was alleged to have been found a number of what appeared to be the simplest type of stone tools, "eoliths," a worked flint, and a large bone implement made from the thigh-bone of an extinct elephant, thought to be *Elephas meridionalis*. Since the latter lived in Europe in the Upper Pliocene and Lower Pleistocene the antiquity of the Piltdown remains was at first referred to the Lower Pleistocene, but it was subsequently shown

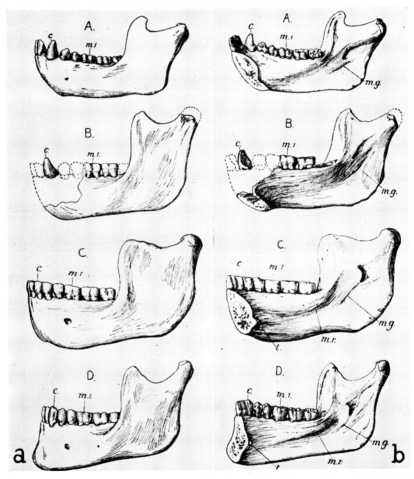

Figure 123. *a*, Left outer and *b*, right inner side of lower jaw of the faked Piltdown Man B compared with that of chimpanzee A, Heidelberg Man C, and Modern Man D. c. canine tooth; m.l = first molar tooth. One-half natural size. (Courtesy, British Museum [Natural History].)

that animal fossils of later date are found in the same gravels as were the Piltdown remains. A test of the fluorine content of the Piltdown bones (the test described in detail in the section on the Galley Hill skeleton, pp. 240-241) showed their fluorine content to be incompatible with an extreme antiquity. The basis of the test is that a form of calcium phosphate, known as hydroxyapatite, is progressively converted to fluorapatite, as fluorine is absorbed from water in the soil. Under the same conditions, and particularly for neighboring fossils, the oldest bones are therefore those with the highest fluorine content. In September 1949, at a meeting of the British Association for the Advancement of Science, Dr. Kenneth Oakley announced the results of the application of the fluorine test on all the available Piltdown materials.

Oakley and Hoskins found that all the animal remains of undoubted Lower Pleistocene age from the Piltdown mélange showed high fluorine content, while all those known to be of later Pleistocene age in the same bed showed a considerably lower fluorine content. All the remains of Piltdown man—and some 20 microsamples were analysed— showed extremely little fluorine. It was concluded that fluorine had been deficient in the Piltdown ground-water since the gravel was accumulated. Nevertheless the test showed conclusively that none of the bones and teeth attributed to Piltdown man belonged to the Lower Pleistocene. However, where the first test failed to be sufficiently discriminating was in obtaining a similar fluorine content for both mandible and cranial bones. The mandible and associated brain-case being of the same age, it was argued, it was probable that they dated from the final settling of the gravel, which from the physiographic evidence, the paleontological findings, and the fluorine tests was now revised downwards as being not earlier than the last interglacial.

The position, then, was that it was still open to scientists to argue about the naturalness of the association of an ape-like mandible with a typically human brain-case, but in the light of the revised dating it was suggested that the probabilities were in favor of mandible and cranial bones belonging together.

In 1951, Montagu examined the Piltdown remains and concluded that on morphological grounds the mandible could not possibly belong with the cranial bones. In July 1953, Dr. J. S. Weiner of Oxford University decided that several things were not as they ought to be about the Piltdown remains. The flatness of the occlusal surfaces of the two molar teeth was quite unnatural and un-apelike, the lack of smooth continuity of biting surface from one molar to the other, the unnaturally heavy wear of the immature canine, the whiteness of the dentine beneath the darkly stained surface of the tooth, all suggested that artificial filing and staining had been the methods by which the superficial appearances had been produced. Proceeding upon this assumption the mandible was subjected to a new fluorine test in which a drilling

Figure 124. Faked "Piltdown" bone implement, made from the thigh-bone of an elephant, and retaining part of the concave inner wall of the marrow cavity A, the smooth hinder surface B, and the outer edge C including the third trochanter; nearly one-third natural size. *b*, accidentally broken hollow, *c*, natural break, *p*, inner wall of perforation from which outer walls have been broken away, *x*, beginning of another perforation. (Courtesy, British Museum [Natural History].)

of deeper substance was analysed. This now yielded a figure of 0.03 per cent, as did the two molar teeth and the canine. The cranial fragments from site I yielded the much higher figure of 0.1 per cent, consistent with the value yielded by specimens of Late Ice Age. The artificial stain which had been used to give the bones an appearance of antiquity had falsified the first fluorine tests. But even before the second test the deeper drilling while in process produced an odor of "burning horn," such as is associated with the drilling of fresh bone, an odor which was absent when the cranial bones were drilled. Furthermore, while the drilling of the mandible yielded shavings of bone as fresh bone does, the cranial bones yielded a fine powder as old bones do. It was now reasonably certain that the mandible was recent and did not belong with the older cranial bones.

Following these revealing findings a whole battery of tests were applied to the Piltdown fragments. Meanwhile, Weiner, Oakley, and

Figure 125. "The Piltdown Committee." Personalities concerned with the Piltdown "discovery." *Back Row:* Mr. F. O. Barlow, maker of the casts, Prof. G. Elliot Smith, anatomist, Mr. C. Dawson, the "discoverer," and Dr. A. S. Woodward, zoologist. *Front Row:* Dr. A. S. Underwood, expert on teeth, Prof. Arthur Keith, anatomist, W. P. Pycraft, zoologist and Woodward's assistant, and Sir Ray Lankester, zoologist. (From the painting by John Cooke, R.A., exhibited at the Royal Academy in 1915.)

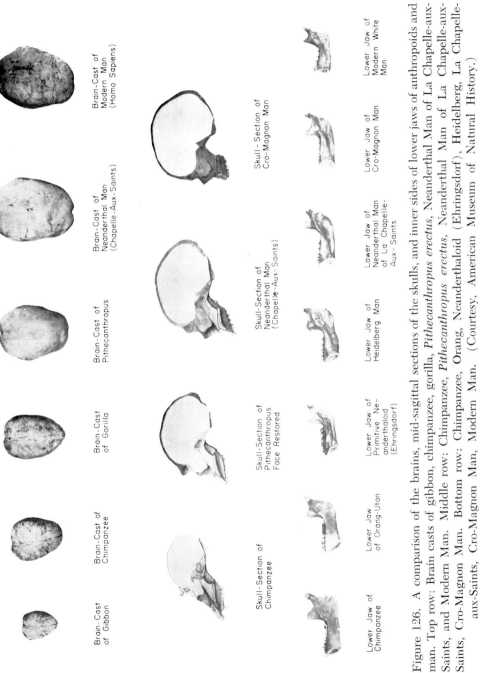

Figure 126. A comparison of the brains, mid-sagittal sections of the skulls, and inner sides of lower jaws of anthropoids and man. Top row: Brain casts of gibbon, chimpanzee, gorilla, *Pithecanthropus erectus*, Neanderthal Man of La Chapelle-aux-Saints, and Modern Man. Middle row: Chimpanzee, *Pithecanthropus erectus*, Neanderthal Man of La Chapelle-aux-Saints, Cro-Magnon Man. Bottom row: Chimpanzee, Orang, Neandertraloid (Ehringsdorf), Heidelberg, La Chapelle-aux-Saints, Cro-Magnon Man, Modern Man. (Courtesy, American Museum of Natural History.)

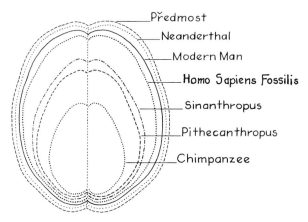

Figure 127. A comparison in brain sizes. Chimpanzee 400 cc. *Pithecanthropus* 860 cc. *Sinanthropus* 1075 cc. *Homo sapiens fossilis* 1300 cc. Modern Man 1400 cc. Neanderthal Man 1450 cc. Předmost 1500 cc.

Le Gros Clark, during the last week of November 1953 published "The Solution of the Piltdown Problem," in which they announced their findings and the conclusion that the Piltdown skull was a fake. In January 1955, "Further Contributions to the Solution of the Piltdown Problem" was published, giving a detailed account of the results of the battery of tests to which the bones had been submitted. This report, the work of a dozen investigators, showed that the mandible, stone artifacts, and the shaped Stegodon (*Elephas planifrons*) "tool" were all faked. The bone "tool" had been shaped with a steel knife from the long bone of a genuine fossil elephant, and the stone artifacts had been artificially stained and introduced into the Piltdown gravels. Four pieces of broken teeth probably representing two molars "associated" with the Piltdown remains have been identified as belonging to the fossil elephant *Elephas planifrons*. Since this species of elephant does not occur in Western Europe the fragments of teeth must have been imported from some foreign source. A *planifrons* from Ichkeul in Tunisia, where the fossil remains of this species are abundant yielded a radioactivity count practically identical with the planted Piltdown *planifrons* teeth. They were artificially stained to match the color of the other Piltdown plants. *Sic transit Eoanthropus dawsoni.*

In 1959 de Vries and Oakley, by radiocarbon dating, showed that the Piltdown skull was 620 ± 100 years old, and that the orang mandible was 500 ± 100 years old. Oakley points out that it is the custom among Dyaks in Borneo to keep orang skulls as fetishes for many

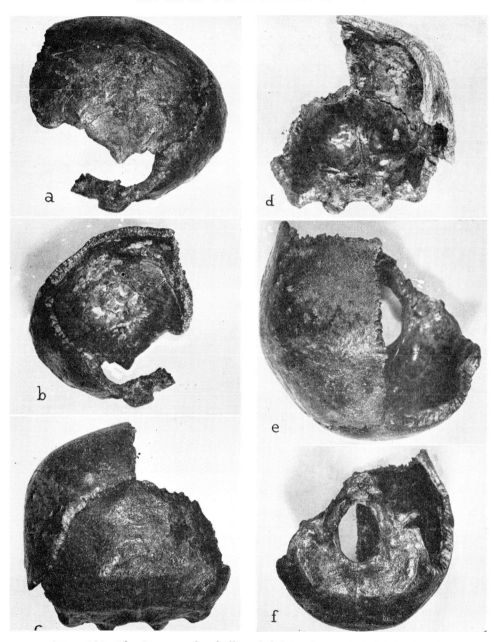

Figure 128. The Swanscombe skull. a, left lateral view, b, left lateral endocranial view, c, occipital view, d, occipital endocranial view, e, vertical view,
f, basilar view. (Courtesy, Dr. G. M. Morant.)

Figure 129A. The Swanscombe skull. Vertical view. (Courtesy, British Museum [Natural History].)

generations, and it was doubtless from such a skull that the mandible was derived.

This is not the place to consider either the possible identity of the forger or his motives. For that story the reader may be referred to Dr. J. S. Weiner's fascinating anthropological "whodunit," *The Piltdown Forgery*, 1955.

The London Skull. In November 1925 most of the occipital and left parietal bones, and parts of the right parietal of a single human skull were found in central London, during excavations for the new Lloyd's building. The age of the deposit in which these bones were found are believed to be Upper Pleistocene. The bones and the brain cast taken from them display an interesting medley of features, some,

Figure 129B. The Swanscombe skull. Occipital view. (Courtesy, British
Museum [Natural History].)

it was at one time thought, bearing close affinities to Neanderthal man.
But careful study of this fragmentary skull reveals that its closest
affinities are with the Cro-Magnon rather than with the Neanderthal
type. It is, indeed, quite possible that the latter were the joint ancestors
of the London Lady (the smoothness of the bones and the weakness
of the muscular impressions indicate the probability that the sex was
female). The cranial capacity has been estimated to have been about
1,260 c.c., some 40 c.c. less than in the average modern English woman.
The slightly greater fullness of the parietal region, and the form of
the bony compartment for the cerebellum sufficiently distinguish this
skull from the Neanderthal type to bring it within the range of the
early neanthropic types.

Swanscombe Man. In 1935-36 at Swanscombe, Kent, in England,
in a deposit which is not later than the second interglacial of the Mid-

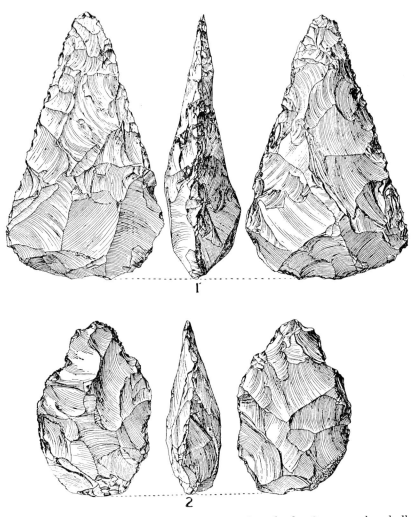

Figure 130. Acheulian hand-axes associated with the Swanscombe skull. 1, found six feet east of occipital bone, 2, found one foot west of occipital bone. (Courtesy, Royal Anthropological Institute.)

dle Pleistocene, an extremely important find was made of a human left parietal and occipital bone. In 1955 the right parietal bone was recovered from the same deposit some 50 feet from the original find. Except for the remarkable thickness and the great breadth of the occipital, these bones are otherwise indistinguishable in form and character from those of modern man, and there can be little doubt that they belonged to an early neanthropic type. Associated with these bones were artifacts of Early Middle Acheulian type, that is to say, representing an industry very appreciably antedating the Late Acheulian and Mousterian industries of Neanderthal man.

The importance of the Swanscombe find lies in the fact that it strongly suggests the existence of a neanthropic type of man in an early geological and cultural horizon.

The cranial capacity of this, probably female, skull is estimated to have been about 1,325 c.c.

Interestingly enough, about the year 1912 portions of a human calvarium together with part of the upper jaw, the whole of the lower jaw, and the first and second cervical vertebrae were found at a depth of eight or nine feet in the alluvial gravel at Swanscombe, but since the skull was of modern type, it unfortunately seems to have been assumed that it could not have been of the geological antiquity indicated by the deposit in which it was found. The present whereabouts of these remains are unknown.

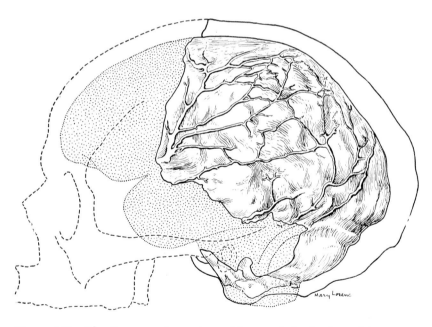

Figure 131. The Swanscombe endocranial cast of the brain and its reconstruction together with the mid-saggital section of the parietal and occipital bones as the basis for a reconstruction of the frontal and facial portions of the skull (reconstruction of the brain alone after Le Gros Clark).

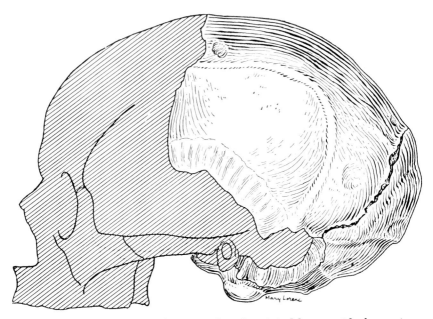

Figure 132. The Swanscombe parietal and occipital bones with the conjectured neanthropic face added.

Quinzano Skull. In a cave in the locality of Carotta, near Quinzano in the commune of Verona, Italy, there was discovered in 1938 a highly fossilized occipital bone which both in its form and measurements closely resembles the Swanscombe occipital. The biasterionic diameter of the Quinzano occipital is 124 mm., and of the Swanscombe occipital 123.5 mm. Found associated with the remains of *Elephas* and other extinct animals in the same state of fossilization, there were also associated stone artifacts of Clactonian and Levalloisian industry. Battaglia, who described the find in 1948, considers that the occipital may have belonged to a female between 40 and 50 years of age. The combined evidence indicates a Middle Paleolithic Riss-Würm age—that is to say, an age approximately the same as that of Swanscombe.

A single occipital bone is hardly sufficient material upon which to establish relationships, even though comparisons are perfectly in order, so that all that can be said about the Quinzano occipital is that it closely resembles that of Swanscombe, and since it is of approximately the same age, Quinzano *may* be related to Swanscombe.

The Galley Hill Skeleton. The Galley Hill skeleton is referred to here at some length for several reasons. Firstly, because up to recent times the skeleton had increasingly come to be accepted as a probable representative of second interglacial man. Secondly, in the first edition of this book the antiquity of the Galley Hill skeleton was forcefully defended. In the summer of 1948 the author was able to study not only the skeleton itself, but also the general geological and stratigraphical conditions of the site from which the skeleton was recovered. In addition, the bones have been subjected to a chemical analysis, the results of which would alone be sufficient to disprove all claims to antiquity of the Galley Hill skeleton. It is for these reasons and also because the story of the Galley Hill controversy illumines the nature of the problems as well as the dangers and pitfalls which confront the paleoanthropologist that a somewhat extended account of Galley Hill man is given here. At the same time the account will provide an opportunity to discuss some of the methods by means of which such problems as were presented by the Galley Hill skeleton can be solved.

The Galley Hill skeleton was found by a workman in the Galley Hill pit, some 500 yards from the quarry in which the remains of Swanscombe man were found in 1935-36. The Galley Hill find was made in September 1888. Mr. Robert Elliot, who saw the bones *in situ* soon after they were found, stated that they were "about two

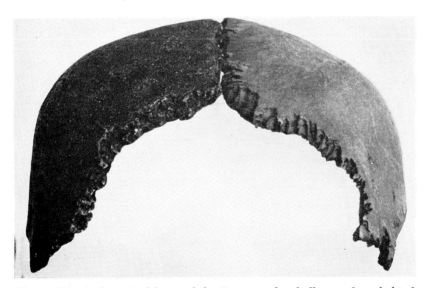

Figure 133. Left parietal bone of the Swanscombe skull, seen from behind, placed in apposition to the right parietal bone of a modern European skull. (From Le Gros Clark. Courtesy, British Museum [Natural History].)

Figure 134. Swanscombe man. Hunting scene. From a painting by Maurice Wilson. (Courtesy, British Museum [Natural History].)

feet above the top of the chalk and eight feet from the top of the gravel, portions of bone were projecting from a matrix of clayey loam and sand. . . .

"The section of gravel was 10 or 11 feet thick, and extended for a considerable distance along the south and east end of the pit; several pot-holes or pipes running from it deep into the Chalk . . . the section on either side of the remains . . . presented an unbroken face of gravel, stratified horizontally in bands of sand, small shingle, gravel, and, lower down, beds of clay and clayey loam, with occasional stones in it—and it was in and below this that the remains were found. We carefully looked for any signs of the section being disturbed, but failed: the stratification being unbroken."

Excavation of the Galley Hill site in 1948 revealed a stratified sandy gravel some eight feet thick, which has been disturbed by the solution of the underlying chalk. The solution of the chalk is due to a downward percolation of carbonic acid laden waters through the gravels. Because this process has been so pronounced at this site no original bones or shells have survived in the gravel. This is a telling bit of evidence. Why should a human skeleton alone have survived?

Analysis of the gravels, sands, and loams at Galley Hill shows that they have been completely decalcified (the pH is 6.8*). A human skeleton could scarcely have survived in such an environment since Middle Pleistocene times. It must therefore be concluded that the bones were introduced after the deposits had become decalcified. Furthermore, analysis of samples of soil which were recovered from the site with the skeleton and subsequently, reveal the presence of sand, silt, and clay. The presence of a skeleton embedded in such a mixed matrix is suggestive of artificial burial.

The fact that Elliot and the local schoolmaster detected no signs of disturbance in the overlying gravel, may simply mean that by the time they saw the remnants of the skeleton protruding from the face, the bulk of any evidence of burial had already been destroyed by the gravel digger. In any event, the deposits could very easily have been of such a nature that traces of disturbance due to burial would have been obscure. McKenny Hughes has shown how easily traces of interment are obliterated in Pleistocene deposits. Even experienced geologists have been known to mistake settled layers of tipped gravel for natural strata. In 1913 Duckworth compared the deformation pattern of the Galley Hill skull with that of skulls recovered from Saxon graves, and concluded that the skeleton of Galley Hill man almost certainly represented a burial of comparatively recent date.

The skull had been described as exhibiting the characters of a primitive type of modern man. The primitive features of the Galley Hill skull when I examined it were entirely wanting. The bones of the skull had been described as thick. I found them to be of the same thickness as those of the average modern male. The mandibular or sigmoid notch of the ramus of the mandible was said to be almost absent. It was. But not because it had never been there, but because the margins forming it had been partly broken away. The last molar tooth was said to be longer than the second. I found the opposite to be true. In short, the skeleton revealed not a single primitive feature. Furthermore, there were no evidences of fossilization. What had deceived most of those who had inspected the bones was the fact that they had been treated with a gelatin which had given them a purplish hue, thus endowing the bones with an appearance of great antiquity. But beneath this the internal structure of the bones is quite like that of relatively recent bones.

---

* pH symbol for hydrogen ion concentration. A pH of 7 indicates equilibrium or neutrality; when the figure is above 7 alkalosis is present, when below 7 acidosis is present.

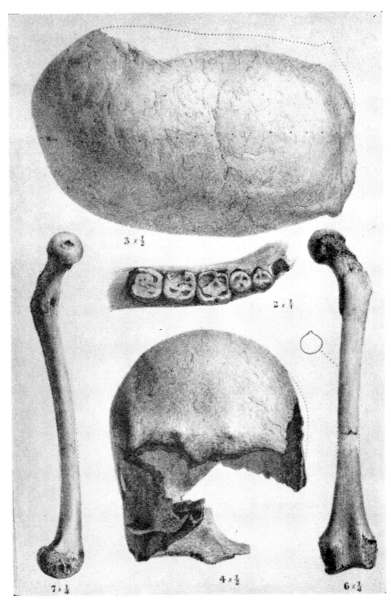

Figure 135. The Galley Hill skeleton. 2, occlusal view of teeth, 3, vertical view of skull. 4, frontal view of skull, 6, left femur frontal view, 7, left femur medial view. (From Newton. Courtesy, the Geological Society of London.)

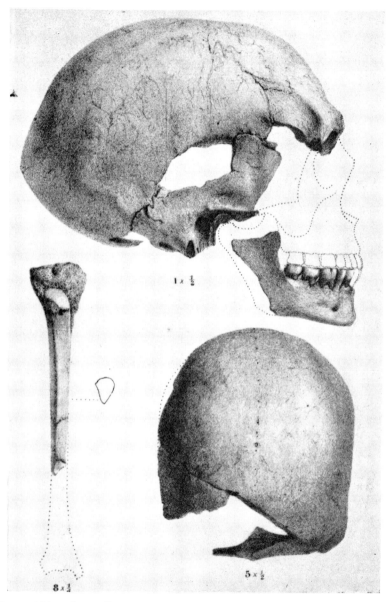

Figure 136. The Galley Hill skeleton. 1, skull and mandible, 2, occipital
view of skull, 3, right tibia. (From Newton. Courtesy, Geological Society
of London.)

The great revival of interest in the Galley Hill skeleton in recent years was due to the discovery by Mr. A. T. Marston of the parietal and occipital bones of a woman in the Barnfield pit at Swanscombe in 1935-36. There was no doubt that these fossils were of Early Paleolithic age. When it was shown that these two bones exhibited no features (except thickness) which distinguished them from those of modern man, interest in the Galley Hill skeleton received a new fillip. At any rate there appeared to be less reason for doubting the antiquity of the latter merely on the score of its modern morphology. Familiar only with the published evidence, many authors, the writer among them, accepted the Galley Hill skeleton as of Early Paleolithic age. Clearly, the question of Galley Hill man's antiquity had become a matter of opinion, if not of actual wishful thinking. What was needed was some sort of delicate test by means of which the relative age of the bones could be accurately determined. Such a test was first devised by Middleton, an English geological chemist, and published in 1844. It was developed by a French geologist, Carnot, in 1893, and in 1895 it was applied by Thomas Wilson of Washington, D.C., to the analysis of the Natchez pelvis (q.v.). The test has recently been revived by Dr. Kenneth Oakley of the British Museum. This test is in the form of a comparative analysis of the fluorine content of bone.

It is known that the fluorine content of bones relative to the soil in which they are contained increases with geological age. This is due to the fact that the main inorganic salt from which bone is formed, namely, hydroxyapatite $(Ca_3P_2O_8)Ca(OH)_2$, a form of calcium phosphate, acts as a trap for fluorine ions, which are usually present in small numbers in most ground waters. The hydroxyapatite crystal units become converted one by one into fluorapatite $CaF_2[Ca_3(PO_4)_2]_3$. Fluorapatite is a stable mineral which is resistant to weathering. Fluorine is not easily leached after it has been fixed in bone. Hence the fluorine content will increase with the passage of time. Owing to the porous character of bone, the fluorine tends to be distributed uniformly throughout the bone.

By spectrographic and delicate microchemical analysis it is possible to determine the amount of fluorine present in any bone. Such an absolute datum taken by itself can give us no idea of the age of bone. It is only when bones taken from different geological strata and from the same locality are compared with one another that an estimate of relative age can be arrived at on the basis of their fluorine content. Bones taken from different localities cannot be compared strata above and below those from which the bones have come in owing to the great variation in the fluorine content of soils in different areas. The bones must be taken from the same locality and from which we are chiefly interested. Bones from the older levels will have a higher absolute fluorine content than those at more recent levels. Bones from the same level as those in which we are chiefly interested should have a similar fluorine content. Applying such comparative chemical tests to bones of known geological age from the Galley Hill-Swanscombe locality, and comparing the results with the fluorine content of five different bones of the Galley Hill skeleton, the following percentages were obtained:

From these figures it will be seen that the highest fluorine content of the Galley Hill bones amounts to but one-fifth of the percentage found in Middle Pleistocene bones, and is only one to three-

TABLE VI

Percentage of Fluorine in Bones from the Swanscombe-Galley Hill Region (Oakley and Montagu)

		Fluorine Per cent
		2.0
		2.8
		2.1
9 Samples of fossil animal bone from loams and gravels in 100-ft. terrace (Middle Pleistocene)		1.7
		1.7
		2.3
		2.0
		2.0
		1.7
Samples of Swanscombe skull		
Occipital bone		c. 1.9
Parietal bone		c. 2.0
		1.0
6 Samples of fossil animal bone from loams and gravels in 50-ft. terrace complex (Upper Pleistocene)		1.2
		1.4
		0.9
		1.1
		1.0
		0.1
5 Samples of recent bones from soil or sub-soil (Postglacial)		0.1
		0.2
		0.3
		0.05
	petrous bone	0.3
	mandible	0.4
5 Samples of Galley Hill skeleton	right tibia	0.4
	limb bone	0.4
	left femur	0.2

Figure 137. The Bury St. Edmunds skull fragment. Showing parts of the frontal and parietal bones.

tenths per cent higher than in recent bones. It is clear, then that the Galley Hill skeleton is much more recent than Middle Pleistocene, and as is shown by comparison with bones from the Upper Pleistocene, is even more recent than that age.

It is safe to say that the Galley Hill skeleton represents the remains of a body which was buried in post-glacial times, and is not more than a few thousand years old.

Bury St. Edmunds. The cranial fragment found at Bury St. Edmunds in 1882, and at one time thought to be of Middle Pleistocene age, has been shown by Oakley to possess an extremely low fluorine content, namely 0.2 per cent, whereas none of the bones from a wide range of the Quaternary deposits in neighboring districts showed less than 0.6 per cent, while none of the specimens from brickearth comparable in age with that of Bury St. Edmunds contained less than 1.6 per cent, a group of facts which renders the high antiquity of the Bury St. Edmunds fragment extremely doubtful.

The Wallbrook Skull. In 1943, during excavation in London for the foundations of the new Western Union House, an almost complete frontal bone was found by a workman about 1,000 yards from the site of the London Skull. Unfortunately, the geological position of the find remains ambiguous, owing to the conditions under which it was retrieved. The evidence, however, strongly suggests that the bone was derived from the red gravel of the Upper Floodplain Terrace of the Pleistocene, and was redeposited in alluvial mud. Its state of fossilization, the traces of earth which adhere to the bone, the statements of the workman who found it and of the electrician who witnessed the find, all indicate that it belongs to the same geological

horizon as the London Skull. The evidence favors an Upper Pleistocene age.

With the exception of a small triangular piece on the right side
and nearly the whole of the glabellar region and pars nasalis, the
whole of the frontal bone is preserved (broken in two pieces which
fit perfectly). The bone is extremely thick, but in every other respect
is in no way distinguishable from that of contemporary man. The
superciliary arches and the supraorbital margins show no excessive
development. The slope, fullness, and 'bossing' of the forehead, are
precisely as in contemporary man, and there is no bilateral narrowing.

The importance of this skull fragment, altogether apart from its
age, is considerable. At the coronal margin the thickness of the bone
is slightly greater than that of the Swanscombe parietal at its coronal
margin. One of the writers of the report on the Swanscombe skull,
Dr. G. M. Morant, considered that the abnormally thick parietal and
occipital bones "suggest forcibly not only that the missing frontal bone
was abnormally thick, but also that it probably possessed a more

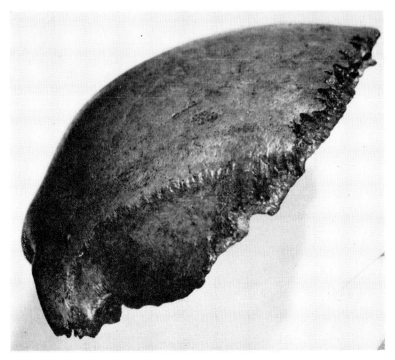

Figure 138. The Wallbrook frontal bone. (Courtesy, British Museum
[Natural History].)

Figure 139. The Wallbrook frontal bone. (Courtesy, British Museum [Natural History].)

massive supraorbital region than any modern specimen." The Wallbrook frontal bone with its thicker coronal border, and supraorbital region which in no way differs from that of modern man, serves to show not only how far wrong one can go in such speculations, but also to underscore the danger of drawing inferences as to the form of the frontal region and face from the thickness of vault bones. The Wallbrook frontal bone is thicker than the Swanscombe parietal, and it is of modern type. In short, the Wallbrook frontal serves to remove yet another objection to the possibility that Swanscombe man possessed a forehead and face like that of contemporary man. We need but one thing to be quite certain—the actual bones themselves!

The Fontéchevade Skulls. In August 1947 in the cave of Fontéchevade, near the village of Montbrun, Department of Charente, France, Mademoiselle Germaine Henri-Martin discovered a human calvarium. This was found beneath the hard stalagmitic floor in the red sandy clay. Associated were crude flint implements consisting mainly of large flakes. These have been assigned to an industry transitional between Mousterian and an earlier period, identical with that found by Abbé Breuil in the lowest archeological horizon at La Micoque, and known as Tayacian. The horizon of the deposit in which the Fontéchevade skull was found is third interglacial. The associated remains of Merck's rhinoceros and a warmth-loving Mediterranean turtle (*Testudo graeca*) help to date the age of the skull. It is about 100,000 years old. It is thus one of the oldest representatives of fossil man ever found in France. It is of interest that it should have come from the very center of the region which has yielded so many remains of Neanderthal man.

Virtually a complete skull-cap was recovered, as shown in Figure 143. Actually the base of the skull is missing as are the supraorbital portions of the frontal bone. The bones are quite thick, varying from 7 to 9 mm. As is the case in most Paleolithic crania the skull is long-headed. The cranial index actually makes the skull mesocranial, for Vallois has calculated it at 78.9. It is of interest to note that the cranial

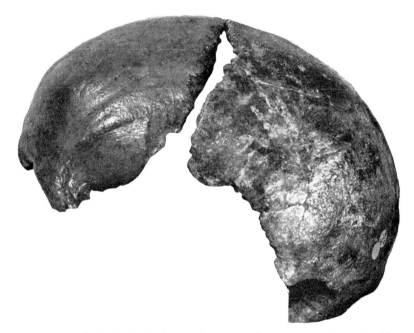

Figure 140. The Wallbrook frontal bone and the Swanscombe parietal bone approximated at the the region of the coronal suture. Left lateral view. (Courtesy, British Museum [Natural History].)

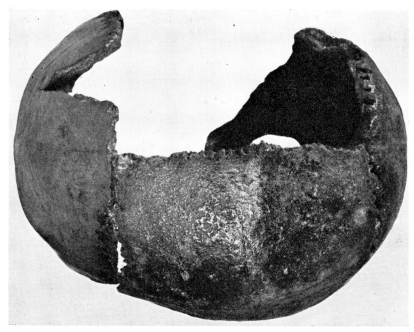

Figure 141. The Wallbrook frontal bone and the Swanscombe parietal bone approximated at the region of the coronal suture. Vertical view. (Courtesy, British Museum [Natural History].)

index is 78.2 in Swanscombe. The cranial capacity of Fontéchevade has been calculated by Vallois to be 1,470 c.c. Fortunately Mlle. Henri-Martin had somewhat earlier, in the same fossil-bearing layer of the cave, discovered a fragment of bone (Fontéchevade I) which is presumed to have belonged to another individual. This represents the frontal glabellar region just over the root of the nose and including a portion of the left orbit exhibiting a supraorbital margin which is as sharp and delicately made as in the most gracile of modern crania. In fact, the gracility of this bone is such that there can be no doubt that it formed part of a skull whose bones were no thicker than those of modern man. Fontéchevade I was adult and probably female.

The form of the brain-box of Fontéchevade II and of the supraorbital region of Fontéchevade I renders it clear beyond any possible shadow of doubt that we are here dealing with a type of man scarcely distinguishable from modern man. And yet this type of man clearly antedated Neanderthal man both culturally and temporally in a region from which a majority of Neanderthal remains have been re-

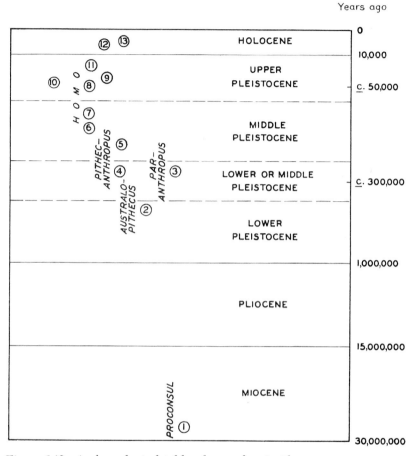

Figure 142. A chronological table of some hominoids.

1. *Proconsul.*
2. *Australopithecus.*
3. *Paranthropus.*
4. *Pithecanthropus modjokertensis.*
5. *Pithecanthropus (Sinanthropus pekinensis).*
6. Swanscombe Man.
7. Steinheim Man.
8. Skhūl V (Mt. Carmel) Man.
9. Florisbad Man.
10. Neanderthal Man.
11. Cro-Magnon Man.
12. Keilor Man.
13. Galley Hill Man.

(From Oakley, Courtesy, Manchester Literary and Philosophical Society.)

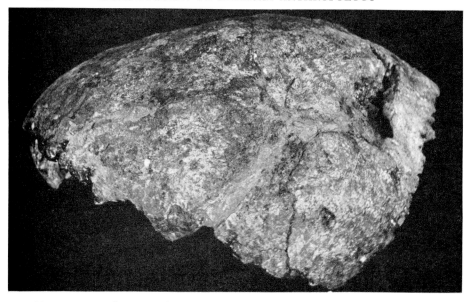

Figure 143. The Fontéchevade skull II. (From Vallois.) Left lateral view. (Courtesy, *Am. J. Phys. Anthrop.*)

covered. It is very likely that Fontéchevade types intermixed with the forerunners of Neanderthal man in Europe.

The great importance of the Fontéchevade skulls lies in the fact that for the first time in the history of the subject we now have indisputable proof of the antiquity of the so-called, or rather mis-called, neanthropic type of man.

In Fontéchevade man then, we see yet another type with whom the forerunners of Neanderthal man may have intermixed, and some more definite evidence for this we see in the physical characters of a possible ancestor of Neanderthal man such as Heidelberg man, and even in such a type as Ehringsdorf.

The Veternica Skulls. In 1956 Malez briefly reported the discovery of a rich paleolithic site in the Veternica cave near the village of Gornji Stenjevec, about 9 kilometers west of Zagreb in Jugoslavia. In the fourth stratum of the cave Malez found three well preserved human crania of young individuals which were of sapiens type. A poorly preserved human femur was also discovered. Associated with these remains were quartz artifacts, suggesting a Mousterian-Aurignacian boundary industry. In the stratum below this, associated with Mousterian artifacts, the skull of an older sapiens individual was discovered. This stratum appears to belong to the second half of the Riss-Würm interglacial.

In still lower strata a rich stone and bone industry of Mousterian type was uncovered.

The importance of this find lies in the fact that the Veternica cave lies in the same valley as Krapina, about 37 kilometers distant where, in 1899-1905, Gorjanović-Kramberger discovered the remains of between 23 and 28 badly broken Neanderthal skulls. Škerlj has recently drawn attention to the fact that one well preserved skull cap of a child, from the Krapina assembly, shows very marked sapiens traits, and few if any neanderthaloid ones. Indeed, the skull exhibits a complete metopic suture, a condition not found in any other known Neanderthal skull (though it occurs in at least one Sinanthropus skull), and as was pointed out by Hrdlička, the sutures are distinctly more serrated than they are in Neanderthal crania, and there are frontal lateral eminences, and there is a shallow depression posterior and parallel to the coronal suture, as in modern Caucasoid crania.

Allowing for the fact that it is difficult to predict the final form of the skull from the juvenile form, and making allowance also for the fact that the Neanderthal juvenile skull was very much more sapiens-like than the Neanderthal adult skull, as we know from the skull of the eight year old La Quina child, and the eight-to-nine year old Teshik-Tash (Uzbekistan) child, and the six year old Gibraltar boy,

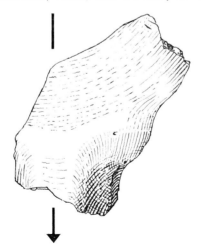

Figure 144. The fronto-naso-orbital fragment of Fontéchevade I. The arrow passes through the middle of the glabella and the nasal process of the frontal bone. Anterior view. Natural size. (Courtesy, Prof. Henri Vallois.)

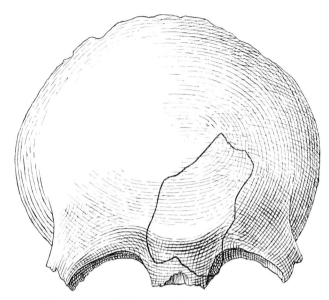

Figure 145. The contour of the Fontéchevade II fragment projected upon the complete frontal bone of a modern Caucasoid. Anterior view. Two-thirds natural size. (Courtesy, Prof. Henri Vallois.)

there is a real question raised by the Krapina child's skull. This question was already raised by Weidenreich in 1945 when he pointed out the marked sapiens-like traits of the Teshik-Tash child's skull, namely, may we not actually have evidence in such skulls, as Weidenreich put it, of "the transformation of Neanderthalian into modern man." Indeed, the probabilities are high that hybridization between neanthropic and neanderthaloid populations, and pre-neanderthaloid populations, occurred more than once and in more than one place, in Western and Central Asia, and as the Veternica evidence (when it is fully published) will show us, in Central Europe and probably elsewhere.

The New Conception of Man's Evolution. It has already been pointed out that in earlier days when but a few fossil remains were available, the extreme differences between such a form as *Pithecanthropus* and another such as modern man, led students to think of these types as representing different genera. They were therefore so distinguished from one another by being given generic names. Today, however, when so many intermediate forms have become available, the apparently extreme character of the first discovered types has con-

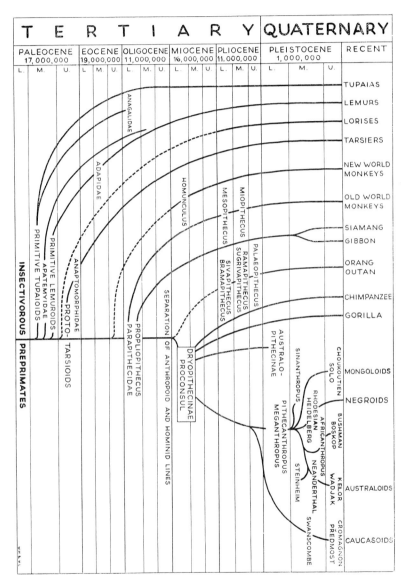

Figure 146. The phylogenetic relationships of the primates in their geological background. The figures refer to the duration of each epoch. (L = Lower, M = Middle, U = Upper).

siderably diminished, and it is now seen that they are all closely related, in many instances in much the same way as the different varieties of man are today related. Weidenreich holds that *Pithecanthropus*, for example, does not differ from *Sinanthropus* any more than does an Australian aboriginal from an Arab. However this may be, our problem continues to be the discovery of the exact nature of these relationships, a problem necessarily for the future, when more material relating both to the morphological and cultural evolution of man has become available.

Meanwhile we see that earlier notions of a linear evolution of man, notions which held that man progressively advanced in a straight line from an ape-like stage toward the stage of neanthropic or the modern type of man, were too simplified. The modern type of man appears to have been differentiated as a distinct type as early as the middle Pleistocene, more than 300,000 years ago, while a distinctly different type like Neanderthal man, which morphologically possessed many more primitive characters, appeared considerably later. Be it noted however, that in spite of the fact that Neanderthal man was the possessor of morphologically more primitive physical characters than early neanthropic man, he was culturally more advanced than the latter, as is evidenced by the artifacts he manufactured and the funerary rites which he practiced. This is an important point because in itself it suggests a later advent in time for Neanderthal man. Even more important is the fact that in one very significant morphological feature Neanderthal man outdistanced neanthropic man, namely, in size of the brain. The average brain size of Neanderthal man (as measured by cranial capacity) exceeded neanthropic man with 1,553 c.c. as against say the 1,325 to 1,457 c.c., of such a type as Swanscombe or Fontéchevade with a cranial capacity of 1,470 c.c. While we know nothing of the range of variation in brain size of these two latter types, nor anything of the possible differences in body bulk which may have had some relation to the difference in brain size, it appears highly improbable that the average cranial capacity of early neanthropic man ever exceeded 1,553 c.c.—the average cranial capacity of Neanderthal males. The interesting fact is that man appears to have attained a large brain size quite early in his career.

It was formerly thought that in the large pulp cavities of the molar teeth, a condition known as "taurodontism," Neanderthal man exhibited a unique specialization which excluded him from the ancestry of modern man. It is, however, now known that far from being a speciali-

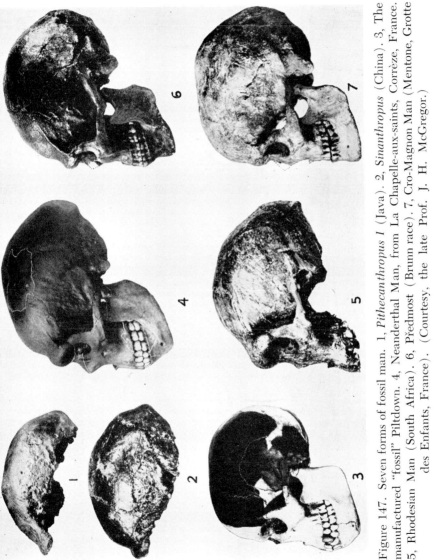

Figure 147. Seven forms of fossil man. 1, *Pithecanthropus 1* (Java). 2, *Sinanthropus* (China). 3, The manufactured "fossil" Piltdown. 4, Neanderthal Man, from La Chapelle-aux-saints, Corrèze, France. 5, Rhodesian Man (South Africa). 6, Předmost (Brunn race). 7, Cro-Magnon Man (Mentone, Grotte des Enfants, France). (Courtesy, the late Prof. J. H. McGregor.)

zation peculiar to Neanderthal man, the condition typically occurs in the orang-utan and chimpanzee, and is by no means rare among various human groups such as the Eskimo and Bushman. Furthermore, taurodontism is sometimes seen in the molars of whites, thus suggesting the possibility of persisting strains of Neanderthaloid ancestry or possibly a tendency toward the appearance of a similar variation in modern man.

The later neanthropic types, who were identical in almost every respect with Europeans of today, namely, the men of Předmost of the Late Aurignacian had, it will be recalled, a cranial capacity of 1,590 c.c. Modern Europeans have to manage on a cranial capacity of 1,400 c.c. more or less.

It appears that Neanderthal man was more advanced in size of brain than both the early neanthropic hominids and their modern descendants.

The difference in the size of the brain between Middle Pleistocene man and modern man has led some students to conclude that the decrease in the size of the brain is to be regarded as a specialization, an evolutionary step in which size of brain is now subordinated to the greater development or increase in the complexity of its cellular structure and organization. It is, however, quite possible that the present size of contemporary man's brain represents the persisting size of the early neanthropic or Swanscombe type of brain *plus* the addition which has accrued from mixture with various other types of man with much larger brains. Although the cranial capacity in Europeans, for example, may vary from 1,000 to 2,000 c.c. the degree of individual diversity, as measured by the coefficient of variation, is rather low, namely, about 8.0. This indicates a relatively high degree of stabilization in brain size. It is quite possible that the evolution of the brain in man is now solely restricted to specialization in internal structure; but it is well to bear in mind the possibility that the enlargement of the brain may continue to be achieved much as it has been in the past, through increase in surface area by the multiplication and deepening of its convolutions, rather than by linear or volumetric increases in size.

It may be that Neanderthal man, with his larger brain, possessed greater potentialities for development than we do, but this is greatly to be doubted, since brain size, within the limits here being considered, bears no relation to mental capacity.

With respect to the human brain it is now reasonably clear that within the limits of the normal, which ranges from a cranial capacity

of 750 c.c. (about 1,000 c.c. in the case of the great French novelist
and wit, Anatole France) to a limit of upwards of 2,000 c.c. in modern
man, with an average of 1,400 c.c., neither cranial capacity, size, form,
nor number of convolutions, has anything whatever to do with intelligence or functional capacity. Not even the number of cells contained in the cortex or in the subcortical regions is significant, but
what is significant is the number of connections which exist between
such cells. In the latter respect it may well be doubted whether
there has been any significant change in the human brain for a long
time.

Instead of a linear evolution of human types we see, on the other
hand, a great diversity of types being produced, and these in turn,
most probably by mixture with one another, producing still other
types.

The principal agency at work in the evolution of man, as in all
other living forms, has been mutation and the action of selection
upon that mutation. Isolation, whether produced by geographic or
other barriers, has undoubtedly played an important part in the
evolution of man. After natural selection has done its work hybridization must be considered a principal agency in the production or
development of new types out of the original materials provided by
mutation. We shall consider these agencies in some detail in the
next chapter.

The new types produced by hybridization would form a group
distinct from their parental types in precisely the same way as the
American Negroes form a group more or less distinguishable from
their African progenitors on the one hand and their white progenitors
on the other. The parental groups would live on as contemporaries of
their hybrid offspring, and might even survive them, even—to use a
lame analogy—as grandparents sometimes survive their grandchildren.
Hence, the possibilities of mixtures of different types with the ever
increasing production of new ones grows increasingly larger.

The widespread distribution of Neanderthal types in the Old
World suggests the possibility of migrations of some early human
groups over extended land surfaces. This, however, is speculative,
for we know practically nothing concerning the movements of early
populations, and in any event in order to account for the wide distribution of Neanderthal types the notion of migration from a single
center is not necessary. The probabilities are that there were many
"centers."

Much valuable light, we have already seen, has been thrown on the evolution of man by recent discoveries in Africa. Another group of finds of fossil man in that continent may be referred to here.

A type which until recently was by some authorities believed to be the earliest representative of neanthropic man yet found, was discovered by L. S. B. Leakey in 1932. This find is represented by a fragment of the mandible consisting of the front portion together with the two right premolars. The discovery was made at West Kanam, on the southern shores of the Kavirondo Gulf of Victoria Nyanza, in Kenya, East Africa. The deposit from which the mandible was recovered was claimed to be of Lower Pleistocene age. A recent uranium analysis of the content of the jaw and Lower Pleistocene fossils from the Kanam site throws considerable doubt upon this claim to antiquity for the Kanam mandible. Lower Pleistocene fossils from the Kanam site yielded a measure of radioactivity equivalent to over 60 c.p.m. U_3O_8, whereas the radioactivity of the Kanam mandible was equivalent to only 10 c.p.m. U_3O_8. Since bone takes up uranium from deposits in which uranium-bearing water circulates (see pp. 286-287 for an account of this) the uranium content of bones from such deposits exhibits a higher rate of radioactivity in those of greater age, while bones of lesser age exhibit a lower rate. The indications are, therefore, that the Kanam mandible belongs to an appreciably later time than the Lower Pleistocene.

The Kanam mandible has been described as if it possessed a well-developed chin. It may well have been so endowed, but the fact is that it is impossible to determine whether it possessed a chin or not since the chin region is pathologically obliterated by a sarcomatous overgrowth which renders identification of normal tissue beyond possibility. However, the form of the alveolar portion of the jaw, which is undisturbed, and the presence of incisor fossae, which generally occur only in mandibles possessing chins, suggest that a chin once was present.

Leakey has also described the fragmentary skeletal remains of three individuals of modern Negroid type from what is thought to be a Middle or Late Pleistocene deposit at Kanjera, in Kenya, associated with artifacts of Acheulian industry. The discovery is somewhat better substantiated than that at West Kanam. Uranium tests corroborate the contemporaneity of the Kanjera skulls with the associated extinct fauna. But it is still an open question whether these deposits may not be of Upper Pleistocene age. The suggestion remains that types of *Homo sapiens*, by the beginning of the Upper Pleistocene, had already early differentiated into distinct ethnic groups and mi-

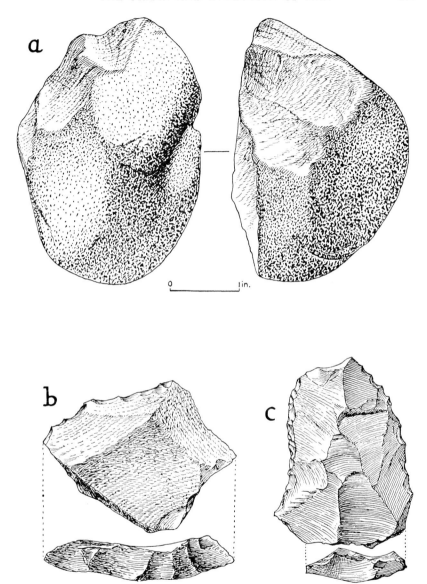

Figure 148. Artifacts of fossil man in Africa. *a*, Oldowan pebble-tool (quartz-ose rock), Kanam beds, Kenya. By courtesy of Coryndon Museum, Nairobi. *b*, Levalloisian flake (lava) associated with "Africanthropus," Lake Eyassi, Tanganyika. *c*, Levalloisian flake-tool (lava) from beds with Proto-Bushman skull, Singa, Sudan. (From Oakley, *Man the Tool-Maker*. Courtesy, British Museum [Natural History].)

Figure 149. The Kanam Mandible. (Upper left), anterior view, (Upper right), right lateral view giving false appearance of chin, (Lower left), occlusal view, (Lower right), basilar view showing part of the tumorous overgrowth. (Courtesy, British Museum [Natural History].)

grated over great distances, even before Neanderthal man had done so.

Leakey has in addition described five crania from Gamble's Cave in Upper Kenya, which were found associated with an Aurignacian industry, and similar crania discovered in Elmenteita, in Kenya, associated with a Mesolithic type of industry.

In 1958, Leakey announced the discovery of two hominid teeth in association with Chellean artifacts at Olduvai Gorge, Tanganyika Territory. Among the Oldowan type tools, stone balls, hand axes, choppers and flakes, were found two lumps of red ochre which were clearly brought to the site by man. The remains of numerous extinct mammals were found on the site including a number of fossil monkeys. The teeth consisted of a lower left second deciduous molar, and a lower left deciduous canine. The molar is very large, having a length 15 mm. and a width of 14 mm. The canine has a length of 7 mm. and a width of 6.1 mm. Leakey believes that the teeth belonged to a true hominid, not of australopithecine type, and probably a man.

With the discovery of *Zinjanthropus boisei* there can be little doubt of the great antiquity of man in Africa. Indeed, in view of the existence of clearly demarcated Middle Pleistocene cultures in Uganda and Kenya territories, there can no longer be the least question as to the existence of man in Africa at a very early period.

In South Africa an important series of finds of fossil human types throws some light on the process of raciation in that country. The fragmentary skeletal remains found in 1914 near Boskop in the Transvaal are of particular interest. These are of a neanthropic type of indeterminate geological age, but almost certainly from the Middle Stone Age of South Africa approximately equivalent to the Last Interglacial Mousterian of Europe. The skull is remarkable for a cranial capacity of about 1,700 c.c., small nipple-shaped mastoid processes, a rather straight-faced profile as in most Europeans, a long head, the breadth being 75 per cent of the length, with a great thickness of the parietal bones at their centers of 13 to 14 mm., probably due to nutritional disturbances in early youth. Stature is estimated at five feet six inches.

Other representatives of the Boskop type which have since been discovered are the Zitzikama woman (1921) with a cranial capacity of about 1,750 c.c., the remarkably pedomorphic Fish Hoek (1928) skeletal remains with a cranial capacity of 1,600 c.c., the Matjes River (1929-34) skeletons with cranial capacities varying from 1,400 c.c. to 1,664 c.c., the Springbok Flats skeleton (1929) with a cranial capacity of 1,500 c.c., the Cape Flats (1929) skull with a cranial capacity of 1,230 c.c., and the Plettenberg Bay skeleton (1931-32).

The Cape Flats skull, found on the Cape Peninsula some 15 miles south of Cape Town is remarkably australoid in its supraorbital ridges and other cranial markings. Drennan, its discoverer, considers it to be a refined advanced version of Saldanha man. It was associated with paleoliths of Stillbay and Wilton industry.

Another extremely interesting type of fossil man found in South Africa is represented by the Florisbad skull (1932). Associated with the cranial remains were artifacts of Mousterian-Levalloisian affinities, and the remains of extinct fauna which endow this skull with, at the least, a Middle Pleistocene age. It thus antedates the Boskop type. The restored skull (Figure 150) exhibits a rather flattish neanderthaloid frontal region with markedly forward and laterally projecting supraorbital toruses. While broader than in Neanderthal man the torus is not continuous as in the latter but is interrupted over the nasal region. The narrow nasal bones are slightly elevated at the

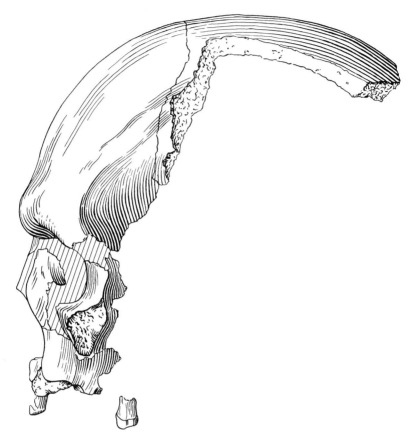

Figure 150. The Florisbad skull. Right lateral view reversed. (From a cast and photographs.)

internasal suture, and the root of the nose is deeply recessed under the overhanging supranasal region. The face is somewhat prognathic. The single much worn tooth recovered, a very long-rooted upper third molar with fused roots, is not in any way remarkable.

The Florisbad skull bears some striking resemblances to the Rhodesian and Neanderthal types, and it has been suggested that Florisbad man represents a type transitional between these palanthropic types and neanthropic man. Florisbad man is conceived to be ancestral to the Boskopoid type, a type which is thought to have ranged from the Cape to Kenya, and from the Indian coast across Central Africa, and which has its modern representatives in the Bushman-Hottentots. The latter are, in fact, simply small Boskopoids.

Galloway sees in the Australoid Florisbad-Boskop types close resemblances to the Wadjak, Keilor, and modern Australian types.

The large brain case and small face of the Boskopoid type has
caused Drennan to suggest that this phenomenon is due to fetalization (pedomorphosis or neoteny), that is to say, the process whereby
the young features of the ancestor are retained in the adult stage of
the descendant. He has further suggested that this process affords a
possible explanation of the mechanism whereby palanthropic was
transformed into neanthropic man. In line with this reasoning Buxton
and De Beer had earlier pointed out that neanthropic man could be
regarded as descended by fetalization (neoteny) from a juvenile stage
of the neanderthaloid type.

Fetalization implies a relative retardation in the rate of body development as compared with the rate of reproductive development,
so that the body does not pass through as many developmental stages
in the descendant as it did in that of the ancestor. Bolk and De Beer
have cited such features as the relatively great size and weight of the
brain, the anterior position of the foramen magnum, brachycephaly,
the character of the cranial flexure, the retarded closure of the cranial
sutures, the absence of brow ridges, the retarded development of the
dentition, the flatness of the face, hairlessness of the body, light color
of the skin, and a number of other features, as evidence of fetalization
in man. That fetalization is a genuine phenomenon there can be little
doubt. As a factor in the evolution and differentiation of man it is
discussed at some length in the next chapter.

Between 1940 and 1942 a Middle Stone Age skull was found in
the Ingwavuma district in the Border Cave in the Lebombo Mountains, South Africa, together with some other human skeletal fragments, and those of an infant of about three months. The Ingwavuma
skull consists of the partial cranium of an adult of about 30 years, of
maximum length 195-200 mm., maximum breadth 140-142 mm., and
auricular-bregmatic height 115 mm. Cranial thickness varies from 5
to 9 mm. Estimated cranial capacity is 1,450 cc. A weak supraorbital
torus is present, together with rather massive superciliary eminences.
Associated were found artifacts of Pietersburg industry, an industry
occurring abundantly in the central area of the Transvaal; there were
some of Levallois technique, and also some Stillbay lanceheads. The
skull compares with the Springbok Flats, which is the only other skull
found associated with artifacts of Pietersburg culture, and with Fish
Hoek which belongs to the closely related Stillbay culture. Morpho-

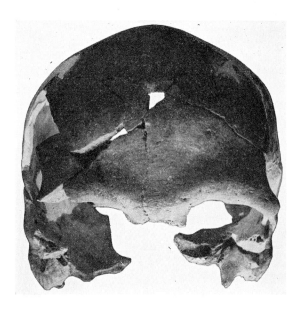

A

→

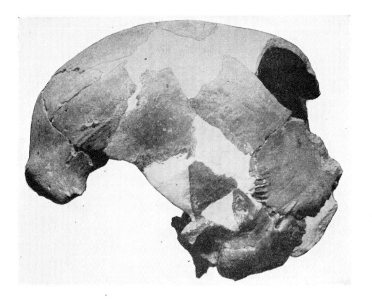

B

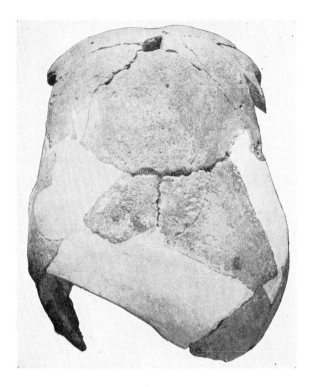

C

Figure 151. The Ingwavuma skull. A, Frontal view. B, Left lateral view. C, Vertical view. (From Wells, Courtesy, *Am. J. Phys. Anthrop.*)

←

logically the Ingwavuma skull stands between the Florisbad and Boskop types.

Without much doubt, then, it may be said that these Boskopoid types stand in the direct line of Bushman-Hottentot ancestry, and that among living ethnic groups the Bushman is perhaps the best provided with fossil ancestors reaching back to a fairly respectable antiquity.

India, Burma, and Thailand have also yielded definite evidence of the handicrafts of early Pleistocene man, some of whom were possibly of neanthropic type, while others were of the type embraced within the pithecanthropoid group, which types and their cultures or industries extended from China and Java into Burma and India.

Incomplete evidence of the existence of Neanderthaloid types in North Africa comes to us in the form of the left half of the maxilla and several teeth from a cave near Tangier. And much further east, from Haua Fteah on the northern Coastal district of Cyrenaica, again in the form of a fragment of the left half of a mandible of which the ramus and part of the body, broken away at about PM_1, and with M_1 and M_3 *in situ*. The radiocarbon date for the Haua Fteah mandible is 34,000 ± 2800 years. The associated industry was Levalloisian-Mousterian, and the geological evidence indicates a Würm II-III interstadial age.

There are also several other sites in North Africa which have yielded implements of Mousterian type, the most typical of which is at Gafsa.

$\rightarrow$

Figure 152. Distribution and Suggested Relationships of the Cultural Traditions of Early Man. Reproduced from K. P. Oakley, *Man the Tool-Maker*, by permission of the Trustees of the British Museum (Natural History), London.

Broken lines have been drawn wherever the connections or time-ranges are mainly speculative.

An encircled letter plotted in relation to the name of a culture shows that fossil remains of a bearer of the tradition have been found in deposits of the age and location indicated. Thus in the European Acheulian Ⓤ indicates the skull found in deposits dating from the end of the second interglacial, at Swanscombe, Kent.

The following is a key to the localities of fossil man:

A, Makapan Limeworks (S. Africa); B, Sterkfontein (South Africa); C, Ternifine (Algeria); D, Kanjera (Kenya); E, Saldanha (S. Africa); F, Florisbad (S. Africa); G, Broken Hill (N. Rhodesia) and Eyasi (Tanganyika); H, Haua Fteah (Cyrenaica); I, Singa (Sudan), Boskop and Matjes River (S. Africa); J, Fish Hoek (S. Africa); K, Sangiran (Java); L, Choukoutien (near Pekin); M, Trinil (Java); N, Galilee; O, Tabun, Mt. Carmel; P, Skhul Cave, Mt. Carmel; Q, Ngandong, Solo River (Java); R, Hotu Cave (Iran); S, Wadjak (Java); T, Heidelberg (Germany); U, Swanscombe (Kent); V, Steinheim (Germany); W, Fontéchevade (France); X, Ehringsdorf (Germany); Y, Gibraltar; Z, La Chapelle-aux-Saints (France); α, Châtelperron and Combe Capelle (France); β, Cro-Magnon (France); γ Predmost (Czechoslovakia); δ, Chancelade (France); ε Cheddar and Aveline's Hole (Somerset), Whaley (Derbyshire).

The remains from A and B belong to Australopithecus; those from K, L, M, and possibly C and T to the *Pithecanthropus* group of men; those from Y and Z to the Neanderthal group; those from E, G, H, N, O, P, Q, V and X are Neanderthaloids showing various degrees of affinity to *Homo sapiens;* remains from D, F, I, J, R, α-ε are referable to *Homo sapiens*.

A possible example of a population descended from a cross between a Neanderthal and a neanthropic type is the North African
Afalou type.

Afalou man is known from some 50 skeletons from Afalou bou
Rummel. These were recovered from a rock-shelter site of Upper
Pleistocene age, where they were found associated with implements
of Oranian (Capsian) culture. Implements of Oranian culture are
closely related to those of Aurignacian origin in Europe. Another
series of the same type, associated with Capsian culture, comes from
Mechta el 'Arbi.

The Afalou type closely resembles the European physical type of
the Middle and Late Aurignacian, that is to say, Cro-Magnon man.
Except for the fact that the nasal aperture is broader, and the upper
face and the length of the vault are slightly shorter, and the latter is
slightly higher, in Afalou than in Cro-Magnon, the two series are in all
other respects remarkably similar.

The fossilized skeleton of an Upper Pleistocene Negroid type
found at Asselar, in the center of the Sahara Desert, some 400 kilometers northeast of Timbuktu, is of some interest because the type is
not unlike that of the Nilotic type living in Africa today. There can
be little reasonable doubt that most African types were already differentiated before the Upper Pleistocene.

Bearing upon this matter of the probable early differentiation of
human ethnic groups is the interesting find made in the Upper Cave
at Chou K'ou Tien of ten human skeletons, which yielded three well
preserved skulls. One skull is of an old male, and this presents the
appearance of an Archaic White or Ainu-like type. Weidenreich thinks
of the "Old Man" as a prototypic Mongoloid; Hooton as more closely
resembling a primitive European white. The second skull is of a
middle-aged woman, and this looks like the skull of an Eskimo. The
third skull, that of a young woman, resembles the contemporary Melanesian type. Weidenreich comments, "The surprising fact is not the
occurrence of palaeolithic types of modern man which resemble racial
types of today but their assemblage in one place and even in a single
family, considering that these types are found today settled in far
remote regions."

The occurrence of these three types within the same Upper Paleolithic population would appear to constitute yet another evidence of
the antiquity of ethnic mixture. It would be difficult to account for
such marked variability within a small breeding population upon any
other hypothesis. It requires, however, to be pointed out, that this

variability does not necessarily mean that Archaic White, Eskimoid, and Melanesoid ethnic groups, entered into the production of these types, but it does mean that admixture between morphologically different ethnic groups most probably occurred, at least to throw up the Eskimoid and Melanesoid types. The "Old Man" probably represents the original type of the group with which the newcomers mixed.

The Singa Skull. In 1924, a fossilized human braincase was found in the river bed at Singa in the Blue Nile Province of the Anglo-Egyptian Sudan. The fossil remains of extinct mammals were found in the same bed, but repeated quarrying had removed any possible evidence of artifacts. These, however, were discovered some 20 miles upstream at Abu Hugar in a fossiliferous limestone conglomerate which is undoubtedly contemporary with the Singa strata. The paleontological, geological, and archeological evidence indicates an Upper Pleistocene age for the Singa skull. The tools consisted of knives, high core scrapers, pounders, but no hand axes. Lumps of red ochre were found in association with the tools. Lacaille considers the industry is most closely paralleled by the advanced Levalloisian or Proto-Stillbay industry of Lochard, South Rhodesia, but that it is somewhat more advanced than the latter, and belongs to the Middle Stone Age of Africa (see Figure 148c).

The Singa skull consists of an almost complete braincase, probably of a middle-aged male. Maximum length is 189 mm. and maximum breadth 155 mm., the cranial index being 82.5, which just makes it brachycranial. Cranial capacity is about 1,575 cc. The skull is large and robust and a supraorbital torus is present. In many respects the Singa skull resembles the Boskop and Bushman skulls, differing from them chiefly in the possession of a supraorbital torus and smaller frontal eminences. The Singa skull resembles the Boskop skull in being both pedomorphic in form and at the same time rather robust. Both skulls are virtually identical in their breadth measurements (155 and 154 mm.) but different in those of length (189 and 205 mm.). Wells, who has described the skull concludes that the Singa skull is related both to the Matjes River and the Boskop type of skull, and that all these skulls represent a proto-Bushman stock modified either by divergent descent or by hybridization.

"Orthogenesis" and "Missing Links." When the time comes for the history of paleoanthropology to be written it may be predicted that two ideas will be found to have been chiefly responsible for the confusion and misdirection of thought which, during the first half of the

twentieth century, characterized the attempt to understand the manner of man's evolution.

The first of these is the conception of orthogenetic evolution, the notion that the evolution of man has been linear, that is to say, in a more or less straight line.

The second is the idea of "the missing link" or "missing links," which, so it was conceived, when recovered would join together the broken parts of a chain of being which would then stretch all the way from some earlier period to our own time. The links being completed in a vertical direction, from below upwards.

Which of these two practically complementary notions has had a more stultifying effect upon the development of our understanding of man's evolution it would be difficult to say. Together their effects have been serious.

The conditioning effect upon students of man's evolution, of such pretty 19th century demonstrations as Marsh's representation of the evolution of the horse neatly arranged in a convincing and orderly succession of types from the tiny Eocene *Eohippus* to the modern horse *Equus* cannot be overestimated. The fact that such a linear arrangement is to a considerable extent arbitrary and puts the chart before the horse, was, and still tends to be, overlooked. A scattergram may be arbitrarily abstracted into one or more straight lines, but it would be quite false to assume that the scattered dots had so arranged themselves. It would also be false to assume that all the dots through which the upper part of the line passed were produced later than those in the region of the lower segment.

Yet the scattering and criss-crossing of variability which occurs during the evolutionary process is vastly more complicated than the most complex of scattergrams. Evolution does not proceed in a straight line, "onward and upward." Evolution is more accurately regarded as a labile reticulate process occurring within the varying environmental matrices of space-time, with repeated intercrossing between different lines, at once convergent and divergent. While very definite trends may be perceived in the evolution of groups, those trends are rarely if ever the result of the addition of variations which add up to straight lines. On the other hand, it is discontinuous particles and processes derived from numerous different sources which are in continuous process of change and interchange in what at times may be likened to a series of eddies, and often resembling a maelstrom, that renders the concept of orthogenetic evolution unacceptable.

In view of the accumulating evidences most students of the evolution of man are in a mood to drop the concept of orthogenetic evolution and the naive idea of "missing links" and to reconsider the evidence on its merits without prejudging it by the measure of some predetermined theory, however hallowed by time or sanctified by authority.

The notion, for example, that neanthropic man represents the culmination, the end product, of a line which commences with *Pithecanthropus* and passes through a Neanderthal phase of development can now be shown to be highly questionable, at least so far as the Neanderthal phase is concerned. The Mount Carmel population, for instance, cannot be accounted for on any other assumption than that they were the products of a neanthropic-neanderthaloid admixture. Such traits as this population exhibited cannot have been produced without the prior existence of a neanthropic type. It is quite likely that the Galilee, Ehringsdorf, and Steinheim types also represent the effects of such admixture, and that they are not the orthogenetic offspring of a neanderthaloid type alone. All these forms of men are, in fact, prior in time to the classic Later Neanderthal type of man, Galilee and Ehringsdorf being of third interglacial and Steinheim of second interglacial date, whereas the Neanderthals proper are of fourth or last glacial age.

From Palestine, France, Germany, and England there is more than strong presumptive evidence of the existence of a neanthropic type before the Later Neanderthal type was fully established.

It is possible, even likely, that a neanthropic type is to be reckoned among the ancestors of Neanderthal man. This is somewhat of a reversal of the traditional view of the relationship, but the facts themselves suggest such an interpretation. It is altogether possible that some proto-Neanderthaloid stock or stocks received infusions of neanthropic genes which then participated in the process of that stock's differentiation into the various neanderthaloid phases which we know. Subsequently these neanderthaloid populations mixed again with neanthropic groups and were eventually absorbed into the neanthropic populations.

The origins of the proto-neanderthaloids are to be looked for in some such stock as the *Pithecanthropus-Sinanthropus* group, through a form possibly such as Solo man, with early representatives such as the first interglacial Mauer and possibly *Africanthropus* types.

The picture which emerges from the evidence as we now have it, quite upsets the older notions of early man recently off the ape-stem waiting for evolution, as it were, to shove him by a series of graduated pushes in an upward direction into a more advanced type. We perceive, rather, a complicated reticular development of human types to a very large extent brought about by such factors as mutation, natural selection, genetic drift, isolation, and hybridization, each of them processes which are at work upon mankind at the present time. Indeed, if we would understand the nature of the processes which were involved in the evolution of man in the past we can do no better than study those which are operative today in producing the diversification and unification of mankind. We shall discuss this subject further in Chapter VI. Before doing so we may conclude the present one with a discussion of early man in America.

Early Man in the Americas. The evidence of archeology and the character of the human skeletal remains thus far discovered indicate that man first arrived in the Americas about 25,000 years ago. The evidence available at the present time strongly suggests that the first Americans entered North America from Siberia, passing across the Bering Straits into Alaska, a distance today of some 56 miles. This distance was certainly much less when the first men to cross over into what is now Alaska navigated it. In winter, when the ice forms, it is possible to walk across the Straits, and it is at any other time easily navigable by boat. Prior to the Eskimo, who arrived in skin boats, man probably reached Alaska by way of the land bridge resulting from the lowered sea level, caused by water being locked in the glaciers.

The crossing of the Bering Straits on foot in modern times has not only been achieved by man, but by man with his sled and sixteen dogs! In February 1938 Dr. John P. Harrington, ethnologist of the Smithsonian Institution at Washington, is reported by the *New York Times* (27 February 1938) as having received a letter from Captain Max Gottschalk of Nome in which he stated that in March 1913, "with my sled, its load of fur and food, and sixteen dogs," he successfully completed the walk between North America and Asia.

The news report states that "It took Gottschalk two and a half days to reach Big Diomede Island, traveling at an angle over the moving ice to allow for the northward current. 'After feeding and resting the dogs,' he says, 'I struck out for Little Diomede Island, which is close by, and easily made it, as the ice between the two islands is grounded.'

"Bill Shroeder, a white man who lived on Little Diomede, followed on snowshoes. He fell through a floe. Gottschalk rescued him, took him back twenty-five miles to Little Diomede Island, where he died.

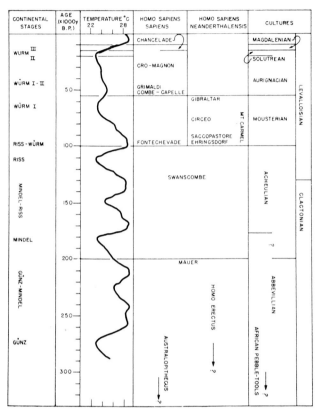

Figure 153. Temperature variations of the glacial Pleistocene and correlation with continental stages, fossil hominids, and industries. The time-scale in this figure is preferred by many to that given in Table VII. (From Emiliani, Courtesy, *Science*.)

Setting out anew, Gottschalk reached Shishmarof six and a half days later, seventy-five miles up the coast from Cape Prince of Wales. 'After resting myself and dogs for several days I left Shishmarof for Nome, 225 miles away by the coast Winter trail,' he adds. His parting shot is that he would never undertake the feat again because of its perils."

The original peopling of America probably took place in a series of waves of immigration, the repeating waves of immigrants subsequently becoming dispersed over the length and breadth of America to the extreme tip of South America, Tierra del Fuego, and the islands south of that, the Navarino Islands. These waves of immigrants probably represented different ethnic groups mostly of Mongoloid type, while a few others may have been of Caucasoid type. This, at least, is what the physical characters of the Indian population of the Americas suggest.

Human skeletal remains, and the evidences of extinct cultures, associated with the remains of extinct species of animals, have been found in North and South America, and recently in Mexico. In the case of the skeletal material both the geological evidence and that relating to the association with extinct animals has been open to some question. The association of cultural artifacts with such animals is, however, indisputable, and it can therefore only be a matter of time before the skeletal remains of early inhabitants of the Americas are found together with those of extinct mammals such as the great bison, camel, horse, mastodon, and ground sloth. Since it is at present not exactly clear when these animals became extinct—it has been suggested that the mastodon may have become extinct less than 1,000 years ago—it is necessary to proceed with great caution in assigning an age to any human remains found in association with them. Ground sloth and great bison had, however, almost certainly died out about 10,000 years ago, the camel possibly earlier. The horse originated in America, spread to the Old World, became extinct in the New World, and was later reintroduced into the New World by the Spaniards. It is, then, possible to assign different cultural artifacts to human beings who must have lived contemporaneously with the animals with whose remains such artifacts have been found. Taken in conjunction with the geological data reasonably accurate determinations of age may be made.

The Natchez Pelvis. Perhaps the most interesting of skeletal remains found in North America is represented by a hip bone which was discovered at Natchez in Mississippi in the year 1845. This bone was recovered from a clayey deposit in a ravine cut by a tributary in a high terrace of yellow loam or loess. The bone was found under the loam together with the bones of extinct ground sloths, horse, mastodon, bison, and other extinct mammals. Charles Lyell, the English geologist, who visited the site shortly after its discovery, calculated that the deposit from which the bone was recovered was more than 100,000 years old. Hence, he conceived that the bone might easily have been intruded into the deposit in which it was found. In view of the uniqueness of the find he concluded, "it is allowable to suspend our judgment as to the high antiquity of the fossil."

In 1895 Thomas Wilson of the National Museum of Washington, having read Carnot's 1893 paper on the fluorine method of dating fossil bones, caused a fluorine analysis to be made of portions of the

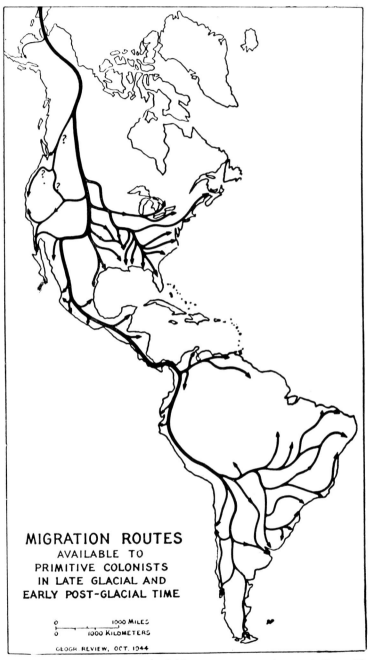

MIGRATION ROUTES
AVAILABLE TO
PRIMITIVE COLONISTS
IN LATE GLACIAL AND
EARLY POST-GLACIAL TIME

Figure 154. Migration routes available to primitive colonists in Late Glacial and Early Post-Glacial Time. (From Sauer. Courtesy, *Geographical Review*.)

Natchez innominate and mylodon bones. This was done by a chemist at the U.S. Geological Survey, on duty at the National Museum. The results obtained led Wilson to conclude that "The human bone is in a higher state of fossilization than is that of the mylodon." But Wilson's paper was speedily forgotten, not being rediscovered until 1951.

Figure 155. Map of areas of Indian culture and principal tribes in North America. (From Collier. Courtesy of Institute of Ethnic Affairs.)

Figure 156. Map of areas of Indian culture and principal tribes in South America. (From Collier. Courtesy of Institute of Ethnic Affairs.)

Meanwhile, in 1948 the author of the present volume, through the courtesy of the Philadelphia Academy of Natural Sciences, took with him to England some pieces of the Natchez bones which, through the kindness of Dr. K. P. Oakley, were submitted to the Government Chemist at London, whose results were then reported by Montagu in 1955. The figures from the Wilson report of 1895 and from the Montagu report of 1955 are as follows:

	Fluorine *Per cent*		Phosphoric Acid *Per cent*	
	Wilson	Montagu	Wilson	Montagu
Natchez innominate	0.38	0.88	20.77	26.2
Mylodon harlani	0.28	0.99	26.59	20.1

These results are in fairly good agreement. Variations between 0.2 and 0.4 per cent for fluorine and 20 to 26 per cent for phosphoric acid may well be encountered in a single specimen. From the above results it will be seen that the Natchez innominate contained a greater amount of fluorine than the mylodon bone. Hence, the probabilities are that the Natchez pelvis is older than that of the associated mylodon. Since the ground sloth *Mylodon harlani* became extinct at least 11,000 years ago, the Natchez human pelvic bone must be assigned at least as great an antiquity, and is probably older.

Midland Man. The only other human skeletal remains of considerable antiquity to be found in North America is represented by the find made near Midland in West-Central Texas in June 1953. This

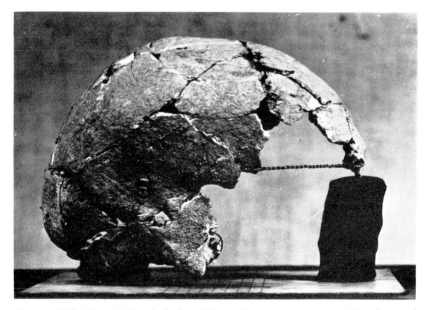

Figure 157. The Midland skull. (From Stewart. Courtesy, University of Texas Press.)

Figure 158. Folsom point and associated bison ribs imbedded in matrix. Folsom, New Mexico. (Photo, Denver Museum of Natural History.)

consists of braincase broken in many fragments with facial and basal portions missing, two portions of the maxilla with seven teeth *in situ,* and a third right molar, two fragmentary ribs, and three metacarpals. The skull is probably that of a female, who at the time of death was about thirty years of age. Projectile points, grinding stones, and a cut bone were found in association.

The discovery was made in a horizon which is pre-Folsom, and radiocarbon dating of the carbon extracted from one of the two associated hearths yielded a date of 20,400 ± 900. Uranium dates for fossil bones from the same locality vary from 15,000 to 19,000 years. Hence, Midland Man is older than 10,000 years and may be about 20,000 years old.

Since the second quarter of the nineteenth century many discoveries of stone implements in association with extinct mammals have been made in the United States, but until recent years when archeological investigations under scientifically satisfactory conditions have become comparatively frequent, such earlier finds were dismissed as doubtful owing to the scientifically unsatisfactory conditions under which they were made. Some of the earlier discoveries, we now have every reason to believe, were probably quite sound. There is, however, no need to speak of them here. In this place we may briefly refer to the few discoveries which are accepted by the majority of scientists as above suspicion. One of the most important of these to date is the discovery near Folsom, New Mexico, in the summers of 1926 and 1927 of peculiar fluted projectile points. In 1927 such a point was found imbedded in the matrix between the ribs of an extinct bison (Figure 158). These points, characterized by longitudinal channels or fluting on each face extending from the base towards the point, have since been found at a number of different sites, the most important of these being the Lindenmeier site in northern Colorado; to this latter site an age of between 9,000 and 10,000 years has been assigned. It is today generally believed that the roughly flaked points found in the Sandia Cave, in Las Huertas Canyon, New Mexico, are not less than 25,000 years old. The Tule Springs site at Vegas Wash in Southern Nevada, with its split, broken, and sometimes burned bones of the camel and mammoth, together with human artifacts, gives every indication of being yet another ancient resting-place of early man. Radiocarbon dating has yielded a calculation of "more than 23,800 years." At still

TABLE VIII

SOME NORTH AMERICAN SITES ASSOCIATED WITH PREHISTORIC MAN

Site	Locality	Years Ago
Borax Lake	Borax Lake, California	4,000 to 7,000
Pinto Basin	Riverside County, California	7,000 to 9,000
Lake Mohave	Lake Mohave, Southeastern California	7,000 to 9,000
Gypsum Cave	Frenchman Mountains, east of Las Vegas, Nevada	7,500 to 9,500
Signal Butte	Near Scottsbluff, western Nebraska	8,000 to 10,000
Russell Cave	Jackson County, Alabama	8,160 ± 300
Simonsen	Simonsen, near Quimby, Iowa	8,430 ± 540
Lindenmeier	South of Colorado-Wyoming boundary, northern Colorado	9,000 to 10,000
Cochise	Whitewater Draw, northwest of Douglas, southeastern Arizona	9,000 to 15,000
Fort Rock Cave	Fort Rock, Oregon	9,188 ± 480
Lubbock	Lubbock, Texas	9,883 ± 350
Folsom	Near Folsom, New Mexico	10,000 to 12,000
Great Salt Lake	Great Salt Lake, Utah	10,000 to 15,000
Natchez	Natchez, Mississippi	11,000 +
Clovis-Portales	Between Clovis and Portales, central-eastern New Mexico	12,000 to 16,000
Ventana Cave	Castle Mountains, southern Arizona	15,000
Midland	Near Midland, west-central Texas	15,100 to 22,000
Sandia	Northern part of Sandia Mountains	15,000 to 25,000
Tule Springs	Near Las Vegas, southeastern Nevada	23,800 ±
Santa Rosa Island	Santa Rosa Island, California	29,650 ± 2,500
Lewisville	Lewisville, Denton County, Texas	37,000 +

Figure 159. Map of North America showing the principal sites from which archeologic evidences of ancient cultures have been recovered. (From Wormington. Courtesy Denver Museum of Natural History.)

→

ALASKA:
1. The Brooks Range
2. The Campus Site (Fairbanks)
3. The Iyatayet Site (Cape Denbigh)
4. The Trail Creek Sites

CANADA:

Alberta
1. Cereal
2. Edmonton
3. Peace River

Saskatchewan
1. Mortlach

Ontario
1. The Brohm Site
2. George Lake
3. Manitoulin Island

Northwest Territories
1. Great Bear Lake
2. The Pointed Mountain Site

Yukon
1. The Engigstciak Site

MEXICO:
1. Tepexpan
1. Santa Isabel Iztapan
1. Tequixquiac
2. Tamaulipas

UNITED STATES:

ALABAMA
1. The Quad Site
2. Russell Cave

ARIZONA
1. Cochise Sites
2. The Lehner Site
2. The Naco Site
3. Ventana Cave

CALIFORNIA
1. The Borax Lake Site
2. Lake Mohave
3. Lower Klamath Lake (The Narrows)
4. The Pinto Basin
5. Santa Rosa Island
6. The Stahl Site (Little Lake)

COLORADO
1. The Claypool Site
2. The Dent Site
3. The Lindenmeier Site
4. The Linger Site
5. The Uncompahgre Plateau
4. The Zapata Site

FLORIDA
1. Melbourne
2. Vero

ILLINOIS
1. The Modoc Rock Shelter

IOWA
1. Turin

KENTUCKY
1. The Parrish Site

MASSACHUSETTS
1. The Bull Brook Site

MINNESOTA
1. The Browns Valley Man Locality
2. The Minnesota Man Locality

MISSISSIPPI
1. The Natchez Pelvis Locality

MISSOURI
1. Graham Cave
2. The Nebo Hill Sites

MONTANA
1. The MacHaffie Site

NEBRASKA
1. The Allan Site
2. The Meserve Site
1. The Lime Creek Site
1. The Red Smoke Site
3. The Scottsbluff Bison Quarry

NORTH CAROLINA
1. The Hardaway Site

NEVADA
1. Fishbone Cave
2. Gypsum Cave
1. Leonard Rockshelter
2. Tule Springs

NEW MEXICO
1. Bat Cave
2. Burnet Cave
3. The Clovis-Portales Area
4. The Folsom Site
5. The Lucy Site
6. Manzano Cave
3. The Milnesand Site
7. The Rio Grande Sites
8. The San Jon Site
6. Sandia Cave
1. The Wet Leggett Site

OREGON
1. Catlow Cave No. 1
2. Fort Rock Cave
3. The Klamath Lake Area
4. Odell Lake
5. The Paisley Caves
6. Wikiup Damsite No. 1

PENNSYLVANIA
1. The Shoop Site

SOUTH DAKOTA
1. The Ray Long Site (Angostura Basin)

TEXAS
1. Abilene
2. Colorado (Lone Wolf Creek)
3. Freisenhahn Cave
4. The Lipscomb Site
5. The Lubbock Site
6. The McClean Site
7. Miami
8. The Plainview Site
9. The Scharbauer Site (Midland)

UTAH
1. Danger Cave
2. Black Rock Cave
2. Dead Man Cave
3. Promontory Cave

VERMONT
1. The Reagan Site

VIRGINIA
1. The Williamson Site

WASHINGTON
1. Lind Coulee

WYOMING
1. Agate Basin
2. The Jimmy Allan Site
3. The Finley Site
4. The Horner Site

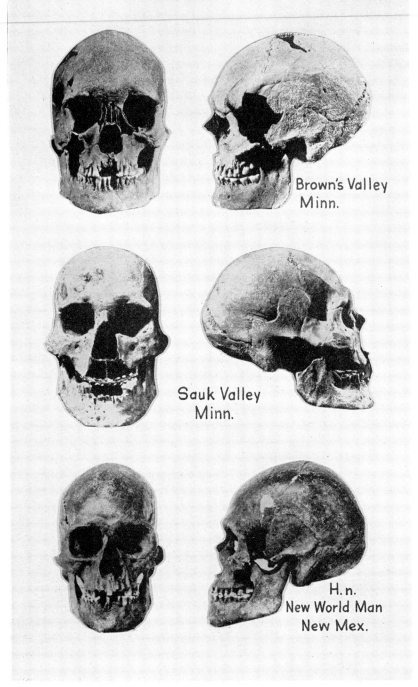

Figure 160. Pre-Columbian Indian types. *Top:* Brown's Valley man, Minnesota. *Center:* Sauk Valley man, Minnesota. *Bottom:* New World man, Cimarron, New Mexico. (Photos Courtesy, Prof. A. E. Jenks and Prof. C. E. Snow.)

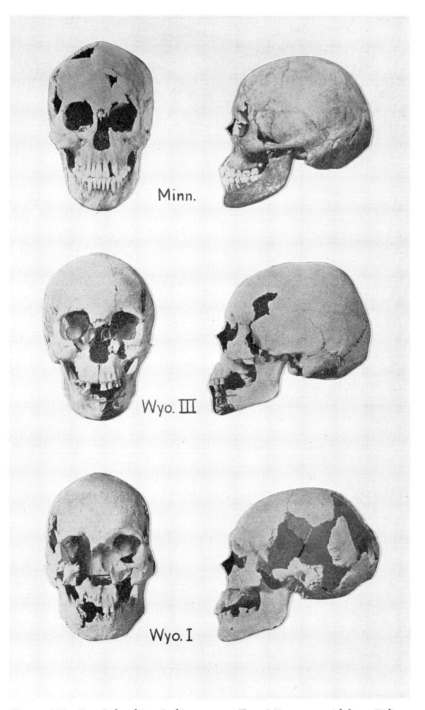

Figure 161. Pre-Columbian Indian types. *Top:* Minnesota girl from Pelican Valley, Minnesota. *Center:* Wyoming III, female from Tarrington. *Bottom:* Wyoming I, male from Tarrington. (Photos Courtesy, Prof. A. E. Jenks and Prof. C. E. Snow.)

another site, on Santa Rosa Island, some 45 miles off the coast of Southern California, a concentration of burned mammoth bones, suggesting that they may have been butchered for a "barbecue," associated with one chipped tool, yielded a radiocarbon date of 29,650 ±2,500 years. Thus, through his artifacts, but not through his skeletal remains, we have definite knowledge of man's existence in North America possibly 35,000 years ago and at least 11,000 years ago.

Some of the better substantiated sites and the ages assigned to them are listed in Table VIII.

These represent but a sampling of the sites which have been investigated, there are many more. Claims which have been made for the antiquity of skeletal remains such as those described as Minnesota man, and for so-called primitive traits in these skeletal remains, cannot be critically supported.

The Punin skull discovered at Punin in Ecuador in 1923 under conditions suggesting considerable antiquity, raises a very interesting question. This skull resembles no type so much as that of the Australian aboriginal. So far only one such skull has been found. On the face of it it does not seem likely that this skull represents a sport or extreme variation not peculiar to the population from which it sprung. This gives rise to the remote possibility of an Australoid contribution to the formation of some part of the South American Indian population.

With reference to this possibility it may be mentioned that between 1835 and 1840 P. W. Lund, a well-known Danish explorer examined some 800 caves in the district of Lagôa Santa in the province of Minas Geraes of eastern Brazil. Six of these yielded the skeletal remains of man. Many of the bones appeared to be highly mineralized and some of the skeletal remains were found in association with those of extinct animals. Lund was convinced of the high antiquity of the remains. The skulls are interesting. Though dominantly of American Indian type they bear some resemblances to the Australian aboriginal type. The average skull is dolichocranial (c.i., 70.5), hypsicranial (high-vaulted, 80.2), broad-palated, broad-cheeked, and prognathic. Viewed from the back (norma occipitalis) the skull is pentagoid in form, with a tendency to the formation of a high crest in the midline sagittally.

The discovery, in 1935, in the Confins cave in the Lagôa Santa region of a complete skeleton, again under conditions suggesting a great antiquity, reopens the question of the antiquity of the Lagôa Santa skeletal remains. The Confins skeleton lay in an extended position, claw marks of rodents on the surface of some of the bones indicate that the individual died where he lay, until he was naturally buried.

The undisturbed stratum in which the skeleton was found bore the remains of extinct animals. There can be little doubt of the antiquity of Confins man, but dating is difficult owing to the lack of an adequate chronology. The skull is clearly of American Indian type, and the sub-nasal prognathism assists to give it a very Mongoloid appearance. The skull is less markedly pyramidal in the vault than most of the earlier Lagôa Santa finds, it is, however, quite clearly of Lagôa Santa type.

On the basis of the fact that certain cultural traits are found both in Oceania and South America, and that it is known that Polynesian navigators traversed great distances in their canoes, it has been suggested that the west coast of South America may have been reached by some boatloads of Pacific Islanders. This is certainly a possibility. However, it would seem most unlikely that such possible trans-Pacific voyages could have been made early and often enough seriously to affect either the populations or the cultures of the New World.

In February 1947 Dr. Helmut de Terra, American geologist, and Dr. Hans Lundberg, Canadian geologist, using an electrical detecting device, made an important discovery of a human skeleton near the village of Tepexpan, in Mexico. At a depth of 1.12m. (three feet and eight inches) in a clearly defined undisturbed layer of pluvial clay they found a remarkably well preserved mesocephalic human skull together with some 50 other portions of the skeleton. The age of the layer in which the skeleton lay has been estimated at between 10,000 and 15,000 years. We have, then, in Tepexpan man among the oldest geologically datable human remains so far discovered in the Americas (Figure 162 bottom).

The almost complete skull is that of an adult male of between 55 and 65 years of age. From the remainder of the skeleton it has been calculated that stature reached 170 cm. (five feet seven inches). Cranial capacity is 1,540 c.c., and the cranial index is 79.89, that is to say, mesocranic. Tepexpan man is the roundest-headed American Indian of early date thus far discovered. That he represents a typical American Indian, though somewhat rounder-headed than most, there can be not the least doubt. Tepexpan man shows no remarkable skeletal features.

One of the best authenticated discoveries of prehistoric man in South America was made in 1937 by Junius Bird. This is the discovery in the Palli Aike Cave in Patagonia of numerous cultural artifacts associated with human skeletal remains as well as the bones of extinct ground sloth and horse. In this and in another cave some 20 miles west the cultural debris was found mixed with animal bones which showed

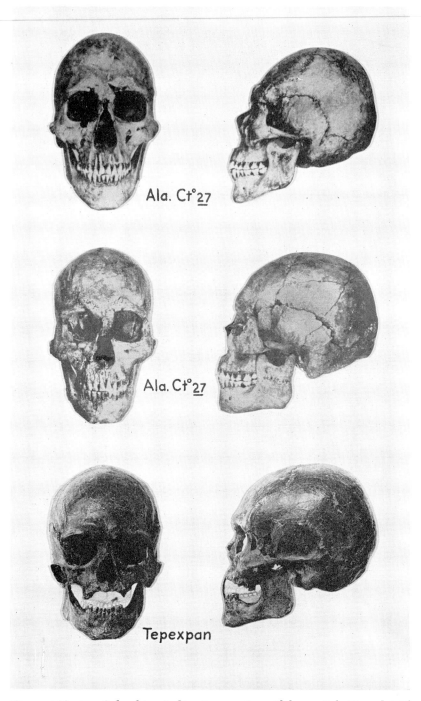

Figure 162. Pre-Columbian Indian types. *Top:* Alabama Sub Mound CT°
27, burial 83, male. *Center:* Alabama Sub Mound CT° 27, burial 84, male.
Bottom: Tepexpan man, Valley of Mexico, male. (Photos Courtesy, Alabama
Museum, and Prof. C. E. Snow.)

clear evidence of treatment by man-made fire and pressure. The age of these remains yielded by the radiocarbon method is 8,639 ± 450 years.

At the present time the evidence indicates that the migration of man into the Americas commenced toward the end of the last great glaciation at a period corresponding to the Solutrean of the Upper Paleolithic of Europe. Further discoveries may show that migration commenced at an earlier period, but at the present time such evidence is wanting, and at most the available evidence permits us to say that the antiquity of man in the Americas is no greater than somewhere between 15,000 and 25,000 years.

METHODS OF DATING

Radiocarbon Dating. The radiocarbon method of dating organic materials was worked out and developed by Professor W. F. Libby at the Institute of Nuclear Physics at the University of Chicago. It was originally not possible to obtain reliable dates by this method beyond 30,000 years, but by a recent refinement of this method it is possible to compute the age of any organic material up to about 70,000 years. This new investigational tool has been particularly useful in the dating of American Indian remains. The method is based on the fact that radioactive carbon (Carbon 14), which is liberated in the atmosphere as a result of the interaction of cosmic rays with nitrogen, is present in all living structures. During the life of the organism an equilibrated and constant percentage of C^{14} is maintained in its carbon structure. This percentage is believed to be the same for every form of life. With death the supply of carbon and C^{14} to the organism abruptly ceases, and the C^{14} atoms disintegrate. It is believed that not only is the concentration of C^{14} the same in all living organisms, but that the rate of C^{14} disintegration after death is also the same. Therefore, if the rate of disintegration of C^{14} can be established for a sample of known age, it becomes possible to check the accuracy of this method of dating. This has been done with considerable success. It has been shown that after 5568 ± 30 years have elapsed one half of the C^{14} atoms have disintegrated. Where formerly some six grams of carbon had to be extracted from specimens before its age could be determined, newer methods have reduced this to about half a gram.

By a most ingenious method the Dutch investigators, Drs. A. Haring and H. de Vries, of Amsterdam and Groningen respectively, have made it possible to determine the age of organic remains up to a period of about 70,000 years. This is done by the method of isotopic enrichment. The CO_2 obtained from the original material is reduced to CO by leading it over zinc at a temperature of $380° \pm 5°$ C. The CO is enriched in five thermal diffusion columns connected in parallel, each column having a length of 430 cm. The enrichment is derived from the abundance of O^{18} in the CO. For the activity measurements the enriched CO is oxidized again by leading it over CuO. Enrichment by a factor of 16 takes about two months, and this enrichment shifts the limit of counting to upwards of 70,000 years.

The Uranium Radiometric Dating Method. A new method for the relative dating of bones and teeth is by radiometric assay of the uranium they may contain. When bones are buried in deposits through which water containing uranium circulates, the calcium atoms in the hydroxyapatite are replaced by those of uranium. The longer the bone is buried the greater the amount of uranium accumulated. The radioactivity of the adsorbed uranium, in the form of the rate of its beta radiations, can be measured since the enamel of a tooth is considerably less absorptive than its dentine, and will therefore be considerably less radioactive, and since fossils from limestone formations and clay accumulate less uranium than those from gravels and sands of the same age, the results obtained must be interpreted with caution, as is the case with the method of fluorine analysis (p. 240). The advantage of the uranium method over the fluorine method is that it does not involve the destruction of the material tested.

The Nitrogen Dating Method. In fresh or recently buried bones the nitrogen content is high, about 4 per cent. With the passage of time, as fluorine increases, nitrogen decreases. Hence, determination of the organic nitrogen content of bones will yield some idea of their relative age. Thus, in a recent (1958) re-determination of the fluorine and nitrogen contents of the bones from several famous sites Oakley obtained the following results:

	Fluorine Per cent	Nitrogen Per cent
Modern bones	0.01	4.0
Neolithic skull	0.3	1.9
Galley Hill skeleton	0.5	1.6
Swanscombe skull	1.7	nil
Fossil mammal bones, Swanscombe gravel	>1.5	traces

The Potassium-Argon Dating Method. This method is still in process of development, but may prove of great importance in the future. Age of organic materials is determined by the ratio of potassium-40 to argon-40 they contain. Potassium-40, a radioactive form of the element, is present in all living things. It decays into argon-40 at the rate of 50 per cent every 1.25 billion years. By determining the amount of potassium-40 that has decayed into argon-40, the passage of time since the specimen had been part of a living system can be determined, since potassium is incorporated into tissues only during life.

A difficulty of the method is that mineral deposits much older than the specimen may have contaminated it, and thus render the age determination dubious. This, however, is a difficulty which need not apply in many cases, and in those in which it does could, possibly, be overcome.

THE CLASSIFICATION OF THE HOMINIDAE

A brief classification of the Hominidae is set out below. This may be used as an alternative to that which has been used in the following pages, or simply as a mnemonic. This brief classification may serve to suggest relationships and also to raise further questions. Some of these may be mentioned here.

Firstly, the admission of *Oreopithecus* to hominid status is still *sub judice*, therefore until the full evidence becomes available the ascription to hominid status remains tentative.

Secondly, the recognition of four genera of australopithecines remains open to some doubt. *Plesianthropus*, at least, may ultimately be demoted to rank as a species of *Australopithecus*.

Thirdly, some workers would be inclined to classify Neanderthal man as a member of the species *erectus*. There is no insuperable objection to such a procedure. It would, in fact, be perfectly legitimate. It should, however, be recognized that the neanderthaloids and neanthropic forms of man were almost certainly not reproductively isolated, and that therefore any specific differences between them must be based on morphological considerations. The suggestion here is that the large size of the brain of the neanderthaloids far outweighs other morphological differences in bringing the neanderthaloids into the species *sapiens* as a subspecies *neanderthalensis*. On this procedure there may be differences of opinion.

A BRIEF CLASSIFICATION OF THE HOMINIDAE

FAMILY HOMINIDAE
  I. SUBFAMILY OREOPITHECINAE
     Genus *Oreopithecus*
     Species *bambolii*

II. SUBFAMILY AUSTRALOPITHECINAE
  Genus *Australopithecus*
  Species *africanus*
  Species *prometheus*
  Genus *Paranthropus*
  Species *crassidens*
  Species *robustus*
  Genus *Plesianthropus*
  Species *transvaalensis*
  Genus *Telanthropus*
  Species *capensis*
  Genus *Zinjanthropus*
  Species *boisei*
  Genus *Meganthropus*
  Species *palaeojavanicus*
III. SUBFAMILY HOMININAE
  Genus *Homo*
  Species *erectus*
  Subspecies *erectus*
  Subspecies *robustus*
  Subspecies *pekinensis*
  Subspecies *soloensis*
  Subspecies *mauritanicus*
  Subspecies *heidelbergensis*
  Species *sapiens*
  Subspecies *rhodesiensis*
  Subspecies *neanderthalensis*
  Subspecies *sapiens*

FOR FURTHER READING, CONSULT:

BIRD, J.: Antiquity and migrations of the early inhabitants of Patagonia, *Geographical Rev.*, 28:250-275, 1938.

———: Before Magellan. *Natur. Hist.*, 41:16-28; 77; 79, 1938.

The official and popular accounts of the discoveries of early man in South America.

BLACK, D.: Asia and the dispersal of the primates. *Bull. Geol. Soc. Am.*, 4: 1925.
A brilliant work on the ecology and dispersal of the primates and early man.

BONIN, G. VON: On the size of man's brain as indicated by skull capacity. *J. Comp. Neurol.*, 59:1-29, 1934.
A lucid and informatively factual study.

BOULE, M., and VALLOIS, H. V.: *Fossil Men.* New York, Dryden Press, 1957.
A standard work on fossil man.

BRAIDWOOD, R. J.: *Prehistoric Men,* 3rd edition. Chicago Natural History Museum Popular Series, Anthropology, No. 37, 1957.
A delightful introduction to the period of man's cultural development before written history began.

BRIGGS, L. C.: *The Stone Age Races of Northwest Africa.* American School of Prehistoric Research, Peabody Museum, Harvard University, Bulletin No. 18, 1955.

A good account, mostly of the Mesolithic and Neolithic, crania of Northwest Africa.

————: *The Living Races of the Sahara Desert.* Papers Peabody Museum of Archaeology and Ethnology, Harvard University, 28:1-217, 1958.
An admirable work.

CLARK, J. D.: *The Prehistory of Southern Africa.* Baltimore, Penguin Books, 1959.
The best account.

CLARK, J. D., and COLE, S.: *Third Pan-African Congress on Prehistory.* London, Chatto & Windurs, 1957.
An invaluable symposium on African Prehistory.

CLARK, W. E. LE GROS: Pithecanthropus in Peking. *Antiquity, 10*:1-5, 1945.
A Review of Weidenreich's "The Skull of *Sinanthropus pekinensis*" which contains, among other things, an excellent discussion of the relationships of the Neanderthaloids to *Pithecanthropus* and *Sinanthropus*.

————: *The Fossil Evidence for Human Evolution.* Chicago, University of Chicago Press, 1955.
A good introduction to paleoanthropology.

COLE, S.: *The Prehistory of East Africa.* Baltimore, Penguin Books, 1954.
A useful survey.

DE VRIES H., and OAKLEY, K. P.: Radiocarbon dating of the Piltdown skull and jaw. *Nature, 184*:224-226, 1959.
The age of the Piltdown skull is shown to be 620 ± 100 years, and the mandible 500 ± 100 years.

EVANS, F. G.: The names of fossil men. *Science, 102*:16-17, 1945.
A constructively valuable criticism of the nomenclature relating to fossil men.

GALLOWAY, A.: Man in Africa in the light of recent discoveries. *South African J. Sc., 34*:89-120, 1937.
An admirable survey up to the date of publication.

————: Physical anthropology in South and East Africa. *Yearbook of Physical Anthropology, 1948. 4*:40-46, 1949.
The survey continued up to date.

HALDANE, J. B. S.: The argument from animals to man: an examination of its validity for anthropology. *J. Roy. Anthropol. Inst., 86*:1-14, 1956.
A brilliant and highly stimulating study.

HARRINGTON, M. R.: Man's oldest date in America. *Natural History, 64*:512-517, 1955.
An illustrated account of the discovery of the Tule Springs site, possibly the oldest camp site in America.

HARING, A., and DE VRIES, H.: Radiocarbon dating up to 70,000 years by isotopic enrichment. *Science, 128*:472-473, 1958.
A detailed account of the method.

HOWELL, E. C.: The evolutionary significance of variation and varieties of "Neanderthal" man. *Quart. Rev. Biol., 32*:330-347, 1957.

————: Upper Pleistocene men of the southwest Asian Mousterian. *Transactions of the Internat. Neanderthal Centennial Congress,* Utrecht, Kemink en Zn, 1958, pp. 185-198.

————: The place of Neanderthal man in human evolution. *Am. J. Phys. Anthropol.,* n.s. 9:379-416, 1951.

————: Pleistocene glacial ecology and the evolution of "classic Neanderthal" man. *Southwest. J. Anthrop.*, 8:377-410, 1952.

————: Upper Pleistocene stratigraphy and early man in the Levant. *Proc. Amer. Phil. Soc.*, 103:1-65, 1959.

An excellent, informative, and stimulating series of papers on Neanderthal man.

————: The Villafranchian and Human Origins. *Science*, 130:831-844, 1959.

A valuable survey of the earliest hominids and their industries.

HOWELLS, W. W.: *Mankind In The Making.* New York, Doubleday & Co., 1959.

An ably written introduction to physical anthropology for the general reader and student.

———— (editor): Early man in the Far East. *Stud. Phys. Anthropol.*, 1:1949. Philadelphia, Wistar Institute.

An important series of studies by five experts.

HRDLIČKA, A.: *The Skeletal Remains of Early Man.* Washington, Smithsonian Miscellaneous Collections, Vol. 83, 1930.

An authoritative and most readable account, covering the material up to the year 1930.

————: *Early Man in South America.* Washington, Smithsonian Inst., Bureau of American Ethnology, Bulletin 52, 1912.

The authoritative and most exhaustive work on the subject.

JENNESS, D. (editor): *The American Aborigines, Their Origin and Antiquity.* Toronto, Univ. Toronto Press, 1933.

Ten papers by different authorities of unusual value and interest.

KEITH, A.: *The Antiquity of Man,* 2 vols. London, Williams & Norgate, Ltd., 1929.

A readable text. Its time-scale, however, is far too contracted. The drawings are frequently inaccurate, though the inaccuracies are such as would not in the least impair the reader's appreciation of the points made by the author.

————: *New Discoveries Relating to the Antiquity of Man.* London, Williams & Norgate, Ltd., 1931; New York, Norton, 1931.

The supplement to the above work.

————: *A New Theory of Evolution.* New York, Philosophical Library, 1949.

Stimulating and readable.

————: *Essays on Human Evolution.* London, Watts, 1946.

A highly controversial but stimulating volume of essays.

KOENIGSWALD, G. H. R. VON: *The South African Man-Apes and Pithecanthropus.* Washington, Carnegie Inst., 1942, publication 530, VIII.

A good discussion together with important illustrations.

————: *Meeting Prehistoric Man.* London, Thames & Hudson, 1956.

A valuable, interesting and anecdotal account of von Koenigswald's discoveries, and those of others, of fossil man in Java.

———— and WEIDENREICH, F.: The relationship between Pithecanthropus and Sinanthropus. *Nature*, 144:926-927, 1939.

An authoritative statement.

LEAKEY, L. S. B.: *Adam's Ancestors,* 4th edition. London, Methuen, 1953.

A readable account of the story of fossil man, containing the discoverer's description of the Kanam and Kanjera finds.

————: A new fossil skull from Eyassi, East Africa. *Nature, 138*:1082, 1936.

A valuable description of the skull of *Africanthropus njarasensis.*

LEVIN, G.: Racial and inferiority characters in the human brain. *Am. J. Phys. Anthropol., 22*:345-380, 1937.

A demonstration of the nonexistence of such characters.

LIBBY, W. F.: *Radiocarbon Dating,* 2nd edition. Chicago, University of Chicago Press, 1955.

The standard treatise on radiocarbon dating.

MACALISTER, R. A. S.: *A Textbook of European Archaeology.* Cambridge & New York, Cambridge University Press, 1921.

The best account of the Paleolithic up to the year 1921. Contains excellent descriptions of the physical types of paleolithic man, and is archeologically admirable.

McCOWN, T. D. and KEITH, A.: *The Stone Age of Mount Carmel,* vol. 2. Oxford, The Clarendon Press, 1939.

The complete description of the skeletal remains. For a critical review, see M. F. Ashley Montagu's "Prehistory," *Am. Anthropol.,* n.s., *43*:518-522, 1940.

McCOWN, T. D.: The antiquity of man in South America. (J. H. Steward, editor) in *Handbook of South American Indians,* vol. 6, Washington, Smithsonian Institution, 1950, pp. 1-9.

MacCURDY, G. G. (editor): *Early Man.* Philadelphia, Lippincott, 1930.

An important symposium covering a wide range of material.

A good survey.

MACGOWAN, K.: *Early Man in the New World.* New York, Macmillan, 1950.

A sound popularly written introduction.

MARTIN, P. S., QUIMBY, G. I. and COLLIER, D.: *Indians Before Columbus.* Chicago, Univ. Chicago Press, 1947.

A good introduction for the student to the archeology of North America.

MONTAGU, M. F. ASHLEY: Genetics and the antiquity of man in the Americas. *Man, 43*:131-135, 1943.

An early discussion of how the problem of the antiquity and wanderings of man in the Americas may be approached by means of the genetic analysis of certain traits.

————: The Natchez innominate bone. *Human Biology, 27*:193-201, 1955.

A historical account of the Natchez pelvis together with the results of the fluorine tests which indicate the contemporaneity of this bone, at the very least, with that of the associated ground-sloth *Mylodon harlani.*

———— and OAKLEY, K. P.: The antiquity of Galley Hill man. *Am. J. Phys. Anthrop.,* n.s., *7*:363-384, 1949.

An analysis of the geological, archeological, chemical, and osteological evidence.

MORANT, G. M.: Studies of Palaeolithic Man. *Ann. Eugenics, 1*:257-276, 1926; *2*:318-381, 1927; *3*:337-360, 1928; *4*:109-214, 1930.

A fundamental series of classical studies on the original crania.

OAKLEY, K. P.: *Man the Tool-Maker.* London, British Museum (Natural History), 4th edition, 1958.

An admirably clear and well-illustrated account of the cultures of prehistoric man.

————: Dating fossil man. *Mem. & Proc. Manchester Lit. & Phil. Soc., 98*:1-20, 1957.

An up-to-date account of methods of absolute and relative dating of fossil remains.

———— and C. R. Hoskins: New evidence on the antiquity of Piltdown Man. *Nature*, 165:379-382, 1950.

A detailed account of the comparative fluorine analysis of the Piltdown bones.

———— and Montagu, M. F. Ashley: The Galley Hill Skeleton. *Bull. Brit. Museum (Nat. Hist.)*, 1:25-48, 1949.

A detailed account of the recent investigation of the Galley Hill site and skeleton, which led to the downfall of the latter.

Paterson, D. G.: *Physique and Intellect*. New York, Century Co., 1930.

A first-rate work on the relation, among many other things, of slope of brow and intelligence.

Piveteau, J.: *Primates et Paléontologie Humaine. Traité De Paléontologie*, 7: 1-657. Paris, Masson et Cie., 1957.

The best descriptive work on the primates and human paleontology available.

Roberts, F. H., Jr.: Developments in the problems of the North American Paleo-Indian. In Essays in Historical Anthropology of North America. *Smithsonian Miscellaneous Collections*, 100:51-116, 1940.

An invaluable discussion of the antiquity of man in North America.

Sellards, E. H.: Early man in America: Index to localities and selected bibliography. *Bull. Geol. Soc. Am.*, 51:373-431, 1940.

An indispensable guide.

Škerlj, B.: Were Neanderthalers the only inhabitants of Krapina? *Bull. Scientifique*, (Yugoslavia), 4:44, 1958.

A brief but important paper raising the question of the contemporaneity of the Krapina Neanderthals and *Homo sapiens* in this region.

Stein, L.: *The Infancy of Speech and the Speech of Infancy*. London, Methuen, 1949.

An extraordinarily interesting attempt to reconstruct the evolution of speech in prehistoric man.

Straus, Jr., W. L. and Cave, A. J. E.: Pathology and posture of Neanderthal man. *Quart. Rev. Biol.*, 32:348-363, 1957.

A thorough demolition of the myth of Neanderthal man's alleged knock-kneed, stooped posture.

Swanscombe Committee: Report on the Swanscombe skull. *J. Roy. Anthropol. Inst., Great Britain and Ireland*, 58:17-98, 1938.

The official report.

Thoma, A.: Metissage ou transformation? Essai sur les hommes fossiles de Palestine. *L'Anthropologie*, 61:470-502, 1957; 62:30-52, 1958.

A valuable examination of the probable causes of the variability of the Mount Carmel Neanderthals.

Vallois, H. V., and Movius, Jr., H. (editors): *Catalogue des Hommes Fossiles*. XIXᵉ Congrès Geologique International, Faculté des Sciences, Alger, French North Africa, 1952.

With the aid of 33 collaborators the essential data is provided concerning site, discoverer, type of industry, principal associated fauna, geology and archeology, character of the remains, repository, casts available, and bibliography. Complete up to 1952. An invaluable volume. Not illustrated.

WEIDENREICH, F.: Some problems dealing with ancient man. *Am. Anthropol., 42:* 373-383, 1940.
An excellent discussion.

———: The "Neanderthal Man" and the ancestors of "*Homo Sapiens.*" *Am. Anthropologist, 45:*39-48, 1943.
A valuable discussion of the relations of the Neanderthaloids to modern man.

———: The skull of Sinanthropus Pekinensis; a comparative study on a primitive Hominid skull. *Palaeontologica Sinica, S.d., S.*127, 1943, p. 1-298, 93 plates.
The official and definitive description of the skulls of the *Sinanthropus* group, containing, in addition, a most valuable discussion of the whole problem of the relationships of fossil man. A highly important volume.

———: The Keilor skull; a Wadjak type from Southeast Australia. *Am. J. Phys. Anthropol., 3:*21-32, 1945.
A comparative study of the Keilor, Wadjak, and Australian skull.

———: Giant early man from Java and South China. *Anthropol. Papers Am. Museum Natur. Hist., New York, 40:*1-134, 1945. 12 plates.
Containing the full description of *Meganthropus palaeojavanicus* and *Gigantopithecus blacki,* together with a valuable discussion of the *Pithecanthropus* problem, a good description of *Pithecanthropus robustus,* and the relation of the giant fossil men to the Pithecanthropus group.

———: *Apes, Giants and Man.* Chicago, Univ. Chicago Press, 1946.
One of the most stimulating books on the origin and evolution of man available at the present time.

———: *Anthropological Papers of Franz Weidenreich 1939-1948.* Compiled by S. L. Washburn and D. Wolffson. The Viking Fund, Inc., New York, 1950.
Thirteen of Weidenreich's important shorter papers on paleoanthropology, together with an obituary, and a bibliography of Weidenreich's writings.

———: Morphology of Solo Man. *Anthropol. Papers Am. Museum Natur. Hist., New York, 43:*205-290, 1951. 31 Plates.
The posthumously published and somewhat incomplete, though altogether admirable description of Solo Man.

WEINER, J. S., OAKLEY, K. P., and CLARK, W. E. LE GROS: The solution of the Piltdown Problem. *Bull. Brit. Mus. (Nat. Hist.), 2:*141-146, 1953.
The communication which exposed the Piltdown skull as a "hoax."

——— *et al.:* Further contributions to the solution of the Piltdown problem. *Bull. Brit. Mus. (Nat. Hist.), 2:*227-287, 1955.
The detailed exposure of the Piltdown fraud by twelve experts.

———: *The Piltdown Forgery.* London & New York, Oxford University Press, 1955.
An absorbing scientific "whodunit" by the scientist principally responsible for the exposure of the Piltdown hoax. Extremely valuable for the light it throws on the hoaxer, and the methods developed to test the age of the various Piltdown fragments.

WEINERT, H.: Africanthropus, der neue Affenmenschfund in Ostafrika. *Ztschr. Morphol. u. Anthropol., 38:*18-24, 1939.
A brief account of *Africanthropus njarasensis.*

WECKLER, J. E.: The relations between Neanderthal man and *Homo sapiens. Amer. Anthropol., 56:*1003-1025, 1954.
A stimulating discussion.

WENDORF, F., KRIEGER, A. D., ALBRITTON, C. C., and STEWART, T. D.: *The Midland Discovery*, Austin, University of Texas Press, 1955.

A full account of the Pleistocene human remains from Midland, Texas.

WILSON, T. M.: On the presence of fluorine as a test for the fossilization of animal bones. *Am. Naturalist*, 29:301-317, 439-456, 719-725, 1895.

A long-forgotten study in which the fluorine test was first applied to the dating of fossil man in the form of the Natchez pelvis.

WUNDERLY, J.: The Keilor fossil skull; anatomical description. *Mem. Nat. Museum*, Melbourne, 13:57-69, 1943.

The official very useful description.

WOODWARD, A. SMITH: *The Earliest Englishman*. London, Watts, 1948.

A first hand account of the discovery and possible significance of Piltdown man by its principal proponent. Well illustrated, and peppered with an assortment of quaint views.

WORMINGTON, H. M.: *Ancient Man in North America*, 4th edition. The Denver Museum of Natural History, Denver, Colorado, 1957.

A wholly admirable, thoroughly documented and illustrated account of the archeology of the American Indian.

———: *Prehistoric Indians of the Southwest*. The Denver Museum of Natural History, Denver, Colorado, 1947.

An excellent volume, supplementing the preceding one.

Chapter V

TIME, MORPHOLOGY, AND NEOTENY IN THE EVOLUTION OF MAN

THE DISCUSSION of the evolution of man in terms of morphology while conveying some notion of the physical changes that have progressively led to the differentiation of the varieties of man fails, however, to tell us what some of the *developmental* mechanisms responsible for those changes may have been.

In the preceding chapter we have seen that such sapiens-like forms as Swanscombe and Fontéchevade antedate in time of appearance morphologically more primitive forms such as Neanderthal man. How can this be? If it is true that evolution progresses from the simple to the more complex or more evolved forms, how can a more evolved form in any species appear earlier than a less evolved one?

The terms "simple," "more complex," and "more evolved" beg some rather fundamental questions. The truth is that evolution does not always proceed from the more simple to the more complex. *Sacculina*, which is an active crustacean, in the earlier stages of its existence, swimming about by means of well-developed appendages, degenerates into a parasitic bag in its later existence which remains attached to the abdomen of a crab.

Is sapiens type of man in fact "more complex," "more evolved" than presapiens man? Are thinner skull bones and absence of supraorbital tori, for example, evidences of greater complexity or advancement? For the idea of progressive advancement is implied in these terms. We think not. Evolutionary change has occurred, but with respect to the traits mentioned it would rather seem that it has progressed from the complex to the simpler. These questions are raised here for the reader to consider, but in this chapter we are concerned with a somewhat different question. It is: By what means did man come into being? What was the process or mechanism by which an apelike creature developed or evolved into a man?

We are aware that genetically the evolution of man was brought about by the accumulation of adaptively favorable mutations acted upon by natural and social selection. But what kind of mutations? Adaptively favorable to what?

Commencing with a consideration of the precursors of man we pass backward in time to the Pliocene, a geological epoch that extended over some 12 million years. Man is essentially a Pleistocene form, so that many of the really important changes leading to the advent of man must have occurred mainly within the Pliocene. All the indications are that Africa is the backdrop against which these evolutionary events were enacted. There is some evidence that in Africa during the Pliocene a number of significant climatic changes occurred principally related to rainfall. The withdrawal of the rainfall further and further northward had the effect of converting vast areas of forested land into open savanna, that is, sparsely-treed plains covered with low vegetation. Such environmental changes shifted the zone of adaptation from a life in the forest to one on the open savanna. Forest dwelling animals if they are to survive on the savanna must become adapted to the demands of an environment altogether different from that afforded by the forest. There are many ways in which different mammalian groups have achieved such adaptations, and even different primate groups, such as the bush babies, some lemurs, and baboons, who exhibit quite a variety of adaptations to life on the savanna or on rocky terrain.

In the case of those apelike forms which comprised the "line" that eventually led to man, their meeting of the challenges of the savanna environment, extending over a period of some millions of years, assumed the form—quite fortuitously—of the development of adaptations enabling the individual to compete increasingly more successfully in the struggle for existence. Since the yield of plant foods on the savanna, as compared with the abundant yield of the forest, is small and varies catastrophically with the seasons, it is an advantage to be able to enlarge one's dietary to include animals. Unlike plants which are stationary and have their roots in the earth, animals are mobile and have their roots in their stomachs. Animals require catching. They have to be chased. Only small game would be attempted at first, and thence one could go on to larger enterprises. But whether large or small those individuals who possessed traits that enabled them to gather in an adequate number of animals would be more likely to survive and bequeath their traits to a larger and more successful progeny, than would those not possessing such traits.

The quest for subsistence would undoubtedly have placed a high premium upon the ability to cooperate, not alone in the hunt, but also in the sharing of food, the care of the young, and the care of the old. All these are highly cooperative activities, and those individuals exhibiting such cooperative traits would be more likely to leave progeny than those who did not.

To judge from the australopithecine remains it would appear that the erect posture was one of the first manlike adaptations achieved by man's early ancestors, probably in the Upper Pliocene. The erect posture frees the hands for manipulatory activities which, accompanied by increasing intelligence, enables one to command the environment more effectively. Intelligence, the ability to scan, forecast, solve problems, and make rapid adjustments to rapidly changing conditions, is at a premium. An animal narrowly confined within the walls of his instinctual equipment will not do as well under such challenging conditions as one that is free to use its intelligence unrestricted by preconditioned determinants of behavior or limited to a narrow range of responses. In short, the animal that becomes increasingly freed from its instinctual drives in arriving at decisions, becomes the driver instead of the driven, and under the unrestricted operation of natural selection would tend to be favored for survival as compared with those who tended to live by their instincts.

By means of such a selective process the immediate forerunners of man would have been increasingly freed from the limiting effects of their instinctual drives, so that by the time hominid status would have been attained virtually the last vestiges of that instinctive system of drives would have disappeared. If instinct is lapsed intelligence enabling the animal automatically to make appropriate responses to a limited range of stimuli, man's freedom from such instinctive mechanisms makes him the one creature whose responses to the environment are potentially unlimited. Man is equipped with potentialities for learning whatever he requires to know in order to grow and develop as a fully adjusted human being. In this respect, also his potentialities are unique, with the maximum capacity for phenotypic adjustment. That is to say, man possesses a genetic endowment which makes it possible for him to adapt himself to every possible environment. Man's phenotypic plasticity is the result of a long history of evolutionary adaptation which has culminated in the most plastically adaptable, the most extraordinarily educable, of all living creatures (see pp. 488-495).

To be educable means to be dependent. If, then, one has to *learn* to be a functioning intelligent being, with learned behavior substituted for instinctually predetermined behavior, an appreciable period of time must be available during which the trained skills of intelligent behavior may be acquired. The developmental mechanism by which this availability of time for learning was ensured appears to have been achieved by means of a process which caused a retention or persistence of the fetal or juvenile plasticity of ancestral forms in the later postnatal developmental stages of the individual. This process by which the young (fetal or juvenile) features of the ancestor are retained in the mature stages of postnatal development is known as *neoteny*—the developmental retention of fetal or juvenile characters in the adult. The suggestion is that many of the changes which led to the appearance of distinctively hominid traits were brought about by neoteny, that man, as the Dutch anthropologist Bolk pointed out, is a fetalized form. Man exhibits the retention of many characters that resemble those of the fetus of apes and man, some of which are listed below.

Neotenous Characters in Man

Retention of cranial flexure	Absence of brow ridges
Long slender neck	Absence of cranial crests
Forward position of foramen magnum	Thinness of skull bones
Orbits under cranial cavity	Globular form of skull
Flatness of face (orthognathy)	Hairlessness of body
Retarded closure of cranial sutures	Lack of pigment in some groups
Large volume of brain	Thin nails
Small face and large braincase	Non-rotation of big toe
Roundheadedness (brachycephaly)	Incomplete rotation of thumb
Small teeth	Prolonged dependency period
Late eruption of teeth	Prolonged growth period

In the fetus of all mammals and most vertebrates the axis of the head forms a right angle with that of the trunk, the cranial flexure. In all mammals, with the exception of man, a rotation of the head occurs during the later stages of development so that the head assumes an orientation that is continuous with the direction of the backbone, as, for example in the adult dog (Figure 163). Man, on the other hand, retains the cranial flexure, his face pointing in a direction at right angles to the axis of his body. The visual axis, the line of sight, of both dog and man is horizontal, the dog's body is also horizontal while that of man is vertical. In the adult great apes the position of the body is in between, being oblique, and the axis of the head is also intermediate, the foramen magnum being situated more posteriorly than it is in either the fetal ape or in man. It thus transpires that man's erect posture is probably due to the retention in postnatal development of a fetal condition which in other mammals is limited only to their intra-uterine state of development. Man's flat-facedness is also a fetal character, and it is an interesting speculation that since orthognathy is limited to the early fetal stages of development in apes, the fetal developmental stage at which the neotenous mutations occurred in man's ancestors that led to orthognathy in man must have occurred fairly early—a point to which we shall return.

The sutures of the braincase remain open in man until all growth has been completed, and long after the brain has achieved its maximum growth (see Figure 221). While in the apes the sutures begin to close within the first few years of life, in man they do not generally commence to close before the end of the 23rd year. It is of considerable interest to note that there is a close correlation between the duration of the early learning period of man—the first six years—and the maximum growth of the brain.

Since the brain's growth in volume is completed by the twentieth year, the cranial sutures must remain open at least until this period of growth has been completed. Occasionally, due to some pathologic cause, the sutures unite in early childhood and prevent the brain from growing, with the result that such children remain mentally

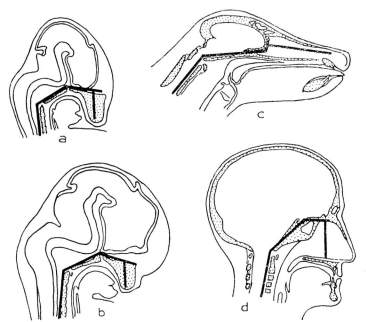

Figure 163. Sagittal sections through the head showing the angle which the head makes with trunk in *a:* embryo dog. *b:* embryo man. *c:* adult dog. *d:* adult man. (From Bolk.)

TABLE IX

GROWTH IN BRAIN AND CRANIAL CAPACITY, BOTH SEXES

Age	Weight gm.	Volume cc.	Cranial Capacity cc.
Birth	350	330	350
3 months	526	500	600
6 months	654	600	775
9 months	750	675	925
1 year	825	750	1,000
2 years	1,010	900	1,100
3 years	1,115	960	1,225
4 years	1,180	1,000	1,300
6 years	1,250	1,060	1,350
9 years	1,307	1,100	1,400
12 years	1,338	1,150	1,450
15 years	1,358	1,150	1,450
18 years	1,371	1,175	1,475
20 years	1,378	1,200	1,500

Source: *Growth and Development of the Child*, Part II, Century Co., 1933, p. 110.

retarded all their lives. The major and fundamental part of human learning takes place during the first six years of life, and, as will be seen from Table IX, it is during this period that the greater part of brain growth is accomplished.

A point of great significance is that the human brain begins its real growth and development at birth, and continues to grow and develop in the functions of a human being, throughout the first two decades of life. The brain of a 3 year old child is almost of the size and weight of that of an adult. By the age of 6 years the brain has generally virtually achieved full adult size. In man the active growth of the brain far exceeds that of any other primate. At birth the mean weight of the brain in Caucasoids is approximately 350 gm or approximately 3.9 times less than its adult weight. The growth of the brain is very different from that of the rest of the body, being quite explosive during the first year when it more than doubles to a weight of 825 gm—a gain of 475 gm. In the second year the gain is almost 275 gm, in the third year about 175 gm, and continues at the rate of about 70 gm up to the end of the fifth year when the brain weight reaches 1230 gm. From the sixth to the tenth year the average increment varies as follows: 19 gm between 5 and 6 years, 8 gm between 6 and 7 years, 46 gm between 7 and 8 years, and 10 gm between 9 and 10 years. After the first decade and to the end of the second decade the increment is less than 3 gm a year—to a total of 1378 gm.

At birth the human brain is only 23 per cent of its adult size, and by the end of the first year the human infant has achieved 60 per cent of its total brain growth; by the end of the third year some 81 per cent. In the great apes the major part of the growth is achieved within the first year. In the rhesus monkey and in the gibbon 70 per cent of the brain growth has been achieved by birth, and the remainder is completed within the first six months. In the great apes the active period of brain growth occurs during the first eleven months, and in man during the first thirty-six months. Complete growth of the brain in man is not achieved until the end of the second decade of life. As Keith has pointed out, in this prolongation of cerebral growth and development we see an important, "if not the most important, feature of human evolution—namely, the time taken to assemble and to organize the myriads of nerve cells and of nerve tracts which enter into the structure of man's brain." This process, as Keith adds, exemplifies the "law" of fetalization or neoteny, and it is this process which is capable of explaining the evolution of that most unique of all traits, the human mind.

It seems reasonably clear that the growth (increase in size) and development (increase in complexity) of the human brain is a neotenous phenomenon. In other words, man preserves something akin to the rate of growth and development characteristic of the fetal brain or preserves and improves upon the rate of growth and development of the infant ape-brain long after the latter has ceased to grow.

The deciduous dentition of the great apes is more like that of adult man than it is like that of the adult apes, so that it is not surprising to find, for example, that the deciduous teeth of the australopithecines resemble more closely the permanent teeth of man than they do those of adult australopithecines.

In the long delayed eruption of both the deciduous and permanent teeth in man we again observe a neotenous trait, the prolongation of the edentulous state of the fetus.

In all the other physical traits listed man more closely resembles the fetal ape than he does the adult. The prolonged postnatal dependency and growth periods are simply prolongations of the fetal dependency and growth periods.

One of the consequences of the prolonged dependency period of man is that it involves a rather long nursing period, and it is presumed that the unique everted mucous membranous lips of man have evolved as an adaptation to the prolonged suckling period of the human infant. Just as the cheeks of the human baby with their suctorial pads of fat are very different from what they are in the later child or adult, so does the character of the lips differ in the

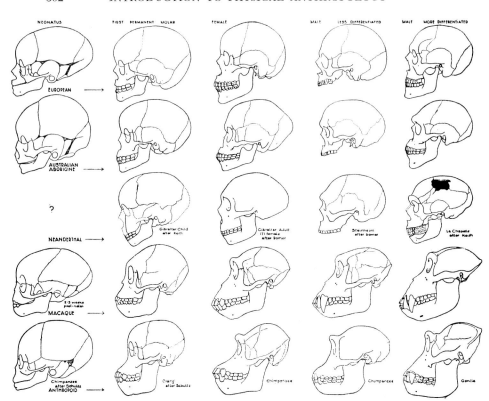

Figure 164. From left to right, showing how the neonatal skull of various primates differentiates to varying degrees of gerontomorphism from a relatively common neonatal form. To facilitate comparison the skulls are all drawn to approximately the same size. (From Abbie. Courtesy, *Trans. R. S. South Austral.*)

baby from what they will later be in the child or adult. The newborn baby's lips are characterized by a median papilla (which is sometimes mistaken for an abnormal condition). This papilla, on each lip, enables the baby to secure a better hold upon the breast.

It is reasonably clear that what is inherited by the organism has in part been acquired as a consequence of interaction of genotype with environment during development. It is during the process of individual development that mutations acquire phenotypic expression. Any mutation which serves to produce a relative retardation of somatic development so that the descendant fails to pass through several of the developmental stages of the ancestor, will result in the descendant exhibiting a pattern of growth which in the adult stage represents a retention of the ancestral fetal or juvenile pattern. Many such cases are known to zoologists and geneticists, in which rates of development, the retention of an embryonic or juvenile character and its extension in the adult, duration of developmental periods, and termination of development are affected by mutations which may have distinct and marked effects upon adult form. Such neotenous mutations may spread rapidly in a small population, and it is suggested that under such conditions the fetal or juvenile developmental stage of a pithecanthropine or similar type could have become very quickly consolidated in the descendant group. A fetalized pithecanthropine, to judge from the juvenile Modjokerto skull, or a fetalized australopithecine, to judge from the juvenile *Australopithecus africanus*, would more closely resemble modern man than these fossil juvenile forms would the adult members of their own type. Spuhler (1954) has shown that the deciduous teeth of the australopithecines are more like the deciduous teeth of modern man, but the permanent teeth are more like those of apes. In almost all the traits in which the juvenile members of these fossil forms differ from the living apes and their own adult forms they most closely resemble modern man, for example, in the comparatively globular form of the skull, the thinness of the skull bones, the absence of brow bridges, the absence of crests, the form of the teeth, and the relative size and form of the brain. We can have little doubt as to the form and characters of the fetal forms of the australopithecine and pithecanthropine types—these would almost certainly more closely resemble the human than the anthropoid. It is by the retention of such fetal and juvenile characters in the adult, particularly in the head region, by neoteny, that a neanthropic type of man could have evolved quite early in the history of the human species. M. R. Drennan, and L. H. D. Buxton and de Beer independently suggested that modern man may not be unrelated to a neanderthaloid type if he can be regarded as descended by neoteny from a juvenile form of the latter. But more recently de Beer has stated, "It is now realized that the ancestor of modern man could not have been Neanderthal man because he appeared later in time than the earliest types of modern man. But if the human ancestor was similar to *Pithecanthropus*, or *Australopithecus*, modern man would have descended from them by retention of features in the juvenile forms of their skulls, which is what is meant by neoteny."

Neotenous mutations appear to have expressed themselves somewhat differently in the different major groups. Mongoloids, for example, are rather more fetalized in their adult characters than are Caucasoids. Negroids exhibit some fetal traits that Caucasoids do not. Below are listed some of the neotenous characters in which Mongoloids and Negroids differ from Caucasoids.

Neotenous Characters in Which Mongoloids and Negroids Differ from Caucasoids

Mongoloids	Negroids	
Less hairy	Less hairy	
Larger braincase	Flat root of nose	
Larger brain	Flattish nose	
More frequently brachycephalic	Small ears	*Bushman-Hottentot*
Broader face		
Flat root of nose		Short stature
Epicanthic fold		Roundheaded (Mesocephalic)
More protuberant eye		Wide separation of eyes
Lack of brow ridges		Epicanthic fold
Greater gracility of bones		Bulging forehead
Shallow mandibular fossa		Relatively large brain
Small mastoid processes		Small face
Stocky build		Horizontal penis

The varieties of mankind that fall into those broad classificatory categories that we today call "major groups" were at one time very small populations, and it is evident that in these populations neotenous mutations occurred somewhat differently in each one. Similar differences in mutation could have occurred among the Pleistocene populations of man. In this manner one could readily explain the appearance of such neanthropic-like types as Swanscombe and Fontéchevade before the advent of such an apparently morphologically more primitive type like Neanderthal man. The fact that Neanderthal man got to look more "primitive" than he appeared to be in his earlier phases of evolution, suggests that our conceptions as to what is "primitive" and what "advanced" in human morphology are in need of careful study. In the Neanderthal group we see that an apparently less primitive-looking morphological type actually preceded a seemingly more primitive-looking type. If this sort of thing could happen in one variety of man it could certainly happen as between different varieties, as we have in fact seen that it happened among the living major groups.

As long ago as 1923 Keith, in commenting on the ideas of Bolk, remarked that "Man's outstanding structural peculiarities have been produced during the embryonic and foetal stages of his developmental history." In 1925 he wrote, "This intrauterine period is one which

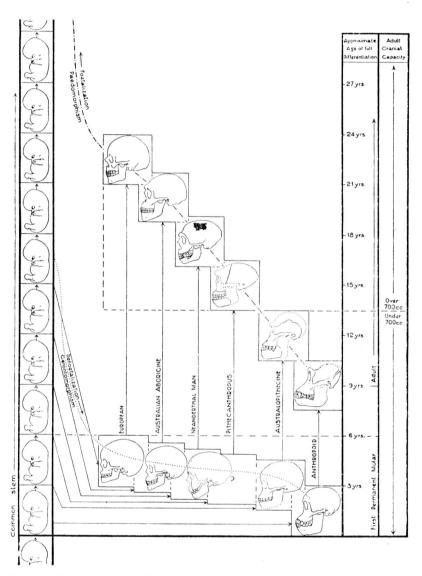

Figure 165. A scheme to illustrate the suggested common primate stem, and the manner in which distinctive forms of various primates have been derived from it by a combination of the processes of pedomorphism and geronto-morphism. (From Abbie. Courtesy, *Trans. R. S. South Austral.*)

gives every opportunity for the working out of new inventions." And, again, in 1947, "It is during the intrauterine phase that nearly all revolutionary changes in structure have been introduced."

Drennan, and more recently Abbie, have argued that anthropologists have paid insufficient attention to the developing uterine organism, that is, the embryo and fetus, and too much attention to the adult form in the study of man's physical evolution. This has, in large part been unavoidable, since most of the fossil remains recovered have been those of adults. Abbie has pointed out that it is really not a sound procedure to attempt to trace human evolution by the comparison of adult forms, and suggests that the only common stem that can be found for the primates lies in an early embryonic series. Practically any of the primates in such an embryonic series could produce a sufficiently generalized precursor of man. Consequently, it would not be necessary to go very far back into primate history to find the ancestral form. And, as Abbie states, "If a common generalized foetal form could be discovered the problem of man's ancestry would be much closer to solution than it is now." As a working hypothesis he visualizes such a form as resembling a human embryo of about 7 weeks' gestation, as shown in Figure 165. Development, at that stage, is that of a generalized primate, with the digits of the hand differentiated but not those of the feet, so that there is not yet any indication whether the great toe will become lined up with the other toes as in man or will become opposable as in the apes. All that is required at this stage is a very small change in order to shift this structure either in the one or the other direction.

In Figure 165 Abbie has provided a simple scheme to illustrate the manner in which distinctive forms of the various primates may have been derived from a common primate fetal ancestor by a combination of the processes of fetalization and gerontomorphism.* Development from the common stem by defetalization or gerontomorphism of vary-

---

* *Gerontomorphism,* the process of phylogenetic change as the result of the modification of adult traits, by means of adult variation, whereby adult ancestral traits become the traits of youthful descendants.

Defetalization, the process whereby development occurs by the loss of fetal traits by their postnatal progression toward more complex adult forms.

Fetalization, the process whereby ancestral or the organism's own fetal traits are retained in the development of the adults of a descendant group.

Pedomorphosis, the process whereby ancestral or the organism's own juvenile traits are retained in the development of the adult descendants of a group. Incorrectly used as a synonym for fetalization.

Neoteny, the process whereby ancestral or the organism's own fetal and/or juvenile traits are retained in the development of the adult descendants of a group. Embraces both fetalization and pedomorphosis.

ing degrees leads through such juvenile forms as those shown in the lower row, which in turn lead to the gerontomorphic forms shown above, but which progressively exhibit, above the 700 c.c. cranial capacity in the adult, a tendency toward the retention of fetal traits in the adult.

Contemporaneity of Morphologically Diverse Forms of Man

How can we account for the presence of probable neanthropic types like Kanjera man, Swanscombe, and Fontéchevade preceding such apparently more primitive types as the Neanderthaloids? Let us consider some of the facts.

The hominid form most resembling the australopithecines is *Pithecanthropus robustus* from the Lower Pleistocene of Java. Middle Pleistocene *Pithecanthropus erectus* of Java, and *Sinanthropus pekinensis* of the same age from China, follow next in morphological significance—which is not necessarily morphological or temporal order. Next follows the Upper Pleistocene Java Solo man. Solo man belongs either to the end of the Third Interglacial or the beginning of the Fourth Glacial. This pithecanthropoid type is undoubtedly a descendant of the older pithecanthropines, and the persistence of Solo man possibly into the Fourth Glacial affords us an opportunity to study the evolution of a hominid group in what seems to have been a thorough geographic isolation from other hominid groups. We may thus observe the trend of evolution from *Pithecanthropus robustus* through *Pithecanthropus erectus* to Solo man. The changes over this great period of time, which we may conservatively put at 500,000 years, are both absolutely and relatively minor—but changes there have been. These changes we know to have affected the brain, in the filling out of the antero-inferior parieto-temporal region, while in the skull the structure of the foramen magnum is unique in that its anterior half faces more or less downwards whereas the posterior half faces backwards. There are other interesting but minor changes. The important fact is that in Solo man we have an insular terminal hominid type which is morphologically clearly descended and but little altered from *Pithecanthropus robustus*. In other words, the rate of evolutionary change in the geographically isolated group of Javanese pithecanthropines was comparatively slow compared with that which appears to have been occurring in other hominid groups elsewhere. It is possible that in Solo man we have an example, in minuscule, of what Simpson has called bradytely, that is, lack of appreciable evolutionary change over a long period of time.

If, as is generally done, we assume a monophyletic origin for man in the Early Pleistocene or Late Pliocene, it should be abundantly clear that to account for such different contemporary morphological types as Solo and Fontéchevade man (each from the latter parts of the Third Interglacial) and such earlier differing contemporaneous (Middle Pleistocene) types as, on the one hand *Pithecanthropus erectus*, and Kanjera and Swanscombe man on the other, it will be necessary to consider every evolutionary process which may possibly have played a role in producing such types.

Evolutionary Rates

Starting as members of a common morphologically similar phyletic group, separated or isolated populations could, as the result of differences in rates of evolution, become significantly differentiated from one another, and this even though the trend or direction of evolution may remain the same. In this manner it would be possible to account for certain phenomena in the evolution of man which upon a naïve or orthogenetic view appear to be irreconcilable.

For our purposes an evolutionary rate may be defined as a measure of morphological change relative to a given period of elapsed time. Simpson has recently fully discussed the varieties of evolutionary rates, and for a discussion of this subject the reader may be referred to his work, *The Major Features of Evolution.* It is now fairly well understood that there has been the widest possible variation in evolutionary rates in the evolution of living forms. Simpson tells us, for example, that, "Of North American mammalian stocks introduced into South America in latest Pliocene and/or early Pleistocene, that is, perhaps from a million to 500 thousand years ago, probably all have become specifically distinct, many have become generally distinct, but none has become so distinct as to be reasonably placed in a new subfamily or family." And Simpson adds that, as he had already noted earlier in his book of other single examples, "this represents an increased average rate of evolution accompanying occupation of new territory." The evolutionary rates of the members of the same groups which remained in North America changed in an appreciable but somewhat lesser degree.

Occupation of new territory, to judge from the wide distribution of fossil man upon the earth, and the wanderings of peoples, appears to have been a not infrequent activity of many prehistoric human populations. Such prehistoric populations seem to have been very small, so that genetic changes could have become rapidly established in them.

As Simpson has pointed out, man as a mammal must be considered to have evolved at a more than average rate, and as a mammal of quite ordinary inherent variability he owes his present great intergroup variation to the fact that he has adapted to a uniquely large number of different habitats—the habitats of man being not merely the differing physiographic environments but including also the different sociocultural environments.

Pedomorphosis, Fetalization, Neoteny

Mutations have, of course, occurred—and occur—in the members of all human populations, but in accounting for evolutionary differences in man it seems unnecessary to assume substantially different mutation rates in different separated early groups of man to account for the contemporaneity of palanthropic and neanthropic types. It is here that the process of pedomorphosis may play a significant role. The original notion of paedogenesis, as he called it, was elaborated by von Baer in 1828, to describe the development of mature germ cells in a larval body. The concept of neoteny was quite clearly discussed by J. E. V. Boas in 1896 as the process by which the young features of the ancestor are retained in the adult stage of the descendant. The concepts of fetalization as proposed by L. Bolk, and neoteny by G. R. de Beer, proterogenesis by O. H. Schindewolf and bradygenesis by A. N. Ivanow, mean pretty much the same thing as paedogenesis or pedomorphosis, except that, strictly speaking, fetalization would refer specifically to fetal stages, while pedomorphosis would refer to young stages. Since the term "neoteny" embraces both these stages as well as the processes of rate implied in Schindewolf's and Ivanow's terms, it is to be preferred as the more comprehensive term.

No one disputes neoteny as a factor of evolution in many lower animal groups. The questions for us to decide, in the light of the evidence, are whether it is at all probable that neoteny has occurred (1) as *a* factor in the evolution of man, and (2) as a factor in the early differentiation of man.

The fact that man belongs to an order of mammals in which most of its members produce a single offspring at a birth (monotocous) made possible the establishment of mutations favoring fetalization. In animals that produce several young at a birth (polytocous) competition between the intrauterine organisms for nourishment and space is considerable. Under such conditions the adaptive advantage lies with rapid development, and the emergence of fetalization becomes impossible because genes favoring a slowing down of development would be eliminated. With one offspring at a birth the case is quite different, and a slowing down of development becomes a great advantage. The longer the single offspring is preserved in the womb, the more leisurely its development can be, and the more likely it is to be preserved for the species. A fetus is, on the whole, better nourished and less exposed to danger than a newborn infant. Under the conditions of life of man's precursors and early man himself, such a prolongation of the intrauterine period of development would have been of great advantage. Genes, therefore, favoring such a prolongation of intrauterine development by a slowing down of the rate of fetal development, would gradually have been established as part of the human genotype by natural selection.

According to the fetalization theory, then, the essential feature of human evolution has been not so much the development of new characters as the retention of embryonic, fetal, and infantile ones. It is interesting to observe that the female of the species exhibits these tendencies rather more markedly than the male.

The future of human evolution, if we are to judge by its past, will probably involve a greater prolongation of intrauterine existence as well as of childhood and a retardation of maturity. Some of the characters now distinguishing adult man will be lost. As J. B. S. Haldane has pointed out, "It was not an embryologist or a palaeontologist who said, 'Except ye . . . become as little children, ye shall not enter the kingdom of heaven'."

Respecting the evolution of such types as Kanjera, Swanscombe, Quinzano, and Fontéchevade, the suggestion is that they constitute possible examples of forms of men in which evolution by neoteny may have played an appreciable role. Neotenous mutations may have occurred with different, but probably insubstantial, frequencies in different early hominid populations derived from a common stock, and hence, by this means, in isolated hominid populations, very appreciable morphologic changes could have been brought about. The selective advantages of such possible neotenous changes is a subject which has received insufficient attention. What was the advantage of thick skull bones, if any, in palanthropic types? What is the advantage of thinner skull bones in neanthropic types? What were the advantages of supraorbital tori in the pithecanthropines and neanderthaloids? What is the advantage of the absence of these tori in neanthropic types? We don't know; we don't even have good theories. We need to think more about these matters much in the manner in which C. S. Coon, S. M.

Garn and J. S. Birdsell have in their book *Race,* with respect to the differences characterizing modern varieties of man. Above all, we need to investigate such matters by experimental means.

Time as a Factor in Evolution

In conclusion, a few words may be added on the dimension of secular time as a factor of evolution. Secular time is the matrix in which evolutionary change occurs. It is a universal constant, but time has no direct control upon evolutionary change. Time provides the constant against which change may be measured. Whatever it is that undergoes change is, however, developmentally influenced by time—change occurring as the result of the interaction of events which occur within time.

Time heals all wounds not because of its passage, but because of the occurrence of events during the passage of time which produce the healing. Were it not for those events no amount of time would be sufficient to produce the healing. Similarly, it should be clear that unless certain events occur no amount of time will serve to produce evolutionary change. However, time being the succession of instants during which events occur, time is obviously necessary for events to occur in. Time is, therefore, a factor or condition of evolution. Evolution needs time.

What we have been attempting to say in the present chapter is that during the same length of secular time, rates of evolutionary change may vary appreciably in isolated populations of the same species. In man, with his somewhat unique breeding habits, and large differences in mobility—some early populations having been confined to a restricted habitat while others wandered over large continental areas, man having reached practically every part of the habitable globe—the possibilities of idiosyncratic variation have been greatly multiplied. Rates of evolutionary change in different early hominid groups during the same length of secular time, exhibited principally as differences in the rate of neotenous mutations—among other factors—are quite sufficient, it is suggested, to explain such apparent anachronisms as neanthropic types of man in the Middle or even Early Pleistocene and a palanthropic type of man in the Upper Pleistocene—always, providing, of course, that we are also finally able to understand the adaptive value of these neotenous changes.

The hypothesis here advanced suggests that commencing with a single hominid ancestral population, which has subsequently separated into several geographically isolated populations, that in addition to such factors as mutation, natural selection, isolation, drift, and the like, neotenous mutations have played an important role in adding to the quanta of morphological difference among such populations. Neotenous mutations occurring at a more rapid rate in some early populations than in others would, at least in part, be responsible for the development of morphologically modernlike types of man at a period contemporary with the flourishing of such types as Pithecanthropus, Heidelberg, and Solo man. The hypothesis suggests that in the latter types neotenous mutations occurred comparatively infrequently.

Neoteny and the Evolution of the Human Mind

A problem perennially puzzling to the student of man has been the manner in which the distinctively human brain and mind have evolved from ape-like counterparts. The mechanism of this evolution has not been understood. N. C. Tappen has pointed out that the "Ancestors of the human group must have made the shift over to symbolic communication to initiate specifically human evolution." This is reasonably certain. But what is required is some explanation of the mechanism by means of which this shift was achieved. As Tappen adds, "Once such a shift toward this new adaptive zone was initiated, a high selective advantage for individuals better adapted to learned behavior and symbolic communication must have ensued."

It is clear that the rate of structural development in man has been appreciably retarded as compared with the rate in apes. It would appear that a similar process was associated with the development of those structural elements which form the physical bases of mind. In other words, as a consequence of neotenous mutations having multiple effects both morphological characters and functional capacities may have been influenced in the hominid-human direction. ("Hominid" refers to the classificatory status of man as a morphological form; "human" refers to the psychological capacities of such a form.) On the other hand the mutations for the strictly morphological changes and those affecting the mental faculties may have occurred quite independently. One thing seems highly probable, namely, that the shift to the human mental status occurred as the result of mutations which caused the retention of the capacity for educability, so characteristic of the juvenile ape, right into the adolescent and/or adult phases of development.

The morphological chasm once separating man from his non-human animal ancestors has been steadily reduced within recent years by the discovery of such extinct forms as the australopithecines of South Africa. Morphologically the australopithecines are not altogether apes (as we have hitherto known them) nor altogether men (as we know them), but something in between—which is exactly what the forms intermediate between apes and men should be, neither altogether the one (apes) nor quite the other (men), but the advent of the past, so to speak, on its way toward the future. The australopithecines habitually stood and walked erectly as ably or nearly as ably as man. The range of brain volume exceeded that of any known ape group, the largest known ape brain being that of a gorilla with a volume of 685 cc., while the australopithecines range in brain volume from 450 to 750 cc. The highest limits of brain volume in the australopithecines fail to fall within the lowest limits of the range of brain volume of modern men of normal intelligence—830 cc.

The brain volume of an australopithecine such as *Telanthropus capenis*, as estimated by Robinson, namely between 850 and 950 cc. is generally agreed to be too high, but 750 cc. is not, and this is within calling distance of the lower limit of the *Pithecanthropus-Sinanthropus* group with a range of 885 to 1225 cc. Robinson believes that *Telanthropus* has virtually bridged the gap between ape and man. The gap seems, however, to be larger than Robinson suggests. Most students are of the opinion that the australopithecines do not constitute the group immediately ancestral to man, though most agree that they are closely related to the hominid ancestral group. The cerebral Rubicon which Keith placed at a mean of 750 cc. is a good distance from having been crossed by the australopithecines. "The Rubicon," writes Keith, "between apehood and manhood, so far as concerns brain volume lies somewhere between 700 cc. and 800 cc.; to be more precise, I would say that any group of the great Primates which has attained *a mean brain volume* of 750 cc. and over should no longer be regarded as anthropoid, but as human." The emphasis here is upon *a mean brain volume*, and the mean brain volume of the australopithecines is 576 cc. This is quite a long way from the mean brain volume of the pithecanthropoids of 881 cc. On the basis of brain volume the australopithecines have not crossed the Rubicon to achieve the status of man.

Whatever conclusion we arrive at concerning the australopithecines on morphological grounds, there can be little doubt on functional grounds, as is evidenced by their tool-making abilities, that at least one group of advanced australopithecines, *Zinjanthropus boisei*, had made the passage from ape to man. Yet, as we have seen, in an earlier chapter, the brain volume of *Zinjanthropus* is estimated as having been below 700 cc. The "Cerebral Rubicon," therefore, must be re-duced downwards. Quite clearly what matters is the genetic change affecting the character of the brain, however small its size, which some-how enables it to function at a hominid conceptual level. Doubtless there are limits below which the size of the brain could not function in such a manner, but they are apparently lower than had previously been considered possible.

It does not seem that many great structural changes would be necessary to produce those qualitative changes that would serve to distinguish the human from the ape mind. It would seem, on the other hand, that the principal, if not the only changes necessary would be those facilitating the ease of symbol usage. What the nature of those changes may be is at present conjectural. Increase in the num-ber of fine connections between cerebral neurons with increased capa-city for growth at axon terminals, resulting in improvement in the association, scanning, and feedback capacities of the brain, is one possibility. Thorndike has suggested that "in their deeper nature the higher forms of intellectual operation are identical with mere associa-tion or connection forming, depending upon the same sort of physio-logical connections but requiring many more of them." This is possibly an oversimplification. However we may describe the structural changes which have undoubtedly taken place in the human brain, they will amount to but the other aspect of what we have already stated, namely, that the difference between the human and ape brain is that the human is more educable. Indeed, educability is the species characteristic of *Homo sapiens*. The juvenile ape is more educable than the adult ape, and the suggestion here is that the preservation of the educability of the juvenile ape into the adult stage in man, by neoteny, serves to explain the evolution of a brain capable of a human mind.

The theory outlined in this section suggests that the shift from the status of ape to the status of human being was the result of neotenous mutations which produced a retention of the growth trends of the juvenile brain and its potentialities for learning into the adolescent and adult phases of development. It is clear that the nature of these poten-tialities for learning must also have undergone intrinsic change, for no amount of extension of the chimpanzee's capacity for learning would yield a human mind.

It is further suggested that evolution by neoteny of the mental faculties has been a gradual process from the commencement of man's origin from the apes. It is questionable whether the shift from the ape to the hominid status was saltatory either for morphological or for mental traits. It may be doubted, for example, that *Pithecanthropus robustus* was as bright as Solo man, though it is highly probable that he was brighter than any of the australopithecines. The progressive increase in the volume of the brain in the fossil Hominidae seems to have been paralleled by a progressive increase in mental capacities. Size of brain seems to have stabilized itself in man, in fact there seems to have been a decline in gross size or dimensions of the human brain since the days of Neanderthal man. This does not, however, mean that the increase in brain mass has come to an end. Increase in mass may be achieved by deepening and multiplication of the number of cerebral convolutions, that is, by increasing the surface area of the brain without increasing its size. There is no reason to suppose that either the quality or duration of man's capacity for learning will not be subject to further evolution.

FOR FURTHER READING, CONSULT:

Abbie, A. A.: A new approach to the problem of human evolution. *Trans. Roy. Soc. S. Australia,* 75:70-88, 1952.
An important study presenting the view that the morphological characters of ancient physical types, particularly Neanderthal man, lie within the range of normal variation, together with an admirable discussion of fetalization or neoteny.

————: Timing in human evolution. *Proc. Linn. Soc. New S. Wales,* 83:197-213, 1958.
Supplementing the foregoing discussion.

Bolk, L.: *Das Problem der Menschwerdung.* Jena, Fischer, 1926.

————: Origin of racial characteristics in man. *Am. J. Phys. Anthropol.,* 13:1-28, 1929.
In both these items Bolk discusses the process of fetalization as a factor in the evolution of men. In connection with man these were the earliest contributions to the subject.

Cuenot, L.: L'homme ce néoténique. *Bull. L'Acad. Roy. Belg., 31:* 1945. *L'Evolution Biologique.* Paris, Masson, 1951.
The article, and part of the book, deal with neoteny in the evolution of man.

De Beer, G.: *Embryos and Ancestors.* Oxford, The Clarendon Press, New York, Oxford University Press, 1958.
Containing an admirable discussion of neoteny in man.

Drennan, M. R.: Pedomorphism in the pre-Bushman skull. *Am. J. Phys. Anthropol.,* 16:203-210, 1931.
A discussion of the role of pedomorphism in producing the traits of the Bushman skull.

Haldane, J. B. S.: *The Causes of Evolution.* London, Longmans, 1932.
A fundamental work, with a good discussion of neoteny in man.

Huxley, J. S.: *Evolution: The Modern Synthesis.* New York, Harper, 1942.
Contains excellent discussions of neoteny in man.

KEITH, A.: Foetalization as a factor in human evolution. In Keith's *A New Theory of Human Evolution*. London, Watts, New York, Philosophical Library, 1949, pp. 192-201.

A good discussion of fetalization in man.

MONTAGU, M. F. ASHLEY: Time, morphology, and neoteny in the evolution of man. *Amer. Anthropol.*, 57:13-27, 1955.

Neoteny in man and as a factor which may account for the early appearance of neanthropic man.

———: Neoteny and the evolution of the human mind. *Explorations* No. 6 (University of Toronto), 85-90, 1956.

On the evolution of the human mind.

Chapter VI

THE CRITERIA AND MECHANISM OF ETHNIC DIFFERENTIATION

THERE exist many distinctive groups of mankind which, as groups, are easily distinguishable from one another. The Chinese and Japanese, for example, are at once recognizable as two members of a very large group the characters of which distinguishes it from all others, and this group has been called the Mongoloid race of man. The African type of man wherever he occurs has been called a member of the Negroid race, and the white wherever he occurs, has been called a member of the White or Caucasoid race. Australian aborigines are in turn distinguishable from all of these, and are therefore spoken of as members of the Australoid race.

But what shall be said of the natives of New Guinea and the Solomons, of the whole region of Melanesia? Are they not a race, the Melanesian race? And what of the Javanese and the peoples of Malaysia, are they not distinct races? How are the peoples of India to be described; the people of Ceylon; and Celebes? The American Indian? And what of the Irish, the Jews, and the Germans, are they all classifiable as races?

These, and many others, are the questions which are asked of the anthropologist, and different anthropologists have had different answers to return to these questions. The answer will, of course, depend upon what is understood by the term "race," and upon this there has not been anything like unanimous agreement. This lack of agreement upon a common meaning for the term, and the utterly abject social and political misuses to which it has been put, has caused the term to fall into disrepute, and even to be altogether rejected by some scientists, so far as its application to man in the modern world is concerned. See Appendix C, pp. 687-691.

The cold light of reason can nonetheless be brought successfully to bear upon even the most passionately discussed of subjects, and whatever the motives may have been of earlier students of the problem of the variety of man, the physical anthropologist of today is ready to revalue his values and to do the best he can to unravel the

317

tangled skein which is the variety of man. In the prosecution of this task the more he has learned about the physical and mental differences existing between the ethnic groups of man the less and less distinct have they become. This in spite of the fact that differences have been sought rather than likenesses.

While authorities have disagreed upon the meaning of the term "race" with reference to man, the layman has generally suffered from no such difficulty. For him "race" has in effect meant any foreign group. For him a foreigner is a member of a different "race" either because of a difference in national origin, religion, language, apparel or appearance. The popular conception of "race" is an unfortunate myth.

All serious definitions of race agree upon the following:

(1) *That the differences which characterize the groups so defined are conditioned by heredity. To the extent that qualities are conditioned by the environment—natural or cultural—they are not considered racial or ethnic characters.*

(2) That mental characters are to a very large extent conditioned by the social environment of the individual and therefore cannot be considered as ethnic characters.

(3) That insofar as nationality is determined by the accident of birth in a particular country, nationality has no necessary connection with ethnic group. Since language is similarly determined, the same holds true for language.

Thus, a person of Japanese parentage may be an American by nationality and speak English only, whereas his parents are Japanese by nationality and speak only Japanese. The grandchildren may be born in different lands in which they grow up as nationals, and speak languages differing from those which their brothers, parents, and grandparents speak.

Language and nationality are not genetically determined and have no inherent relation whatever to the genetic factors which constitute the fundamental determinants in the development of the physical characters of man. Language is culturally determined, nationality is politically determined, membership in any major or ethnic group of man is determined by heredity. In order to arrive at an objective, scientifically satisfactory classification of mankind into different ethnic groups it is clear that neither language, nor nationality, will help us, though language may reveal past contact between groups. We must approach the problem instead through the study of the hereditary characteristics of such groups.

The Criteria of Analysis and Classification

There are many ways in which one may ask questions about the variety of man, and the kind of question asked will largely determine the character of the answer returned. It has frequently been the case that each student has devised his own definition of "race" and has then attempted to classify the varieties of mankind according to the terms laid down in that definition. As T. H. Huxley remarked many years ago, "I speak of 'persistent modifications' or 'stocks' rather than of 'varieties' or 'races,' or 'species,' because each of these last well-known terms implies, on the part of its employer, a preconceived opinion touching one of these problems the solution of which is the ultimate object of science; and in regard to which, therefore, ethnologists are especially bound to keep their minds open and their judgments freely balanced." (*On the Methods and Results of Ethnology*, 1865.) We have had classifications by hair, pigmentation, head shape, eye-color, and combinations of some or all of these characters, and a great many more. Some of these classifications have been bad, some have been better than others, but none has been scientifically satisfactory, in the sense of being able to provide us with really workable accounts of each group of mankind supposedly exhibiting the characters which distinguish them from each other.

The reason for this is simple: The kind of discontinuous, clear-cut differences which so many investigators have preconceivedly assumed to exist between the varieties of man were simply not to be found at the level at which they were looked for. Anyone can perceive certain clearcut differences between a Negro and a white at a glance, but Negro and white are in a sense extreme types, in the sense, that is, of presenting "extreme" differences in pigmentation and hair form. Even so, white and black cease to be easily distinguishable where there has been some degree of admixture, so that in America, for example, many persons of Negro-white ancestry readily pass for white. In the latter case the problem would be to say just when a person ceased to be a Negro and became a white. And that precisely is one of the great difficulties which the anthropologist encounters when he attempts to refine his classifications to embrace all the varieties of man. The transitions between the latter are often indeterminable. Where one group leaves off and the other begins it is frequently impossible to say. As Darwin remarked in *The Descent of Man* (1871), "It may be doubted whether any character can be named which is distinctive of race and is constant."

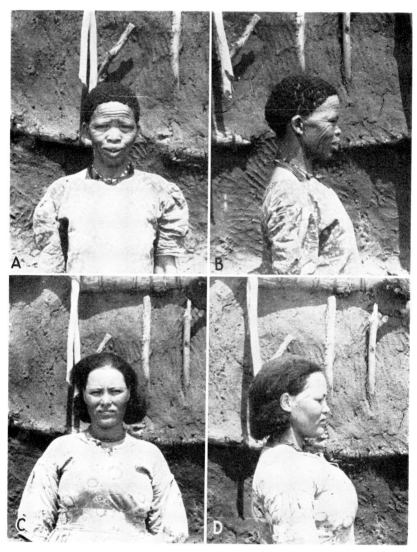

Figure 166. An example of the results of admixture between two "extreme" types, Bushman and Caucasoid. *A:* Unmixed Bushman woman, frontal view. *B:* lateral view. *C:* Daughter of the preceding by a white man, frontal view. *D:* lateral view.

Figure 166—Continued
E: Daughter's white husband and their daughter. F: Bushman mother, hybrid daughter and granddaughter. G and H: The granddaughter. (From Tobias. Courtesy, *Man*.)

Groups of mankind that are unique for all the characters we can examine do not exist. Hence, in the past the anthropologist selected a few distinctive characters by the use of which he attempted to delimit several large groups of mankind from one another. In a mixed population he claimed, by this means, to be able to distinguish the various races entering into its composition, and in this way he often arbitrarily created races which in fact had no existence outside his method or his imagination. Such arbitrarily drawn lines between one group and another have in fact served to obscure the real truth, namely, that in nature no such line exists, and that it is the systematist alone who introduces such divisions into nature. Were such arbitrary practices helpful in throwing some light upon the problem of the relationship of the varieties of man to one another, there might be some justification for continuing their use. But as they have been misused in the past they are distinctly not helpful. On the contrary, they have served to obscure the problem and to delay its solution. This is not to say that attempted classifications of mankind are undesirable, indeed, they *are* desirable, but the criteria used in their creation must be soundly based, and not arbitrarily selected. Unfortunately, such criteria have until recently been of the latter order rather than of the former, with the result that great masses of measurements have been accumulated which gave us at best a rather unsatisfactory description of the groups to which they have reference, and tell us disappointingly little concerning either the origins or the relationships of the groups involved.

Racial classifications are intended to have (*a*) a pragmatic meaning, and (*b*) a biological basis, but it frequently happens that the two intentions clash. The problem of the *existence* of ethnic groups is totally distinct from the problem of their *delimitation*. It is one thing to know that such groups exist, it is quite another to be able to delimit and define them. Lines between groups do not exist, but steep or flat places in geographic or character gradients do. The concept of character gradients refers to the fact that as one passes from place to place in a given direction, the physical characters of the inhabitants of the territories traversed change more or less gradually. Neighboring populations tend to resemble one another more closely than do geographically more remote ones. This is the phenomenon of character gradients. Such populations are usually called *clines* in animal biology. It must be the task of the physical anthropologist to recognize and study the significance of such gradients or clines in man.

Until recent years, the anthropologist has been forced to rely upon the external characters of the body for his analysis and classificatory purposes. This, principally, has been the reason for his failure to trace the relationships of the varieties of man to one another, and what is more important, the mechanism of these relationships, because external characters (the phenotype) represent the expression of a large number of individually inherited patterns of genes (the genotype) in interaction with the environment. Furthermore, taxonomic exercises in the classification of assemblages of phenotypical (external) characters do not lead to the clarification of their significance for the simple reason that it is not assemblages of characters which undergo change as such in the development of the individual and of the group, but single units, the genes, which, in interaction with the environment, determine those characters. This is what the science of genetics has made irrefragably clear.

It is the inheritance of separate traits, and not aggregations of traits, which must be studied, because it is the genes or potentialities for the former and not the latter which are inherited, although linkages and clusters of such traits may, and do, occur.

The materials of evolution are not represented by continuous, rigidly articulated determinants of particular aggregates of characters, but by discontinuous packages of chemicals; each little packet interacting with the others as an independent unit, being only partially responsible for the ultimate form of any character, since it is not independent in its action but is influenced by the presence of other similar packages of chemicals. These chemical packages are the genes, which are chemically best described as giant self-reproducing nucleo-protein molecules.

It has been estimated that about 5,000 different genes enter into the making of the most popular of all experimental animals in the geneticist's laboratory, the fruit fly (*Drosophila melanogaster*). Man has 23 pairs of chromosomes, almost six times as many as *Drosophila*. Allowing that this is an extrapolation it may be reasoned that if *Drosophila* with four pairs of chromosomes has about 5,000 genes then it is possible than man has about 30,000 genes in the chromosomes of his sex cells. Spuhler has arrived at a similar figure by another method and Evans reasons that there must be well over 5,000 genes, probably between 10^4 and 10^5. Each of these genes retains both its independence and its individual character more or less indefinitely, although they are probably all inherently variable and, in time, capable of mutation. For these reasons any conception of the nature of human variation which operates as if inheritance were a matter of the transmission of gross aggregates of characters is erroneous and stultifying. It is potentialities, implying limits, which are inherited, not characters.

The facts of human variability are best explained by genetic analy-

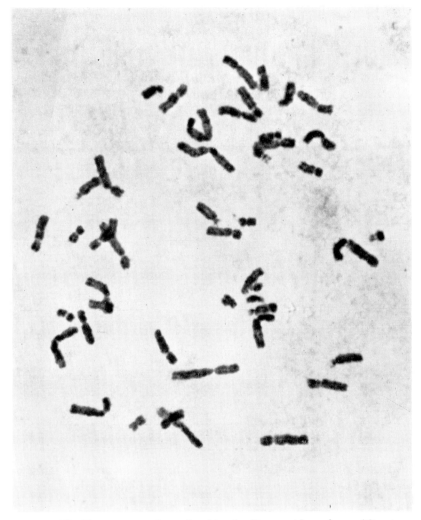

Figure 167. Chromosomes from the skin of a Caucasoid newborn. (Courtesy, Dr. E. H. Y. Chu.)

sis, since the fundamental units involved in producing that variability are the genes.

Very briefly, in each individual (zygote) there are 46 chromosomes or 23 pairs of chromosomes. One member of each of these 23 pairs is derived from the mother and the other member from the father. When the reproductive or germ cells (gametes) are formed, the members of each pair of parental chromosomes or genes separate from each other so that each reproductive cell has one or the other member of each pair but not both. This is known as the principle of gametic purity or segregation. At fertilization the arrangement into gene pairs is restored. Pairs of genes located in different chromosomes assort independently of each other. The genes derived from the mother will not, however, tend to stay together, nor will those derived from the father, but each gene will be assorted independently of the other. This is the principle of independent assortment.

Each member (*allele*) of a gene pair is specifically similar to the other, thus, for example, genes for eye color will always pair together, so will genes for nose shape, but an eye color gene and a nose shape gene will never pair, though they may occur in the same chromosome and may be transmitted together on the same thread in the whole or a part of a chromosome. When such genes are found in association they are spoken of as *linked* genes. Linkage may be defined as the tendency for two or more genes to remain together without recombination. It is obvious that a very large number of genes must be linked. This linkage would definitely put a limit upon the number of possible variations which could occur were it not for the fact that the segments of similar chromosomes are capable of exchanging parts, a process known as *crossing over*. In this way genes that were originally situated on the maternal thread in one chromosome may become attached to the paternal thread of genes in another chromosome, in this way former linkage associations are broken up and new ones created. The limitation of genetic combinations which linkage brings about is counteracted by the possibilities of recombination through crossing over. Linkage and crossing over regulate the degree and amount of reassortment of genes. The facts of segregation and independent assortment together with the phenomenon of crossing over should make it clear that in man, with his many thousands of genes, the number of gene combinations thus rendered possible is of a very large order indeed, i.e., at least $2^{30,000}$, and that, therefore, the genetic variability of man is likewise very great. (see p. 475).

To this explanation of the fundamental mechanism of genetic variability must be added the fact that while the genes themselves remain stable, their expression will change according to the conditions under which they develop. That is to say, any character is the product of interaction between the genetic make-up and the environment, and not of the one or the other alone.

Furthermore, in the course of time any gene may undergo a permanent structural change, thus giving rise to a new character or, what is more usual, to some part of a new character, a new hereditary variation. Such a change is known as a mutation. A character may be defined as any structure, function or trait of an organism. At one time it was considered that mutation was a relatively rare process taking the form of perceptible major changes. Today, however, all those small variations which occur in the individual which are of a discontinuous character, that is to say, which vary either in number (meristic) or in presence or absence (qualitative), as opposed to normal continuous variation by degree of difference (quantitative), are regarded as due to mutation and recombination. The mode of inheritance is exactly the same for discontinuous as for continuous variation; in the former a few genetic factors are involved, each producing a major effect, in the latter many genetic factors are involved which produce small additive effects, in the shaping of a character. Modern students are generally agreed that mutations and recombinations furnish the only source of new variation.

The formation of new species in lower animals is explained by the geneticist as being brought about by the gradual accumulation of mutations and the effects of recombinations until a certain threshold is passed which signifies the evolution of a new species. In man there is the additional factor, as a consequence of his migratory habits, of frequent hybridization, a factor which greatly contributes to the process of diversification.

The variation due to recombination in living groups of mankind is so great that such "groups" can only be distinguished by statistical methods and in statistical terms. As Julian Huxley has put it, "In such groups the *mean values* for characters, though still useful, no longer have the same theoretical importance. The *range of variation* of characters is of far greater practical importance, as is also the range of qualitatively different recombination types. The two resultant race-concepts are fundamentally dissimilar."

In order to understand how the varieties of mankind came to possess such characters as they now exhibit, it should be obvious that making omelettes out of the very ingredients, the genes, which it is necessary to isolate and to map, will be of no assistance whatever. The frequencies with which such genes occur in different groups must be studied.

If we arbitrarily recognize, say, forty genes as entering into the determination of the shape of the head, then it should be evident that measuring the shape of the head will tell us no more than what the shape of the head is. By such means we can never hope to learn how the shape of any particular head or group of heads came to be as it now is, and that is the significant point. But by experimental studies on lower animals, on the genetics of the inheritance of each bone and its relation to shape of the head, it may eventually be possible to transfer the knowledge thus gained to the analysis of the genetics of cephalic architecture in man. Even so it will always remain true that craniometric similarities by no means necessarily indicate genetic affinity.

Furthermore, the work of Boas on the descendants of immigrants into the United States, of Shapiro and Hulse on the descendants of Japanese in Hawaii, and of Dornfeldt on the descendants of Eastern European Jews in Berlin, has shown that the potentialities of head shape, as well as other characters of the body, can be significantly modified by the environment. To put it more accurately, latent gene potentialities for head shape express themselves differently in different environments. (See pp. 529-537).

Hence, if we are to trace the relationships of the varieties of man to one another, it is necessary that we rely on criteria which possess a more permanent character than the shifting sands of head shape. Such criteria should, as far as possible, be unequivocally objective in character, as much as possible unaffected by environmental factors, and as little as possible subject to mutation. Such characters are available in the blood groups, in the M-N in the Rh-Hr blood types, and in the hemoglobin and haptoglobin types of man.

The Landsteiner Blood Groups O, A, B, and AB

The genetic mechanism of the blood groups is now well understood, and their distribution throughout the world has been widely studied. The four principal blood groups of man are denoted by the letters O, A, B and AB. There are several subgroups of A and AB to which reference will be made later (pp. 366-367). The four blood groups are determined by the fact that the red blood corpuscles (erythrocytes) contain two different antigens denoted by the letters A and B. An antigen is a substance which injected into the blood of an animal results, after some time, in the appearance of antibodies in its blood serum. The antibodies are known as agglutinins and the antigens which produce them are known as agglutinogens. The agglutinogens or blood group substances can be present either singly, as in blood group A and in blood group B, or together as in blood group AB, or be altogether absent as in blood group O.

In the presence of the serum (or plasma) of certain other persons

TABLE X

THE AGGLUTINOGENS AND AGGLUTININS OF BLOOD GROUPS
O, A, B, AND AB

Blood Group	Agglutinogen (In red corpuscles)	Agglutinin (In serum)	Approximate Frequency (%) Among Caucasoids
O	None	anti-**A** and anti-**B**	40
A	A −	anti-**B**	40
B	− B	anti-**A**	15
AB	A and B	None	5

the agglutinogens, with the exception of blood group O, cause the red blood corpuscles to form clusters or clumps, that is, to agglutinate. The agglutination is produced by the two agglutinating substances, the agglutinins anti-**A** and anti-**B**, which are found in the blood serum of some persons.* The blood plasma (or serum) is the medium in which float the red blood corpuscles containing the agglutinogens. Once the blood corpuscles are agglutinated, the agglutinins may then proceed to destroy (hemolyse) them.

If a person is of the same blood group as another with whose blood serum some of his own red blood corpuscles are mixed the latter will remain evenly dispersed. This is due to the fact that members of the same blood group do not carry the antibodies which would agglutinate their own blood corpuscles. This is illustrated in Table X.

It should be clear on purely empirical grounds and from this Table, that the blood serum could not, and does not, normally carry substances which would cause its own red blood cells to agglutinate. It is therefore the rule (Landsteiner) that if an agglutinogen is absent from the red blood corpuscles of a person, then the corresponding agglutinin is present in the serum of that person. In blood transfusion it is important to avoid introducing blood containing agglutinogens that can react with agglutinins present in the serum of the recipient, otherwise the introduced blood will be destroyed or agglutinated, damaging the kidneys and even causing the death of

---

* In conformity with the recommendations of the Committee on Medicolegal Problems, regular type is used for symbols for agglutinogens, phenotypes, and blood group systems; **boldface** type is used for symbols for antibodies and the corresponding factors defined by them; and *italics* for symbols for genes and genotypes. The blood factors are the serological attributes by which agglutinogens are identified, and, in general, each agglutinogen has multiple blood factors which characterize it (see p. 348).

TABLE XI

DETERMINATION OF BLOOD GROUPS WITH TWO TEST SERA, ANTI-**A** AND ANTI-**B**

	Known Serum Anti-**A** (Blood Group B)	Known Serum Anti-**B** (Blood Group A)	Blood Group
Agglutination of the unknown blood corpuscles	−	−	O
	+	−	A
	−	+	B
	+	+	AB

+ = clumping of red cells   − = no clumping

the recipient. It will readily be seen that the blood groups can be determined by testing the unknown blood corpuscles with anti-**A** and anti-**B** sera, or by allowing the unknown serum to act on known corpuscles of A and B. The manner in which this may be done is shown in Tables XI and XII. In Table XIII is shown the usual effect which follows upon adding a donor's blood corpuscles to a receiver's serum.

In populations of European origin the commonest blood group is O, this occurs in about 40 per cent of the population. Since blood group O contains no agglutinogens it was formerly given to receivers irrespective of their blood groups; persons of blood group O were therefore called "universal donors." The **A, B** agglutinins of blood group O are diluted and neutralized in the recipient's body so that they are incapable of damaging the cells of the other blood groups. It happens, however, that some persons of blood group O possess agglutinins of high titer; the use of their blood is therefore dangerous since the antibodies may react in spite of dilution. For this reason donors of the same blood group are, whenever possible, used. Since persons belonging to the least common blood group AB, about 5 per cent of the population, possess no agglutinins they were until very recently considered to be capable of receiving the blood of any other

TABLE XII

DETERMINATION OF BLOOD GROUPS OF SERA WITH KNOWN BLOOD CORPUSCLES A AND B

	Known Corpuscles A	Known Corpuscles B	Blood Group
Agglutination by the unknown serum	+	+	O
	−	+	A
	+	−	B
	−	−	AB

+ = clumping of red cells   − = no clumping

TABLE XIII

THE USUAL EFFECT OF ADDING A DONOR'S BLOOD TO A RECEIVER'S SERUM

Agglutinins in receiver's serum	Agglutinogens of Donor's Corpuscles			
	(Group A) A	(Group B) B	(Group AB) A and B	(Group O) None
(Group A) anti-**B**	Compatible	Agglutinated	Agglutinated	Compatible
(Group B) anti-**A**	Agglutinated	Compatible	Agglutinated	Compatible
(Group AB) none	Compatible	Compatible	Compatible	Compatible
(Group O) anti-**A**, anti-**B**	Agglutinated	Agglutinated	Agglutinated	Compatible

group, and were therefore called "universal recipients." But the red blood corpuscles of such "universal recipients" were occasionally clumped by the introduced donor's agglutinins. For these reasons the use of so-called "universal donors" and "universal recipients" is restricted today to special cases. Blood group A occurs in about 40 per cent of persons of European stock, and blood group B in from 10 to 15 per cent.

It has already been stated that the heredity of the blood groups is well understood. The hereditary characters of man, as in all animals and plants, are largely determined by genes. Genes, we have already seen, are the complex nucleoproteins which are carried in the rod-like structures which occur in the nuclei of cells, and these rod-like structures, the chromosomes, occur in pairs. Each chromosome generally carries hundreds of genes. The essential message-carrying molecule consists of deoxyribonucleic acid (DNA). Each gene in the chromosome has a gene corresponding to it in the other member of the pair of chromosomes, at the corresponding position or locus.

During the development of the reproductive cells (sperm and ova) these pairs of chromosomes separate (reduction division or meiosis) and each sperm or ovum (the gametes) contains only one of each kind of chromosome, thus forming an exception to the general rule that each cell contains a pair of each kind. When a sperm fertilizes an ovum, the maternal and paternal gametes contribute their chromosomes to restore the arrangement by pairs. The genes contributed by the parents may be like or unlike, that is, the genes in one member of a pair of chromosomes may match or be unlike those in the opposite member of the pair. It is now known that the blood group to which a

TABLE XIV

DETERMINATION OF GENETIC CONSTITUTION OF HUMANS WITH
REGARD TO BLOOD GROUPS A-B-O

Genes Derived from Parents		Genotype	Blood Group (Phenotype)
O	O	OO	O
A	A	AA	
A	O	AO	A
O	A	OA	
B	B	BB	
B	O	BO	B
O	B	OB	
A	B	AB	AB
B	A	BA	

person belongs depends upon which pair out of six possible pairs of genes he has inherited from his parents, only one pair of which each parent himself can have possessed. Each of the genes in such a pair is called an allele, and is designated by the italicized letters used for the agglutinogens, A, B, and O. There is only one gene on each chromosome for the agglutinable properties of the red corpuscles. There are, therefore, a total of two in each individual. The genetic constitution of human beings with regard to the blood groups is therefore determined in the manner shown in Table XIV.

Genes A and B are of equal expressive value and therefore the substances which they determine occur together as recognizable agglutinogens. O is masked by or recessive to A and B which are therefore dominant to it, so that O is not expressed in the presence of the alleles A or B. Thus, for a person to belong to group O both of the parents must have carried the gene, either in a homozygous condition, where both genes were alike, or in a heterozygous condition, where one gene in each parent was O and the other either A or B. In the

TABLE XV

THE GENE COMBINATIONS OR GENOTYPES YIELDING
THE PHENOTYPES OR BLOOD GROUPS

Genotype	Phenotype
OO	O
AA or AO	A
BB or BO	B
AB	AB

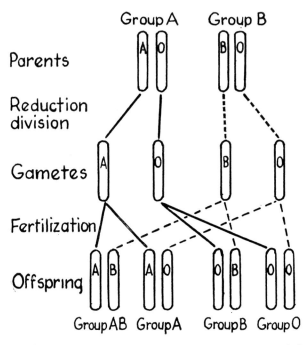

Figure 168. Chromosome diagram showing the transmission of the genes in the mating of two persons, one of blood group A and the other of blood group B, each being heterozygous for blood group O.

former event, all the children would belong to blood group O, as for example is the case among such South American Indian tribes as the Chulpie of Argentina, the Guarani of Paraguay, and the Onas, Yámanas, and Alakalufs of Tierra del Fuego; in the latter event the offspring could belong to any one of the four blood groups. The mode of transmission of the genes in the latter case is illustrated in Figure 168. From these facts it will be seen that the blood group genes yield six genotypes and four phenotypes as shown in Table XV.

By tracing the distributions of the genes for such traits as are exemplified by the blood groups in the different populations and varieties of man, the anthropologist can expect to discover precisely what the hereditary bases are of the differences and likenesses involved. By a simple mathematical procedure known as gene frequency analysis it is now possible to calculate the number or percentage of genes present in a given population for any character in that population the mode of inheritance of which is known. The term *frequency* denotes the percentage of a particular gene as determined in a particular population. The frequencies of the genes A, B, and O in any population are conventionally denoted by the letters p, q, and r respectively. In any population, therefore, in which these genes occur their sum should be equal to 100, thus $p + q + r = 100$. The frequency of the A gene, denoted by the letter p is obtained by extracting the square root of the sum of the frequencies of groups B and O and subtracting from 100. The frequency of the gene B, denoted by the letter q, is obtained by extracting the square root of the sum of the frequencies of groups A and O and substracting the result from 100. Finally, the frequency of the O gene, denoted by the letter r, is obtained by subtracting from 100 the sum of the calculated frequencies of the A and B genes, or by taking the square root of the frequency of group O. Other methods of computing these gene frequencies are available but these need not concern us here.

Table XVI shows the kind of distribution of the blood groups O, A, B, and AB, together with their gene frequencies, as encountered in human populations. The populations in this Table were selected on the basis of their ethnic status alone. The distribution of the blood groups and their gene frequencies were omitted from consideration for the purposes of this Table, for it was desired to show in what relationships a number of populations selected at random would fall in respect of their blood groups. The populations were then arranged in order of the diminishing gene frequency, q, of blood group B. If the reader will now carefully examine Table XVI he will discover something of the virtues of blood group gene frequency analysis and also something of its limitations.

It will be observed that there is a marked tendency for Asiatic Mongoloids to exhibit the highest frequencies of the gene q (B). On the other hand the lowest frequencies of B are encountered in the North and South American Indians and Eskimos. This is interesting, since on archeological and physical grounds the evidence is clear that the American Indians and the Eskimos are closely related. Were we to rely upon analyses of the four blood groups we should certainly not suspect a relationship between the Asiatic and the American Mongoloids. We find the latter very high in O, whereas the former tend to be comparatively low in O. The frequency of A, however, appears to be similar in both groups, moreover the subgroup A_2 is absent in both. In short, in the present state of our knowledge we could not rely exclusively upon the four blood groups to prove relationships between populations. However, in conjunction with other

TABLE XVI

DISTRIBUTION OF THE BLOOD GROUPS IN RANDOM SAMPLES OF HUMAN POPULATIONS

(Arranged in order of *diminishing* frequency of gene Bq)

Population	Investigator	Number of Subjects	Blood Groups (%)				Frequencies of Genes (%)		
			O	A	B	AB	p	q	r
Ainu	Wellisch 1935	205	36.0	19.5	38.5	6.0	14.6	26.3	60.0
Asiatic Indians	Wiener et al. 1944	156	34.0	25.0	37.2	3.8	18.5	26.1	58.3
Tatars (Tatar Republic)	Gerasimov (*vide* Boyd 1939)	641	28.2	31.3	33.3	7.2	24.0	25.0	53.0
Congo Pygmies	Jadin 1935	1 032	30.6	30.3	29.1	10.0	22.7	21.9	55.4
Chinese (New York)	Wiener et al. 1944	138	31.1	32.6	27.5	8.5	23.4	20.2	55.8
Hottentots (S.W. Africa)	Pijper 1935	506	34.8	30.6	29.2	5.3	20.1	19.3	60.5
Japanese (Nagasaki)	Furuhata 1933	6 387	28.0	37.9	22.8	11.3	28.3	18.4	52.9
Filipinos (Philippines)	Simmons 1945	382	45.0	22.0	27.0	6.0	15.2	18.1	67.1
Indonesians (C. Java)	Buining 1934	215	48.8	18.1	27.0	6.1	11.9	17.3	69.8
Chinese (Canton)	Dornanns 1929	992	45.9	22.8	25.2	6.1	15.2	16.6	67.6
Negroes (West Africa)	Muller 1927	325	52.3	21.5	23.0	3.2	13.6	14.5	72.4
Russians (Odessa)	Rubashkin 1929	1 831	31.8	33.4	17.4	4.6	31.9	13.7	56.4
Italians (Sicily)	Nicoletti (*vide* Boyd 1939)	540	45.9	33.4	17.3	3.4	21.3	11.8	67.8
Samoans	Stephenson 1935	500	58.6	17.0	19.4	5.0	10.3	11.8	76.6
Fijians	Simmons et al. 1942	200	43.5	34.0	16.5	6.0	22.2	11.6	65.9
Papuans (Schouten Ids.)	Bos 1932	611	63.7	15.4	18.5	2.4	9.2	10.8	79.8
Egyptians (Cairo)	Sharaf 1930	962	47.4	27.0	15.0	10.6	17.4	10.1	68.9
American Whites (New York)	Wiener 1944	1 077	41.7	37.8	13.9	6.6	24.4	10.0	64.6
American Negroes (New York)	Wiener 1944	582	45.8	27.2	19.8	7.0	27.8	9.0	63.7
Italians (Florence)	Ferraro (*vide* Boyd 1939)	214	42.0	43.0	11.7	3.3	27.4	8.5	64.8
Danes	Rosling 1929	2 534	43.9	41.1	11.3	3.7	25.9	8.2	66.3
Irish (Dublin)	Boyd and Boyd 1937	399	55.2	31.1	12.0	1.7	18.6	7.6	74.4
American Whites	Snyder 1929	20 000	45.0	41.0	10.0	4.0	25.7	7.1	67.2
Scottish	Matta (*vide* Boyd 1939)	746	49.6	36.6	9.5	4.3	22.4	6.5	70.4
English	Fisher and Taylor 1940	106 477	45.2	43.2	8.5	3.1	27.0	6.0	67.0
Bushman (S.W. Africa)	Pijper 1932	268	60.4	28.0	7.8	3.7	17.3	5.9	76.8
Eskimo (Greenland)	Freuchen 1932	340	43.5	47.1	7.3	2.1	29.2	5.4	66.0
French (S.E. France)	Vallois 1941	2 882	46.7	44.4	6.9	1.9	27.1	4.8	68.3
Basques	Chalmers et al. 1949	805	51.1	43.5	4.1	1.2	25.6	2.6	71.7
Australian Aborigines	Birdsell and Boyd 1940	267	53.2	44.7	2.1	0.0	26.0	1.4	72.9
Maori (North Island)	Graydon et al.	267	41.2	58.1	0.2	0.2	35.2	0.4	64.2
Indians (Navaho)	Nigg 1926	457	72.9	26.9	0.2	0.0	14.5	0.1	85.4
Eskimo (Labrador) mixed	Sewall 1934	56	46.5	53.5	0.0	0.0	31.8	0.0	68.2
Eskimo (Labrador) unmixed	Sewall 1934	143	55.6	44.4	0.0	0.0	25.0	0.0	75.0
Indians (Kwakiutl)	Gates and Darby 1934	94	92.6	7.4	0.0	0.0	3.7	0.0	96.3
S. A. Indians (Tierra del Fuego) unmixed	Lipschutz et al. 1946	34	100.0	0.0	0.0	0.0	0.0	0.0	100.0

serological traits, and to some extent alone, they can be used as indicators. For example, taken alone, the presence of the Congo Pygmies and Hottentots in the Asiatic Mongoloid group supports the belief of some anthropologists that the Hottentots have some Mongoloid ancestry, and raises a question in connection with the Pygmies. Interestingly enough the South African Bushmen who live cheek by jowl in the same territory as the Hottentots, and who are physically scarcely to be distinguished from the latter, are nevertheless very low in B. Questions are raised which suggest further researches which may ultimately lead to the answers.

It will be seen from Table XVI that the Asiatic Mongoloids, the American Mongoloids, and the whites of various origins seem to form independent clusters on the basis of their blood groups and gene frequencies. There is, then, evidence here of a relative intragroup homogeneity, although clearly of a very variable kind.

The hundreds of investigations which have been carried out on the blood groups of different populations are sufficient to convince us that by such means alone we shall never solve the problem of the composition and interrelations of such populations. In conjunction, however, with the information derived from the distribution of the blood types M-N and Rh-Hr the indications are that we have in this method a most valuable, though admittedly partial, approach to the analysis of the problem of the variety of man. The type of information we may expect to secure by this means may be illustrated by the following examples.

A colony of Hungarian gypsies were found by Vérzar and Weszeczky to have A-B-O blood group frequencies more like those of the Hindus of Northern India than those of the Hungarians. On checking the history of this group on the basis of the structure of their language, a philologist discovered that the ancestors of this colony of gypsies had migrated from India some 500 or more years earlier. This case underscores the fact that ethnic origins cannot be determined by the analysis of blood group frequencies alone, though such analysis can suggest them. Such indicated origins must generally be supported by appropriate additional data.

The same investigators found that a colony of Germans living in Hungary were characterized by A-B-O blood group frequencies which more closely resembled those of the Germans of Heidelberg, from which their ancestors had migrated 200 years previously, than those of their fellow Hungarian citizens.

In Wales it has recently been found that a significant number of

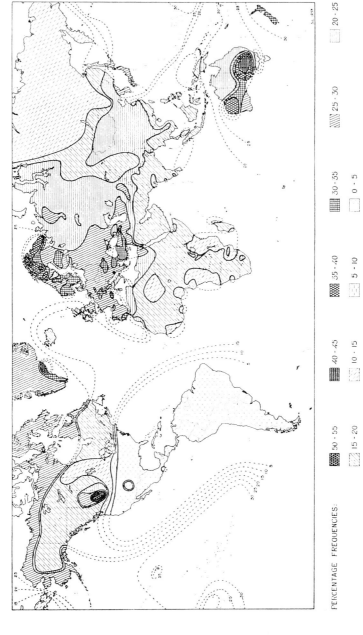

Figure 169. Distribution of blood group gene A in the aboriginal populations of the world. (From Mourant. *The ABO Blood Groups*, 1958. Courtesy, C C Thomas.)

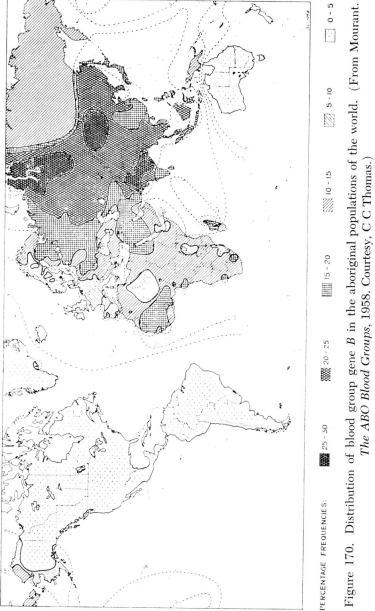

PERCENTAGE FREQUENCIES:

Figure 170. Distribution of blood group gene *B* in the aboriginal populations of the world. (From Mourant. *The ABO Blood Groups*, 1958. Courtesy, C C Thomas.)

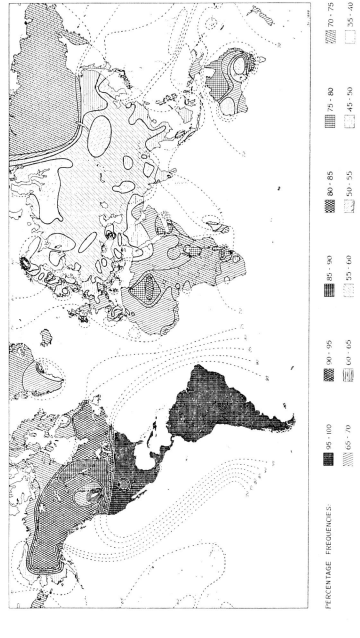

Figure 171. Distribution of blood group gene *O* in the aboriginal populations of the world. (From Mourant. *The ABO Blood Groups*, 1958. Courtesy, C C Thomas.)

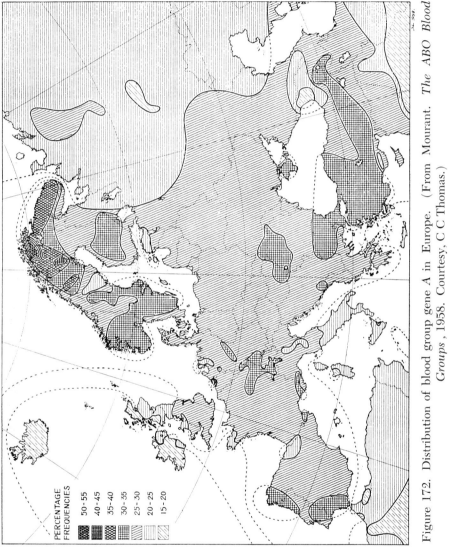

Figure 172. Distribution of blood group gene A in Europe. (From Mourant. *The ABO Blood Groups*, 1958. Courtesy, C C Thomas.)

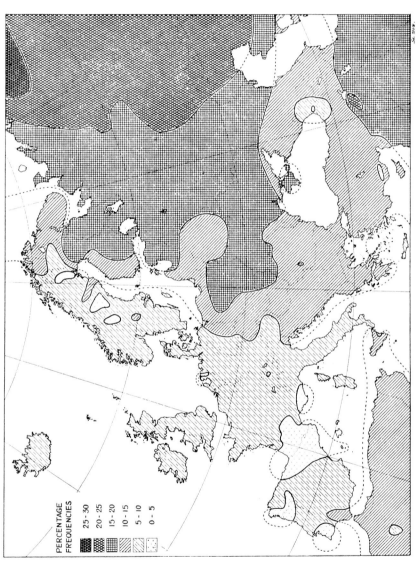

Figure 173. Distribution of blood group gene *B* in Europe. (From Mourant. *The ABO Blood Groups*, 1958. Courtesy, C C Thomas.)

PERCENTAGE
FREQUENCIES

25 - 30
20 - 25
15 - 20
10 - 15
5 - 10
0 - 5

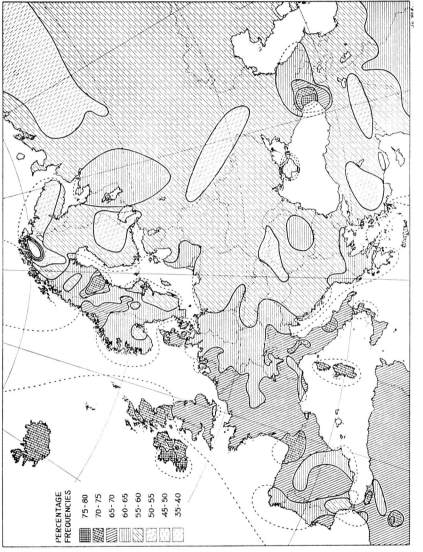

Figure 174. Distribution of blood group gene O in Europe. (From Mourant. *The ABO Blood Groups*, 1958. Courtesy, C C Thomas.)

persons bearing Welsh names made up a distinctively different population in their blood group gene frequencies from those bearing English names. The north and south Welsh are different in regard to blood group frequencies, the former resembling the Scots and Irish, while the inhabitants of south Wales, even those bearing Welsh names, are almost as high in the frequencies of certain blood groups (A in particular) as the southern English.

The population of New Zealand is mostly derived from English and Scottish immigrants. The blood groups of the non-Maori New Zealand population exhibit frequencies intermediate between those of the English and the Scots. On the other hand the mixed and the unmixed Maoris respectively show somewhat different frequencies.

Candela has shown that there is good reason to believe that blood group B was either introduced into Europe or augmented in that area between the 5th and 15th centuries A.D. by the Asiatic armies which invaded Europe during the lapse of those ten centuries. This he has been able to show by combining the data of history, physical anthropology, and the analysis of the blood groups. Candela very properly points out that the results of his studies illustrate the necessity of combining such data rather than to attempt to interpret the blood groups from their purely geographical distribution. This is, of course, not always possible, but in general, it should be obvious, that by means of genetic analyses such as are typified by the blood groups it would be possible to discover the composition of any apparently homogeneous population, and to determine what were the proportions of the different blood groups that entered into its composition.

Methods are now available for the study of the effects of the mixture of different populations on gene frequencies. But here again gene frequency analysis while indicating relationships requires additional supportive data if conclusions of any value are to be drawn. For example, the distribution of Rh types among Puerto Ricans is suggestive of a Negroid-Caucasoid mixture. However, it is also known that American Indians have also contributed to the ancestry of the Puerto Ricans, as is methodologically confirmed by the presence among them of a high frequency of shovel-shaped incisors—a Mongoloid trait.

If, as some students have suggested, mankind was originally characterized by a number of distinct populations, some of which were predominantly of blood group O, while others were predominantly of blood group A or B, it would follow that the present

TABLE XVII

Blood Group Frequencies in New Zealanders, Descendants Mainly of English and Scottish Settlers, in English and Scotch, and in Unmixed and Mixed Maori Showing the Probable Effects of European Admixture Upon the Blood Group Frequencies of the Latter

Population	Investigator	Number Examined	Percentage Distribution of Blood Groups				Gene Frequencies		
			O	A	B	AB	p	q	r
New Zealanders	Staveley & Godley 1950	2,802	53.0	35.5	8.8	2.6	21.2	5.8	72.8
Scotch	Fisher & Taylor 1940	10,969	52.0	34.2	10.4	3.3	20.7	6.9	72.2
Northern English	Fisher & Taylor 1940	8,716	48.6	40.3	8.5	2.5	24.5	5.8	69.5
Southern English	Fisher & Taylor 1940	106,477	45.2	43.1	8.5	3.0	26.7	6.0	67.2
Maori, Unmixed	Graydon & Simmons 1945	267	41.2	58.1	0.7	0.0	35.2	0.4	64.2
Maori, Possibly settler admixture	Godley 1946	835	45.3	48.6	4.1	1.9	29.6	2.9	67.2

distribution of the blood groups resulted from hybridization succeeded by varying intervals and degrees of isolation. The analysis of that distribution by the gene frequency method, in conjunction with other data, is obviously the method most capable of throwing some light on the history of that process. More refined methods will undoubtedly become available in the future, but even now it is of interest to observe, and not without significance, that certain distinct patterns in blood group distribution can be recognized when the blood groups of different peoples are plotted on a map. (See Figures 169-174).

Populations which at different times have received contributions to their common gene pool from other hybridizing populations can, at least speculatively, be more or less broken up into their blood group components by means of gene frequency analyses, and thus, to a certain extent something of the biological character of the population can be conjectured.

Since the blood groups of late prehistoric populations can in some instances and to a limited degree be ascertained by tests carried out on their skeletal or mummified remains,* it may in the future become possible to follow something of the biological and migratory history of such populations, and by this means possibly also something of their origins may be revealed.

Blood Types M, N and MN

The three blood types M, N, and MN are determined by a single pair of genes designated by the letters M and N. When a chromosome in which the gene M is located pairs with a chromosome containing gene M the resulting blood type is M. When a chromosome containing gene M pairs with a chromosome with the N gene the resulting blood type is MN. When pairing is between chromosomes containing N genes at each of their corresponding loci the blood type is N. This is clearly expressed in Table XVIII.

In man the so-called M and N agglutinogens only rarely have corresponding natural iso-agglutinins, hence it is hardly ever necessary to take them into consideration in making transfusions. The test sera are usually obtained from rabbits which have been injected with human blood of types M and N, and which have as a result developed agglutinins against the agglutinogens.

The M and N genes are without dominance. Since they are quite

---

* Other blood factors, like **M, N,** and **Rh,** have thus far not been determined successfully on skeletal or mummified remains.

TABLE XVIII

THE HEREDITY OF BLOOD TYPES M, N, AND MN

Genes Derived From Parents		Genotype	Blood Type
M	M	MM	M
M	N	MN⎫	MN
N	M	MN⎭	
N	N	NN	N

independent in their inheritance of all other blood groups and types, their distribution in human populations is anthropologically of considerable interest. Something of this distribution is shown in Table XIX.

Table XIX has been arranged in order of decreasing occurrence of blood type N. From this Table it will be seen that the first five populations, the Papuans, Australian aborigines, Fijians, Indonesians, and the Ainu show an excess of N over M, unlike the remaining twenty populations in which M is always more frequent than N. It is interesting to find the Australian aborigines and the Ainu agreeing in their high frequency of N in view of their long suspected relationship on physical

TABLE XIX

PERCENTAGE DISTRIBUTION OF THE BLOOD TYPES M, N, AND MN
(In order of decreasing percentage of blood type N)

Population	Investigator	Number of Subjects	M	N	MN
Papuans	Graydon & Simmons 1945	200	7.0	69.0	24.0
Australian Aborigines	Birdsell & Boyd 1940	730	3.0	67.4	29.6
Admiralty Islanders	Simmons et al. 1947	112	14.3	46.4	39.3
Fijians	Simmons et al. 1942	200	11.0	44.5	44.5
Ainu	Kubo 1936	504	17.9	31.9	50.2
American Negroes	Wiener et al. 1945	227	26.0	30.0	44.0
Maori (North Island)	Graydon et al. 1946	267	24.3	26.6	49.1
Congo Pygmies	Jadin 1934	92	29.3	26.1	44.5
Indonesians	Simmons et al. 1942	296	30.4	24.0	45.6
Filipinos	Simmons & Graydon 1945	382	25.9	23.8	50.3
Irish (Dublin)	Boyd & Boyd 1937	399	30.0	23.3	46.7
Basques	Chalmers et al. 1949	383	29.5	21.9	48.5
Chinese (New York)	Wiener et al. 1944	138	31.9	21.7	46.4
Russians (Leningrad)	Blinov 1935	701	32.0	21.3	46.7
Danes	Wellisch 1935	1 485	30.0	21.2	48.9
American Whites (N. Y.)	Wiener et al. 1945	6 129	29.2	21.2	49.6
Egyptians	Boyd & Boyd 1937	419	26.2	20.7	53.1
Australian Whites			27.1	20.5	52.4
English	Harley 1936	200	32.0	19.5	48.5
Japanese	Ischizu 1935	2 001	27.8	18.3	53.8
Chinese (Hong Kong)	Ride 1935	1 029	33.2	18.2	49.6
Asiatic Indians	Wiener et al.	156	40.4	16.0	43.6
Eskimos (Labrador & Baffinland)	Sewell 1939	144	31.2	16.0	52.8
Chinese (Boston)	Boyd & Boyd 1943	101	38.6	15.8	45.5
Welsh (North Wales)	Boyd & Boyd 1937	192	30.7	14.0	53.3
Amer. Indians (Washington)	Landsteiner & Wiener 1942	120	56.7	4.2	39.1
Mexican Indians	Wiener et al. 1945	98	61.2	3.1	35.7
Eskimo (E. Greenland)	Fabricius-Hansen 1939	569	83.5	0.8	15.7

TABLE XX

THE MNSs BLOOD GROUP SYSTEM

Phenotypes	Genotypes
MS	*MSMS* or *MSMs*
Ms	*MsMs*
MNS	*MSNS, MSNs,* or *MsNS*
MsNs	*MsNs*
NS	*NSNS* or *NSNs*
Ns	*NsNs*

grounds, and it is equally interesting to find the Papuans associated in this respect with the Australians. The Fijians and the Indonesians might have been predicted to have fallen close together in respect of the percentage of N. The percentage of all three blood types are strikingly similar in the American Negroes and in the Congo Pygmies, but as a combined group these do not significantly differ from the distribution found in other populations. Thus, in Western Europeans, American whites, American Negroes, Congo Pygmies, Chinese, and Japanese, and proportions of the three types are roughly 29 per cent M, 21 per cent N, and 50 per cent MN.

While, on the whole, the Asiatic Mongoloids tend to be relatively high in N, the American Mongoloids are exceptionally low in that blood type.

The MNSs Blood Group System

In 1947, an **S** blood factor was discovered which was soon shown by Sanger and Race to be related to the M and N agglutinogens, with phenotypes and genotypes as shown in Table XX. There are two possible ways in which the MNSs blood system is controlled, one is by four allelic genes, *MS, Ms, NS,* and *Ns,* where **S** is regarded as a mutation in the *M* and *N* genes, rendering the red corpuscles agglutinable by anti-**S** serum, the other where S and s are alleles linked with the *M* and *N* genes. Upon the latter hypothesis, two loci on a single chromosome appear to be involved, with one locus occupied either by *M* or *N,* and the other either by *S* or *s. M, N, S,* and *s* determine corresponding antigens. The test sera anti-**M**, anti-**N**, anti-**S**, and anti-**s** render possible the recognition of the distribution of the four genes in human populations with comparative ease. A sampling of the distribution of MNSs phenotypes in different human populations is shown in Table XXI.

The Rh-Hr Blood Types

Even more valuable than the blood groups and the M-N blood types in the genetic investigation of mankind are the Rh-Hr blood types.

When the blood of a rhesus monkey is injected into rabbits or guinea pigs a serum is obtained which has the property of agglutinating the blood of approximately 85 per cent of white persons, quite independently of the blood groups and M-N blood types to which they may belong. Such persons possess an agglutinable factor of some complexity on the surface of their red blood corpuscles, and this (from the first two letters of the name of the *rhesus* monkey, in which it was discovered in 1937 by Landsteiner and Wiener) is now called the Rh factor. Persons possessing this factor are said to be Rh-positive, persons lacking it are said to be Rh-negative. We now know that there are

TABLE XXI

Distribution of MNSs Phenotypes in Some Human Populations.
Tested with Anti-**M**, −**N**, and −**S**

Population	Investigator	No. Tested	Phenotypes %					
			MMS	MsMs	MNS	MsNs	NNS	NsNs
Australian Aborigines	Sanger 1950	178	0.0	7.9	0.0	35.4	0.0	56.7
Papuan Pygmies	Graydon et al. 1958	137	0.0	0.7	0.0	19.0	1.5	78.8
Maori	Simmons et al. 1951	148	0.7	25.0	7.4	43.9	4.0	18.9
Malay Aborigines	Polunin & Smith 1953	107	2.8	57.9	2.8	30.8	0.0	5.6
Malayan Negritoes	Polunin & Smith 1953	102	12.7	44.1	8.8	24.5	3.9	5.8
Japanese	Lewis et al. 1957	145	2.1	24.1	9.6	42.0	4.9	17.3
Ainu-Japanese	Simmons et al. 1953	414	2.1	16.8	19.3	24.8	25.3	12.0
Chinese, N. Y.	Miller et al. 1951	103	4.7	32.1	4.8	42.9	1.1	14.3
Eskimo	Chown & Lewis 1952	67	26.9	38.8	7.5	22.4	0.0	4.5
Blackfoot Indians	Chown & Lewis 1952	39	23.1	25.6	33.3	15.4	2.6	0.0
British Columbia Indians	Chown & Lewis 1952	300	22.7	37.0	9.0	25.7	1.0	4.7
Blood Indians	Chown & Lewis 1952	241	43.1	31.9	18.7	5.8	0.0	0.4
Cree Indians	Chown & Lewis 1956	165	39.0	12.1	21.8	23.0	0.0	4.2
Navaho Indians	Ikin & Mourant 1952	97	28.8	48.4	15.5	7.2	0.0	0.0
Diegueño Indians, Calif.	Pantin & Kallsen 1953	39	43.6	12.8	20.5	17.9	0.0	5.1
Brazilian Indians	Pantin & Junqueira 1952	74	10.8	8.1	47.3	32.4	0.0	1.3
Mapuche Indians, Chile	Sandoval & Henckel 1954	59	28.8	22.0	28.8	11.8	6.7	1.7
Negroes, N. Nigeria	Chalmers et al. 1953	159	3.8	13.2	18.9	35.8	3.1	25.2
Negroes, Congo	Nijenhuis 1953	70	15.7	20.0	10.0	37.1	2.8	14.3
Negroes, U. S. A.	Miller et al. 1953	580	6.9	17.2	16.5	33.1	6.0	20.2
Tswa Pygmies	Allison et al. 1953	33	0.0	9.1	15.2	29.4	15.1	21.2
Amba Pygmoids, Uganda	Ikin et al. 1952	113	4.4	16.8	15.9	35.4	5.3	22.1
Bushman	Zoutendyk 1953	188	7.4	30.3	7.4	35.1	1.6	18.1
Hottentot	Zoutendyk et al. 1955	201	13.4	42.8	12.0	22.9	0.9	8.0
Bantu, S. Africa	Shapiro 1953	205	9.7	23.9	12.2	36.6	3.4	14.1
Gorkhas, Nepal	Bird et al. 1957	200	20.0	28.0	13.5	31.0	2.5	5.0
Chenchu, S. India	Simmons et al. 1953	108	19.4	11.1	32.4	14.8	15.7	6.5
Caucasoids, U. S. A.	Wiener et al. 1953	394	22.3	9.4	26.9	22.1	6.8	12.4
English	Race & Sanger 1950	1419	20.8	7.5	26.7	22.7	7.2	15.1
Welsh	Ikin et al. 1952	116	17.2	13.8	31.0	15.5	7.1	14.6
Scottish	Ikin et al. 1952	527	19.9	7.0	26.4	27.5	4.2	15.0
Dutch	Nijenhuis & Van Loghem 1953	171	18.1	9.3	29.8	19.8	5.8	16.9
Italians	Ceppellini 1951	727	24.5	10.7	25.6	22.1	5.1	11.9
Yemenite Jews	Dreyfuss et al. 1952	104	36.5	18.3	20.2	21.1	1.0	2.8
Yemenite Arabs	Lehmann & Ikin 1953	111	30.0	21.6	20.7	13.5	2.7	5.4

three principal Rh-factors, the original **Rh**$_0$ which is by far the most powerful antigenically and clinically most important, and **rh'**, and **rh"**. Type rh blood lacks all three factors so that it can therefore be safely used in cases of intragroup incompatibility due to Rh factors.

The three elementary factors or antigens **Rh**$_0$, **rh'**, and **rh"**, have three theoretically possible contrasting factors designated **Hr**$_0$, **hr'** and **hr"**.[*] Every blood, with rare exceptions, possesses either an Rh factor or an Hr factor or both, derived from the pairs of contrasting factors **rh'-hr'**, and **rh"-hr"**. The Hr factors are less antigenic (that is, less capable of stimulating the formation of specific reacting substances) than the Rh factors. The three elementary Rh factors, it is now known, (together with the Hr factors **hr'** and **hr"**) determine 8 agglutinogens, as shown in the following diagram:

Agglutinogens

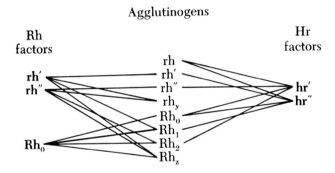

At first there were believed to be five Rh agglutinogens together with the blood type possessing no Rh agglutinogens, the rh type, determined by six major allelic genes designated R^1, R^2, R^0, r', r'' and r. Since every person has but one pair of Rh genes, one derived from the maternal pair and the other from the paternal pair, the possible ways in which these six genes can be combined in pairs are 21. In other words, 21 genotypes are possible which express themselves in eight Rh blood types or phenotypes. The Rh type of the individual is therefore the expression of his genotype determined by a single pair of genes, each allele or member of the pair being derived from the opposite parent. The 21 possible genotypes (not all of which

---

[*]Actually sera giving the expected reactions for anti-**hr'** and anti-**hr"** have been found, but not for anti-**Hr**$_0$. Instead of anti-**Hr**$_0$ a related anti-serum, anti-**hr** has been found, and recently the symbol anti-**Hr**$_0$ has been applied to a serum reacting with almost all blood cells except in individuals homozygous for so-called super Rh genes.

are at present serologically recognizable) and the eight Rh blood types are shown in Table XXII.

In reality there are probably more than a dozen Rh genes. To the six principal allelic Rh genes which have been referred to above four recently discovered additional Rh genes must be added. These are the genes R^z, r^y R^{1w}, and r'^w making a total of ten completely identified Rh genes, written in *italics*, as follows: r, r', r'^w, r'', r^y, R^0, R^1, R^2, R^{1w}, and R^z. The first five genes belong to the Rh-negative set of the gene *rh*, and the last five genes to the Rh-positive set of gene *Rh*. Each gene determines a corresponding agglutinogen. The agglutinogen molecule is characterized by specific properties which determine the specific combination of an antigen with its corresponding antibodies—it is these properties of the agglutinogen molecule that constitute the blood factors, and each agglutinogen has properties for many blood factors. For these reasons it is desirable to distinguish between agglutinogens and their serologic attributes, the blood factors. Hence, the symbols

TABLE XXII

RH BLOOD TYPES, GENOTYPES AND PHENOTYPES

Union of Genes Derived From Parents		Genotype	Rh Phenotype*
r	r	rr	rh
r	r'	$r'r$ $\rbrace$	rh'
r'	r'	$r'r'$	
r	r''	$r''r$ $\rbrace$	rh''
r''	r''	$r''r''$	
r'	r''	$r'r''$	rh'rh'' (rh$_y$)
r	R^0	R^0r $\rbrace$	Rh$_0$
R^0	R^0	R^0R^0	
r	R^1	R^1r	
R^0	r'	R^0r'	
R^0	R^1	R^1R^0 $\rbrace$	Rh$_1$
r'	R^1	R^1r'	
R^1	R^1	R^1R^1	
r	R^2	R^2r	
R^0	r''	R^0r''	
R^0	R^2	R^2R^0 $\rbrace$	Rh$_2$
r''	R^2	R^2r''	
R^2	R^2	R^2R^2	
r'	R^2	R^2r'	
r''	R^1	R^1r'' $\rbrace$	Rh$_1$Rh$_2$ (Rh$_z$)
R^1	R^2	R^1R^2	

*As determined using only antisera anti-**Rh**$_0$, anti-**rh'**, and anti-**rh''**.

TABLE XXIII

PARTIAL LIST OF RH-HR ALLELIC GENES, THEIR CORRESPONDING AGGLUTINOGENS, AND THE REACTIONS WITH 13 OF THE AVAILABLE RH-HR ANTISERA (WIENER'S THEORY OF MULTIPLE ALLELIC GENES).

Gene	Agglutinogen	Reactions with antisera of specificity												
		Rh_0	Rh^A	rh'	rh^{w_1}	rh^x	rh_1	rh''	rh^{w_2}	hr'	hr''	hr	hr^v	Hr_0*
r	rh	−	−	−	−	−	−	−	−	+	+	+	−	+
r^v	rh^v	−	−	−	−	−	−	−	−	+	+	+	+	+
r'	rh'	−	−	+	−	−	+	−	−	−	+	−	−	+
r'^w	rh'^w	−	−	+	+	−	+	−	−	−	+	−	−	+
r''	rh''	−	−	−	−	−	−	+	−	+	−	−	−	+
r^y	rh_y	−	−	+	−	−	−	+	−	−	−	−	−	+
R^0	Rh_0	+	+	−	−	−	−	−	−	+	+	+	−	+
R^{0v}	Rh_0^v	+	+	−	−	−	−	−	−	+	+	+	+	+
$\bar{R}^0$	$\overline{Rh_0}$	+	+	−	−	−	−	−	−	−	−	−	−	−
$\bar{R}^{w_1}$	$\overline{Rh^{w_1}}$	+	+	−	+	−	−	−	−	−	−	−	−	−
R^{0a}	Rh_0^a	+	−	−	−	−	−	−	−	+	+	+	−	+
R^1	Rh_1	+	+	+	−	−	+	−	−	−	+	−	−	+
R^{1w}	Rh_1^w	+	+	+	+	−	+	−	−	−	+	−	−	+
R^{1x}	Rh_1^x	+	+	+	−	+	+	−	−	−	+	−	−	+
R^2	Rh_2	+	+	−	−	−	−	+	−	+	−	−	−	+
R^{2w}	Rh_2^w	+	+	−	−	−	−	+	+	+	−	−	−	+
R^z	Rh_z	+	+	+	−	−	−	+	−	−	−	−	−	+

(From Wiener Courtesy, *Science*.)

*This symbol was originally applied to an antibody (also called anti-d), which appears to be non-existent. These two uses of the symbol are not to be confused.

for genes are customarily printed in *italics*, while the symbols for antibodies and their corresponding blood factors are printed in **boldface** type. For example, as may be perceived from Table XXIII gene r gives rise to agglutinogen rh, which is characterized by the blood factors, hr', hr'' hr, and Hr_0, and so on throughout the Table XXIII. Further serving to maintain the distinction between genes and agglutinogens, the latter are printed in regular type, the "h" of "rhesus" is retained and superscripts and subscripts used, as follows: rh, rh', rh'^w, and rh'', rh_y, Rh_0, Rh_1 Rh_2, Rh_1^w, and Rh_z. With ten Rh genes the number of theoretical Rh genotypes is increased to 55 with 28 corresponding serologically distinguishable phenotypes. These are shown in Table XXIV. Of the four recently discovered genes, r^y, r'^w, and R^z are extremely rare in whites, r^y being so rare that there is practically no data on it at all, though the suspicion is that it may occur less rarely in Mongoloids, while R^z is known to occur in 3 to 6 per cent of Asiatics, American Indians, and Australian aborigines.

The distribution of the Rh types in human groups promises to be anthropologically more enlightening than that of any other sero-

TABLE XXXV

THE Rh-Hr PHENOTYPES AND GENOTYPES

(From Wiener & Wexler. *Heredity of the Human Blood Groups, 1958.* Courtesy, Grune & Stratton)

Desig-nations	2 Rh phenotypes Approximate frequencies in N Y C whites (%)[3]	Reaction with anti-Rh₀ (or anti-rhesus)	12 Rh phenotypes Desig-nation[†]	Approximate frequencies in N Y C whites (%)[3]	Reaction with Anti-rh′	Anti-rh″	Anti-rhᵂ	28 Rh-Hr phenotypes Desig-nation	Approximate frequencies in N Y C whites (%)[3]	Reaction with Anti-hr′	Anti-hr″	Anti-hr	55 Genotypes[*]
Rh negative	15	−	rh	14 4	−	−	−	rh	14.4	+	+	+	rr
			rh′	0.46[*]	+	−	−	rh rh	0 46	+	+	+	r′r
								rh′rh	.0036	−	+	−	r′r
			rh″	.004	+	−	+	rh″rh	.004	+	+	+	r″r
								rh″rhᵂ	.00006	−	+	−	r′rᵂ or r′rᵂ
			rhᵧ	0 38	−	+	−	rh″rh	0 38	+	+	+	r″r
								rh″rh″	.0025	−	−	+	r″r
			rhʸ	.01	+	+	−	rh′rh″	.006	+	+	+	r′r″
								rhᵧrh	.008	+	−	+	rᵧr
								rhᵧrh′	.0001	+	−	−	rᵧr′
								rhᵧrh″	.0001	−	+	−	rᵧr″
								rhᵧrhᵧ	.000001	−	−	−	rᵧrᵧ
			rhᵧᵂ	.00005	+	+	+	rh′ᵂrh″	.00005	+	+	−	r′ᵂr″
								rhᵧrh′	.000001	+	−	−	rᵧr′ᵧ
Rh positive	85	+	Rh₀	2 8	−	−	−	Rh₀	2 8	+	+	+	R⁰R⁰ or R⁰r
			Rh₁	50 7	+	−	'	Rh₁rh	33.4	+	−	+	R¹r, R¹rᵖ or R⁰r′
								Rh₁Rh₁	17 3	+	−	−	R¹R¹ or R¹r′
			Rh₁ᵂ	3 3	+	−	+	Rh₁ᵂrh	1.6	+	−	+	Rᵂr, R¹ᵂr⁰ or R⁰r′ᵂ R¹r′ᵂ, R¹ᵂr′, R¹ᵂrᵂ, Rᵂr′ᵂ, or R¹ᵂr′ᵂ
								Rh₁ᵂRh₁	1.7	+	−	−	R¹Rᵂ, R¹ᵂr′ or R¹ᵂr′ᵂ R¹R¹ᵂ, R¹ᵂrᵂ or R¹ᵂr′ᵂ
			Rh₂	14.6	−	+	−	Rh₂rh	12.2	−	+	+	R²r, R²r⁰ or R⁰r″ R¹R² or R¹r″
								Rh₂Rh₂	2.4	−	+	−	R¹R² or R¹r″
			Rh₂	13 2	+	+	−	Rh₁Rh₂	13.5	+	+	+	R¹R², R¹r″ or R²r′ R¹r, R²R⁰ or R¹r′
								Rh₂rh	0.2	+	−	+	R²r, R²R⁰ or R¹r′ R²r′, R²r′ or R¹r′
								Rh₂Rh₂	.03	−	+	−	R²R², R²r″ or R¹r″ R²R², R²r″ or R¹r″
								Rh₂Rh₂	.07	+	+	−	R²R², R²r″ or R¹r″ R²R² or R²r′
								Rh₂Rh₂	.0008	−	−	−	R²R² or R²r″
			Rh₂ᵂ	0 6	+	+	+	Rh₁ᵂRh₂	0.6	+	+	+	Rᵂr², Rᵂr″ or R²r′ᵂ R¹ᵂR², R¹ᵂr″ or R²r′ᵂ
								Rh₂ᵂRh₁	.008	+	+	−	Rᵂr², Rᵂr″ or R²r′ᵂ R¹ᵂR², R¹ᵂr″ or R²r′ᵂ

[*] This table does not include hypothetical genes $R^{r''}$ and $r'^{''}$, which, if they exist at all, are very rare.

[†] In this table Rh₁ is used as a short designation for Rh₀′, rh₁ is short for rh′ᵂ and Rh₁ is short for Rh₀ᵂ

[*] The reduction in the frequency of type rh′ as compared with that given in earlier charts can be attributed to recognition of bloods of type Rh₁ (containing Rh₀ variant) which are now included in type Rh, instead of rh′ The agglutinogens Rh₀, Rh₁ and Rh₂, and their corresponding genes R⁰, R¹ and R² are not given here, because this would serve unnecessarily to complicate the chart, by increasing the number of possible genotypes to 91. Also, no attempt is made to include certain rare exceptional bloods, such as those lacking both factors rh′ and hr′, and/or lacking both rh″ and hr″, etc.

[3] Based on the estimated gene frequencies, r = 0.38, r′ = .005, r″ = .0001, r′ᵂ = .00005, r″ᵂ = .00005, R⁰ = .027, R¹ = .041, R¹ᵂ = .015, R² = .002, and R²ᵂ = .02

TABLE XXV

DISTRIBUTION OF THE RH BLOOD TYPES

(As Determined by the Use of 3 Sera: Anti-Rh_0, Anti-rh′, Anti-rh″)

Population	Investigators	Number of Subjects Tested	(Rh+)	rh	Rh_1	Rh_2	$Rh_1 Rh_2$	Rh_0	rh′	rh″	rh′rh″
Papuans	Simmons et al. 1946	100	100.0	0	93.0	0	7.0	0	0	0	0
Admiralty Islanders	Simmons & Graydon 1947	112	100.0	0	92.9	0.9	6.2	0	0	0	0
Fijians	Simmons & Graydon 1947	110	100.0	0	89.1	1.8	9.1	0	0	0	0
Filipinos	Simmons & Graydon 1945	100	100.0	0	87.0	2.0	11.0	0	0	0	0
New Caledonians (N & NW)	Simmons & Avias 1949	243	100.0	0	77.4	2.1	20.5	0	0	0	0
Loyalty Islanders	Simmons & Avias (Incomplete)	103	100.0	0	77.7	2.9	19.4	0	0	0	0
Indonesians	Simmons and Graydon 1947	200	100.0	0	74.0	2.5	22.5	0.5	0	0	0
Australian Aborigines	Simmons et al. 1948	234	100.0	0	58.2	8.5	30.4	1.3	1.7	0	0.5
American Indians (Mexico)	Wiener et al. 1915	95	100.0	0	48.1	9.5	41.2	1.1	0	0	0
American Indians (Oklahoma)	Wiener et al. 1946	105	100.0	0	40.0	17.1	39.1	2.9	0.9	0	0
Maoris	Simmons et al. (Incomplete)	32	100.0	0	25.0	31.0	41.0	3.0	0	0	0
Japanese	Miller and Taguchi	180	99.4	0.6	51.7	8.3	39.4	0	0	0	0
Japanese	Waller and Levine	150	98.7	1.3	37.4	13.3	47.3	0	0	0	0.7
Chinese	Wiener et al. 1944	132	98.5	1.5	60.6	3.0	34.1	0.9	0	0	0
Asiatic Indians (Moslems)	Wiener et al. 1945	156	92.9	7.1	70.5	5.1	12.8	1.9	2.6	0	0
American Negroes	Wiener et al. 1944	223	91.9	8.1	20.2	22.4	5.4	41.2	2.7	0.7	0
American Negroes	Levine et al. 1945	135	92.6	7.4	23.7	16.3	4.4	45.9	1.5	0.5	0
Puerto Ricans	Torregosa et al. 1945	179	89.9	10.1	39.1	19.6	14.0	15.1	1.7	0.5	0
White, Americans	Wiener et al. 1946	766	87.5	12.5	54.7	14.9	14.0	2.2	0.9	0.6	0
White, Americans	Unger et al. 1946	7,317	85.3	14.7	53.5	15.0	12.9	2.2	1.1	1.3	0.01
White, English	Fisher & Race 1946	927	85.2	14.8	54.9	12.2	13.7	2.3	0.7	0.7	0
White, English	Murray 1946	1,038	84.7	15.3	54.8	14.7	11.6	2.3	0.6	0.7	0
White, Australians	Simmons et al. 1945	350	85.1	14.9	54.0	12.6	16.6	0.6	0.9	0.6	0
White, Hollanders	Graydon et al. 1946	200	84.6	15.4	54.0	12.3	17.7	1.5	1.5	0	0
White, French	Bessis 1946	501	83.0	17.0	51.5	13.6	13.0	3.6	0.4	0.8	0
Basques	Chalmers et al. 1949	383	69.5	28.8	55.1	7.8	6.0	0.6	1.8	0	0
Basques	Etcheverry 1947	250	64.4	—	—	—	—	—	—	—	—
Swiss Walsers (Tenna.)	Moor-Jankowski & Huser 1958	38	60.5	39.5	—	—	—	—	—	—	—

logical trait. Something of this distribution in samples of various populations may be seen from Table XXV.

It will be observed from Table XXV that type rh is absent or virtually so from the blood of all groups with known Mongoloid traits. It will also be observed that there is virtually complete absence of the type rh in the Australian aborigines and in the Papuans of New Guinea. Furthermore, that while the distribution of the 8 Rh types in the Australian aborigines roughly resembles that seen in the Mongoloids, with the exception of a complete absence of type rh the pattern even more closely resembles that seen in whites. This pattern is very different in the Papuans. The Mongoloid plus Caucasoid character of the Rh blood types in the Australian aborigines is extremely interesting for the reason that the latter have usually been classified with the Archaic Caucasoid stock which is of more or less remote Asiatic origin. In the character of their Rh blood types the Australian aborigines may therefore be exhibiting the evidences of a relationship with stocks of Mongoloid character on the one hand and Caucasoid character on the other. The fact that the Australian aborigines are very low while Negroids are very high in Rh_0 contraindicates a Negroid component in the ancestry of the Australian aborigines. These brief remarks should serve to indicate the manner in which analysis of the blood types may be utilized in anthropological studies. Already this type of analysis has served to indicate remote and unsuspected possible relationships among human ethnic groups, and to confirm some which have been suspected on other grounds.

The Rh blood types promise to be among the most useful genetic traits in the study of the biological relationships of human groups, but it is only in combination with the analysis of many other genetically conditioned traits, and by an analysis of each of these traits in relation to the others that these types will have their greatest value.

R. A. Fisher originally proposed the theory that the rhesus blood types are controlled by three genes, D, C, E, with their alleles d, c, e. A single chromosome can carry either a D or a d gene but not both, hence there are three possible genotypes DD, Dd, and dd, and the same is, of course, true for the C and E genes and their alleles. Under this nomenclature an individual who is Rh positive possesses one or two D genes which control the presence of the D antigen. An Rh negative individual does not possess a D gene. The D is by far the most frequently present antigen and producer of its corresponding antibody.

Fisher postulated that the genes controlling the Rh antigens were all closely situated together on the same chromosome, $\begin{smallmatrix} D \\ C \\ E \end{smallmatrix}$ on the one

chromosome and $\begin{smallmatrix} d \\ c \\ e \end{smallmatrix}$ on the homologous chromosome. Hence, during the reduction division it is unlikely that these genes will become widely separated from one another on each chromosome, and hence, highly likely they will reappear in close relation to one another. The exchange of chromosome material during the reduction division between homologous chromosomes, called *crossing-over* has not been observed to occur, a fact which renders the Fisher three-gene hypothesis somewhat dubious. Additional alternative antigens of those already known, such as C^w and D^u are considered to be alleles occurring at the C and D loci. If the Rh blood groups are controlled by three genes segregating together, then the six alleles, C, c, D, d, and E, e, (omitting from consideration the rare alleles C^w and D^u) result in 8 different combinations or chromosomes, as listed below.

According to this theory the child inherits the three-gene combination from each parent, so that if the genotype of one parent is *CDE/cde*, then the child receives *either* CDE or cde from that parent. Since two chromosomes carrying Rh genes are present in every body cell (the diploid number of chromosomes) this means that the 8 different combinations can yield 36 different Rh genotypes, the addition of the alleles C^w and D^u make possible ten more combinations of which only five have been determined, namely C^wDe, C^wde, CD^ue, cD^uE, and cD^ue, making a total of 13 and yielding 91 genotypes.

r	cde
r'	Cde
r''	cdE
r^y	CdE
R^o	cDe
R^1	CDe
R^2	cDE
R^z	CDE

The number of ways in which n things can be selected in pairs is derived from the formula:

$$\frac{n}{2}(n+1).$$

Wiener has pointed out that the distribution of the *Rh* (rhesus positive) and *rh* (rhesus negative) genes can best be accounted for on the hypothesis that, at least during postglacial times, ethnic mixture must have been the most important factor influencing the pattern of that distribution.

In addition to the A-B-O and Rh systems a number of other blood groups have been discovered which are now to be described.

The P Blood Groups

The P blood groups were discovered by Landsteiner and Levine in 1927. Individuals having the P agglutinogen on their red blood corpuscles are called P-positive and those lacking it are known as P-negative. This additional property of the blood is due to a pair of allelic genes P and p situated at a single locus on the chromosome. Individuals with one or two P genes are P-positive, while those with pp are P-negative. The **P** factor is inherited as a simple dominant.

In 1951 Levine and his co-workers found an antibody, anti-Tj^a which reacted with the red cells of 3000 random group O individuals, but not the cells of the donor herself or of three of her offspring. Sanger subsequently found that the **Tj**^{a} factor is part of the P blood group system, when 15 Tj(a—) individuals from 9 families were all found to be P-negative. When anti-Tj^a serum was absorbed with P-negative blood until it ceased to react with the absorbing blood, there remained in the serum an antibody fraction that gave reactions corresponding to anti-**P**. Instead, then, of a pair of genes the P system is best accounted for by the postulation of three allelic genes P^1, P^2, and p at the P locus. The P^1 gene determines the agglutinogen previously called P, which besides factor **P** also has factor **Tj**^{a}; gene P^2 determines the P-negative agglutinogen having factor **Tj**^{a}, and gene p determines the agglutinogen Tj(a—). The genetic facts are set out in Table XXVI.

The **P** factor occurs with a frequency of 98 per cent in Negroids, 80 per cent in Caucasoids, and about 30 per cent among Chinese and Japanese. In Table XXVII a sampling of populations among which the frequency of the **P** factor has been determined is given in order to show the kind of variation encountered.

The Kell Blood Groups

The Kell blood groups were discovered independently by Coombs,

TABLE XXVI

THE P SYSTEM OF GENES AND BLOOD GROUPS

Genes Derived From Parents		Genotype	Blood Factors
P^1	P^1	P^1P^1	
P^1	P^2	P^1P^2	P, Tj^a
P^1	p	P^1p	
P^2	P^2	P^2P^2	Tj^a
P^2	p	P^2p	
p	p	pp	None known to date

TABLE XXVII

DISTRIBUTION OF THE P BLOOD GROUPS IN SOME HUMAN POPULATIONS

Population	Investigator	Number Tested	Phenotypes %		Genes %	
			P+	P−	P	p
English	Ikin et al. 1952	1166	76.59	23.41	51.61	43.39
Scottish	Ikin et al. 1952	527	75.52	24.48	50.52	29.48
Irish (Northern)	Ikin et al. 1952	106	78.30	21.70	53.42	46.58
American Whites	Wiener & Unger 1944	237	74.26	25.74	49.27	50.73
Germans	Dahr 1942	6478	73.62	26.38	48.64	51.36
Austrians	Speiser & Mohl 1953	240	70.83	29.17	45.99	54.01
French	Moullec & Kherumian 1952	2305	78.31	21.69	53.43	46.57
Norwegians	Brendemoen 1950	1162	74.87	25.13	49.87	50.13
Norwegian Lapps	Allison et al. 1952	183	78.14	21.86	53.25	46.75
Swedes	Jonsson 1947	1089	76.31	23.69	51.33	48.67
Swedish Lapps	Allison et al. 1952	193	60.10	39.90	36.84	63.16
Danes	Henningsen 1949	2345	78.85	21.15	54.01	45.99
Dutch	Van Loghem & Berkhout 1948	300	80.50	19.50	55.84	44.16
Egyptians	Moharram 1942	1000	77.50	22.50	52.57	47.23
West African Negroes	Barnicot & Lawler 1953	114	97.37	2.63	83.78	16.22
Nigerians	Chalmers et al. 1953	29	93.10	6.90		
Kikuyu (Kenya)	Henningsen 1950	66	96.97	3.03	82.59	17.41
Somali	Goldsmith 1952-53	233	72.10	27.90	47.18	52.82
Bantu (S. Africa)	Shapiro 1951	500	86.80	13.20	63.67	36.33
American Negroes	Miller et al. 1950	300	98.33	1.67	87.08	12.92
Todas (S. India)	Lehmann & Cutbush 1952	60	45.00	55.00	25.84	74.16
Irula (S. India)	Lehmann & Cutbush 1952	80	53.75	46.25	31.99	68.01
Andamanese	Lehmann & Ikin 1953	16	75.00	25.00		
Chenchu (S. China)	Simmons et al. 1953	95	73 68	26.32	48.70	51.30
Chinese (New York)	Miller et al. 1950	190	32.63	67.37	17.92	82.08
Negritos (Malayan)	Polunin & Sneath 1953	96	75.58	24.42	50.58	49.42
Senoi (Malayan)	Polunin & Sneath 1953	101	79.21	20.79	54.40	45.60
Ainu	Simmons et al. 1953	100	72.00	28.00	47.08	52.92
Maori	Simmons et al. 1951	153	90.20	9.80	68.70	31.30
Palauans (Micronesia)	Simmons et al. 1953	112	79.46	20.54	54.68	45.32
Australian Aborigines (C. Australia)	Simmons et al. 1957	100	23.00	77.00		
Thais, Bangkok	Simmons et al. 1954	100	30.00	70.00		
Australian Aborigines, (S. Australia)	Simmons et al. 1954	140	65.00	35.00		
Cook Ids. Polynesia	Simmons et al. 1955	256	45.70	54.30		
New Guinea	Semple et al. 1956	318	57.20	42.80		
N. Guinea Pygmies	Semple et al. 1956	91	63.00	37.00		
N. Britain, Baining	Semple et al. 1956	38	89.50	10.50		
N. Britain, W. Nakanai	Simmons 1956	46	35.00	65.00		

Mourant and Race in 1946, and by Wiener and Gordon in 1947. They are determined by a pair of allelic genes K and k, each of which gives rise to a particular agglutinogen. The genotypes are therefore KK, Kk, and kk. The Kell-positive type (KK, Kk) occurs in about 7 per cent of Caucasoids, and the Kell-negative (kk) in about 93 per cent.

In 1949 Levine and his co-workers discovered a second antibody which clumped the blood cells of most K-negative individuals, that is to say, those carrying the k gene the allele of K. Originally designated anti-Cellano (after the patient) this antibody is now called anti-k. Gene k causes the formation of the additional agglutinogen k which is detectable in both the homozygote and the heterozygote, as seen in Table XXVIII. This fact, therefore, renders it possible by the use of the anti-k serum to separate the homozygous from the heterozygous sections of the Kell-positive population. Something of the distribu-

TABLE XXVIII

GENOTYPES AND PHENOTYPES OF THE KELL BLOOD GROUPS

Genes Derived From Parents		Genotype	Blood Factors
K	K	KK	**K, Kp**^{b}
K	k	Kk	**K, Kp**^{b}**, k**
k	k	kk	**k, Kp**^{b}
K	k^p	Kk^p	**K, Kp**^{b}**, Kp**^{a}**, k**
k	k^p	kk^p	**k, Kp**^{b}**, Kp**^{a}
k^p	k^p	k^{p}k^p	**Kp**^{a}**, k**

tion of the Kell blood groups among the ethnic groups of man may be gathered from Table XXIX.

A third gene in the Kell series k^p, allelic to K and k, discovered by Allen and Lewis in 1957, gives rise to the blood factor **Kp**^{a}. When Fudenberg, in 1956, tested red cells of a Kell-negative man with anti-**Kp**^{a} serum he obtained an exceptionally strong reaction, such as one would expect from individuals of genotype k^pk^p, hence the resulting blood factor is assigned the symbol Kp^b. Allen and Lewis have suggested that with the four antisera anti-**K**, anti-k, anti-**Kp**^{a} and anti-**Kp**^{b}, some ten genotypes and 9 phenotypes are theoretically possible. However this may be there is at the present time convincing evidence

TABLE XXIX

DISTRIBUTION OF THE KELL BLOOD GROUPS. SAMPLES TESTED WITH ANTI-K

Population	Investigator	Number Tested	Phenotypes %	
			Kell+	Kell−
Australian aborigines	Simmons *et al.* 1955	58	0.00	100.00
Thais, Bangkok	Simmons *et al.* 1954	100	0.00	100.00
Chinese, Southern	Simmons *et al.* 1954	103	0.00	100.00
New Guinea	Simmons *et al.* 1956	98	0.00	100.00
Polynesians	Simmons *et al.* 1957	108	0.00	100.00
Malaysians	Polunin & Smith 1953	210	0.00	100.00
Chinese, N.Y.C.	Miller *et al.* 1951	103	0.00	100.00
Eskimos	Chown & Lewis 1952	67	0.00	100.00
Blackfoot & Blood Indians	Chown & Lewis 1953	280	0.00	100.00
Athapascan Indians	Chown & Lewis 1953	203	0.49	99.51
Brazilian Indians	Pantin & Junqueira 1952	423	10.17	89.83
Bantu, South Africa	Shapiro 1953	705	0.57	99.43
American Negroes N.Y.C.	Miller *et al.* 1948	200	3.50	96.50
West African Negroes	Barnicot & Lawler 1953	114	1.75	98.25
Bushman	Zoutendyk *et al.* 1953	106	10.38	89.62
Norwegian Lapps	Allison *et al.* 1952	183	12.02	87.98
Swedish Lapps	Allison *et al.* 1952	151	0.66	99.34
Walser Isolates, Switzerland	Ikin *et al.* 1957	76	15.00	85.00
Italians (Ferrara)	Ceppellini 1953	178	3.37	96.63
English	Dunsford 1949	566	7.26	92.74
Swiss	Hässig 1952	616	7.31	92.69
Dutch	Van der Heide *et al.* 1951	538	8.55	91.45
Poles	Kelus *et al.* 1952	1000	11.30	88.70

TABLE XXX

DISTRIBUTION OF THE LUTHERAN BLOOD GROUPS IN SOME HUMAN POPULATIONS

Population	Investigator	Number Tested	Phenotypes %	
			Lu(a+)	Lu(a−)
Asiatic Indians	Lehmann & Cutbush 1952	343	0.00	100.00
Malayan Negritos	Polunin & Smith 1953	105	0.00	100.00
Aboriginal Malays	Polunin & Smith 1953	46	0.00	100.00
Australian aborigines	Sanger et al. 1951	178	0.00	100.00
New Guinea	Sanger et al. 1951	141	0.00	100.00
Eskimos	Chown & Lewis 1952	25	0.00	100.00
Blood Indians	Chown & Lewis 1953	97	0.00	100.00
Brazilian Indians	Pantin & Junqueira 1952	73	16.44	83.56
Diegueño Indians (Calif.)	Pantin & Kallsen 1953	58	3.45	96.55
Bushman	Zoutendyk 1953	106	0.00	100.00
Bantus, South Africa	Shapiro 1953	205	5.37	94.63
West African Negroes	Barnicot & Lawler 1953	114	7.02	92.98
Somalis	Goldsmith 1952-53	233	8.58	91.42
Italians (Ferrara)	Ceppellini 1953	279	3.94	96.06
Norwegian Lapps	Allison et al. 1952	183	4.37	95.63
Dutch	Van der Heide et al. 1951	541	6.84	93.16
Danes	Mohr 1951	220	9.09	90.91
English	Ikin et al. 1952	1166	6.09	93.91
Welsh	Ikin et al. 1952	116	0.86	99.14
Scottish	Ikin et al. 1952	527	5.50	94.50
Irish (Northern Ireland)	Ikin et al. 1952	106	8.49	91.51
Walsers, Switzerland	Ikin et al. 1957	76	5.00	95.00
Greeks	Dunsford 1953	36	2.78	97.22

for only 3 alleles, K, k, and k^p which can only yield 6 genotypes. The conditions appear to be as set out in Table XXVIII. (Recently, however, Chown has obtained evidence for a blood type lacking all four factors, **K**, **k**, **Kp**^{a}, and **Kp**^{b}, presumably determined by a special gene K^o.)

The Lutheran Blood Groups

The Lutheran blood groups were discovered by Callender and Race in 1946. The Lutheran blood groups are determined by a pair of allelic genes Lu^a and Lu^b, the latter being dominant, and each gene determining the corresponding blood factor **Lu**^{a} and **Lu**^{b}. The three possible genotypes are Lu^bLu^b, Lu^aLu^b, Lu^aLu^a. Something of the distribution of the Lutheran blood groups among the ethnic groups of man is shown in Table XXXI. As will be perceived from this Table the distribution of the Lutheran blood groups is of some interest, for while the Lutheran positive (Lu^a) gene is not frequent in any population, the differences in its frequency as between some populations is not without significance. For example, southern Asiatic Indians do not seem to possess the gene at all, nor do the aborigines of Australia or New Guinea or the Eskimos. Among Europeans it ranges from 3 to 5 per cent, among Africans from zero to about 9 per cent. Among American Indians it is either absent or very low, but among Brazilian Indians the gene frequency for Lu^a has been reported as high as 8.6 per cent.

The Duffy Blood Groups

The Duffy blood groups were discovered by Cutbush, Mollison and Parkin in 1950. This blood system is determined by a pair of allelic genes Fy^a and Fy^b, the dominant gene being Fy^a, each determining the corresponding blood factor $\mathbf{Fy^a}$ and $\mathbf{Fy^b}$. The three possible genotypes are Fy^aFy^a, Fy^aFy^b, and Fy^bFy^b. The first two of these genotypes giving rise to the phenotype Fy(a+), and the third to the phenotype Fy(a—). A sampling of the ethnic distribution of the Duffy blood groups is given in Table XXXI. The frequency of the gene

TABLE XXXI

THE DISTRIBUTION OF THE DUFFY BLOOD GROUPS IN SOME HUMAN POPULATIONS TESTED WITH ANTI-$\mathbf{FY^a}$

Population	Investigator	Number Tested	Phenotypes % Fy(a+)	Phenotypes % Fy(a—)
Australian aborigines	Simmons *et al.* 1954	49	100.00	0.00
Thais, Bangkok	Simmons *et al.* 1954	100	100.00	0.00
Cook Ids., Polynesia	Simmons *et al.* 1955	254	92.1	7.90
Maoris	Simmons *et al.* 1955	53	71.7	28.30
Polynesians	Simmons *et al.* 1957	118	74.6	25.40
Papuans	Simmons *et al.* 1956	252	100.00	00.00
New Britain, W. Nakainai	Simmons *et al.* 1956	46	100.00	00.00
New Britain, Bainings	Semple *et al.* 1956	22	100.00	00.00
New Guinea Pygmies	Semple *et al.* 1956	30	100.00	00.00
Eskimos	Chown & Lewis 1952	7	100.00	00.00
Blackfoot Indians	Chown & Lewis 1953	39	97.44	2.56
Chippewa Indians, Unmixed	Matson & Levine 1953	161	98.14	1.86
Chippewa Indians > ¾ Indian	Matson & Levine 1953	128	92.97	7.03
Chippewa Indians < ¾ Indian	Matson & Levine 1953	206	81.55	18.45
Diegueño Indians, California	Pantin & Kallsen 1953	58	89.66	10.34
Brazilian Indians	Pantin & Junqueira	73	00.00	100.00
Bantu, South Africa	Shapiro 1953	365	11.78	88.22
Bushman	Zoutendyk *et al.* 1953	108	15.74	84.26
American Negroes	Miller *et al.* 1951	200	26.00	74.00
Chinese, N.Y.C.	Miller *et al.* 1951	103	99.03	0.97
Ainu-Japanese	Simmons *et al.* 1953	51	98.04	1.96
Asiatic Indians	Cutbush & Mollison 1950	55	92.73	7.27
English	Ikin *et al.* 1952	1166	65.52	34.48
Welsh	Ikin *et al.* 1952	116	69.83	30.17
Scottish	Ikin *et al.* 1952	527	66.79	33.21
Irish (Northern Ireland)	Ikin *et al.* 1952	106	65.09	34.91
Norwegian Lapps	Allison *et al.* 1952	183	96.72	3.28
Swedish Lapps	Allison *et al.* 1952	70	80.00	20.00
Dutch	Van der Heide *et al.* 1951	212	59.91	40.09
Swiss Walsers	Ikin *et al.* 1957	76	74.00	26.00
Swiss	Hässig 1952	527	64.71	35.29
Italians (Milan)	Ceppellini	115	66.96	33.04

TABLE XXXII

Distribution of the Kidd Blood Groups in Some Human Populations

Population	Investigator	Number Tested	Phenotypes % Jk (a+)	Phenotypes % Jk (a−)
African Negroes	Ikin & Mourant 1952	105	95.24	4.76
American Negroes	Rosenfield et al. 1953	305	92.79	7.21
Sea Dyaks (Borneo)	Sweetman et al. 1953	31	100.00	0.00
Eskimos	Chown & Lewis 1952	7	100.00	0.00
Indians (Br. Columbia)	Chown & Lewis 1952	146	61.64	38.36
Blood Indians	Chown & Lewis 1953	194	92.27	7.73
Blackfoot Indians	Chown & Lewis 1953	39	87.18	12.82
American whites N.Y.C.	Rosenfield et al. 1953	726	76.72	23.28
Chinese N.Y.C.	Rosenfield et al. 1953	103	52.43	47.57

ranges from zero among Brazilian Indians, to 6 to 14 per cent in Negroids, to a mean of about 50 per cent in Caucasoids and a range of between 40 and 70 per cent, and is highest in Mongoloids, in some Mongoloid populations approaching 100 per cent.

The Kidd Blood Groups

The Kidd blood groups were first described by Allen, Diamond and Niedziela in 1951. This blood group system depends upon a pair of allelic genes Jk^a and Jk^b each determining a corresponding blood factor **Jk^a** and **Jk^b** and three genotypes Jk^aJk^a, Jk^aJk^b, Jk^bJk^b. The first two genotypes giving rise to the phenotype Jk(a+), and the third to phenotype Jk(a−). As will be seen from Table XXXII showing the ethnic distribution of the Kidd blood groups, there are some anthropologically interesting differences, the gene for the Kidd positive factor being present in 100 per cent of Sea Dyaks in Borneo, and similarly frequent in Eskimos, quite high in Negroids (70 to 80 per cent), in slightly over 50 per cent of Caucasoids, in about 30 per cent of Chinese, and in from 30 to more than 70 per cent in American Indians.

The Lewis Blood Groups

The Lewis blood groups were discovered by Mourant in 1946. The genetics of the Lewis blood groups at the present time is not entirely clear, and these blood groups would appear to be characterized by some unique features, chief among which is the fact that the agglutinogen can only be demonstrated as present on the red blood corpuscles when both parents transmit the gene. In other words, the Lewis-positive factor appears to be inherited as a recessive. The pair of genes involved, Le^a and Le^b are responsible for the corresponding blood factors **Le**^{a} and **Le**^{b}.

In 1948 Grubb drew attention to the fact that individuals who are Lewis-positive Le(a+) are non-secretors of the A-B-O blood group substances in their saliva, whereas those individuals who were Lewis-negative Le(a—), with a few exceptions, were secretors of the A-B-O blood substances. Individuals who are Lewis-positive and non-secretors of A-B-O blood group substances do, however, secrete Le^a blood group substance in their saliva, while the majority of those who are Lewis-negative also secrete Le^a blood group substance in their saliva. It is of interest to note that chemical studies reveal that the Lewis substance is a mucopolysaccharide chemically almost indistinguishable from the A-B-O substances.

The heredity of the **Le**^{a} factor parallels that of the secretor/non-secretor trait. For example, parents who are both Le(a+) would both be non-secretors of the A-B-O blood group substances, and would have

TABLE XXXIII

The Distribution of the Lewis Blood Groups in Some Human Populations Samples Tested With Anti-Le^a

Population	Investigator	Number Tested	Le (a+)	Le (a—)
Australian aborigines, South	Simmons *et al.* 1954	164	7.30	92.70
Australian aborigines, Central	Simmons *et al.* 1957	125	100.00	00.00
N. Britain, W. Nakanai	Simmons *et al.* 1956	46	11.00	89.00
Thais, Bangkok	Simmons *et al.* 1954	100	23.00	77.00
Cook Ids. Polynesia	Simmons *et al.* 1955	256	17.20	82.80
Maoris, N. Z.	Simmons *et al.* 1955	49	29.00	71.00
Kapingas, Polynesia	Simmons *et al.* 1955	20	45.00	55.00
Polynesians	Simmons & Graydon 1957	138	14.50	85.50
Kedayans, Borneo	Simmons & Graydon 1952	104	18.27	81.73
Melanaus, Borneo	Simmons & Graydon 1952	100	14.00	86.00
Javanese	Simmons & Graydon 1951	40	40.00	60.00
Marshallese	Simmons *et al.* 1952	390	25.90	74.10
Palauans	Simmons *et al.* 1953	169	11.24	88.76
Trukese	Simmons *et al.* 1953	112	13.39	86.61
Kapingas	Simmons *et al.* 1953	44	45.45	54.55
Ainu-Japanese	Simmons *et al.* 1953	338	35.21	64.79
Southern Chinese	Simmons *et al.* 1950	71	15.49	84.51
Chenchu	Simmons *et al.* 1953	98	9.18	90.82
Blackfoot Indians	Chown & Lewis 1952	39	0.00	100.00
Blood Indians	Chown & Lewis 1952	241	0.00	100.00
Otomis, Mexico	Salazar Mallen 1949	81	9.88	90.12
Mexicans, Mexico City	Salazar Mallen 1949	199	11.56	88.44
English	Grubb & Morgan 1949	212	22.17	77.83
Norwegians	Brendemoen 1949	285	21.75	78.25
Dutch	Van der Heide *et al.* 1951	164	20.12	79.88
Poles	Kelus *et al.* 1952	500	22.80	77.20
Italians (Milan)	Ceppellini 1952	118	18.64	81.36
Swiss Walsers	Ikin *et al.* 1957	100	5.00	95.00
New Guinea Pygmies	Graydon *et al.* 1958	116	0.00	100.00

children similarly endowed, that is, all of whom would be Le(a+)
and non-secretors. Parents who are both Le(a—), on the other hand,
have children who are Le(a+) as well as Le(a—), thus indicating
that the factor **Le**[a] behaves in inheritance as a recessive. This suggests
that the gene *Le*[a] is the same as or is related to the non-secretor gene
se, and that gene *Le*[b] is the same as the secretor gene *Se*. Something
of the ethnic distribution of the Lewis trait is shown in Table XXXIII.

The Diego Blood Group

The Diego blood group was discovered by Levine and his co-
workers in 1954. The Diego factor is apparently inherited as a simple

TABLE XXXIV

DISTRIBUTION OF THE DIEGO BLOOD GROUP PHENOTYPES
IN SOME HUMAN POPULATIONS

Population	Investigator	No. Tested	Phenotypes % Di(a+)	Di(a—)
Australian Aborigines, Cent.	Simmons *et al.* 1957	112	0.0	100.0
Australian Aborigines, Cape York	Simmons *et al.* 1958	50	0.0	100.0
Polynesians	Simmons *et al.* 1957	80	0.0	100.0
Maoris	Lehmann *et al.* 1958	92	0.0	100.0
Caucasoids	Levine *et al.* 1956	2600	0.0	100.0
Eastern Papuans	Simmons *et al.* 1957	23	0.0	100.0
New Britain	Simmons *et al.* 1957	74	0.0	100.0
Marshallese, Micronesia	Sussman *et al.* 1956	129	0.0	100.0
Eskimos, Hudson Bay	Lewis *et al.* 1956	156	0.0	100.0
Sea Dyaks, (Iban) Sarawak	Colbourne *et al.* 1958	85	0.0	100.0
Land Dyaks, Sarawak	Colbourne *et al.* 1958	61	4.9	95.1
Japanese	Arends & Layrisse 1956	65	12.3	87.7
Chinese, Canton	Arends & Layrisse 1956	100	5.0	95.0
Japanese	Lewis *et al.* 1957	145	6.8	93.2
Bushman, C. Kalahari	Weiner & Zoutendyk 1959	114	0.0	100.0
Warrau, Winikina, Venezuela	Layrisse *et al.* 1958	72	0.0	100.0
Guajiros, Ziruma, Venezuela	Layrisse *et al.* 1955	152	5.3	94.7
Caribs, Santa Clara, Venezuela	Layrisse *et al.* 1955	49	14.3	85.7
Caribs, Cachama, Venezuela	Layrisse *et al.* 1955	121	35.5	64.5
Caribs, Rio Negro, Venezuela	Nunez Montriel 1957	125	25.6	74.4
Piaroas, Amazon	Layrisse & Arends 1956	24	12.5	87.5
Guahibos, Amazon	Layrisse & Arends 1956	76	14.5	85.5
Kaingang, Paraua, Brazil	Junqueira *et al.* 1956	48	45.8	54.1
Caraja, Mata Grosso, Brazil	Junqueira *et al.* 1956	36	36.1	63.9
Quechua Indians, Peru	Allen 1958	308	24.0	76.0
Blackfeet Indians	Chown (Layrisse) 1958	66	4.5	95.5
Apache Indians	Gershowitz (Layrisse) 1958	100	2.0	98.0
Surinam Indians	Nijenhuis (Layrisse) 1958	73	16.4	83.6
Negroes, Gold Coast	Layrisse & Arends 1957	107	0.0	100.0
Negroes, Miranda, Venezuela	Layrisse & Arends 1957	150	7.3	92.7
Negroes, Yaracuy, Venezuela	Layrisse & Arends 1957	119	3.4	96.6
Negroes, Canada	Lewis *et al.* 1956	35	0.0	100.0
Negroes, Brazil	Junqueira *et al.* 1957	120	0.0	100.0
Negroes, U. S. A.	Stern (Layrisse) 1958	27	0.0	100.0
Caucasoids	Layrisse & Arends 1957	1400	0.0	100.0
Arabs, Iran	Nijenhuis (Layrisse) 1958	100	0.0	100.0

dominant *Di*, the allele being *di*. Anthropologically the Diego factor is proving quite interesting, being extremely rare in Caucasoids, and having been found in frequencies from 2 to 45 per cent in American Indians, in about 8 to 12 per cent of Japanese, in about 2.5 per cent of Chinese, and it is uncommon among unmixed Negroids, Eskimos, and Polynesians (see Table XXXIV).

The Hunter and Henshaw Blood Groups

The Hunter antigen Hu, was discovered by Landsteiner, Strutton and Chase in 1934. The Henshaw antigen He, was discovered by Ikin and Mourant in 1951. The Hunter and Henshaw genes are closely linked with the MNSs system, but whether the genes involved are alleles of one another or not is at present unknown. The Hunter antigen is found in about 7 per cent of American Negroes, 22 per cent of West African Negroes, and in 0.5 per cent of American Whites. The Hunter gene almost invariably travels together with the *N* and *Ns* genes. The Henshaw gene in Papua is predominantly associated with *Ns*, in West Africa with *Ns*, in Congo Negroes with *MS*, in Hottentots with *MS*, in Cape Coloured with *Ms*, in South African Bantus it is random in distribution with respect to *MNSs*, and in Bornean Sea Dyaks it appears to travel with *MS*. The Henshaw antigen occurs in 2.7 per cent of West Africans, in 2.1 per cent of Nigerians, in 4.3 per cent of Gold Coast Negroes, in 3.3 per cent Bushman and Hottentots, and in about 7 per cent of Bornean Sea Dyaks.

The Sutter Blood Group

The red-cell antigen Js[a] discovered by Giblett in 1958 belongs to the new blood group named by its discoverer after the patient (J.S.) the Sutter blood group. The Sutter blood group promises to be of great value as an anthropological marker, since it has thus far only

TABLE XXXIV-A

DISTRIBUTION OF THE SUTTER BLOOD GROUP PHENOTYPES
IN SOME HUMAN POPULATIONS

Population	*Place*	*Investigator*	No. Tested	Phenotypes % Js(a+)	Js(a−)
American Negroes	Seattle	Giblett 1958 & 1959	440	19.5	80.5
Bushman, C. Kalahari	So. of Ghanzi	Wiener & Zoutendyk 1959	72	4.2	95.8
Bushman, C. Kalahari	At Ghanzi	Weiner & Zoutendyk 1959	42	7.1	92.9
American Whites	Seattle	Giblett 1958 & 1959	500	0.0	100.0
Paraujano Indians	W. Venezuela	Layrisse & Layrisse 1959	120	2.5	97.5
Goajira Indians	W. Venezuela	Layrisse & Layrisse 1959	119	0.8	99.2
Irapa Indians	W. Venezuela	Layrisse & Layrisse 1959	138	0.0	100.0
Macoita Indians	W. Venezuela	Layrisse & Layrisse 1959	57	0.0	100.0

been found to occur in Negroes, and hence will be of service in the study of gene flow from Negroid into non-Negroid populations. As will be seen from Table XXXIV-A it has thus far not been found in a single Caucasoid, but occurs in about 19.5 per cent of Seattle Negroes. It has not been found in any South American tribes thus far examined, with the exception of those having a history of some Negro admixture, such as the Arawak tribes, the Paraujanao and the Goajira. Unpublished studies on Belgian Congo Negroids by Giblett on eight different tribal samples of about 100 each reveal a variability of Js^a positives of from 5 to 26 per cent. Similar variability in West African tribes seems also to exist. Such variability may be due to genetic drift.

A pair of allelic genes Js^a and Js^b are probably involved in the Sutter blood group, giving rise to three genotypes and two phenotypes, as follows:

Genotypes	Phenotypes
Js^aJs^a	Js(a+)
Js^aJs^b	Js(a+)
Js^bJs^b	Js(a−)

The Blood Genes as Genetic Indicators

The comparatively stable nature of the blood genes renders them of great potential value in the tracing of ethnic relationships. It is, however, not to be expected that it will be possible to solve anthropological problems with respect to ethnic relationships merely by turning to blood gene frequency tables, as one would look up the definition of a word in a dictionary or the answer one is seeking in a table of logarithms. This is particularly worth emphasizing in view of the fact that neither the evolutionary nor the ethnic implications of the characters of the blood are quite clear. There can, however, no longer be much doubt that the serological traits of man are not adaptively neutral, but that they are in fact of some adaptive value. Evidence for this is slowly but surely emerging, and we shall deal with this on pp. 372-382.

At the present time we can see that certain more or less distinct patterns exist in the distribution of man's serological traits, and furthermore, that a fair amount of correlation exists between these blood frequency patterns and certain patterns of distribution of human populations. Thus far, however, no linkages between blood traits and anatomical traits have been discovered. Such linkages as have been established between blood groups and other traits, have been limited to families and are not characteristic of populations. One such family linkage was demonstrated by Renwick and Lawler in 1955. These workers found that in some families the nail-patella syndrome was associated with group B, while in others the dominant gene for this condition travelled with the O and A genes. This is quite an exciting discovery for it tells us that the gene for the normal development of nails and knee-caps is situated at the same locus as the A-B-O genes—as is the abnormal nail-patella gene. The condition, sometimes called hereditary onycho-osteodysplasia, is one in which the finger nails and knee-caps are poorly developed or the latter may be absent, occasionally the elbows are dislocated, and the pelvic bones may have extra growths. In 1953 Chalmers and Lawler demonstrated linkage between elliptocytosis, that is, oval instead of the normal circular disc type red corpuscles, and the Rh gene complex. In some families the gene for oval cells travelled on the same chromosome as R^2, in some with r and in others with R^1.

It has already been pointed out that the genetic mechanism governing the inheritance of the blood traits is well understood, in contrast to the situation which prevails with regard to almost all other anthropological criteria, the inheritance of but a few of which is at best but imperfectly understood. In the case of the serological traits a particular gene is responsible for a particular antigen in the red blood corpuscles, whereas in such traits as skin color, hair form, and the like, a number of genes are involved. Furthermore, in respect of the genetic relations of populations to one another the serological genes are much more significant than those for discontinuously distributed traits like skin color and hair form.

Further, the blood trait genes can serve as ethno-serological *indicators,* much as radioactive sodium ions act as "tags" in biochemical researches, enabling the biochemist to identify the stages through which a chemical reaction passes, and the changes which occur in the substance under investigation.

For this to be possible in ethno-serological studies it is necessary first to identify the source of the blood group factor which one proposes to use as an indicator. This is by no means an easy task in all instances, in view of the shuffling and reshuffling of populations which has occurred since the earliest times. However, it seems almost certain that all the B in Europe and in eastern Asia, as well as a little of the B in Southeastern Asia and the Pacific area, is derived from the brachycephalic central Asiatic Mongoliod pool exemplified by the

TABLE XXXV

GENE SERIES O, A_1, A_2, B

Genotypes	Phenotypes
OO	O
A_1A_1 } A_1O } A_1A_2	A_1
A_2A_2 } A_2O	A_2
BB } BO	B
A_1B	A_1B
A_2B	A_2B

Buriat type. Group B in Indonesia (including Madagascar), and in most of Indo-China is attributable, on the other hand, to relatively late colonization from India.

The account given in the preceding pages of the blood groups is accurate as far as it goes. Since 1910 it has been known that there are two sorts of A blood, designated A_1 and A_2, with A_1 apparently dominant over A_2. It has been postulated that there are four rather than three genes involved, namely O, A_1, A_2, and B, giving rise to 10 genotypes and six phenotypes, as shown in Table XXXV.

Subgroup A_2 is anthropologically of considerable interest, for from the many studies which have thus far been carried out on various populations this subgroup (see Table XXXVI) appears to be absent in the Australian aborigines, Papuans, all Mongoloids, and Polynesians. At the present time, omitting from consideration the mixed American Negroes among whom both A_2 and A_1 occur, A_2 appears to be largely if not entirely limited to whites of European origin.

In mixing with Mongoloids in eastern Asia the assumption is that some groups of the Archaic Caucasoid divisions acquired large amounts of group B, and corresponding portions of Mongoloid genes; such a group is represented by the Ainu. The Australian aborigines, on the other hand, are exceedingly low in B, and many coastal tribes are wholly lacking in it. Possibly as a result of mixture with a Negroid stock they now possess somewhat greater amounts of O, together with greater amounts of melanin pigments in the skin than the Asiatic Archaic Caucasoids. In addition to the striking difference in the frequencies of A_2 in the Caucasoid and the Archaic Caucasoid

TABLE XXXVI

DISTRIBUTION OF THE SUBGROUPS OF A AND AB

(In order of *increasing* frequency of gene p_2)

Population	Investigator	Number of Subjects	Frequencies of Blood Groups %						Frequencies of Genes			
			O	A_1	A_2	B	A_1B	A_2B	p_1	p_2	q	r
Mexican Indians	Wiener et al. 1945	98	90.8	6.1	0.0	3.1	0.0	0.0	3.1	0.0	1.6	95.3
American Indians (unmixed)	Landsteiner et al. 1942	120	73.3	25.8	0.0	0.8	0.0	0.0	13.9	0.0	0.5	85.6
Indonesians	Simmons et al. 1945	296	51.7	22.6	0.0	21.3	4.4	0.0	14.6	0.0	13.8	71.9
Fijians	Simmons et al. 1945	200	43.5	34.0	0.0	16.5	6.0	0.0	22.5	0.0	12.0	66.0
Papuans	Simmons et al. 1946	455	42.9	27.5	0.0	21.3	8.4	0.0	19.9	0.0	16.1	65.5
Australian Aborigines	Wilson et al. 1944	649	43.9	56.1	0.0	0.0	0.5	0.0	25.1	0.0	0.0	74.9
Hawaiians	Nigg 1930	413	36.5	60.8	0.0	2.2	0.5	0.0	28.2	0.0	1.8	60.4
Maoris (North Island)	Graydon et al. 1946	267	41.2	58.1	0.0	0.7	0.0	0.0	35.2	0.0	0.4	64.2
American Indians (mixed)	Landsteiner et al. 1942	155	58.1	31.6	3.2	4.5	2.6	0.0	18.1	2.1	2.9	76.2
Caucasians (Tiflis)	Boyd & Boyd 1937	268	57.5	25.4	3.7	10.1	1.0	0.0	14.8	2.4	6.4	75.8
Basques	Chalmers et al. 1949	383	51.1	37.3	6.2	4.1	1.0	1.5	21.5	4.1	2.6	71.7
American Negroes	Wiener et al. 1943	189	48.1	19.6	6.8	22.8	1.6	0.0	12.2	4.8	14.5	69.4
Germans	Dahr et al.	416	40.1	37.5	7.0	11.3	3.3	1.1	23.4	5.3	8.4	63.3
English (Hertfordshire)	Shenley	900	42.1	35.8	8.0	10.1	3.1	0.8	21.9	5.9	7.4	64.9
Egyptians (Cairo)	Matta 1937	516	26.6	29.1	6.6	27.1	7.0	0.9	21.3	6.0	21.7	51.6
Irish (Dublin)	Boyd & Boyd 1937	400	55.5	21.7	9.5	11.8	3.1	3.8	12.5	6.1	7.6	74.3
Russians	Blinov 1935	763	33.7	30.8	7.6	20.8	7.0	0.8	20.6	6.2	15.8	58.1
Dutch	Graydon et al. 1946	200	46.5	30.5	9.0	13.9	4.5	3.1	18.2	6.3	6.3	68.2
American Whites	Wiener et al. 1943	1,077	41.7	29.0	8.9	12.4	5.2	0.5	18.1	6.5	10.0	64.6
Danes	Clausen	1,853	40.0	32.7	9.8	16.3	2.8	1.4	20.2	7.3	9.2	63.3
Welsh (North Wales)	Boyd & Boyd 1937	190	47.3	21.6	11.6	10.3	2.6	2.3	13.0	7.9	10.8	68.8
Swedes	Wolff & Jonsson	1,200	37.9	36.9	9.8	15.8	3.9	0.5	22.9	8.5	7.9	61.6
Finns	Mustakallio	7,120	33.9	32.3	10.7	15.8	4.4	1.2	20.1	9.3	12.3	58.2
Basques (San Sebastian)	Boyd & Boyd 1937	64	51.5	31.2	15.6	1.6	0.0	2.9	17.3	10.2	1.1	71.6

major groups there is also a fundamental difference between them in the frequency of the M-N blood types. It has already been seen that whereas in whites of European origin the frequency of M is always in excess of that of N, among the Australian aborigines M is scarce and N very high. In the Ainu also, the N factor is more frequent than in the rest of the world populations, but less so than in the Australian aborigines. This may be the result of admixture with carriers of Mongoloid genes or it may be the effect of their more markedly Caucasoid genotype. In being virtually 100 per cent Rh positive the Australian aborigines fall into the Mongoloid pattern, but not so, as we have already seen, with respect to their remaining Rh types which follow the Caucasoid pattern.

This brief discussion will suffice to indicate the manner in which the genes for the blood groups and blood types may be used as indicators. For it is obvious, for example, that if it is established that the central Asiatic Mongoloids were the source of European B, then we could use that information to estimate the extent to which the Mongoloids have contributed to the genetic composition of a given population.

In the example which has been cited, a close correlation has been demonstrated between the frequencies of the "new" blood group gene B and the proportions of the "new" somatic (Mongoloid) genes. The latter, being for the most part genetically dominant, are easily discernible in the resultant ethnic mixture. The presence of this close correlation makes us more confident in the application of the method to those other problems of ethnic mixture in which the somatic genes, being recessive, may have failed to leave a visible impression on the phenotype.

The new science of population genetics has already thrown considerable light upon those micro-evolutionary changes that constitute the evolutionary process. The studies of Glass and his collaborators on the American Dunker religious isolate demonstrating the effects of genetic drift on blood group gene frequencies, and of Allison on sickling are but two outstanding examples of the work that is being done in this field.

While the blood groups and blood types are not chemically quite the same in the apes and monkeys as they are in man, their distribution in these non-human primates is of some assistance in helping us to understand the nature of the possible factors involved in the distribution of the blood groups throughout the world as we find them at the present time.

While some species of monkeys possess two of the blood group factors, there is a striking tendency for many other species to exhibit but a single blood group, generally either A or B. This is not the case in the anthropoid apes. Thus, the two mountain gorillas thus far tested belong to group A, the 13 lowland gorillas thus far tested to group B. Of the 133 chimpanzees tested, 117 are A and 16 are O. Out of 24 orangs tested nine were A, 10 were B, and five AB. The 11 gibbons tested yielded two A, seven B, and two AB.

Group substances are absent from the red blood corpuscles of gorillas and monkeys, but are present in the tissues and secretions. Thus, a group A monkey has A in its saliva, but anti-B in its serum but no A on its red blood corpuscles (Wiener, Candela and Goss).

With the exception of 10 per cent of chimpanzees group O is lacking in the apes. In man group O occurs in all populations in frequencies varying from 50 per cent to as high as 100 per cent of the O gene.

On the basis of these facts it could be argued the stock from which man, in common with the great apes, was derived, possessed all four blood groups, and that different genes suffered extinction in different isolates of apes and of early man. In such case the pattern of distribution of the blood groups in early man would have been the same or very similar to what it is among the anthropoid apes today. From this we would have to conclude that the present distribution of the blood groups was, in man, brought about by intermixture or hybridization. Furthermore, it could be argued that blood group O in man was originally of very low frequency, and probably limited to a few groups, being subsequently diffused through hybridization. On the other hand it could be argued that these differences indicate that man is only remotely related to the anthropoid apes.

The blood of all chimpanzees thus far tested contains agglutinogens similar to but not identical with the human agglutinogens M and N. The orang-utan, the gibbon, and the catarrhine monkeys exhibit M agglutinogens of progressively more different kinds. An M-like agglutinogen has been found in only one species of platyrrhine monkey (Wiener and Landsteiner).

It was at one time thought that all chimpanzees were Rh negative, since the first animals tested seemed to be so. But in 1953 Wiener et al., showed that in 4 chimpanzees which they tested in every case the Rh_0 factor was present, thus all 4 were Rh positive. Subsequently 4 additional chimpanzees tested have been shown to be Rh positive. It is now reasonably certain that the first chimpanzees tested were also Rh positive, for owing to the chemical differences the chimpanzee blood failed to react with the anti-rhesus guinea-pig serum used originally. When, however, the chimpanzee's cells are treated with proteolytic enzymes (ficin) and are tested with human anti-Rh_0 serum they are strongly agglutinated. It is probable that all chimpanzees are Rh positive. Possessing, as they do, blood factors Rh_0 and hr', but not rh' and rh", they curiously most resemble in this respect the Negroid major group (Wiener).

The indication gains strength that the Rh negative blood type constitutes a relatively recent mutation in man's biological history, appearing possibly in the upper paleolithic somewhere in western Europe.

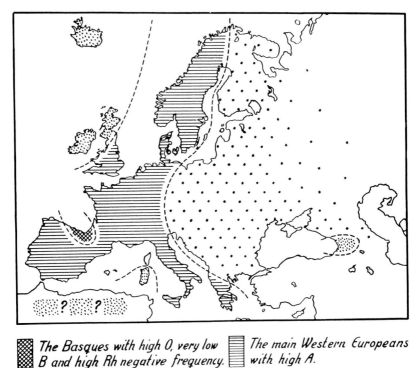

The Basques with high O, very low B and high Rh negative frequency.

The main Western Europeans with high A.

The Celts and other peripheral peoples with high O.

The Slavs and other Eastern Europeans with high B.

Figure 175. Blood groups of the Basque People. (From Chalmers, Ikin, and Mourant. Courtesy, *Am. J. Phys. Anthrop.*)

This suggestion has recently been rendered more than plausible by the discovery that the linguistically unique Basque people are characterized by an extraordinarily high frequency of the Rh-negative gene. In a total of 250 Basques Etcheverry (1947) found that 35.6 per cent were Rh-negative. This is more than twice the highest percentage hitherto known for any human group. In a sample of 383 Basques Chalmers and his co-workers (1949) found the percentage to be 29.0 per cent. Later observations suggest that 26 per cent is probably nearer the true frequency for the Rh-negative trait in the Basques. The Basques as well as populations containing a large Basque element show a high frequency of group O persons. In this they resemble Icelanders, Scots, Irish, northern Welsh, and Sardinians. The Basques, however, are unique among all the peoples of Europe in their very low frequency of group B. Such facts together with their extraordinarily high Rh-negative constitution suggest that the Basques are a relict population which has remained isolated from the general stream of western European admixture.

It is of interest to mention here that in 1945 Boyd and Montagu by plotting the distribution of Rh gene frequencies on a small scale map, were led to conclude that the highest frequency of Rh-negative was to be found in the borderland region between northern Spain and southern France, in other words, the Basque country. Boyd and Montagu also concluded that it seemed probable that the Rh-negative gene originated in a population in this general region. Mourant (1947) and Etcheverry (1947) independently suggested that the Basques are the present-day representatives of a population from which the Rh negative gene in Europeans is derived.

In 1958, Moor-Jankowski and Huser reported on the Rh frequencies, as well as other serological and anthropological traits, characterizing isolated village populations of Switzerland. In these small populations, isolated from one another by mountain barriers, even higher frequencies of Rh-negative were encountered than among the Basques. The details for the three populations showing the highest Rh-negative frequencies are as follows:

Population	Village	No.	Rh-Negative %
Eastern Walsers	Davos-Sertig	34	32.4
Eastern Walsers	Wiesen	66	34.5
Western Walsers	Tenna	38	39.5

It is of interest to note that the population showing the highest Rh-negative frequency is considered to be the most isolated. As among the Basques Moor-Jankowski found, among these isolated Swiss

TABLE XXXVII

The Genotypes and Phenotypes of the Secreting Factor

Genotype	Phenotype
SS	Secretor
Ss	Secretor
ss	Non-Secretor

populations, a high frequency of blood group O (50%) and an extremely low frequency of blood group B (5.3%), the corresponding frequencies for the Basques being 54.7 per cent and 3.4 per cent.

The similarity of the Basques and Walsers in these serological traits probably represents an example of the effects of the same genetic processes at work in two different populations, rather than an example of the origin of these two populations from the same stock with similar frequencies of serological traits. This kind of parallel variation has almost certainly occurred again and again in widely separated populations, and hence underscores the necessity of caution in interpreting gene frequency distributions for serological traits.

The Secreting Factor

The blood group factors may also be demonstrated in the saliva, gastric juice, mucous secretions, and urine of some persons. Such persons are termed "secretors." Persons whose saliva or other body fluids are nearly free of these factors (in water soluble form) are termed "non-secretors." The heredity of the secreting factor is simple, two genes being involved, one of which is dominant S, and the other is recessive s, thus giving rise to three genotypes (Table XXXVII).

The secreting type occurs in 78 per cent of Berlin whites, 84.2 per cent of New York whites, and 61.2 per cent of American Negroes.

The simple hereditary mechanism of the secreting factor and the ease with which it may be tested, renders it admirably suited to ethnic studies.

Sickling

Another trait of the blood which is genetically of promising anthropological value is the tendency of the red blood corpuscles (erythrocytes) in some members of Negroid populations to assume a peculiar sickle shape when placed in an oxygen-deficient medium. A drop of blood of such an individual when sealed under a cover-slip on a slide with vaseline will, when observed under the microscope at varying intervals up to three days, show a high proportion of erythrocytes of bizarre oat, sickle, or holly leaf shapes. This condition is known as sickling or the sickle cell trait. In American Negroes sickling occurs in frequencies ranging from 4.3 to 15.0 per cent, with a mean of about 8.0 per cent. In about 1 out of 40 of those individuals whose cells are capable of sickling, severe chronic anemia develops as a result of excessive destruction of their erythrocytes. This condition is known as sickle cell anemia. In July 1949 Neel showed that the gene responsible for sickling is carried in heterozygous condition in individuals showing the sickle cell trait, and in homozygous condition in those with sickle cell anemia. In November 1949 Pauling and his coworkers corroborated this discovery by showing that normal and sickle cell anemia hemoglobin exist in roughly equal proportions in sickle trait hemoglobin preparations. The gene responsible for sickling is identifiable with one of an alternative pair of alleles (allelic genes are situated at corresponding loci in a pair of chromosomes), as Hb^A and Hb^S, where Hb^A is the gene controlling the normal hemoglobin molecule A, and Hb^S is the gene controlling the deficient hemoglobin molecule S of sickle cell anemia. In normal unaffected persons there is a complete absence of the deficient gene Hb^S and two doses of the normal allele is present, as $Hb^A Hb^A$. In sickle cell anemia the somatic cells carry two doses of the sickle cell gene, as $Hb^S Hb^S$, and show a complete absence of the normal gene. In the heterozygous state $Hb^A Hb^S$ there is a 40 per cent deficiency in the hemoglobin, the 60 per cent normal hemoglobin being sufficient to protect most heterozygotes against a full expression of sickle cell anemia. The sickling gene is therefore seen to behave as a dominant, which in the heterozygous condition may not produce more than a mild anemia, but in the homozygous state produces full-fledged sickle cell anemia.

The immediate cause of the sickling phenomenon and of the hemolysis of sickle cell anemia is the replacement of part or all of the normal hemoglobin of the red blood corpuscles by a form of hemoglobin which, in the reduced state, has a very low solubility and crystallizes inside the cell and results in its breakdown. The sickle-cell trait carrier (who is usually heterozygous) has less than half of this abnormal kind of hemoglobin S, while most of the sickle-cell anemics, who are usually homozygotes, have nearly 100 per cent of it, usually with some of the fetal type (F) of hemoglobin as well. The conditions are as set out at the head of the next page.

In the present volume the term *sickle-trait carrier* is used to describe the heterozygous carrier trait, *sickling* to refer to both the

Allele	Allele	Condition	Hemoglobin	
Hb^A	Hb^A	Normal	A	100% Normal
Hb^A	Hb^S	Sickle-trait carrier	A	55–75% Normal
			S	25–45% Sickling type
Hb^S	Hb^S	Sickle cell anemia	S	80–100% Sickling type

carrier state and the homozygous *sickle cell anemia* condition and *sicklemia* as a synonym for the latter.

The phenomenon of sickling occurs mainly in Negroid populations, and principally in Africa. But it has also been reported among the populations of several Greek villages and cities, and among Dravidian-speaking populations of Southern India, and in Sicily. These are interesting associations. The sickling trait is most prevalent in areas where malaria is common, and it appears that sickling is an adaptive trait directly related to a malarial environment. In 1954, Allison examined the children of a small African village and found that 46 per cent of the non-sicklers were infected with malaria, as against only 28 per cent of the sicklers. Furthermore, the non-sicklers tended to suffer from malaria in a more severe form. Allison innoculated 15 adult sicklers and 15 adult non-sicklers with malarial parasites. Fourteen of the non-sicklers came down with malaria, but only two of the sicklers. These findings have been corroborated by other workers, and it is now clear that the sickle-cell trait confers real advantages upon the heterozygous carrier against malaria. The persistence of the sickle-cell trait, then, would be the result of a balance between the pressure of malaria, which tends to increase the frequency of the gene, and that of sickle cell anemia, which tends to eliminate it. The AS heterozygotes have a much better chance of surviving and leaving progeny behind them than the AA hemoglobin homozygotes, and certainly considerably greater than the SS hemoglobin homozygotes, most of whom die in early childhood, hence, the advantages possessed by the heterozygotes counterbalance the disadvantages of the homozygotes, a situation known as *balanced polymorphism*. Balanced polymorphism refers to the fact that when the adaptive value of the heterozygote is greater than that of the homozygotes, natural selection will act to preserve a balanced distribution of the genes involved.

The increased resistance of the heterozygotes, it should be stated, is principally to one type of malaria, the malignant tertian type due to the *Plasmodium falciparum*. The resistance of the heterozygote is probably due to the fact that this parasite is better able to grow on hemoglobin A than on hemoglobin S.

It would seem reasonable to conclude that the frequency of the Hb^S gene in a population is significantly related to the exposure of that population to malaria. Hence, it is not surprising to find it in regions where the population has been exposed for many generations to the invading parasite. As malaria is gradually eliminated in those parts of the world in which it was formerly endemic, the genes will no longer be in equilibrium with the environment, and a new genetical equilibrium will evolve. It should be possible to measure this.

Finally, it may be mentioned that sickle cell anemia can now be successfully treated by the oral administration of a carbonic anhydrase inhibitor, acetazolamide (Diamox), by controlling the reduction of hemoglobin the drug suppresses sickling.

As illustrative of the caution necessary in interpreting the signifi-

TABLE XXXVIII

DISTRIBUTION OF SICKLEMIA IN UGANDA

Language Group	Tribe	Number Examined	Percent of Sicklemia	Frequency of Gene S	Frequency of Gene s
HAMITIC	Bahima	166	2.4	1.3	98.6
	Sebei	124	0.8		
	Suk	128	3.9		
	Karamojong	156	3.2		
	Teso	416	17.8	9.3	90.6
NILOTIC	Lango	278	27.0	13.7	86.2
	Acholi	141	27.0		
	Jaluo	130	28.0		
	Lugbara	120	21.0		
	Kakwa	101	25.0		
	Aiur	114	25.0		
	Jonam	109	26.0		
	Madi	109	3.0		
BANTU	Bairu	139	2.0		
	Banyuaranda (Bahutu)	496	8.0	4.7	95.2
	Banyoro	91	12.0		
	Batoro	120	12.5		
	Baganda	740	19.0	9.9	90.0
	Bakonjo	102	18.0		
	Barundi	108	19.0		
	Bakenyi	88	26.0		
	Basoga	241	29.0	16.0	83.9
	Bagishu	207	30.0		
	Baamba	140	45.0	25.8	74.1

After Lehman and Raper, 1949; and Elsdon-Drew, 1950.

cance of the frequency differences in the distribution of such a trait as sicklemia, reference may be made to the valuable work of Lehmann and Raper (1949) on the distribution of sicklemia in the Uganda. Lehman and Raper investigated nearly 5,000 Uganda Negroes from 24 different tribes for sicklemia. Their findings are shown in Table XXXVIII. From this table it will be observed that the Hamitic tribes show a relatively low frequency of sicklemia, with the exception of the Teso. The fact of interest here is that the Teso is the only Hamitic-speaking tribe which exhibits marked Negroid physical traits. The Nilotic tribes are much alike in the frequencies of sicklemia, excepting the Madi who live on the Sudan border. Unlike the two previous groups the Bantu-speaking tribes are remarkably homogeneous in the frequencies of sicklemia. These findings were at first interpreted as indicating that in Uganda incidence of sicklemia is inversely proportional to the contact the various tribes have had with the Hamitic invaders. Allison (1954) explained such differences as primarily due to differences in malarial severity, the sickling heterozygotes having a greater chance of surviving in malarious regions. As Lehmann and Raper point out, there are populations in which either of these two explanations may be sufficient, but some other explanation seems to be called for in such a territory as Uganda where there exist large differences in sickling rates between not widely different ethnic groups living in closely similar malarial environments. These investigators point out that severe malaria, which might not by itself cause death, may be converted into a lethal condition by other disadvantages, the selective death-rate thereby being expanded. The explanation for the differences in the sickling rate may then be, at least in part, explained, by the differentially high wastage of life associated with existence in a non-literate society.

In a valuable study of the ecology of the sickle-cell gene from the anthropological standpoint, Livingstone (1958) has shown how the distribution of the sickle-cell gene in West Africa has come about as a consequence of the interaction of selection and gene flow. Gene flow referring to the process of gene movement as a result of both migration and hybridization.

In plotting the distribution of the sickle-cell gene in West Africa it is observed that the higher frequencies are generally to be found in the south, there being some indication of a north-south gradient. *Plasmodium falciparum* malaria follows a similar gradient. However, there are many highly malarious regions of West Africa in which sickling is of low incidence.

Correlating languages with the distribution of sickling, the indications are, on the whole, that the tribes with a low incidence of sickling are probably the indigenous tribes of West Africa who have been forced back into such areas as Portuguese Guinea and Eastern Liberia, where they have been somewhat isolated. It is only in contemporary times that the sickle-cell gene is being introduced to these tribes.

Agriculture not being more than 6,000 years old in Africa, there is some reason to believe that the slash-and-burn agriculture practiced is related to the complex epidemiology of malaria in West Africa, and to the selective advantage of the sickle-cell gene. The major vector of malaria is the mosquito *Anopheles gambiae*. The only places in which *A. gambiae* cannot breed are: (1) very shaded water, (2) water with a strong current, (3) brackish water, and (4) very alkaline or polluted water. In a tropical rain forest there would be few places in which *A. gambiae* could breed, the trees effectively shading the ground, and the absorbent humus leaving very few stagnant pools. It is only when man cuts down the forest that *A. gambiae* is provided with an abundance of breeding places. The soil loses its humus and becomes laterized. Virtually impervious to water, the soil now holds it in puddles. Further breeding places are provided by the village settlement in the thatch of its huts and its abundant refuse.

Hunting populations do not destroy the forest, and show a very low incidence of malaria. The Pygmies of the Ituri Forest are a good example. They are said not to suffer from malaria, and are known to show lower frequencies of the sickle-cell gene than surrounding populations, presumably having acquired this gene by admixture with their Negro neighbors.

It would seem, then, that the spread of slash-and-burn agriculture has been responsible for the spread of the selective advantage of the sickle-cell gene, and that therefore the sickle-cell gene represents a comparatively recent genetic response to a disease which, in certain parts of the world, at least, has been influencing the evolution of man. Haldane's suggestion that disease may have been a major factor in controlling the size of human populations with the advent of the agricultural revolution, receives considerable support from Livingstone's study of the ecology of sickling.

Blood Groups and Disease

In recent years a number of independent investigators have found evidence which indicates that persons belonging to different blood groups may differ substantially in their susceptibility to certain diseases of adult life. In 1951, Struthers in Glasgow, Scotland, drew attention to a significant relationship between the frequency of blood group A and bronchial pneumonia. Carter and Heslop, in 1957, on a larger series in London were unable to confirm this. In 1953 Aird, Bentall, and Roberts, comparing the blood groups of 3,632 individuals suffering from cancer of the stomach with a control series free of the disease, concluded that "the frequency of blood group A is greater and the frequency of blood group O less in patients suffering from cancer of the stomach than in the general population of the locality in which they live." For example, in Newcastle they found that blood group A occurred in 43.6 per cent of the individuals with cancer, but in only 37.4 per cent of the controls who were free of the disease. In other localities the figures were as follows: Leeds, 47.9 cancer, 40.3 control; Manchester, 44.5 cancer, 38.4 control; Liverpool, 44.7 cancer, 39.6 control; Birmingham, 57.0 cancer, 44.4 control; London, cancer 46.0, 42.2 control; and Scotland, 36.4 cancer, 32.5 control.

The consistency with which blood group A is in every case significantly more frequent in the cancer victims than in those free of the disease is impressive. However, Speiser in Vienna and Wallace in Glasgow were unable to find any association between cancer and the A-B-O groups in large series of individuals examined by them. Nor have some other investigators been able to find such an association. On the other hand, Haddock and McConnell found a significantly high frequency of blood group A in cases in which the cancer arose in the body of the stomach as compared with growths affecting the pylorus or the antrum of the stomach.

As the evidence now stands duodenal ulcer appears to be about 40 per cent more common in individuals of blood group O than in individuals of other groups. There are no differences in individuals of A, B, and AB groups. Duodenal ulcer apparently occurs more frequently in non-secretors than in secretors (Clarke et al.). Gastric ulcer also appears to be more common in individuals of group O. Individuals of group A have about a 20 per cent greater chance of developing cancer of the stomach than those of either group O or B. Individuals of group A also have about a 25 per cent greater chance of developing pernicious anemia than the individuals of other groups. Group A individuals are also more likely to develop diabetes mellitus. McConnell, Ryke, and Roberts, who found this association in Scotland in 1956, interestingly enough found that the association existed only in men in their series.

In 1954 Aird and his associates claimed that in a series of 3,011 cases from three localities in England the frequency of blood group O was significantly higher in patients with peptic ulcers (that is, ulcers affecting either the stomach or duodenum) than in the control series. This relationship has since been confirmed by more than half a dozen different investigators. While there remains some question as to the significance of the association between blood group O and stomach ulcers, the association between duodenal ulcer and blood group O seems to be definitely established.

Claims for the association of certain blood groups with diseases of various other kinds are at the present time being studied by a number of investigators, and we shall await their findings with interest.

Meanwhile, it requires to be pointed out that the association between blood groups and disease by no means implies a causal relationship. There is no evidence that it is blood of a certain type which produces the susceptibility to disease. It seems rather more likely that if an association exists between blood groups and disease—and this is denied by some authorities like Wiener and Wexler, Unger, and Manuila—the blood groups may simply represent indicators of some other factor or factors with which they are associated and which are more directly related to the susceptibility to certain types of disease—but what these other factors may be is at present a matter for conjecture only. A clue to the kind of possible factors involved has been provided by Dr. A. J. Cain of Oxford. Dr. Cain points out that secretors pour a considerable amount of the antigens from their salivary glands into the commencement of the digestive system, the mouth. This at once suggests that something is being taken into the body, as part of the food, which it is advantageous to neutralize as quickly as possible. In 1948 Renkonen and in 1949 Boyd and Reguera independently discovered that the seeds of many leguminous plants widely used for food, such as the lima bean, contain large quantities of blood-group agglutinins which can be neutralized by secretors. This suggests that these antibodies may have a deleterious effect on some parts of the absorptive epithelial lining of the digestive tract. Cain points out that while such action may be of little importance to civilized man, it might have been of considerable significance under the far more strenuous conditions under which man lived in the prehistoric period. The finding of Clarke and his collaborators that secretors had a considerably lower incidence of duodenal ulcer as compared with non-secretors of the A-B-O blood group antigens strongly suggests the actual nature of the deleterious action. Thus, secretors would have a definite selective advantage in this respect.

It would appear, then, that far from being of neutral adaptive value the blood groups in fact constitute excellent examples of balanced polymorphism. The blood group genes are not inert, static entities but dynamically active participants in the process of natural selection, the polymorphism of the blood groups clearly being based on a balance of selective advantages and disadvantages.

Haptoglobins

In recent years a new group of serological traits have become available for anthropological studies which may prove of considerable value, these are the *haptoglobins*, so called because they are plasma protein a_2-globulins which bind and act as carriers of free hemoglobin (*hapto*, Gr. seize). By thus binding the hemoglobin the haptoglobins prevent the excretion of the hemoglobin molecule through the kidney, and protect the body from loss of precious iron or the blockage of the lower functional unit of the kidney (nephron). For the method of determining the haptoglobins see pp. 593-594.

Three types of haptoglobin groups have been distinguished, each probably determined by a pair of autosomal incompletely dominant genes, as follows:

Phenotypes	Genotypes
Haptoglobin 1-1	Hp^1Hp^1
Haptoglobin 2-1	Hp^2Hp^1
Haptoglobin 2-2	Hp^2Hp^2

It has recently been suggested that a fourth group exists characterized by a complete lack of haptoglobins, but the question that has yet to be answered is whether populations lacking haptoglobins do so for genetic or environmental reasons. Diseases of the liver and also hemolytic conditions can cause the disappearance of haptoglobins for considerable periods of time. Ahaptoglobinemia can also be produced by other conditions, hence, the lack of haptoglobins may in some, if not in all, cases be due to environmental conditions. Caution is therefore necessary in interpreting the results obtained on any population lacking them. Recently Oliver *et al.* found that haptoglobin values are low in hepatocellular failure, and high in biliary obstruction and secondary carcinomatosis. The distribution of the haptoglobin groups in various populations thus far investigated is shown in Table XXXIX.

The distribution of the haptoglobin groups in Table XXXIX is arbitrarily given in order of increasing frequency of the 1-1 phenotype. This strongly brings out the fact that Caucasoid populations are characterized by comparatively low 1-1 and high 2-2, while Negroids are high in 1-1 and low in 2-2. The differences in the phenotypic frequencies in the haptoglobin groups in each of these populations indicates that a true polymorphism exists. The polymorphism may be the result of a balance of selective factors such as are operative in the case of the blood groups in relation to susceptibility to disease, and possibly other conditions. The differences in the frequencies of 1-1 and 2-2 in Caucasoid and Negroid populations suggests that each haptoglobin group carries with it advantages which are selectively significant in one particular ecologic niche but not in the other, as, for example, in tropical as compared with temperate climates. In tropical climates low 2-2 may afford advantages which do not obtain in temperate climates.

Abnormal Hemoglobins

Another group of hematological traits which may prove of anthropological value are the non-sickling abnormal hemoglobins. These abnormal variants of normal hemoglobin A have been designated by the following letters in the order of their discovery: C, D, E, G, H, I, J, K, L, M, and N. Normal adult hemoglobin is designated A, fetal hemoglobin, some of which may still be found in the infant's blood up to its fourth or sixth month, is designated F. The letter B is omitted since it had at one time been used for sickle-cell hemoglobin. Most of the abnormal hemoglobins are probably all alleles of the normal gene A, for they appear to behave in a simple Mendelian manner, but this has been proved conclusively only for hemoglobins A, S and C.

TABLE XXXIX

HAPTOGLOBIN GROUPS IN VARIOUS POPULATIONS

Population	Place	Investigator	No. Tested	% 0-0	% 1-1	% 2-1	% 2-2
English	Oxford	Allison *et al.* 1958	218	2.7	10.1	55.5	31.7
American whites	Chicago	Sutton *et al.* 1956	54	—	11.1	53.7	35.2
Australian aborigines	N. Queensland	Butz-Olsen 1958	123	—	12	68	20
Norwegian	Norway	Fleischer & Landevall 1957	1000	—	13.2	46.2	40.6
Basque	Spain	Allison *et al.* 1958	107	0.9	14.0	45.7	39.3
Australian whites	Queensland	Butz-Olsen 1958	100	—	14	58	28
Finnish	Helsinki	Mäkelä *et al* 1959	891	0.2	14.5	43.3	42.0
Swedish	Sweden	Larrell & Grubb 1957	46	—	15	50	35
French	Paris	Moullec & Fine 1959	406	—	15.3	49.7	35.0
Danish	Denmark	Galatius-Jensen 1958	2050	0.2	16.0	47.2	36.6
Swedish	Sweden	Beckman 1959	220	—	18.6	50.0	31.4
Canadian whites	Toronto	Smithies 1955	49	—	21.1	50.5	28.4
Swedish	Sweden	Nyman 1958	160	—	21	41	38
American Negroes	Seattle	Giblett 1959	406	4.2	26.4	48.0	21.4
Negro-white hybrids	Venezuela	Rodríguez & Arends 1959	208	—	27.4	54.8	17.8
Australian aborigines	Cent. Australia	Butz-Olsen 1958	100	—	40	47	13
Negroes	Liberia, Ivory C.	Sutton *et al.* 1956	142	—	48.6	42.2	9.2
Negroes	Nigeria, W.	Allison *et al.* 1958	99	32.3	53.5	11.1	3.0
Bushmen	Bechuanaland	Barnicot *et al.* 1959	113	1.8	1.6	35.4	52.2
Hottentots	Namaqualand	Barnicot *et al.* 1959	59	—	30.5	42.4	27.1
Cape Coloured	Springbok	Barnicot *et al.* 1959	88	—	19.3	55.7	25.0
Zulus	Johannesburg	Barnicot *et al.* 1959	116	2.6	31.0	41.4	25.0
Italians	Berra, N. Italy	Harris *et al.* 1958	119	—	16.8	48.0	35.2
Italians	Naples	Harris *et al.* 1958	93	—	10.7	47.3	42.0
Sardinians	Illorai	Harris *et al.* 1958	147	—	12.2	50.8	37.4
Sicilians	Catania	Harris *et al.* 1958	107	—	15.0	49.5	35.5
English	London	Harris *et al.* 1958	114	—	17.6	48.2	34.2

There have been reports in which hemoglobin variants were inherited in a manner suggesting more than one locus.

The abnormal hemoglobins are characterized by restricted distributions, a fact which renders them unusually interesting. For example, while hemoglobin S is found all over tropical Africa, and also in certain parts of India and among a certain proportion of American Negroes, hemoglobin C has thus far only been discovered in West Africa, in about 2.5 per cent of American Negroes, and in about 1 per cent of Cape Coloured in Cape Town. The suggestion is that the latter two populations derived their hemoglobin C from West African ancestors. This hemoglobin has not been found in East Africa or in Uganda, nor among northern Nilotes of the Southern Sudan. But on the Gold Coast it has been found with a frequency of 28 per cent among the Dagomba of the north. In the southern Gold Coast the frequency is 10 per cent. Further east, in Western Nigeria it was found with a frequency of 7 per cent among the Yoruba, but among the ethnically related but more isolated Igala east of the River Niger it is completely lacking. Lehmann therefore suggests that it would seem that hemoglobin C has arisen somewhere near the Gold Coast and is now spreading southwards and eastward, and that in this hemoglobin we may actually be witnessing the relatively recent birth of a new gene and its early dissemination.

Hemoglobin D has been found in 4.2 per cent of Australian aborigines, and in 2 New York Negroes, and in about 1.8 of Sikhs, in about 1 per cent of Punjabis and in some Gujeratis in India. Hemoglobin E has been found in 13 per cent of Siamese and in an equal number of Burmese, in 4 per cent of Veddas, and it has been found in a Turkish family and in a Persian girl.

Hemoglobins G, H, I, J, K, L, and M, have thus far been found in single families only. Hemoglobin N has been found among Liberians and in some 0.3 per cent of Portuguese Guinea Negroes.

A study of 708 Eskimos, 200 Aleuts, and 44 Indians in Alaska for abnormal hemoglobins found that only normal hemoglobin A was present in their blood—a finding which suggests that abnormal hemoglobins do not occur in the members of these populations, or if they occur are extremely rare.

In the serological traits we have anthropological characters which for the first time provide us with a means of actually breaking through the phenotypical external characters, and determining the genetic character, the genotype, of a population. This, of course, is true only for a very few other traits in addition to the serological traits. Future

TABLE XL

The Genotypes and Phenotypes of Tasting and Non-Tasting PTC

Genotype	Phenotype
TT	Taster
Tt	Taster
tt	Non-Taster

researches will undoubtedly yield many more such traits which will then become usable in the same way in the genetic analysis of populations.° One such trait which may next be discussed is in the form of a taste-reaction, and should provide the reader with an idea of the great variety of traits which lend themselves to genetic analysis.

Tasting and Non-Tasting

PTC are letters which stand for a white crystalline powder known as phenyl-thio-carbamide. A single crystal placed on the back of the tongue as soon as it is dissolved in saliva, or else dissolved in and drunk from a glass of water,† is experienced by most persons as a rather bitter taste. Such persons are known as "tasters." Those who are unable to taste PTC are known as "non-tasters." Two genes are involved, one of which is dominant (T), and the other recessive (t), both giving rise to three genotypes (Table XL). The gene T is dominant for tasting and the gene t recessive for non-tasting, the non-tasters always being homozygous (tt) for that gene.

In the human populations thus far investigated interesting differences have been found in the proportions of non-tasters to tasters. The percentages of tasters are listed in Table XLI. Interestingly enough the investigation of the taste reaction of 27 chimpanzees to PTC revealed that seven animals or 26 per cent were non-tasters, a proportion falling well within the range of that encountered in man in whom the range is from 0.2 to 73.3 per cent non-tasters. Since it is hardly conceivable that the relations of the genes to one another has remained the same over the 800,000 or more generations since the separation of the anthropoid and hominid stocks, the erroneous inference was made that over this enormous period of time the heterozygotes (Tt) for this apparently valueless character have enjoyed a selective advantage over both the homozygotes (TT, tt), and this in both the lineage of the evolving chimpanzees and in that of evolv-

---

° See pp. 583-587.

† For the method of testing, see pp. 584-585.

ing man. There are, apparently, about equal numbers of T and t genes in the chimpanzees (and in some human populations) yielding, as would be expected,

$$
\left.\begin{array}{l}
25 \text{ per cent } TT \\
50 \text{ per cent } Tt \\
25 \text{ per cent } tt
\end{array}\right\} \begin{array}{l} \text{tasters} \\ \\ \text{non-tasters} \end{array}
$$

Under conditions of genetic isolation the proportions of the genes and their phenotypic expression will remain constant, and are then said to be in equilibrium.

From Table XLI it will be seen that the variation is such in the proportions of tasters to non-tasters as to indicate significant differences in gene frequencies with respect to the T and t genes. The study of these gene frequencies in different populations should be particularly rewarding. The genetic analysis of taste-reactions in the non-human primates and in human populations may serve to throw a unique light upon such important problems as the relationship of primate groups to one another, the stability or instability of certain combinations of genes, and their selective value.

Indeed, considerable light has recently been thrown on the adaptive value of PTC tasting by Kitchin and his co-workers (1959). It has been known since 1942 (Richter & Clisby) that when rats are fed PTC they develop marked thyroid hyperplasia. Subsequent work has established that the thiocarbamides in general are active goitrogenic substances. They occur naturally in such foods as turnips, brussels sprouts, rape, and especially kale. Kitchin *et al.* determined the PTC threshold in 447 patients with thyroid disease, and in a normal control group of 265 individuals. They found that in 246 patients with adenomatous (nodular, neoplastic) goiter 97 individuals or 39.3 per cent were non-tasters (genotype tt). This is a significantly high incidence, when compared with the normal controls with an incidence of 29.4 per cent or when compared with the frequency of non-tasters in any other English sample (See Table XLI). Of this group of adenomatous non-tasters 60 per cent were males and 36.6 per cent females.

In 133 patients with toxic diffuse goiter only 22 individuals or 16.6 per cent were non-tasters, and there was no difference in the sex distribution. Thus, there was a significant excess of tasters (genotypes TT, Tt) among the patients with toxic diffuse goiter.

The taster/non-taster genotypes appear, then, to be of importance in determining the type of thyroid disorder that may develop, that is, whether it shall be nodular or diffuse. If, as these findings suggest, non-tasters (*tt*) are more susceptible to thiocarbamides, it is possible that the homozygous tasters (*TT*) are even less susceptible than the heterozygous tasters (*Tt*). The assumption is that such insusceptibility to thiocarbamides renders the thyroid more prone to toxic diffuse goiter, and in this way one of the natural restraining mechanisms to thyroid homeostasis is removed. This could result in a highly sensitive thyroid which might react more vigorously to psychic stimuli by way of the hypothalamus and pituitary.

Biochemically the differential taste response to PTC is confined to substances with the chemical grouping —N—C—. They are all

$$\underset{\parallel}{\text{—N—C—}}\atop{S}$$

active reducing agents, and their biological action is to inhibit tyrosinase and the synthesis of thyroxine. This effect occurs within the thyroid, is uninfluenced by the treatment with iodine, and results in thyroid hyperplasia under the stimulus of pituitary thyrotropin.

To complete the story ecologically: Goitrogenic substances allied to PTC occur in many vegetables which are fed raw to cattle in winter. Goitrogens have been isolated from cow's milk following feeding with kale. Cow's milk could therefore be an important source of goitrogens in man. Such ingestion of goitrogens would occur only in winter, since in spring and summer cows are usually grass-fed. If this were so, cycles of seasonal involution and hyperplasia would occur in the thyroid, particularly in non-tasters of PTC, and it is precisely this pathological sequence that is known to give rise to adenomatous goiter in later life.

Undoubtedly the bimodal taste response in different populations is yet another example of balanced polymorphism.

How the present differences in the frequency distribution of the blood group, blood type, secreting, sicklemia and taste-reaction genes were probably produced, as well as the many other differences which are to be found in the different major and ethnic groups of man, may best be considered below.

Our knowledge of none of the traits here discussed is at present sufficient to permit us to reconstruct the relationships of the major and ethnic groups of man to one another. Attention has here been given to an account of these traits principally because they provide the type of criteria which modern physical anthropology is beginning to use, and of which it will make ever increasing use in the future. The mechanism of the inheritance of these traits has been described

TABLE XLI

ABILITY TO TASTE PHENYL-THIO-CARBAMIDE IN HUMAN POPULATIONS

Population	Place	Investigator	No. Tested	Per Cent Tasters
Australian Aborigines	South Australia	Simmons et al. 1954	85	27.0
Australian Aborigines	Central Australia	Simmons et al. 1957	74	50.0
Australian Aborigines	South Australia	Simmons et al. 1954	152	50.7
New Guinea	Mount Hagen	Semple et al. 1956	330	54.2
Welsh	Five towns	Boyd & Boyd 1937	237	58.7
Eskimo, Unmixed	Labrador & Baffin Id.	Sewall 1939	130	59.2
Asiatic Indians, Chenchu	Madras	Simmons et al. 1953	132	62.1
Germans		Gottschick 1937	183	62.3
Danish	Copenhagen	Hartmann 1939	596	62.8
Russians	Zagorsk (N. Moscow)	Boyd & Boyd 1937	486	63.2
Arabs	Syria (interior)	Hudson & Peter 1934	400	63.5
Russians	Kharkov	Boyd & Boyd 1937	161	64.6
American Whites	Montana	Matson 1938	291	64.6
New Britain	Nakanai	Simmons et al. 1956	352	65.3
Malays	Singapore	Lugg & Whyte 1955	50	66.0
Yemenites	Yemen, Israel	Yunovitch 1934	59	67.7
Armenians	Syria	Berberian 1934	294	68.0
Danes	Denmark	Mohr 1951	314	68.2
Ashkenazic Jews	Israel	Yunovitch 1934	245	68.5
English	London	Harris & Kalmus 1949	441	68.5
American Whites	Washington, D. C.	Parr 1934	439	69.1
Eskimo, Mixed	Labrador & Baffin Id.	Sewall 1939	49	69.4
Central Europeans		Gurevitch et al. 1951	647	69.6
Norwegians	Norway	Merton 1958	266	69.6
American Whites	New York & vicinity	Blakeslee 1932–35	400	70.0
English	Oxford	Race & Sanger 1958	801	70.0
Asiatic Indians, Rarhi Brahmin	West Bengal	Das 1956	845	70.0
American Whites	Columbus, Ohio	Snyder 1932	3 643	70.2
Swiss	Zurich & vicinity	Botsztein 1942	544	70.4
English	Merseyside	Kitchin et al. 1959	265	70.6
Finns	Helsinki	Allison & Nevanlinna 1952	202	70.8
Scottish	Glasgow	Riddell & Wybar 1944	60	71.7
Irish	Dublin	Boyd & Boyd 1937	398	71.8
Europeans	Singapore	Lugg & Whyte 1955	50	72.0
Sephardic Jews	Israel	Yunovitch 1934	175	72.0
Kapingas	Micronesia	Simmons et al. 1953	54	72.0
Ashkenazic Jews	Sao Paulo, Brazil	Saldanha & Beçak	244	72.1
Belgians	Liege	Creteur 1952	572	72.7
Copts	Cairo, Egypt	Boyd & Boyd 1937	110	73.6
English	London	Falconer & Fisher 1947	629	73.7
East Georgians	Tiflis	Boyd & Boyd 1937	121	74.5
Basques	San Sebastian	Boyd & Boyd 1937	98	74.5
Melinde Arabs	Kenya, E. Africa	Allison 1951	63	74.6
Egyptians	Cairo	Hickman & Marcos 1934	208	75.9
Spaniards	N. E. Spain	Pons 1955	306	75.2
Brazilian Whites	Rio	Kalmus 1957	225	75.8
American Negroes	Alabama	Howard & Campbell 1934	533	76.5
West Georgians	Tiflis	Boyd & Boyd 1937	218	78.0
Palauans	Palau, Pacific	Simmons et al. 1953	198	78.8
Mohammedans	Cairo	Boyd & Boyd 1937	459	78.9
Polish Jews	Sao Paulo, Brazil	Saldanha & Beçak 1959	102	79.6
Flathead Indians, Mixed	Montana	Matson 1938	442	82.6
Trukese	Truk, Pacific	Simmons et al. 1953	126	81.7
Brazilian Whites	Rural	Kalmus 1957	332	81.9
Cook Islanders	Cook Islands	Simmons et al. 1955	215	83.7
Chinese	Singapore	Lugg & Whyte 1955	50	84.0
Malay		Thambipillai 1956	237	84.4
Asiatic Indians	Madras	Lugg & Whyte 1955	50	86.0
Mixed American Indians	Lawrence, Kansas	Levine & Anderson 1932	110	87.2
Brazilian Negroes & Mulattoes	Brazil	Kalmus 1957	355	88.5
Puerto Ricans	Puerto Rico	Thieme 1952	3,229	88.8
Chinese	London	Barnicot 1950	66	89.4
Flathead Indians, Unmixed	Montana	Matson 1938	30	90.0
American Negroes	Ohio	Lee 1934	3,156	90.8
New Hebrideans	New Hebrides	Simmons et al. 1954	196	90.8
Japanese	Japan	Fukuoka 1936	921	91.0
Japanese	Brazil	Kalmus 1957	89	91.0
Maoris	New Zealand	Simmons et al. 1951	157	91.7
African Negroes	Kenya, E. Africa	Lee 1934	110	91.9
Polynesians	Easter Id., etc.	Simmons et al. 1958	116	92.1
American Indians	Alberta	Matson 1938	310	92.4
Japanese	Japan	Rikimaru 1936	8 824	92.9
Japanese	Sao Paulo, Brazil	Saldanha 1958	295	92.9
Chinese	Formosa	Rikimaru 1936	5,933	92.9
Swedish Lapps	N. Sweden Nevanlinna	Allison & Nevanlinna 1952	62	93.0
Norwegian Lapps	Norway	Allison & Nevanlinna 1952	78	93.2
Ainu	Hokkaido	Simmons et al. 1953	328	93.6
American Indians, Unmixed	Lawrence, Kansas	Levine & Anderson 1932	183	93.9
Chinese	Washington & N. Y.	Chen & Chain 1934	167	94.0
Thais	Bangkok	Simmons et al. 1954	56	94.6
Ainu-Japanese	Hokkaido	Simmons et al. 1953	175	94.8
Formosans	Formosa	Rikimaru 1936	1,756	94.8
African Negroes, Shilluk	Sudan	Lee 1934	805	95.8
Negritos, Kintak	Kampang LaPong, Malaya	Lugg 1957	50	96.0
Negritos, Senoi	Perak	Lugg 1957	50	96.0
Giriama, Eastern Bantu	Kenya, E. Africa	Allison 1951	208	96.2
American Indians	Northern Alberta	Matson 1940	559	96.9
African Negroes	London	Barnicot 1950	74	97.3
American Indians, Navaho	Ramah, New Mexico	Boyd & Boyd 1949	269	98.2
Brazilian Indians	Brazil	Kalmus 1957	163	99.8

in order to show to what extent such traits may be relied upon for tracing the physical relationships of man.

THE MECHANISM OF DIFFERENTIATION OF THE MAJOR AND ETHNIC GROUPS OF MAN

In the last chapter we saw that early man was already differentiated into a number of recognizable types, that there was good reason to believe that mixture had occurred between some of these types, and that from some of these mixtures several of the varieties of man as we now know them probably were evolved.

When, in this connection, we use such a word as "evolved" we have a very definite series of processes in mind, and it is these processes, which we shall now consider, which give a definite meaning to what we understand by the evolution of the ethnic groups of man. Such evolutionary processes are at work before our eyes at the present time in every part of the world, where the barriers between different isolates are being broken down or else erected. This is particularly true of the United States where one can observe and study the effects of both processes in action. But this is to anticipate.

When two or more populations are isolated from one another they may be spoken of as *isolates*. It does not matter how large or small the population is. Isolation may be defined as the state or condition of separation from other groups which limits or prevents interbreeding between them. Within any population there are generally a number of different groups which may remain more or less distinct by virtue of marriage regulations, chance factors, or recognized barriers, which serve to maintain the distinctness of the group. Such groups are also *isolates*. Natural geographic barriers such as distance, seas, rivers, forests, and mountains, serve to maintain the independence of isolates. Out of the way villages with poor communications with the outside world provide good examples of isolates in our own country, and still more so in Europe. In western society the tendency to marry into one's own class serves to maintain what may be called the *class isolate*, while the tendency to marry a person of the same religion serves to maintain the *religious isolate*. When, as is usually the case, both are combined, as among Jews, or Catholics—particularly Catholics of Irish and Italian descent—where Jews tend to marry Jews of the same class, and Catholics tend to marry Catholics of the same class and national origin, easily recognizable social isolates are produced, and these are often miscalled "races."

Factors similar to those involved in the production of the isolates just mentioned have probably been operative throughout the long history of mankind, but there have also been others.

Whether we think of the earliest types of man as arising from a common ancestral stock or from several different stocks, ultimately makes very little difference to our understanding of the differentiation of mankind. If they originated from different ancestors and were different to begin with, some of them must have met and interbred and produced hybrids who, in turn, did likewise, and some of the results of these mixtures may have given rise to existing varieties of mankind. A strong case could be made out for this polygenic theory of the origin of the varieties of mankind, but not quite as strong as that which can be made out for the monogenic theory which postulates the origin of the varieties of mankind from a common ancestral stock. One of the principal objections to the polygenic theory is that the living varieties of man so closely resemble one another in all their physical and mental characters that it would be difficult to conceive of them as having originated from distinct lines by a process of convergence. Also while it makes it more difficult to account for the existing differences, the monogenic theory seems to be more in accord with the facts, and with the evolutionary processes involved in the production of other varieties of living creatures.

Our present knowledge is not by any means adequate to provide an entirely satisfactory explanation of the mechanisms of ethnic differentiation in man. Much basic research will have to be carried out before that becomes possible; but by utilizing the findings of geneticists on other animal groups as well as on man it will be possible to give the reader some idea of the nature of the probable mechanism or processes involved in the evolution of the ethnic groups of man. We may begin with the following postulates:

1. The original ancestral human population, living in a circumscribed region of the earth, was genetically relatively heterogeneous.
2. By migration at different times away from the original ancestral population and habitat, individual families or groups of families became dispersed over great distances.
3. Some of the groups thus dispersed became geographically isolated from one another, and remained so isolated for more or less considerable periods of time over many generations.
4. In all these isolated groups the following factors came into play as conditions leading to evolutionary change:

i. *Natural selection*   v. *Hybridization*
ii. *Mutation*   vi. *Sexual selection*
iii. *Isolation*   vii. *Social selection*
iv. *Genetic drift*

Natural Selection

By natural selection is meant the preservation through the action of the environment of such variations as arise and are beneficial to the organism under its conditions of life. Because they adapt the organism to those conditions such variations are called adaptive. Under the selective action of the physical environment those individuals who are lacking in the necessary adaptive characters or qualities tend either (i), to go on to occupy different niches in the environment, or (ii), to leave a lesser progeny behind them, or (iii) to die out while those who possess the necessary qualities survive and procreate. Natural selection may, then, be regarded as the creative force which out of the raw materials of mutation determines not only which organisms shall survive, but also which among the many millions of possible organisms will in fact arise.

Darwin's own definition of natural selection may be given here. It is from the introduction to *The Origin of Species*, 1859, page 5:

"As many more individuals of each species are born than can possibly survive; and as, consequently, there is a frequently recurring struggle for existence, it follows that any being, if it vary however slightly in any manner profitable to itself, under the complex and sometimes varying conditions of life, will have a better chance of surviving, and thus be *naturally selected*. From the strong principle of inheritance, any selected variety will tend to propagate its new and modified form."

Natural selection is a convenient shorthand phrase for the effects of the differential reproduction of different types. It is an immediate and automatic consequence of the basic property of the genetic materials, autocopying, but with occasional erroneous variations—mutations. Autocopying results in multiplication and competition. The autocopying process is the means by which the genetic materials replicate themselves, the errors in the precision with which this is sometimes done, mutations, result in conferring different degrees of biological advantage or disadvantage on those who inherit them. The net effect is differential fertility down the generations, that is, natural selection. The result will be that favorable new mutations or favorable combinations of old mutations will tend to become established as normal in the stock in the place of less favorable ones. The probability of any organism having come into being fortuitously without the operation of natural selection is so great that R. A. Fisher has aptly described natural selection as "a mechanism for generating an exceedingly high degree of improbability."

Since natural selection is automatic and blind and neither purposeful design nor foresighted planning is involved in its action, its results are always relative to the particular environment in which the organism is living, as well as to its particular structure and habit. Adaptive traits are adaptive only in relation to environments in which organismal structure and function fit harmoniously.

Judging from its distribution it is practically certain that skin color is an adaptive character, that is to say a character which has selective value. In man, with few exceptions darkly pigmented skins are geographically distributed in high temperature-sunlight-humidity regions, lightly pigmented skins in regions of lower temperature-sunlight-humidity conditions.

The marked geographic gradients shown by pigmentation in warm-blooded lower animals have been subsumed in Gloger's rule. This rule states that melanin pigmentation tends to increase in the warm and humid parts of the species range. High humidity together with high temperature promotes the formation of black pigmentation (eumelanins), while aridity with high temperature promotes the formation of the reddish, yellowish- and reddish-brown pigments (phaeomelanins). The phaeomelanins tend to be reduced under cooler conditions even if arid, as do the melanins under extreme cases such as the polar regions. The maximum depth of pigmentation is found in humid and hot climates, the minimum in arctic climates. Heat and aridity, as in subtropical deserts, tends to promote yellowish- and reddish-browns, while lower temperature and aridity, as in steppes, tends to promote greys and grey-browns.

With the exception of color varieties which do not occur in man such as greys and grey-browns, and allowing for the shifts which have occurred as a consequence of migration, these relations between climate and skin color would seem to apply equally to man as to lower animals.

It may be that the broad nose of the Negro and the narrow nose of whites also represent adaptive characters. The work of Thomson and Buxton suggests that air at higher temperatures is breathed more easily through a broad than through a narrow nose. A broad nose permits the maximum exhalation of heated air from the lungs, and in hot climates where heat dissipation is desirable a broad nose would be a selective advantage. It has been suggested that the narrow nose represents an adaptation to cold climates where the temperature of the air must be adjusted to the proper warmth and humidity. As Negus has shown, this interpretation receives no support from the conditions found among lower animals, close-set and large nostrils far apart follow no climatic rules. Kenney points out that most human desert dwellers have a slender nose, which has the advantage of providing cooling and saturation of the inspired air before its exposure to the respiratory surfaces. Weiner reëxamined Thomson and Buxton's original data and found that the broad nose correlated rather more significantly with external absolute humidity (exchange of water from nasal epithelium to inspired air) than with air temperature and humidity.

Populations living in regions of extreme cold, such as those of the Arctic Circle, Siberia, Alaska, and Greenland, tend to be relatively short, and well padded with fat. They present a surface area which is less than that exhibited by populations which have been long resident in regions of high temperature. The latter would appear to be built to radiate as much heat as possible—the former as little as possible. Flat padded faces, flattish noses, and "double" upper eyelids—the epicanthic folds—appear to be adapted to protect the exposed and vulnerable face and eyes from cold.

Body weight is also correlated with mean temperature, the tendency being for high body weights to be associated with low temperature, and low body weight to be associated with high temperatures, while medium body weights occur in more temperate regions. The selective advantage of such body-weight relations to temperature may be deduced from the fact that for a given stature lower body weight at higher temperatures yields an advantageous ratio of body surface area to mass, thereby facilitating the maintenance of body heat balance. Accumulation of fat in cold climates provides insulating qualities which appreciably affect body heat loss. A decrease of surface is of advantage for the maintenance of body heat in a cold environment. Since larger bodied individuals have a smaller surface in proportion to mass—volume and mass increasing as the cube of the linear dimensions and surface only as the square—a larger body size serves to reduce heat radiation, and a smaller body size to increase it. These facts are resumed in Bergmann's rule which states that the smaller-sized members of a population are to be found in the warmer parts of the range, the larger-sized members in the cooler areas.

Allen's rule, which states that the protruding parts of the body, such as limbs, ears, and noses are relatively shorter in the cooler parts of the species range than in the warmer parts is to some extent also applicable to man. Tropical peoples tend to be of slighter build and to show a greater degree of linear development in the limbs, the limbs being increased in length compared with trunk length, and their diameter reduced. This is also true of the neck. To some extent the migratory habits of man may have played havoc with this particular ecological rule. The application of Bergmann's and Allen's rules to man have been seriously and cogently questioned (Wilber), on the ground that the inadequate data has been improperly interpreted, and that in any event, man has never responded to his environment in a passive manner, but has always done everything within his power to control and shape the environment to his requirements. But while this is undoubtedly true, it should be remembered that ecological rules are generalizations to which exceptions can be found in every group, but that by and large they do apply to most populations of a species. The studies of Newman and of Roberts on New and Old World human populations lend strong support to the view that ecological rules apply to man as well as to other animals.

The action of natural selection varies under different conditions, and the rate at which it operates depends upon the character or quality involved. Thus, for example, where inherited lack of immunity to certain diseases such as sleeping sickness, malaria, and tuberculosis, is involved, natural selection would operate very rapidly, and those lacking immunity to these diseases would in a relatively short time tend to die out, while those possessing some degree of immunity would tend to survive and grow stronger.

The gradual dying off of individuals possessing a white skin in a tropical humid climate, so that only those with a dark skin remained, would probably take a very considerable amount of time. There is, however, no direct evidence that in this particular respect, such a differential action of natural selection ever occurred in the development of man.

It must be observed here that in addition to its creative action in the preservation of progressive adaptations, natural selection also operates in favor of those individuals who are already preadapted. Preadaptive traits predispose individuals to take advantage of the environment into which, by chance, they may be thrown. It may be, for example, that the broad nose of Negroids is such a character, that in a particular environment already existing persons with broad noses were able to adapt themselves to the conditions of that environment so efficiently that any other form of nose would have been at a disadvantage in comparison, that hence the broad nose persisted. Natural selection expressed itself here in the preservation of a pre-existing character which was probably characteristic of all or most Negroids to begin with. It is unnecessary, therefore, always to assume that if a character or quality has survived another character or quality not as well adapted to the conditions of the environment must have died out.

The survival and diffusion of mutations has, to a large extent, been dependent upon natural selection, and since it is quite certain that mutation has played a considerable role in the evolution of man, it goes without saying that natural selection has played an equally important role.

The evidence points to the fact that natural selection has been the principal arbiter of man's evolution. Unfortunately, what is involved in the process of natural selection has not always been too clear to many writers on the subject. Ever since the publication of Darwin's *On the Origin of Species by Means of Natural Selection, Or the Preservation of Favoured Races in the Struggle for Life,* in November 1859, most writers have dwelt on the "struggle" aspect of natural selection while altogether omitting to consider its very important cooperative aspects. Since 1859 a great deal of evidence has been accumulated which renders it quite clear that cooperation is an indispensable part of the "struggle" for existence. If, instead of thinking, as the social patterns of the nineteenth century suggested, of "struggle" as the ruthless competition between individuals for survival we think rather of "struggle" as endeavor or drive to survive we shall be nearer the truth. Involved in the process of endeavoring to survive there are cooperative as well as competitive elements. The distribution of adaptive characters throughout a group is achieved by cooperation as well as by competition. Organisms possessed of certain selective advantages need the cooperation of their fellow organisms in order to be preserved. If natural selection secures the differential survival or perpetuation of different genotypes, then quite clearly cooperation is an integral part of the process without the action of which the survivors could not long be preserved. It is the cohesive effect of natural selection as represented by its cooperative aspect which secures the perpetuation of the species. It should be fairly evident that no animal group could possibly survive without the cooperative aspect of natural selection to sustain and integrate it. Competition without the cohesive effects of cooperation is powerless to preserve anything. "Favoured races" are not preserved by conflict but by cooperation. By cooperation is meant the support which animals given one another in the struggle for existence. As Kropotkin put it in his great book *Mutual Aid*, "If we resort to an indirect test, and ask Nature: 'Who are the fittest: those who are continually at war with each other, or those who support one another?' we at once see that those animals which acquire habits of mutual aid are undoubtedly the fittest. They have more chances to survive, and they attain, in their respective classes, the highest development of intelligence and bodily organization."

These are most important ideas for the reader to grasp, since the principle of the struggle for life *against* others has, in the past, been greatly overemphasized, while the principle of cooperation has been unwarrantably neglected. Natural selection favors the cooperative as opposed to the disoperative struggle for survival. As Burkholder has put it, "The most important basis for selection is the ability of associated components to work together harmoniously in the organism and among organisms. All new genetic factors, whether they arise from within by mutation or are incorporated from without by various means, are accepted or rejected according to their cooperation with associated components in the whole aggregation."

The unfortunate habit of thinking in terms of the struggle for existence, by means of which, it is believed, the fittest, that is "the fightingest," are alone selected for survival while the weakest are ruthlessly condemned to extinction, is not only an incorrect view of the realities, but is a habit of thought which has done a considerable amount of harm. Only by omitting any reference to such an important evolutionary force as the principle of cooperation, and by viewing evolution as a process of continuous conflict between all living things can man be led to conclude that survival or development depends upon successful aggression. Omitting important facts and basing their arguments on incomplete and false premises the tough Darwinians, but not Darwin himself, could only arrive at false conclusions. In 1944 a group of distinguished biologists resumed the principle of cooperation in the statement that the probability of survival of individual or living things increases with the degree with which they harmoniously adjust themselves to each other and to their environment. So far as man is concerned it is particularly necessary to remember, as Haldane has said, that "in so far as it makes for the survival of one's descendants and near relations, altruistic behaviour is a kind of Darwinian fitness, and may be expected to spread as the result of natural selection."

As we shall see (pp. 491-494) cooperation has almost certainly played a role of the first importance in the evolution of man.

Mutation

Mutation defines the condition in which a particular gene undergoes a permanent change of some sort, resulting in a transmissible hereditary modification in the expression of a trait. A mutation is, in fact, the result of a failure of precision in the basic autocopying exhibited by the genes. It is mainly small mutations that are important in evolution. Indeed, the selective advantages of most mutations are so small as to be undetectable in any one generation. But such mutations, operating on the scale of geological time, are capable of producing all the observed phenomena of biological evolution. Mutations provide the raw materials of evolution for natural selection to turn into the improvably "finished article." Mutations of genes for some traits have almost certainly occurred independently at different rates, and have affected different traits. Thus, for example, in one isolate mutant genes may have appeared and ultimately become scattered throughout the population, as for instance, may have been the case in the original production of "black" skin color among Negroes.

If we assume that "white" was the primitive skin color of man, then in one isolate mutant genes resulting in a brownish skin color may have appeared, while in still another isolate mutation in the direction of a yellowish skin may have occurred, and by subsequent mutation "black" skin may have made its appearance. However, it is possible that these skin colors were already in existence among the earliest groups of man. In this connection it is of interest to note that chimpanzees present some, at least, of the varieties of skin color found among the living groups of *Homo sapiens.* In different geographic races of these animals individuals are encountered that are completely black or brown skinned, and others in which face, hands, and feet, may be black and the remainder of the body white or brown. But nothing like the kind of variability in skin color that occurs in man is encountered in any non-human primate. There can, therefore, be little doubt that mutation has played some part in providing the raw materials for the great variety of skin colors seen in man.

Mutation of hair-form genes to yield the present variety of hair form would give a better, and probably more accurate picture of the manner in which such problems may be discussed and investigated.

Thus a genetically relatively heterogeneous population from which groups have migrated and become isolated from one another, may by random variation in gene frequencies, and the change in the expression of genes themselves, produce new gene combinations which differ from group to group and thus serve to define the differences existing between such groups. This random variation or recombination together with the occurrence of mutation may be considered as the primary or basic conditions for the evolution of all animal forms. That these processes have played such a fundamental role in the evolution of mankind appears to be a justifiable inference from the facts.

Quite as important are those factors which act upon the shifting pattern of the genetic apparatus and influence its course. These are the secondary factors, such as environment, natural selection, hybridization, sexual, and social selection, inbreeding, and so on, factors which have been unremitting in their action upon the primary one, though the character of that action has been very variable.

Here it is principally desired to emphasize the fact that in the character of the action of gene mutation, we have positive evidence that variation is a natural process which is constantly proceeding in all human groups. But while in man variation brought about by mutation has probably been very great, it has in many discussions too often been permitted to overshadow the variation which has been produced by the action of the secondary factors. Mutations not anthropologically significant occur frequently in man. It is also probable that over long stretches of time more significant mutations occur in one or another human group. But where we know so little the concept of mutation must be used with extreme caution, for it is the one which is readily abused, since almost everything can be "explained" by an appeal to mutation.

It should be clear that while mutation presents the raw material of evolution it does not tell us how that evolution comes about. We know that mutations occur, the real problem is to discover how they (the mutant genes) become differentially distributed, increasing in one group and not in another. If we find that skin color in man has largely arisen as the result of mutation it still remains necessary to explain why some skin colors became localized as, for example, white in Europe, yellowish in a large part of Asia, and black in Africa. Kinky hair, like most other characters, is due to the interaction of several genes (no one knows how many). In order to become established in a population there must be some agent which brings the mutants together and thus ensures their perpetuation. What this agent is we do not know, though it may be strongly suspected that it is selection of some sort.

Bearing these facts in mind, it may then be safely said that some of the physical differences existing between the living varieties of man probably represent the end effects of small gene mutations fitting harmoniously into gene systems which remain relatively unaltered. It is unlikely that the number of genes involved in these differences exceeds more than a very small proportion of the total number carried by each member of the group.

Individuals in whom such mutations occurred—for mutations occur in individuals, not in groups—would have to reproduce if the mutation is to survive. Now, an important point to grasp here is that early populations of man consisted of very small breeding groups, much as among the food-gathering and hunting nonliterate peoples of today. In such small groups a mutation, if it possessed some selective advantage, could establish itself fairly rapidly, in the course of several generations. Under favorable conditions a mutant gene might have a better chance of perpetuating itself in a small population, and in a small population a mutant gene might easily be lost by not being perpetuated in reproduction. In any event, it should be stressed that even when a mutation has considerable adaptive value its spread through a population is extremely slow. Favorable mutations might become distributed through the whole or only through a portion of the population. In the former case, we would have an isolate distinguished by a unique character for which every member was homozygous; in the latter case we would have a situation ready for the further operation of selective factors. Through the agency of limiting factors or social selection those possessing the mutant character gradually become separated from those not characterized by it, and a new group buds off, as it were, from the old, to form a more or less distinct geographic race. This we know to occur in all other forms of life which have been studied, and there is no reason to believe that the same processes have not occurred in the case of man, though definite evidence for this is wanting.

In environments where life is not easy, and the struggle for survival determines the maintenance of small bands rather than large ones, such budding-off of isolates is a perfectly natural process.

Isolation

By isolation is here meant the separation of a group from all other groups of the same species, so that breeding takes place largely or entirely within the isolate. Under such conditions small breeding groups tend to become distinct from others as a result of the unique fixation of mutations which occurs; and the process thus defined becomes temporarily genetically stable, and a type of man distinguishable, in some one or more characters, from all others may thus become established. That isolation is a cause of differentiation has already been remarked. "This," as Julian Huxley says, "is due to the nature of the evolutionary process, which proceeds by the presentation of numerous small mutative steps, and the subsequent incorporation of some of them in the constitution by selection, or in some cases by Sewall Wright's 'drift.' The improbability of the mutative steps being identical in two isolated groups, even if they be pursuing parallel evolution, is enormously high," hence, the fact that no two isolates are ever alike.

It is in this manner that geographically or otherwise isolated groups have doubtless become the source of novel types of mankind, but it should not be supposed that any group of man has ever been completely isolated throughout the whole course of its history. Here, of course, the element of time enters. There can be little doubt that some groups of man have, in the course of their history, been isolated for considerable periods of time, but sooner or later contact is generally established with some other group, and interbreeding occurs. The introduction of new genes for a time produces a certain amount of heterozygosity, and results in a greater variability of the group. If, after such intermixture, the group continues to breed in isolation, there is again produced an equilibrated distribution of genes to result once more in a relatively stable group. The group will now be different in genotype (in the type of its genes, i.e., in its heredity), and may or may not be different in the appearance of its members, in its phenotype. Whether the group will show any phenotypical difference among its members will depend upon the numbers involved in the original crossings, and upon the characters possessed by each of the mating groups, as well as upon whether marriage is random or otherwise with respect to certain traits. No population, however, ever becomes homozygous for all its traits, the fact being that all populations maintain a considerable measure of heterozygosity.

Genetic Drift

It has already been pointed out that throughout the greater part of his history the numbers entering into the constitution of the various breeding populations of man appear to have been very small. Fleure and Graham Clark have independently estimated that the total population, for example, of Britain in Upper Paleolithic times, under a subglacial climate, was between 250 and 2,000, probably nearer 250 in winter months. In the Lower Paleolithic it is unlikely that the population of Britain ever comprised more than a dozen bands. Peoples of the lower hunter stage of cultural development at the present day rarely if ever attain a breeding population size of 1,000. According to Krzywicki's survey tribes numbering more than 500 individuals were a rarity among the Australian aborigines. Such tribes were at least reproductively partially separated from other tribes.

In such partially isolated small populations another factor comes into play. This is the 'accident' of the *breeding structure* of small populations which renders it possible for particular mutant genes or gene combinations to survive. Under such conditions genes for traits which are 'neutral,' that is, which possess neither a positive nor a negative adaptive value, may spread throughout the particular population. The smaller the population and the more isolated it is the more likely is it that a mutation will become fixed in all its members and its normal allele lost. On the other hand the mutant gene may be completely extinguished, and the mutation wholly disappear.

This accidental increase or decline of mutant genes, resulting in spontaneous random variations in gene frequencies, has been termed *genetic drift* or the Sewall Wright effect. As a result of genetic drift small populations commencing with similar genetic structure when more or less isolated from one another, even though they continue to live under similar environmental conditions, will in the course of time come to exhibit certain differences. In this way the accident of genetic drift may produce non-adaptive divergence. Given the inherent variability of the genic system an important factor in genetic drift is isolation. Isolation may then be regarded as in itself a condition of evolution. But the determining factor in genetic drift is small population size.

Random local differentiation as a consequence of genetic drift has undoubtedly played an important role in the evolution of man, but on the whole not nearly as important a role as natural selection. In interaction with natural selection genetic drift has probably been responsible for the establishment of a number of adaptively valuable traits in the human species.

In less isolated larger populations genetic drift is of limited importance, owing to the more extended and intensive opposed action of selection.

Hybridization

By hybridization is understood the crossing of individuals differing from one another in one or more genes or characters.

Two kinds of hybridization may be distinguished, (a) the sexual process in general which produces gene recombinations which serve as raw material for selection, genetic drift, etc., this is generally referred to as Mendelian recombination, and (b) intercrossing of distinct populations. Both types of hybridization have played important roles in the evolution of mankind.

Hybridization between populations leads towards the disappearance of racial distinctness, except insofar as it produces intermediate racial groups on geographic boundaries, or within a larger population. It is precisely such intermediate groups which under conditions of geographic or social isolation will develop as geographic races. In short, two of the most important processes in the evolution and diversification of mankind have undoubtedly been isolation and hybridization followed by isolation. This is likewise true of most living organisms. It is to a very considerable extent through hybridization that the whole great process of phenotypical change occurs. When two groups of somewhat different genotypes mix, there is an exchange of genes to form completely new combinations or systems of gene pairs. Numerous dominant genes for which the other parent is recessive are supplied to the hybrid, so that characters or qualities which would not normally be expressed appear, and establish themselves. It is to this kind of rearrangement of genes, to heterosis, that the phenomenon of hybrid vigor is believed to be due, that is, the condition, as a result of hybridization, in which the offspring exceed both parents in size, fecundity, resistance or other adaptive qualities. In the history of man's progress hybrid vigor may have played an important role in infusing new strength into long isolated groups, and in enabling them to adapt themselves to changes in environment. In the crossing of contemporary ethnic groups however, there is no good evidence of hybrid vigor. The gene differences between human populations do not appear to be significant enough to produce hybrid vigor, although the offspring produced are biologically healthy in every way.

When it is stated that hybridization is an important process in the diversification of mankind, it should also be obvious that it is one of the most important processes in the unification of mankind, for hybridization always leads to a union of the characters of the hybridizing populations in the resulting hybrid population, and to intra-populational variation. It is only when a newly formed hybrid group becomes isolated that the new pattern of genes is able to establish itself as in some respects a unique population.

The American Negro is an example of the simultaneous differential action of both processes. On the one hand social barriers effectively limit his biological participation in the reproductive structure of the white population, and on the other hand an appreciable number of individuals of Negroid ancestry are continually entering the ranks of the white population. And this in spite of the asymmetric sexual relations which prevail between the two groups, the only relationship (covertly) allowed being between white men and Negro women. Stuckert (1958) estimates the number of "whites" now in the United States with some Negro ancestry at about 30 million.

By hybridization there is not simply produced a mixture of genes between different populations, but what is vastly more important the new combinations of genes thus produced expresses itself in a new pattern, something so significantly unlike anything which has appeared before as to justify being called a new type. The American Negroes, for example, exhibit a number of such new types, and such types are also to be seen in the numerous offspring of crosses in Hawaii and elsewhere in the world. To keep to the example of the American Negroes, there are three possible ways in which the African Negroes introduced into America might have produced a new ethnic group or groups: (1) by being freely permitted to marry with members of the white population, so that all differences between Negro and white would eventually have been completely eliminated through the more or less equal distribution of their genes throughout the population, with the resultant emergence of a new Negro-white type; (2) by white men mixing with Negro women, which has almost wholly been the case in America, so that while the white population remained relatively unchanged, the Negro population underwent modification in the direction of the white type; and, (3) by segregation of the mixed individuals as a separate breeding isolate from the relatively unmixed Negro population.

It is quite probable that in the evolution of the geographic races of man such processes have been more or less continuously at work. Factors such as sexual and social selection may have played a more or less consequential part in the evolution of the varying types of man, the tendency in the past, however, has been for many biologists to overemphasize the importance of the first factor and to neglect the second.

Sexual Selection

Ever since Darwin first developed the conception in *The Descent of Man* (1871) sexual selection in man has come to mean the selection of the most preferred females by males possessing certain characteristics, the males so distinguished tending to crowd out those males who do not possess them in the matter of reproduction. The traits of such males and their preferred spouses are thus likely to be perpetuated through sexual selection. The traits thus selected by the successful males are likely, in the course of time, to bring about modifications in the females, and by this means eventually in the whole population. Functionally sexual selection could be defined as the process of selecting mates on the basis of a preferred standard of beauty or other desirable quality, so that in the course of time the sexually preferred type would become the dominant one in the group, and perhaps cause the non-preferred type to become a separate isolate, or even to die out.

For example, in a group in which kinky hair was preferred to straight hair, the straight-haired individuals would find fewer and fewer mates, until the gene for straight hair ceased to exist altogether, or the kinky-haired would mate with kinky-haired, and straight-haired with straight-haired, and thus two distinct types would be formed. The preference of dark Negro males for lighter females in America is an illustration of the manner in which sexual selection operates to maintain the phenotypic variability of the Negro skin. The preference of brunets of one sex for blonds of the other, and vice versa, is an illustration of how sexual selection serves to maintain a balanced distribution of such types. Since the differentiation of human groups could, at least in part, be brought about through the sexual selection of traits possessing no survival value, that is, no adaptive value, this is a possible factor to be considered in any discussion of the evolution of man. Many observers have remarked that in existing literate and non-literate societies males appear to have a preference for females who preserve a certain number of infantile traits, such as the high forehead, high cheeks, long eyelashes, retrousse nose, pouting lips, shorter stature, and the like. Indeed, this is the type of female most valued by Hollywood and movie-going audiences everywhere. And it may well be that the selection of such females during the course of man's biological evolution has played a significant role in contributing to the present form of *Homo sapiens*. It is, however, difficult to evaluate with any degree of security the part that sexual selection has played in the history of man's evolution. When we turn to non-literate societies for enlightenment upon this point, we find that in such societies everyone usually marries, but that certainly the most proficient hunter is likely to be the most-married. The less desirable males and females, however, usually have no difficulty in finding a mate, so that their characteristics are not eliminated.

In civilized societies a certain amount of sexual selection occurs, males principally selecting females for their beauty. The effect of such selection if long continued undoubtedly serves to perpetuate those traits that are considered beautiful. But it should be remembered that there will always be a majority of individuals mating who are not beautiful, and these will transmit their characteristics to descendant generations.

Social Selection

By social selection is meant the regulation of breeding by artificially instituted barriers between socially approved individuals or groups within a population, so that mating occurs between individuals pre-ferred by such social standards, rather than at random. Under such conditions strong isolating mechanisms are developed which, in the course of time, may produce considerable modifications in a population. Where, as in America, there are a variety of colored populations, black, brown, and "yellow," social barriers more or less successfully tend to keep these groups separate from one another and from the white population. In this way such barriers act as isolating mechanisms akin to natural physiographic isolating factors, which have a similar effect in maintaining the genetic differences between isolated groups.

We may suggest, then, in broad outline, the means by which the evolution of human groups has occurred. Commencing with a single genetically relatively heterogeneous population from which small groups have separated and become more or less isolated from one another, it is possible to see how by the action of selection on intrinsic changes in the character of genes and their action (mutation) new combinations of genes may be preserved and distributed throughout a group and thus serve to differentiate it from others. The selection may be either natural, social, or sexual, or any combination of these. In the previous edition of this book we wrote, "As in all other animal groups we may suspect that natural selection has played the most significant role in the differentiation of mankind. Our suspicion needs critical observations to support it. These are, at present, lacking. They must be gathered. Studies must be instituted to determine the adap-tive value of certain traits. Skin color is one of the most obvious of such traits. What is the adaptive value of the different skin colors under different environmental conditions? Temperature, ultra-violet radiation, humidity, and aridity? To what environmental conditions is each skin color best adapted?"

Skin color remains the unsolved problem it is, but since the above words were written our suspicion as to the part played by natural

selection in the evolution of man has been given the strongest confirmation by the findings relating to the adaptive value of such traits
as sickling and blood groups and disease.

It has been said that the broad-cheeked faces of the Mongoloids
living in the high steppe lands of Asia are well padded with fat.
Whether this is so, in fact, remains to be determined. It has, however,
been suggested that such a face is very well adapted to tolerate the
strong cold winds which blow in these regions. This is an example
of the kind of problem which abounds in anthropology, and which
for the want of the necessary facilities for research goes begging. The
application of thermocouples to the cheek regions of representative
samples of Mongoloids and non-Mongoloids ought to be sufficient to
tell us whether the Mongoloid face is more likely to be resistant to
windy insults than the non-Mongoloid.

Brachycephaly, in some populations at any rate, seems to have
some adaptive advantage over dolichocephaly. But what this advantage may be future research alone can tell us. With a progressive increase in stature, there has been a progressive tendency to maintain
the infantile headform in the adult at a cephalic index of about 81.0.

Skin color, head form, face form, eye color, hair color, hair form,
and nose form, are a few of the more obvious traits the adaptive value
of which has yet to be determined. Until this has been done it will
not be possible to arrive at a clear understanding of the manner in
which these traits have been evolved.

In addition to natural selection and mutation another important
evolutionary factor is that of genetic drift or the random variation in
gene frequencies which tend to occur in partially isolated small populations. This process is essentially complementary to the action of
natural selection, and hence may result in the establishment of non-
adaptive gene combinations. It has already been remarked that the
frequency distributions of the blood groups give every indication of
having been produced in this way. It is likely that other traits have
been established in the same manner. Studies in the size of prehistoric
populations, populations being understood to be breeding units, and
in the demography of living nonliterate peoples are therefore very
necessary. The demographic number and the genetically effective
population are not the same things. The latter, the breeding unit, is
always smaller. In dealing with man at any stage of cultural development it is generally observed that demographically a hierarchy of
populations obtains. Some being larger than others, occupying larger
territories, and some being more effectively isolated, so that exchanges

of genes between populations, as well as accidental gene losses, may vary considerably in rate, number, and kind. The isolating barriers may be geographic, sheer distance, or social. These are matters which call for more detailed study than they have yet received. It has already been mentioned that the breeding populations of man in prehistoric times were small, rarely if ever exceeding one thousand individuals. For example, it has been estimated that the population of England and Wales in the latter part of the Old Stone Age probably never reached much more than two thousand individuals. Occasionally we have direct evidence of hybridization between diverse populations such as the "palanthropic" Neanderthaloids and the "neanthropic" types of Mount Carmel. For the rest basic data are wanting and are urgently in need of collection.

Hybridization can easily be overemphasized as a factor in the evolution of man, but it can also be underemphasized. The problem in which we are primarily interested is to discover how the diversity of races arose in the first place. When we speak of hybridization between races we thereby state that this diversity already exists. It tells us nothing concerning the process of initial diversification. Hybridization, however, can be invoked to explain partially, at least, the origin of some intermediate types which may eventually become distinct races. On the other hand, there is always the possibility that the intermediate types arose by the same mechanisms as the parent types. Clearly, then, the concept of hybridization is one which must be used with great caution, since by its misuse it becomes a simple matter to create all sorts of so-called "secondary races" out of "primary races."

There can be little doubt that hybridization has played an important role in the evolution of man, but the extent of that role is a problem which calls for the kind of investigation which has scarcely yet been undertaken. The fact that in the course of man's history intersterile species have not developed would strongly suggest that hybridization between geographic races of man has been the rule. The divergent variability encountered in mankind as a whole would thus be due to the ensuing simple gene recombinations. This crossing and criss-crossing of human races has been visualized as a reticulum or network, and has been called reticulate evolution. As Huxley points out, man's history of progressively increasing "migration and crossing has led to a progressive increase of general variability.

"Man is the only organism to have exploited this method of evolution and variation to an extreme degree, so that a new dominant type in evolution has come to be represented by a single world-wide species instead of showing an adaptive radiation into many intersterile species. Doubtless this is due to his great tendency to individual, group, and mass migration of an irregular nature, coupled with his mental adaptability which enables him to effect cross-mating quite readily in face of differences in colour, appearance, and behaviour which would act as efficient barriers in the case of more instinctive organisms" (354).

The whole problem of sexual selection as a factor in the evolution of prehistoric populations remains uninvestigated. It has been indicated that there is good reason to believe that its role has probably been overestimated.

In short, much fundamental work needs to be done before we shall understand the mechanism of ethnic differentiation. The little, however, that we know of man's evolutionary history appears to conform to the conclusion established by Sewall Wright that the potentialities for rapid evolution are greatest in a large species which is separated into partially isolated groups. Such partial discontinuities favors diversity by local adaptation and also by genetic drift and the establishment of non-adaptive combinations. The fact that the discontinuities or isolates are only partially so, renders considerable the variance of the total diversity potentially available to the species as a whole.

Increase in the availability of this variance has proceeded at an increasingly more rapid rate within the historic period. Dobzhansky has pointed out that the merging in the human species of small population groups in a more or less freely interbreeding whole may be regarded as one of the most important of recent evolutionary events. This process today is being markedly accelerated by the increasing facility of contact between populations or segments thereof.

As the evidence accumulates the distinctive differences between "genera" and "species" of fossil man become less and less marked, just as they do for non-human primates. We begin to suspect that all known forms of man, fossil and living, existing at any one time level belong to a single polytypic species.

A polytypic species has been defined as a group of actually or potentially interbreeding natural populations which is reproductively isolated from other such groups. The actual or potential interbreeding populations are usually more or less separated by geographic barriers, so that an appreciable amount of geographic variation in characters is encountered. Such populations are the polytypes, subspecies, or geographic races which together comprise the species. A population may be defined as any contiguously distributed grouping of a single species which is characterized by both genetic and cultural continuity through several generations.

Quite clearly the whole of mankind comprises a single polytypic species consisting of a large number of geographic races. Exact knowledge concerning the number of human geographic races, their distribution, and rate of gene exchanges between them, is virtually completely wanting. The data which will lead to such exact knowledge remain to be collected.

The racial variability which mankind exhibits is of the kind which in a large number of other animal groups is known to be peculiar to small geographically partially isolated populations. Groups of populations which do not occur together, which exclude each other geographically, are termed *allopatric*. Populations which occur together, whose areas of distribution overlap or coincide, are termed *sympatric*. Man is essentially a member of a sympatric polytypic species. Partial reproductive separation of small populations maintained by geographic barriers is a necessary condition in the production of the observed differences. As Dobzhansky says, "Racial differences cannot persist if races come to inhabit the same territory, for in such a case the races, lacking reproductive isolation, would exchange genes, the differences between them would gradually be erased, and finally they would fuse into a single variable population." Now that the world has, indeed, become "the same territory" the amalgamation of all varieties of man into a single variable population is but a matter of time. If, then, we are to understand the manner in which these geographic races came into being before this process is completed we cannot too long delay the initiation of the necessary investigations.

Definition of an Ethnic Group and Major Group

Thus far our discussion of the mechanism of ethnic group differentiation has been principally in genetic terms. We have seen that the manner in which groups of mankind are formed may best be understood in terms of the processes whereby certain genes acquire different frequencies in different isolates whether or not they are derived from the same ancestral population. A species, we saw, may be regarded as a more or less genetically closed system because it does not regularly exchange genes with other species, while subspecies or geographic races are genetically open systems, since they do exchange genes with other races within the species. Mankind was defined as a single sympatric polytypic species. The basis of that definition was geographic variation. The varying types of which mankind is comprised are seen to be the more or less geographically separated representatives of a single species. Such geographically separated groups were called *geographic races*. The geographic boundaries separating such geographic races are largely continental. The barriers to free gene-flow are oceans, seas, and mountain chains. In our own time we observe that the geographic barriers between such races are increasingly breaking down with the result, particularly in Europe, America, and latterly in the Pacific, that there has been much intermixture between the members of all such populations. Gene exchanges between numerous formerly separated populations are now occurring with great rapidity. It is no longer possible to distinguish many of these populations as geographic races. Hence, in order to avoid the confusion which otherwise inevitably results we need some term by which to distinguish recognizable groups of man that are not reproductively isolated from one another. The genetical definition of a race is a population which differs in the frequency of some gene or genes, which is actually exchanging or capable of exchanging genes across whatever boundaries separate it from other populations of the species. Such a definition as an analytic tool is invaluable, but its usefulness for the practical purposes of classification waits upon the analysis of data which have for the most part yet to be accumulated. Races in this sense have yet to be delimited in man. The truth is that the genetical definition of race would admit so many populations under the term as to result in a *reductio ad absurdam*. The problem of what we wish to call races is clearly arbitrary. Since most genetic differences are quantitative we would first have to specify what level of frequency difference we would accept. Then we would have to consider the position with regard to all loci which have been studied, a complicated exercise in multivariate analysis which would scarcely solve the problem.

The pre-genetical physical anthropologist has used purely morphological criteria for his classificatory purposes. For example, all black-skinned people with kinky head hair were distinguished as belonging to the Negroid major group, all white-skinned people as belonging to the White or Caucasoid major group, and yellow-skinned peoples as belonging to the Mongoloid major group. Within these major groups populations were recognized which differed from one another in virtue of a more or less statistically distinguishable assemblage of physical traits. Such populations were and are still called races. Unfortunately for this form of "race" classification people who look alike may be genetically quite unlike in certain significant traits, while people who look unlike may be genetically very like. Furthermore, by arbitrarily selecting certain traits and treating them as criteria of "race" it is possible to create any number of artificial taxonomic "races," and even to sort these out of a single population. As Huxley says, "So-called 'racial types' may be mere recombinational segregants, thrown up from a highly mixed population, without any continuity of descent through the same phenotype or genotype from the original stock which they are held to represent." The so-called "Nordic" racial type is almost certainly such an artificial "race." If we add to these considerations the political and highly emotional distortions which the term has undergone during the last hundred years, it becomes more than ever necessary to distinguish between the *scientific* usage of the term race and its *unscientific* usage. It is perhaps no exaggeration to say that no term in the English language has been so consistently misused as the word "race." In view of all these facts it were better to use some non-committal term which leaves the matter of rigorous definition and classification open till such time as the necessary data have been secured. For this purpose the term *ethnic group* has been suggested.*

Since, in the next chapter, we shall be giving an account of the principal ethnic groups of mankind we may here define the terms which are there to be used.

All living mankind comprises the single species *Homo sapiens,* a species which consists of a number of populations which individually maintain certain differences from one another by means of isolating mechanisms such as geographical and social barriers. In addition to the effects of other influences these differences will vary as the power of the isolating mechanisms vary. Where these barriers are of low power neighboring isolates will intergrade or hybridize with one another. Where these barriers are of high power, such isolates will tend to remain distinct or replace each other geographically or ecologically.

Such isolates constitute *ethnic groups,* which anthropologically are defined as arbitrarily recognized groups which in virtue of the possession of a more or less distinctive assemblage of physical traits, through a common heredity, are statistically distinguishable from other groups within the species.

It is observed that most of these ethnic groups tend to form certain clusters, according to their resemblances in certain characters. For example, black skin yields a whole cluster of Negroid groups; white skin yields another cluster of White or Caucasoid ethnic groups, and

---

* For a fuller discussion of the use of term see Appendix D, pp. 692-699.

yellowish skin the cluster of Mongoloids; while chocolate-brown to brownish-white skin associated with abundant wavy head hair yields the Australoid or Archaic White cluster. These clusters of characters suggest that some of the ethnic groups exhibiting them may be, in respect of these characters, more closely related than they are to the members of other clusters. As we shall see for this suggestion there is a fair amount of factual support.

It is customary to call such clusters "stocks." This term is, however, objectionable because it suggests an ancestral group from which other populations arose. It is, therefore, preferable to use a term which suggests its purely arbitrary character, namely, *major group*.

A major group is comprised of a number of ethnic groups classified together on the basis of their possession of certain common characters which serve to distinguish that major group from others. For example, the black skin color, tightly curled hair, and everted lips of the Negroids together constitute a combination of characters which serve to distinguish the arbitrarily recognized cluster of ethnic groups they represent from all other ethnic groups.

It should be clearly understood that a major group is a purely working device, a classificatory convenience arbitrarily created as a working hypothesis. In some cases it does not work, in many others it does. When and if it ceases to be useful it should be dropped.

Ethnic group and divisional differences simply represent more or less temporary expressions of variations in the relative frequencies of genes in different parts of the whole species. Such a conception rejects altogether the all-or-none conception of "race" as a static condition of fixed differences. It, of course, denies the unwarranted assumption that there exist any hard and fast genetic boundaries between any groups of mankind and asserts their common genetic unity in diversity. Such a conception of the variety of man cuts across national, linguistic, religious, and cultural boundaries, and thus asserts their essential independence of genetic factors.

FOR FURTHER READING, CONSULT:

ALLEE, W. C.: Where angels fear to tread: A contribution from general sociology to human ethics. *Science*, 97:518-525, 1943.

An important discussion of the principle of cooperation and the part which it has played and could play in the future evolution and development of mankind.
———— *et al.: Principles of Animal Ecology.* Philadelphia, Saunders, 1949.

The fundamental treatise on the interrelation between living organisms and their environment.
————: *Cooperation Among Animals.* Revised ed. New York, Schuman, 1951.

————: *Animal Aggregations.* Chicago, University of Chicago Press, 1931.
Two standard works on cooperation among animals, the first is the more popularly written, the second is more complete, but out of print.

ANDREWARTHA, H. G., and BIRCH, L. C.: *The Distribution and Abundance of Animals.* Chicago, University of Chicago Press, 1954.
A fundamental work concerned with answering the question: How does the environment influence the animal's chance to survive and multiply?

BOYD, W. C.: Critique of methods of classifying mankind. *Am. J. Phys. Anthropol.,* 27:333-364, 1940.
A valuable and very clear exposition of the case for the blood groups in the classification of mankind.

————: *Genetics and the Races of Man.* Boston, Little, Brown & Co., 1950.
A very readable book on the application of genetical methods of analysis to the problems of human raciation.

CANDELA, P. B.: The introduction of blood-group B into Europe. *Human Biol.,* 14:413-443, 1942.
An admirable study illustrative of the manner in which the gene frequency method of analysis, together with a study of the historical data, may throw light on ethnic origins and relationships.

COLIN, E. C.: *Elements of Genetics,* 3rd edition. New York, McGraw-Hill, 1956.
An excellent exposition of the laws of heredity with particular reference to man.

COON, C. S.: Some problems of human variability and natural selection in climate and culture. *Am. Naturalist,* 89:257-280, 1955.

————: Climate and race. In *Climatic Change* (edited by H. Shapley), Harvard University Press, 1954, pp. 13-34.
Two stimulating papers.

COWLES, R. B.: The black skin and human protective coloration. *J. Entomol. & Zoology,* 42:1-4, 1950.
A cogent discussion of black skin as a trait of selective value because of the protection it affords the individual in effectively concealing him from predators.

CRICK, F. H. C.: Nucleic acids. *Scientific American,* 197:188-200, 1958.
An admirable discussion of the nature of the gene and the manner in which genes probably duplicate themselves.

DAHLBERG, G.: An analysis of the conception of race and a new method of distinguishing races. *Human Biol.,* 14:372-385, 1942.
A criticism of the existing anthropological conception of race, with an interesting proposal for the proper handling of the problem.

————: *Race, Reason and Rubbish.* New York, Columbia University Press, 1942.
An excellent introduction to the principles of heredity with especial reference to the problems of human variation, and an equally excellent discussion of the problem of race, by a leading authority.

DAVIS, A.: The distribution of the blood-groups and its bearing on the concept of race. *Political Arithmetic* (edited by L. Hogben), New York, Macmillan, 1938, p. 503-531.
A very clear and important discussion.

DOBZHANSKY, T.: *Genetics and the Origin of Species.* New York, Columbia Univ. Press, 3rd edition, 1951.
One of the most important analyses of the species problem in the light of genetics to be published in our time.

————: The genetic basis of evolution. *Scientific American, 122*:32-41, 1950.
An admirably clear discussion.

————: *Evolution, Genetics, and Man.* New York, Wiley, 1955.
Evolution treated as a living subject with especial reference to man.

————: *The Biological Basis of Human Freedom.* New York, Columbia University Press, 1956.
A most stimulating book in which the interaction of competitive and cooperative factors in evolution is ably discussed.

DUNN, L. C. and DOBZHANSKY, T. H.: *Heredity, Race, and Society.* Revised edition. New York, Pelican Books, 1952.
An excellent elementary introduction to genetic anthropology.

EVANS, R. D.: Quantitative inferences concerning the genetic effects of radiation on human beings. *Science, 109*:209-304, 1949.
An important paper on, among other things, the probable number of genes in man.

FISHER, R. A.: *The Genetical Theory of Natural Selection.* The Clarendon Press, Oxford, 1937. Reprinted New York, Dover Books, 1958.
A fundamental work on the theory of natural selection, with a discussion of biological problems relating to man, and the rise and fall of civilizations.

————, FORD, E. B. and HUXLEY, J. S.: Taste-testing the anthropoid apes. *Nature, 144*:750, 1939.
On the genetics of the taste reactions of the anthropoid apes to PTC (phenyl-thio-carbamide).

GALTON, D. A. G. (editor): Haematology. *Brit. Med. Bull., 15*:1-88, 1959.
A fundamental series of fifteen studies in hematology.

GOLDSMITH, K. L. G. (editor): Blood groups. *Brit. Med. Bull., 15*:89-174, 1959.
Fifteen basic studies on the blood groups. This is an indispensable work for the student of anthropology.

GRÜNEBERG, H.: *Animal Genetics and Medicine.* London, Hamish Hamilton, 1947.
A survey of inherited diseases in laboratory rodents, valuable for its discussion of the physiological channels through which genes produce their physiological effects.

HALDANE, J. B. S.: *Heredity and Politics.* New York, Norton, 1938.
A brilliant series of papers on human biology.

————: The blood-group frequencies of European peoples, and racial origins. *Human Biol., 12*:457-480, 1940.
An important study, somewhat technical, but admirably demonstrative of the manner in which blood-group frequencies are studied in relation to the problem of varietal and ethnic group origins.

————: *New Paths in Genetics.* New York, Harper, 1942.
On the genetics and biochemistry of development.

HARRIS, H.: *Human Biochemical Genetics.* London and New York, Cambridge University Press, 1959.
A valuable examination of the biochemical states the genetics of which are more or less well understood.

HERRICK, C. J.: *The Evolution of Human Nature.* Austin, University of Texas Press, 1956.
A most readable and stimulating work by the doyen of neuroanatomists.

HOGBEN, L.: The concept of race. *Genetic Principles in Medicine and Social Science.* New York, Knopf, 1932, pp. 122-144.

The best critical analysis of the anthropological conception of race yet written.

HUXLEY, J. S. and HADDON, A. C.: *We Europeans: A Survey of Racial Problems.* New York, Harper, 1936.

An admirably clear survey written in collaboration by a distinguished biologist and a distinguished anthropologist.

HUXLEY, J. S.: *Evolution: The Modern Synthesis.* New York, Harper, 1942.

A magnificent synthesis of modern knowledge expository of the process of evolution. With Dobzhansky's and Mayr's books, indispensable reading.

————: *Touchstone for Ethics.* New York, Harper, 1947.

Julian Huxley and his grandfather T. H. Huxley discuss evolution and ethics.

————: *Evolution in Action.* New York, Harper, 1953. Also available in paperback, New York, New American Library, 1956.

A brilliant thought-provoking book, which terminates in the development of a thoroughgoing evolutionary humanism.

————: *New Bottles for New Wine.* New York, Harper, 1957.

A delightful and informative collection of essays on subjects of anthropological interest.

INGRAM, V. M.: How do genes act? *Scientific American, 198:*68-74, 1958.

An important study in which the actual change in the gene which leads to sickle cell anemia is demonstrated.

JONXIS, J. H. P., and DELAFRESNAYE, J. F., (Editors): *Abnormal Haemoglobins.* Springfield, Illinois, Thomas, 1959.

An international symposium, and the best single work on the abnormal hemoglobins.

————, and HUISMAN, T. H. J.: *A Laboratory Manual on Abnormal Haemoglobins.* Springfield, Illinois, Thomas, 1959.

The best available work on the determination of the abnormal hemoglobins.

KROPOTKIN, P.: *Mutual Aid.* Boston, Porter Sargent, 1955.

The classic work on cooperation. Indispensable reading. To be regarded as a continuation rather than as a corrective of Darwin's *Origin of Species.* First published between 1890 and 1896 in the *Fortnightly Review,* and as a book in 1902, and many times reprinted since, the above edition reprints Huxley's "Struggle for Existence" manifesto, to which Kropotkin's *Mutual Aid* constitutes the reply.

KRZYWICKI, L.: *Primitive Society and Its Vital Statistics.* London, Macmillan, 1934.

A valuable pioneering study of the primitive community, its size, and vital statistics.

LAWLER, S. D., and LAWLER, L. J.: *Human Blood Groups and Inheritance.* Cambridge, Massachusetts, Harvard University Press, 1957.

A short and readable account of the blood groups, their genetics, and clinical use.

MAYR, E.: *Systematics and the Origin of Species.* New York, Columbia Univ. Press, 1942.

A most valuable discussion of taxonomical principles in the light of modern genetics, in relation to the old and the new systematics.

———— (editor): *The Species Problem.* Washington, D.C., American Association for the Advancement of Science, 1957.

A valuable symposium.

MONTAGU, M. F. ASHLEY: *Man's Most Dangerous Myth: The Fallacy of Race,* 3rd edition, New York, Harper, 1955.
An examination and criticism of existing conceptions of race both anthropological and popular in the light of history, biology, genetics, sociology, and psychology.
————: The origin and nature of social life and the biological basis of cooperation. *J. Soc. Psychol.,* 29:267-283, 1949.
A theory of the origin and nature of social life and an exposition of the principle of cooperation.
————: *On Being Human.* New York, Schuman, 1950.
A study in the meaning of cooperation.
————: *Statement on Race,* 2nd edition. New York, Schuman, 1952.
An extended exposition and discussion of the UNESCO Statement on Race.
————: *Darwin, Competition, and Cooperation.* New York, Schuman, 1953.
A discussion of the development of the Darwinian conception of competition, and the somewhat neglected cooperative factors which have played a role in evolution.
————: *Human Heredity.* New York, World Publishing Co., 1959.
Stressing the importance of the environment, and containing a census of genetically conditioned disorders, together with a list of counseling centers.
MOURANT, A. E.: *The Distribtuion of the Human Blood Groups.* Springfield, Thomas, 1954.
————: *The ABO Blood Groups.* Springfield, Thomas, 1958.
The most thorough and exhaustive works on the anthropological aspects of the ABO blood groups, with numerous tables, and maps. All work up to the end of 1957 is reported in the second volume.
————: Blood groups and anthropology. *Brit. Med. Bull.,* 15:140-144, 1959.
A valuable discussion and summary.
MULLER, H. J., LITTLE, C. C. and SNYDER, L. H.: *Genetics, Medicine, and Man.* Ithaca, New York, Cornell Univ. Press, 1947.
An admirable work on the principles of heredity and their application to man in health and disease.
NASMYTH, G.: *Social Progress and the Darwinian Theory.* New York, Putnam, 1916.
An extremely important book in the tradition of Kropotkin, on cooperation versus disoperation.
NEWMAN, M. T.: The application of ecological rules to the racial anthropology of the aboriginal New World. *Amer. Anthrop.,* 55:309-327, 1953.
A test of the applicability of Bergmann's and Allen's rules to man in the New World.
PATTEN, W.: *The Grand Strategy of Evolution.* Boston, Badger, 1920.
One of the truly great books of our century. An eminent biologist's analysis of the nature of life and of evolution in the light of the principle of cooperation.
RACE, R. R. and SANGER, R.: *Blood Groups in Man,* 3rd edition. Springfield, Thomas, 1958.
The standard work, authoritative and probably one of the few existing technical works to which the adjective "charming" could be applied.
ROBERTS, D. F.: Body weight, race and climate. *Am. J. Phys. Anthropol.,* n.s. 11: 533-558, 1953.

A valuable study lending some support for the applicability of Bergmann's and Allen's rules in man.

ROBERTS, J. A. FRASER: *An Introduction to Medical Genetics,* 2nd edition. New York, Oxford University Press, 1959.
The best and most lucid work of its kind.

————: Blood groups and disease. *Brit. Med. Bull., 15:*129-133, 1959.
An excellent account of the findings to date.

SCHEINFELD, A.: *The New You and Heredity.* Philadelphia, Lippincott, 1950.
By far and away the best popularly written account of heredity, covering a vast territory including race. Beautifully, clearly illustrated by the author.

SCHIFF, F. and BOYD, W. C.: *Blood Grouping Technic.* New York, Interscience, 1942.
A manual for clinicians, serologists, anthropologists, and students of legal and military medicine. An indispensable work of great practical value. Specially constructed tables and nomographs greatly simplify the task of computing gene frequencies.

SHEPPARD, P. M.: Blood groups and natural selection. *Brit. Med. Bull., 15:* 134-139, 1959.
A valuable discussion of the evidence.

SIMPSON, G. G.: *Evolution.* New York, Columbia Univ. Press, 1953.
A brilliant discussion of the rates of evolutionary processes, and of the manner in which populations become genetically and morphologically differentiated.

————: *The Meaning of Evolution.* New Haven, Yale University Press, 1949.
The best of all books on the history of life and its significance for man.

————, PITTENDRIGH, C. S., and TIFFANY, L. H.: *Life: An Introduction to Biology.* New York, Harcourt Brace, 1957.
An exemplary work, probably the best introduction to general biology in any language.

SPUHLER, J. N.: *On the number of genes in man. Science, 108:*279, 1948.

STERN, C.: *Principles of Human Genetics.* 2nd ed. San Francisco, W. H. Freeman & Co., 1960.
An able, conservatively written, text covering the whole field of human genetics.

SYMPOSIUM: *Origin and Evolution of Man.* Cold Spring Harbor, L.I., Cold Spring Harbor Symposia on Quantitative Biology, *XV:vii*-425, 1950.
A valuable symposium in which geneticists, anthropologists, and zoologists participate, containing some fundamental contributions.

WEINER, J. S.: Nose shape and climate. *Am. J. Phys. Anthropol.,* n.s. *12:*1-4, 1954.
A helpful discussion.

WIENER, A. S.: The Rh factor and racial origins. *Science, 96:*407-408, 1942.
An excellent paper illustrating the manner in which conclusions may be arrived at as to ethnic origins, from a study of the present distribution of *Rh* and *rh* genes.

————: *Blood Groups and Transfusion.* Springfield, Ill., Thomas, 1943.
A standard work on the subject, very readable, and containing an exhaustive account of the anthropology of the blood groups.

————, CANDELA, P. B., and GOSS, L. J.: Blood-group factors in the blood, organs and secretions of primates. *J. Immunol., 45:*229-235, 1942.
An important paper.

———— and WEXLER, I. B.: *Heredity of the Blood Groups.* New York, Grune & Stratton, 1958.

The best short account of the heredity of the blood groups.

WILBER, C. G.: Physiological regulations and the origins of human types. *Human Biology,* 29:329-336.

A criticism of the application of the rules of ecology to man. For a reply to this paper see S. M. Garn, A comment on Wilber's "Origin of Human Types." *Human Biology, 30:*338-340, 1958.

SYMPOSIUM. *Genetics and Twentieth Century Darwinism.* Cold Spring Harbor Symposia on Quantitative Biology, *24:*xv + 321, 1959.

An invaluable series of papers and discussions on the mechanisms of evolution.

OSCHINSKY, L.: A reappraisal of recent serological, genetic and morphological research on the taxonomy of the races of Africa and Asia. *Anthropologica,* n.s. *1:*1-25, 1959.

Chapter VII

THE MAJOR GROUPS AND ETHNIC GROUPS
OF MAN

In the preceding chapter we saw that the major and ethnic groups of man must be regarded as more or less temporary isolates, which may be arbitrarily delimited and distinguished as such. We saw, too, something of the manner in which such isolates have been produced. In the present chapter a brief account will be given of the major groups and more prominent ethnic groups of man which have been recognized by physical anthropologists.

It should, however, be clearly understood that the classification here offered is both a tentative and a temporary one, and is merely calculated to give the reader little more than the names by which he may refer to certain arbitrarily distinguished groups of mankind. It must always be remembered that such names are only labels for convenient abstractions which help us to appreciate broad facts, and that a major or ethnic group is, in most cases, an abstraction which exists in our own minds alone.

The truth is that we know far too little about mankind to be able to make any efficient classification of it. The older school of physical anthropologists utilized a purely arbitrary selection of external or phenotypical characters in order to make their classifications. They could hardly have done otherwise, but their classifications have never been satisfactory for the simple reason that it is impossible to define most populations in terms of external characters alone. I have no desire to perpetuate this type of classification here or to perpetrate another along similar lines. It is, however, the duty of an expositor to present the conventional anthropological view of the major groups and principal ethnic groups of mankind, before it finally bows gracefully out of existence to make way for the genetical analysis of mankind. There is, however, a real question as to whether any classification of continuously varying groups into discrete categories can ever be anything more than artificial.

The classifier of the "races" of man has hoped to be able to reduce the great variety presented by mankind to some sort of comprehensible system. This he has attempted to do by arbitrarily recognizing certain physical distinctions between groups of mankind, distinctions based on external characters such as the shape of the head, stature, hair form, hair color, hair distribution, eye form, eye color, skin color, and the like. The classifier has always tried to select characters which remained *constant,* and which he thought to be largely uninfluenced by the environment. By this means the classifier of mankind has generally been led to a definition of "race" which typically takes the following form: "A race is a group of individuals or a population with the same or similar external characters, which have been determined by their common heredity or descent."

Apart from the fact that such a definition would logically lead to the recognition of a red-headed race, a color-blind race, and a deaf-mute race, it makes possible the arbitrary creation of any number of "races" on the basis of any physical characters the classifier chooses to select. Furthermore, it obscures basic facts, and does not actually achieve what the classifier sets out to do, for such a definition does not delimit his "races" from either species or even genera. Finally, the notion of common heredity or descent seems inevitably to lead to the utterly erroneous idea of "pure races," the like of which there never were. The realities of the situation are that human groups represent not static but fluid aggregates characterized by very variable characters in process of undergoing more or less constant change. For this reason it has been difficult for the practical demand of the classifier to be met that the "races" of man be well limited and well defined units. The approach to the problem of raciation in man has, in the past, been unsound, for unfortunately the description of external characters can tell us very little concerning either the genetic history or present relationships of the groups described. Hence, the real interest of the physical anthropologist must be in those dynamic processes whereby human groups come to exhibit the kind of variability or changes they now display. Classification regarded as a preliminary step in the service of this interest is to be welcomed.

The reason why systematic exercises in the classification of external characters can never succeed in elucidating the relationships of different groups of mankind to one another is, as we have already more than once pointed out, that it is not assemblages of characters which undergo change in the formation of the individual and of the group, but single units which affect the development of those characters, the genes. The fact is that there is no such thing as a "race" in the older conventional sense or in the popular sense. We have already seen that geographic and local races of mankind do exist, and that genetically the process of raciation may best be understood in terms of the frequencies with which the genes in interaction with the total environment, express themselves in varying distributions of phenotypical characters, the degree of significant association of which is best assessed by statistical methods.

In the genetic sense a race may be defined as a breeding population differing in the incidence of certain genes from other populations within the species. Such a population is actually or potentially capable of exchanging genes across whatever boundaries separate it from other populations. It is a *genogroup*.

Since the same types of physical characters may have very different origins, the only way in which their origin can be traced is by tracing the distribution of the genes determining them, that is to say, by the very opposite method by which the classification below has been arrived at. This classification represents an attempt to reduce the classificatory schemes of the older school of anthropologists to a single simple scheme, combining both the vices and the virtues of most of them. It is based on certain external physical characters which are specified below, and which are very roughly capable of distinguishing the groups described. The reader should bear in mind that this, together with most other classifications, based on external characters alone, is a highly debatable one, and will very probably eventually turn out to be more or less nonsensical. Finally, the reader should remember that description is not analysis.

Bearing these cautions in mind we may now proceed with the attempt to give some of these abstractions some semblance of form.

THE MAJOR GROUPS OF MANKIND

Three major groups of mankind may be distinguished: The *Negroid*, the *Caucasoid*, and the *Mongoloid*. As a subdivision of the Caucasoid larger than an ethnic group may be distinguished the *Australoid* or *Archaic Caucasoid* sub-complex. This classification is based upon the common possession by each of these groups of a few physical characters which, in general, serve to distinguish them from one another. These characters are: Skin color, form and character of the hair and its distribution, form of the head and proportions of the body.

The Negroid Division

Among the Negroids the skin is typically dark brown, but is often black, and even yellowish-brown in some groups. The head hair varies from tightly curled to pepper-corn in form (sparsely distributed tufts), and as a rule there is a marked paucity of hair over the rest of the body (glabrousness). The head is long, the nose is broad and flat with wide nostrils, the ears small, there is some prognathism (forward projection of the upper jaw), and the lips are thick and everted.

The development of a deeply pigmented skin was probably early diffused throughout the group, for it is highly probable that the black skin has proven of distinct survival value to peoples living in hot humid climates. In association with this type of skin there occurs a large number of sweat glands which, by their excretion, serve to reduce the temperature of the body, and which in addition serve to maintain a salty film of moisture over the skin which assists to keep it cool.

There are a fairly large number of Negroid groups which are anthropologically known, but a still larger number which are anthropologically unknown. In general Negroids may be classified as African and Oceanic. Under African Negroids may crudely be distinguished the following ethnic groups:

The True Negroes
The Forest Negroes
The Nilotic Negroes or Nilotes
The Half-Hamites or Nilo-Hamites
The Bantu-Speaking Negroes
The Bushman
The Hottentots
The Negrillos

Geographic Distribution of African Negroids

A line drawn from the mouth of the Senegal River on the West Coast of Africa through Timbuktu to Khartoum in the Anglo-Egyptian Sudan, and from thence down to the western borders of Abyssinia around to the south-east, and finally from the Juba River to the Indian Ocean, divides Africa into a northern light-skinned third inhabited by Hamitic and Semitic speaking Caucasoids, and a southern two-thirds essentially Negroid.

Admixture among the peoples and cultures of these two great regions has been more or less continuous for many generations.

The Hamites. The influence of the Hamitic-speaking peoples has been considerable upon Negro Africa, much more so than the more recent influences of the Semitic-speaking peoples. A few words are therefore necessary concerning the Basic Mediterranean Hamitic-speaking peoples, usually called Hamites, though "Hamitic" is a linguistic and not a physical category. The so-called Hamites are divided into two major branches, the Northern and the Eastern.

The cradle-land of the Hamites is generally agreed to be Asiatic, perhaps the Arabian peninsula or even further east.

The Northern Hamites include the Berbers of Cyrenaica, Tripolitania, Tunisia, and Algeria (the Libyans), the Berbers of Morocco, the Taureg and Tibu of the Sahara, the Fula of Nigeria, and the extinct Guanche of the Canary Islands.

The Eastern Hamites are composed of the ancient and modern Egyptians, the Beja, Nubians, Galla, Somali, Danakil, and most Ethiopians.

Among the Hamites skin color varies all the way from white to black; head hair varies from straight to frizzly; the face is never prognathous; the lips vary from thick to thin, but are almost never everted as in the Negro; there is, in general, a paucity of body hair. The head is mesocephalic (cephalic index 76.0), and stature is medium, about 1.65 m. (five feet five inches). The Hamites are more fully described on p. 456.

The True Negroes

The home of the so-called True Negroes is West Africa, from the mouth of the Senegal River to the eastern boundary of Nigeria, with the French Sudan, some part of the Cameroons and the Congo representing the central and southern extensions of the type. (The remainder of Negro Africa consists of Negroes hamiticized to a greater or lesser degree, namely, the Bantu, the Nilotic Negroes or Nilotes, and the Half-Hamites.

The physical characters of the true Negroes may be summarized as follows: Skin black, hair woolly, nose broad and flat, average height 1.73 m. (five feet eight inches), thick often everted lips, moderately long head (cephalic index 73-75), considerable prognathism, body-build burly, relatively long-legged, long-armed.

New World Negroes. The New World Negroes for the most part represent the somewhat mixed descendants of true Negroes of West African origin, and some northwestern Bantu. In general the New World Negro differs from the Old World Negro in the following observable features: Greater height, larger ears, lighter pigmentation, and a narrower nose. These differences, and others, are due to admixture mostly with whites.

Figure 176. A Nilotic Negro of the Tagala People of the Sudan. (Courtesy, Musée de l'Homme, Paris.)

The Forest Negro

Over a wide area of tropical Africa, extending from the Senegal River in the west to the Sudan, Uganda, and Northern Rhodesia in the east, and in the south to Lower Angola, there occurs a rather barrel-chested, short-legged, long-armed, stocky type of Negro characterized by a markedly protrusive lower face, retreating chin, prominent cheekbones, and a somewhat sloping forehead. The head is generally long (dolichocephalic), the root of the nose low, and the bridge flat. The lips are markedly everted. Stature varies considerably, averaging between 1.65 m. (five feet five inches) to 1.75 m. (five feet nine inches). It is supposed that the forest Negro is closely related to the pygmies who live within part of the range of the former in the equatorial forests of Africa, especially in the Congo region.

The Nilotic Negroes or Nilotes

The long-legged, slim, tall, very dark inhabitants of the Sudan and the Upper Nile Valley are long-headed (cephalic index 71-74), and the face is not as protrusive nor the forehead as sloping as in the forest or true Negroes. Average height is 1.78 m. (five feet ten inches) or slightly more. The nose is generally broad, but in some groups narrow, as among the Somalis and the Shilluk, and though the hair remains woolly, the evidence of Hamitic admixture is clear.

The probabilities are that the Nilotes represent the result of admixture between true Negroes or Negroes of the forest type and some early Hamitic or Ethiopian stock. The Hamitic type is best seen in the Shilluk of the west bank of the Nile of the eastern Sudan, and also among the Dinka, the Kavirondo, Jaluo, and others. Westermann's classification of the Nilotes on linguistic grounds conveys some idea of the peoples involved.

1. The High Nilotic group comprising Mittu, Madi, Abukaya, Abaka, Luba, Wira, Lendu, and Moru.
2. The Middle Nilotic group, comprising Shilluk, Anuak, Beir, Jur, Belanda, and numerous other peoples of Eastern Uganda, Acholi, Lango, Aturu, and Jaluo.
3. The Low Nilotic group, comprising Dinka and Nuer.

In view of their appreciable Hamitic admixture the Nilotes are sometimes spoken of as Negroids rather than Negroes.

The Half-Hamites or Nilo-Hamites

The Half-Hamites or Nilo-Hamites are limited to East Africa and East Central Africa. They occupy the greater part of Kenya Colony, that part of the Uganda which runs northwards to the Sudan bound-

Figure 177.   Hamiticized Nilote of Assouan, Sudan. (Courtesy, Musée de l'Homme, Paris.)

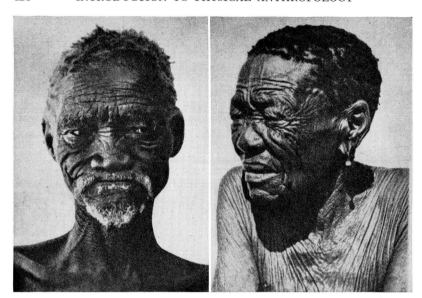

Figure 178a. Old Hottentot Man and Woman, South-West Africa. (From L. Schultz, *Aus Namaland und Kalahari*, 1907. Courtesy, Gustav Fischer, Jena.)

ary, as well as much of the northern portion of Tanganyika Territory. The Half-Hamites are the result of mixture of Hamite with Negro. Typical Half-Hamite tribes are the Masai, the Nandi group (comprising Nandi, Kipsigis, Keyo, Suk, Barabaig, and Dorobo) and the Teso group (Teso, Kuman, Karamajong, Turkana, and Toposa).

Skin color varies from light chocolate to very dark brown. Sometimes the skin is described as having a reddish tinge. The hair is woolly, the nose varies from broad and flat to moderately narrow, the lips are usually full but not everted, the cheekbones high, prognathism slight, average stature is about 1.73 m. (five feet eight inches), while the Ba-Hima of the Uganda are extremely tall. On the whole, however, the Half-Hamites are not as tall as the Nilotes. The head among the Masai, Nandi, and Turkana is long (cephalic index 73-74), but the cephalic index among the Suk is about 77 (mesocephalic).

The Bantu-Speaking Negroes

"The Bantu-Speaking Negroes" is a phrase which embraces a great conglomeration of peoples inhabiting the enormous expanse of territory which includes central and southern Africa. A line drawn from the mouth of the Rio del Rey a little south of 4° N. lat., on the

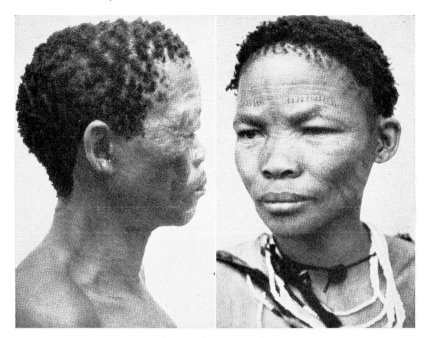

Figure 178b. Adult male and female Bushman. (Courtesy, Dr. M. Gusinde.)

west coast to the mouth of the Juba River a little below the equator 43° long., demarcates the upper limits of the distribution of the Bantus or Bantu-Speaking Negroes, who thus occupy the southern two-thirds of black Africa. The phrase describing these peoples is a very crude, purely temporary one, and is merely used for convenience in order to refer to a fairly large number of African peoples of differing physical type who have thus far been insufficiently studied by physical anthropologists, and of whom it is at the present time not possible to give a satisfactory account, nor even to say of how many ethnic groups they may be composed. As a whole they are customarily described as follows: Hair of usual Negro type, skin color varies from yellowish-brown to black, though dark chocolate is the prevalent hue, average height is 1.67 m. (five feet six inches), the head is typically dolichocephalic, though mesocephalic groups occur, some with lower stature. In the "typical Bantu" the skin is usually less dark, stature shorter, head less elongated, forehead flatter, prognathism less marked, nose generally more prominent and narrower than in the true Negro.

The Bantu-speaking peoples of central and southern Africa present a great variety of types. They are essentially Negro peoples mixed with Hamitic, Negrillo and in the south, with Bushman-Hottentot elements. A rough classification on geographical, cultural, and historical bases, makes it possible to group the Bantu as follows:

1. *Eastern Bantu:* From Uganda in the north, through Kenya Colony, Tanganyika Territory, Northern Rhodesia, Nyasaland, and Mozambique north of the Zambesi.
2. *Southern Bantu:* South of the Zambesi and Kurene Rivers, covering the vast area which includes Southern Rhodesia, the southern half of Mozambique, east and central parts of the Union of South Africa, Swaziland and Bechuanaland Protectorates, Basutoland, and South-West Africa.
3. *Western Bantu:* From the Atlantic north of the Kurene River to North-West Rhodesia and the Rift Valley (the line of the Great Lakes), and extending in the north-west to French West African possessions and the Southern Cameroons.

Bushman

The Bushman is now mainly confined to Southern Angola, the central and northern parts of the Kalahari Desert, and the northern half of South-West Africa, where Tobias has estimated that some 50,000 survive. In earlier times, as evidenced by rock-paintings and other typical Bushman artifacts such as digging stick weights of perforated stone, the ancestors of the contemporary Bushman once occupied the greater part of tropical East, East-Central, and Northern Africa, as well as Uganda and Southern Sudan, and the whole of South Africa.

The Bushman presents so distinctive an appearance as to be distinguishable at a glance from all other Africans, save the Hottentot. The average height of the Bushman is 1.58 m. (five feet two inches), but there are a large proportion of pygmoid individuals, and also many tall ones. They are slightly built, with well-shaped limbs and small hands and feet. Arms and legs are long in relation to length of trunk —possibly an example of Allen's rule. On the head 12 to 20 hairs are either tightly coiled into spiral tufts or little rolls termed "peppercorn," which seem to leave bare areas on the scalp. The body is almost completely devoid of hair, though a sparse growth on the face is generally present; the head is mesocephalic (cephalic index 75-76), the face small, broad and flat, and somewhat pentagonoid. There is generally no or only a very slight protrusion of the lower face. The entire integumentary upper lip is of medium height and arches convexly forward, while the membranous lips vary from medium thick to thin, and are light rose in color, they are not as thick or as everted as in the typical Negro. The nose is short and flat and very broad, seen in profile it appears concave. The root of the nose is usually depressed. The cheekbones are broad and prominent, the forehead is either vertical or bulging, and usually narrow. The chin is pointed. The eyes are set rather wide apart, and the opening between the eyelids is narrow, often appearing slightly oblique owing to the remarkable fullness of the upper lid, and the fact that a prominent fold of skin usually curves round from above it to the side of the nose and completely covers the medial angle of the eye, the so-called Mongoloid or epicanthic fold. The ears are small and circular or squarish, and usually lobeless. Skin color varies from light yellowish-brown to reddish- and copper-brown. The skin is very dry and lean, except on the upper parts of the thighs and especially the buttocks which, in the females particularly, are frequently the seat of immense deposits of fat forming, as one wit has remarked, a sort of morphological bustle, a condition known as steatopygia. It has been suggested that this trait is of some adaptive value, the fat thus laid up being drawn upon during periods of starvation, thus helping to sustain life. This suggestion is, however, contradicted by the fact that under conditions of starvation, and in otherwise emaciated women, the deposit of buttock fat is not selectively utilized. In both sexes the forward lumbar curvature is greatly exaggerated. In the females there is a peculiar elongation of the labia minora, the so-called "Hottentot apron" or "tablier égyptien." There is a suspicion that this may be a form of artificial genital deformation. Steatopygia is apparently not as well developed among the Northern Bushman as it is among the Southern Bushman; according to Gusinde the Northern Bushman of both sexes develop only a more or less noticeable lordosis. The Bushman skin characteristically falls into deep wrinkles and folds, especially on the face, even in fairly young and well-nourished individuals. In males the normal position of the penis is horizontal rather than pendulous, and the scrotum is contracted.

Skin color, skin wrinkling, broad cheekbones, eye and nose form, the presence of a so-called Mongoloid sacral spot in infants, are traits which have suggested to some students that the Bushman is the result, among other things, of a Mongoloid admixture. It has been suggested that the Bushman is the descendant of a group which draws its origin from intermixture of the so-called Boskop type (see p. 259) with a Mongoloid group, and some pygmoid group, possibly also with some early proto-Hamitic stock. All this is, however, speculative to the highest degree. How such a suggested admixture came about, if it ever did, no one knows, though there is some hope that future studies

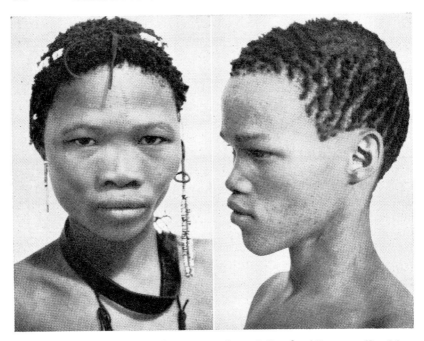

Figure 179a. Young Bushman Female and Youth. (Courtesy Dr. M. Gusinde.)

will throw more light upon what is at present an anthropological enigma. The alleged Mongoloid influence is, in spite of superficial appearances, a good illustration of the dangers involved in attempting to deduce ancestral origins and relationships from external characters. The skin color of the Bushman conforms to Gloger's rule that yellowish- or reddish-brown pigments prevail in hot arid climates. Since the Bushman type in the form of the Boskopoids (see pp. 259-263) is known to have lived in the southern half of Africa at least since the Middle Pleistocene, their skin color is almost certain to prove to be not a trait inherited from some conjectured Mongoloid ancestor, but an adaptation to the climate of a desert or semi-desert nature. In this connection Gusinde states, "The bodily form of the Bushman-race clearly shows a remarkable adaptation to their desert environment; the light color of their skin blends well with their desert surroundings; their light weight, delicate structure, and long legs render possible prolonged running in desert sands."

Since there are many Bushmen with flat nasal roots who do not possess an epicanthic fold, while there are others with well-developed

Figure 179b. Hottentot Woman showing steatopygia. (Courtesy, Musée de l'Homme, Paris.)

nasal roots who do exhibit it, the epicanthic fold in the Bushman is therefore not related to a flat nasal root, but is inherited as an independent trait, the genes involved for epicanthic fold and nasal root being independent entities.

The bluish-gray so-called Mongoloid sacral spot seen in the Bushman infant is not unique to Mongoloids, for it occurs in 90 per cent of Negro infants, and it also occurs in some white and American Indian infants. In short, there is really no reason whatever to assume a Mongoloid component in the ancestry of the Bushman. The flat root of the nose, the epicanthic fold, the regional deposition of the fat, the hairlessness of the body, and the general characters of the skull are all fetalized or neotenous traits (see pp. 295-316). When we turn to the A-B-O blood group frequencies in the Bushman we observe the following typical picture, the tribes are the Auen and Kung of South-West Africa:

Tribe	Investigator	No.	O	A	B	AB	p	q	r
Auen	Pijper 1932	280	53.9	31.1	5.4	9.6	22.5	7.6	6.79
Kung	Pijper 1932	268	60.4	28.0	7.8	3.7	17.3	5.9	9.86

The strikingly low B gene frequency of the Bushman is in marked contrast with the high B gene frequencies of Mongoloids. On morphological and serological grounds the Bushmen are essentially Negroid, probably descended from an ancient Negroid stock from which they remained isolated for a sufficiently durable period of time to undergo the genetic changes that now distinguish them.

The Hottentots

Scattered over the western part of South Africa, in what was formerly their homeland range from the Kurene River in the north to the Cape Peninsula in the south, and extending inland to the Kei River, live the remnants of the Hottentots. The Hottentots are physically scarcely distinguishable from the Bushman, the chief points of difference being a taller average stature of 1.62 m. (five feet four inches), a longer narrower head (cephalic index 73), and a somewhat more prognathous face. There are also some blood group frequency differences, as follows:

Investigator	No.	O	A	B	AB	p	q	r
Pijper 1935	506	34.8	30.6	29.2	5.3	20.2	19.3	60.5
Zoutendyke et al. 1955	213	37.1	32.4	24.4	6.1	21.7	16.7	61.6

It will be seen that while Bushman and Hottentot resemble each other in most blood group frequencies they differ significantly in the frequency of the B gene, occurring as it does about three times as frequently in the Hottentots as it does in the Bushman.

The Hottentots are believed to be the result of admixture between Bushman and early invading Hamites, from whom they received the linguistic and cultural traits that distinguish them from the Bushman. It is considered that the admixture occurred in the north, possibly in the region of the Great Lakes, and that the Hottentots reached South Africa long after the Bushman had established himself there. The surviving Hottentots in South-West Africa are estimated at about 24,000. The Hottentot of the Cape hybridized with Europeans and East Indian slaves, and constituted the basis of the present "Cape Coloured," "Griqua," and "Rehoboth half-breeds."

Because of their close physical relationship the Bushman and Hottentots are becoming better known as the *Khoisan,* the first half of the term (actually *Khoi-Khoin*) being derived form the Hottentot's own name for themselves, the second half (*San*) from their name for the Bushman.

The Pygmies

At one time some anthropologists regarded the pygmies as the most primitive surviving branch of mankind; others, with even less justification, inclined to assign that rank to the Australian aborigines, but whatever the truth may be the fact is that we know of no early types of man that in any way resemble the pygmies, and there certainly seems to be insufficient reason to regard them as primitive simply because they are short and inhabit either marginal, island, or central areas, that is, refuge areas. The evidence suggests that they are best regarded as relatively early variants of the Negroid major group, from which they differ in a number of important features.

Average stature is 1.42 m. (four feet eight inches), hair is black and woolly, skin color varies from yellowish-brown to black, the nose varies from broad and flat to straight and moderately broad with the tip upwardly directed, the upper lip tends to be deep and convex, the lips in general are moderately thick, eyes rather large and prominent, face short, the body is often covered with a light downy hair, the head normally varies between meso- and brachycephaly, but dolichocephalic types occur both in Africa and New Guinea; both markedly prognathous and slightly prognathous types are known to occur.

The pygmies have an interesting distribution, being found in the interior of the Malay Peninsula and East Sumatra, in the Andaman Islands in the east of the Bay of Bengal, in the Philippine Islands, in Netherlands New Guinea, and in the Congo region of Equatorial Africa. On the basis of this geographic distribution together with certain associated physical differences the pygmies have been distinguished as falling into three groups, namely, the African, the Asiatic, and Oceanic groups. The African pygmies are known as *Negrillos*, the Asiatic and Oceanic pygmies being known as *Negritos*. Several distinct ethnic groups may be recognized.

The African Pygmy or Negrillo

Among the shortest of the pygmies with an average height of 1.43 m. (four feet eight and a half inches), the African pygmy is a native of the equatorial forests of the Congo, typically he has a short trunk, short legs, and long arms, woolly dark rusty-brown head hair, yellowish

Figure 180. Three Hottentot girls. The one on the right is the offspring of a Hottentot mother and a white father of European origin. (Courtesy, Musée de l'Homme, Paris.)

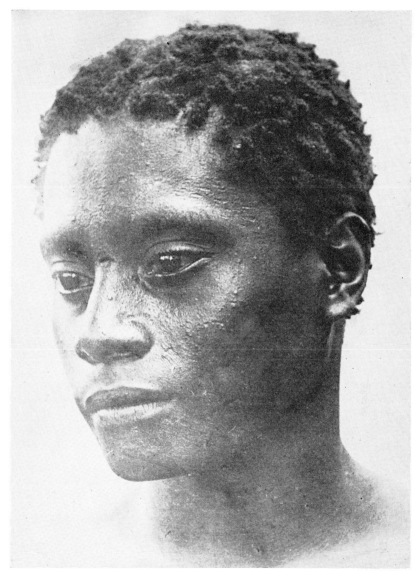

Figure 181. A young Andaman male. (Courtesy, Musée de l'Homme.)

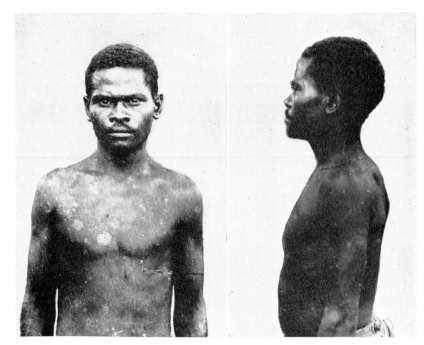

Figure 182. Young Negrito Aeta male, from Zambales, Luzón, Philippine Islands. (Courtesy, Musée de l'Homme, Paris.)

downy hair on the body, ordinarily black hair in arm-pits and on pubes; the skin though frequently very dark includes reddish-yellow and yellowish-brown shades. The head is mesocephalic (cephalic index 79.0), the face short and broad. The nose is very flat and broad, the wings of the nostrils being both broad and high, the most characteristic feature of the nose being that it is both broad and overhanging at the tip. The eyes tend to be protuberant, the upper jaw prognathic. Cranial capacity is 1,300 c.c. Gates suggests that the Negrillos have arisen through inbreeding of individuals heterozygous for a simple dwarf mutation.

The Asiatic Pygmies or Negritos

Andamanese

Inhabitants of the Andaman Islands in the east of the Bay of Bengal, the Andamanese or Mincopies are a well-proportioned people of an average height of 1.48 m. (four feet ten inches); the woolly hair is black in color, with a reddish tinge, body hair is very scanty, skin color varies from bronze to sooty-black, the head is brachycephalic (cephalic index 82.5), the face is broad at the cheek-bones, the lips are full but not everted, the jaws do not project, the nose is straight, and not flat. Cranial capacity is 1,269 c.c.

Semang

Inhabitants of the central region of the Malay Peninsula and of East Sumatra, the Semang are of an average height of 1.52 m. (five feet), well-proportioned, mesocephalic (cephalic index 79.0), the black head hair is woolly or frizzly with a reddish tinge, body hair is scanty, skin color dark chocolate brown, the face round, the lips not thick, the nose flat and broad, the upper jaw slightly projecting. This is the type which has been described as "infantile"; the adult type is long-faced, relatively thin-lipped with a narrower-looking nose, short torso, and longer extremities. Cranial capacity is 1,338 c.c.

The Philippine Negritos

Inhabitants of the widely scattered regions of Luzón, Mindanao, Palawan, Panay, and other Philippine Islands. As typical of the Philip-

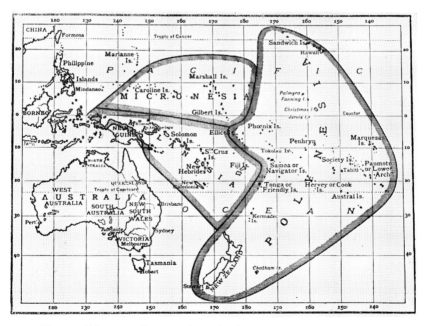

Figure 183. Map showing the Ethnological Divisions of Oceania.

TABLE XLII

A-B-O Blood Group Frequencies of Pygmies

Population	Place	Investigator	No.	O	A	B	AB	p	q	r
African Pygmies	Congo	Various	2,573	45.1	29.3	21.8	19.0	19.0	13.7	66.3
Andaman Islanders	Andamans	Various	66	17.1	51.0	22.0	10.1			
Negritos	Malaya	Polunin & Sneath 1953	269	59.1	24.5	14.5	1.9	14.2	8.5	77.2
Aeta	Zambales	Schebesta 1952	155	50.9	32.9	12.2	3.8	20.4	8.4	71.4
New Guinea Pygmies	Nassau Mts.	Semple et al. 1956	139					7.5	13.9	78.6

pine Negrito we may consider the Aeta, who represent the dominant number and are probably purest in type. They are inhabitants of the northernmost of the larger Philippine Islands, namely, Luzón. The Aeta have an average height of 1.42 m. (four feet eight inches), the frizzly head hair is dark brown to black in color, and is frequently abundant on face and body; skin color is sooty brown; the head is brachycephalic (cephalic index 82), the nose short, flat, and broad, the lips moderately thick. Cranial capacity is 1,415 c.c.

The Oceanic Pygmies or Negritos

New Guinea Pygmies

Inhabitants of the central range, through almost the whole length of New Guinea, the average height of the New Guinea pygmies is 1.445 m. (four feet nine inches), the head hair is black and woolly, and is abundant on face and body, skin color is yellowish-brown, the nose is short, broad, and flat, the upper lip is deep and convex, the head varies from dolichocephalic to mesocephalic.

The superficial resemblances of the pygmies have inclined many students to consider them as closely related. Their peculiar distribution would tend to support this view. The significant differences which now characterizes each of the known pygmy groups may be due to isolation and some admixture with the peoples in the regions in which they have lived, and in which they now live.

There is a certain amount of evidence which indicates that the representatives of a widespread pygmoid stock formed the earliest populations of Malaysia and the Pacific Islands. The peculiar distribution of the pygmies, in marginal or peripheral areas, at the extremities of continents, as the Andamanese on the islands of the southern extremity of India; in central areas, as the Semang of Malaysia, the New Guinea, and Congo Pygmies; and the Philippine Pygmies is very suggestive. It looks as if these are the "refuge areas" left to peoples that at one time had a much wider distribution. On the other hand, it is

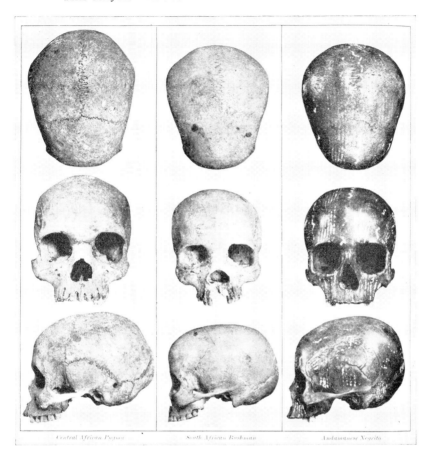

Figure 184. Skulls of the Central African Negrillo, South African Bushman, and Andaman Negrito. (From Sullivan, Courtesy, American Museum of Natural History, New York.) *Top row:* Vertical view showing the rhomboidal contour, parietal eminences, and narrow frontal region. The braincases overhang the face and cheek bones so that these are not visible. The proportion of the breadth to the length is greater than in most other Negroid groups. *Middle row:* Frontal view showing the low, broad nasal opening. In the Andaman skull the nasal opening is somewhat narrower and higher, and note the great height of the orbital openings in the Andaman skull and the Negrillo skull. The faces are small in comparison with the size of the braincase. *Bottom row:* The Negrillo is prognathous, the Bushman orthognathous, and the Andaman only slightly prognathous. The foreheads are vertical in all three, but markedly so in the Bushman. The occipital regions are projecting, and the mastoid processes are small in all three skulls. These skulls all appear rather juvenile, with the Bushman most strikingly so.

quite possible that the different pygmy populations have in some or all cases arisen independently of one another as a result of gene mutation in environments favoring small stature. The blood group frequencies of the pygmies are interesting but not very illuminating, although, as will be seen from Table XLII, with the exception of the Andaman Islanders, there is a certain consistency between them.

Oceanic Negroids

The Oceanic Negroids are inhabitants of the territory of New Guinea and the great group of islands extending to the east all the way to the Fiji Islands. The natives of the New Guinea region are known as Papuans, and are said to be more strikingly Negroid than those who inhabit the numerous islands extending to the east, the Melanesians. The distinction, however, is perhaps rather more geographic than physical. Strictly speaking the terms Papuan and Melanesian refer to two languages rather than to physical types. Though superficially resembling African Negroes in their general characters, the Oceanic Negroes differ from the former in several particulars. They are, on the whole, less pedomorphic than the African Negroes. Hair tends to be more abundant and less tightly coiled, the lips less thick and everted, the jaws less protrusive, and the chin less receding. The forehead is rounded and not so sloping, and the nose is often strongly hooked.

Papuans

The Papuans are said to be the more Negroid of the Oceanic Negroids. There is, however, no evidence at all that they differ in any significant manner from the Melanesians, and it is best to recognize them as a geographic rather than as a physical group. They cannot be treated as linguistic groups since Melanesian is spoken on the south-east and parts of the north-east coast of New Guinea. If the term "Papuan" be retained it must be on the strict understanding that it refers to Melanesians who are natives of the whole island of New Guinea, and not merely limited to the south-eastern part of the mainland, which is today known as Papua. Many distinct local types are recognizable, such as the pale-skinned Hula, the stalwart brown Huon Gulf people, the pygmy Buangs, the black New Georgians, the tall dark Kiwai, the stocky yellow-brown Hagen people, the slightly taller Chimbu, and the slender Bena-Bena.

Hair is black, somewhat frizzly, and abundant on the face; the nose is broad, often prominent and convex, with tip frequently turned down, skin color is dark chocolate or sooty brown, average height is about 1.68 m. (five feet six inches). Long-headed and broad-headed types occur, the forehead sloping with fairly marked brow ridges, the lips are of medium thickness.

Melanesians

Hair usually frizzly, but sometimes curly and even wavy, usually slight on face and body; skin color is dark chocolate, sometimes very dark, sometimes copper-colored; stature is short to medium; long-headedness prevails generally, forehead rounded, and brow ridges usually not prominent; nose somewhat broad, sometimes straight with less fleshy tip.

The Distribution of the Negroids

The markedly discontinuous distribution of the Negroids presents an interesting problem. Africa and southeastern Asia and Oceania are quite a long way from one another. The Negroids of today are, generally, poor seafarers; were their ancestors so, too? It is difficult to say. Melanesians often make voyages by sea in small outrigger craft of 50 miles or more. There is no reason to suppose that their

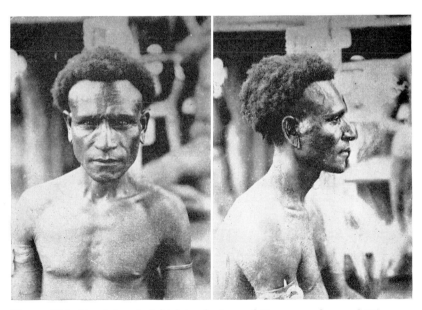

Figure 185. Frontal and right lateral views of Papuan male, aged 35 years, from New Guinea. (Courtesy, Musée de l'Homme, Paris.)

ancestors could not do likewise. It is quite possible that the Oceanic Negroids are the result of Negrito and Archaic White admixture.

Evidences of a very ancient Negroid substratum in the existing peoples of India, Burma, Assam, Persia, and Arabia are not wanting. The persistence of Negroid types among these populations suggests the possibility that a Negroid population once inhabited southern continental Asia, and that migrant groups from this population eventually populated the areas to the east and west, while in the continental homeland the Negroid population was absorbed by other groups in intermixture.

The Australoid or Archaic Caucasoid Sub-Division

Into this sub-division fall four of the most interesting varieties of mankind, the Australian aborigines, the Veddahs of Ceylon, the Pre-Dravidian peoples of India, and the Ainu of Japan. These four groups bear a close resemblance to one another, and to the so-called "white" or Caucasoid peoples. The evidence of their physical characters, of their geographic distribution, and of pre-history, suggests a considerable antiquity for these four groups, while from their physical characters alone it seems clear that their nearest affinities are with the Caucasoids, and that they are best regarded as a Caucasoid sub-division.

The Australian Aborigines

The Australian aborigines are frequently regarded as physically the most primitive of the surviving ethnic groups of man. This belief is based largely upon the fact that the skull is considered to present certain "primitive" features, such as the relatively large size of the palate and teeth, the fairly pronounced brow-ridges, small cranial capacity, sloping forehead, and receding chin. The Australoid skulls found at Wadjak in Java, and the Wadjak-like skull found at Keilor in south-eastern Australia, suggest an Asiatic origin for the Australian aborigines. Unfortunately, there is neither archeological nor any other kind of evidence which tells us how long the aborigines have been in Australia. The highly mineralized Talgai skull found in Queensland in 1884 is of doubtful age. The Keilor skull thought to be of Middle Pleistocene age has been fixed by radiocarbon dating at $6,546 \pm 250$ years. The Cohuna skull, found in 1925 some 10 miles south of the Murray river in Victoria is almost certainly recent. Save for the great cranial capacity of Keilor (1,593 c.c.) none of these skulls differs in any way from that of the modern Australian aboriginal. The question

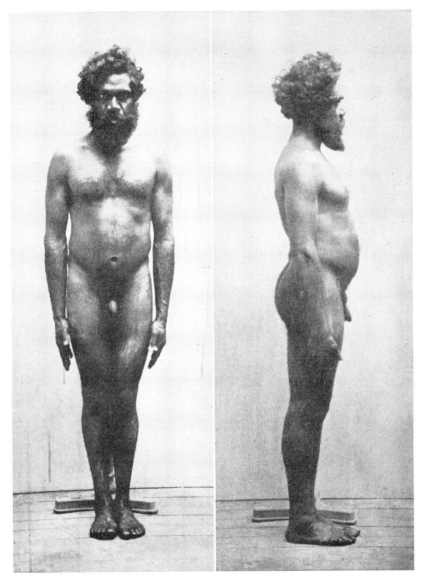

Figure 186. Frontal and lateral views of an Australian aboriginal male, aged 30 years, height 5 feet 6 inches. (Courtesy, Musée de l'Homme, Paris.)

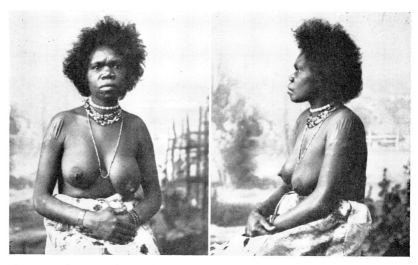

Figure 187. Frontal and left lateral views of young Australian aboriginal female. (Courtesy, Musée de l'Homme, Paris.)

of the antiquity of the aboriginal in Australia is quite open, and no one at the present time knows the answer to it.

In his external features the Australian aboriginal presents the following characters: Head hair is wavy, but curly, woolly, and straight forms are not infrequent, varying from light brown to black in color. In children the hair is sometimes very light brown, and occasionally quite fair, but it usually darkens before adult age is reached. Facial and body hair are abundant. The head is dolichocephalic (cephalic index 73.0), the vault is gable-shaped, and the cranial capacity about 1,280 c.c. The forehead is sloping and the brow-ridges extremely well developed. The nose is broad, depressed at the root, fleshy at the tip, but otherwise not flat but quite prominent; the ears are large and long; the face is rather short, the lips full but not Negroid; there is a moderate degree of prognathism, the chin is weak. Skin color varies from a reddish to a chocolate brown. Stature is very variable, averaging about 1.65 (five feet five inches).

Several morphological types have been distinguished, the (Caucasoid) Murrian type of southeastern Australia, the (Melanesian-Papuan) Carpentarian type of the Gulf of Carpentaria, the Desert type of Central Australia, said to be a blend of the Murrian and Carpentarian types, and the Negrito-like Tasmanoid types, the Barrineans near Lake Barrine, of the rain forest refuge areas in the Cairns and Atherton districts of Northern Queensland.

The Australian aborigines may be explained as an archaic Caucasoid group modified in the Negroid direction by admixture with some Negroid group on the one hand, and some Oceanic admixture on the other. Thus, possibly trihybrid in origin, the Australians remain dominantly Caucasoid, a view abundantly supported by the fact that when Australian aboriginal and white are crossed the hybrid loses most of the typically "primitive" characters of the aboriginal. That the earliest Australoids were of Asiatic origin is rendered probable by the existence of groups bearing a striking resemblance to the Australian aborigines both in their physical and blood group characters in central and southern India (Pre-Dravidians), in Ceylon (the Veddahs), and in Japan (the Ainu).

The extinct Tasmanians, the last of whom (see Figure 189) died in 1876, were physically chiefly distinguishable from the Australian aborigines by virtue of their rather woolly Negroid hair. The Bass Straits, between Australia and Tasmania represents a distance of 120 miles.

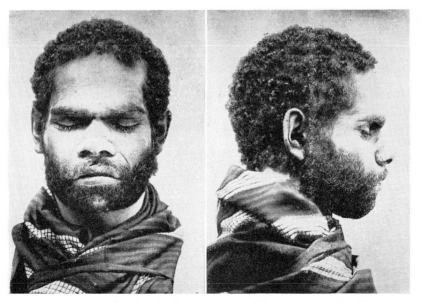

Figure 188. Frontal and right lateral views of Tasmanian male. (Courtesy, Musée de l'Homme, Paris.)

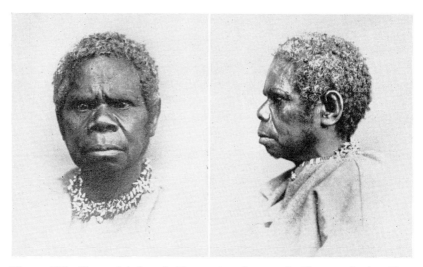

Figure 189. Truganini, female Tasmanian aboriginal. She was the last Tasmanian to survive, dying May 8, 1876. Frontal and lateral views. (Courtesy, Tasmanian Museum, Hobart, Tasmania.)

The Veddahs

The Veddahs of Ceylon are a people of small body size, the average stature being just 1.52 m. (five feet). Head hair is black with a reddish tinge in some cases, fine and wavy or slightly spirally coiled, except for a sparsely distributed growth of hair in the chin region, and an even more sparse attempt at growth on the upper lip, the rest of the body is totally devoid of the adult type of hair, except at the pubes and the arm-pits. If any hair is present it is of the infantile type, known as lanugo. Eyebrows are feebly developed, and eyelashes are sparsely represented. Skin color is chocolate brown, and is very "matt" in appearance; the head is the smallest to be found in any living hominid group, the average cranial capacity being 1,250 c.c. in the male, is very dolichocephalic (cephalic index 70.5), the forehead is slightly sloping, and the brow ridges are only moderately developed, though they may be quite prominent in some individuals, there is no protrusion of the lower face except occasionally; the lips are of medium thickness, and the chin generally somewhat receding; the nose is depressed at the root, but below this rises to form a squat triangular eminence, with expanded wings with rounded nostrils, opening forwards as much as downwards, the tip is often depressed,

the face is short and broad. The characters of the skull bear very striking resemblances to that of the Australian aboriginal, and interestingly
enough, to that of the Bushman, but as in so many other characters
the closest affinities of the Veddahs are with the Pre-Dravidian peoples
of central and southern India; craniologically there seems to be no
difference between them whatever. In this connection it should be
recalled that the island of Ceylon is merely a detached portion of the
southern mainland of India.

The Pre-Dravidians

The Pre-Dravidians of central and southern India constitute the
oldest and most primitive populations of that land, and comprise many
local types which differ in some degree from one another. While now
mainly limited to the Deccan (southern India) and to Central India,
there is reason to believe that the Pre-Dravidians formerly extended
their range over the greater part of India. At the present time the Pre-
Dravidians make their homes, for the most part, in the jungles.
Typical tribes are the Kadir (who are somewhat Negroid in appearance), the Kurumba, Paniyan, and Irula of the Deccan, the Bhil,
Gond, and Kandh, of northern central India, and the Oraon and Ko-
larian of Chota Nagpur. Like the Veddah the Pre-Dravidians are
rather short, the average stature being 1.57 m. (five feet two inches),
the hair is very dark brown to black in color, varying from wavy to
very curly; hair on the rest of the body is very scanty, though facial
hair may provide a moderate beard; skin color is black, the head is
dolichocephalic (cephalic index 73.0), the nose very broad, depressed
at the root, and flat, the forehead is somewhat sloping, the brow-ridges
but slightly or moderately prominent, some protrusion of the lower
face is present, and the lips are often quite thick, while the chin is
generally somewhat receding.

The physical characters of the Pre-Dravidians strongly suggest admixture of a Negrito with a Proto-Australoid type at some early period
in their development.

A very closely related Pre-Dravidian type is to be found in the southern portion of the Malay Peninsula, this is the Sakai or Senoi, a people
who live mainly in southern Perak and northern Selangor. Head hair is
long, wavy or curly, while some individuals have hair which very
closely approaches frizzly, the hair is black with a reddish tinge, skin
color varies from yellowish-brown to dark brown, the head is mesocephalic (cephalic index 78.0), the nose broad and flat, prognathism
is slight, the chin somewhat receding, the lips moderately thick but not

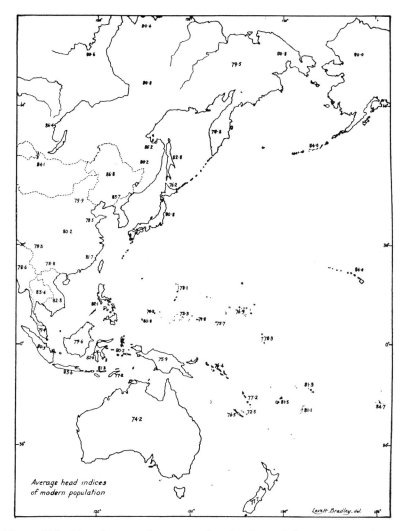

Figure 190. Map showing the average head indices of the recent populations of Eastern Asia, Australia, and Oceania. (From Weidenreich. Courtesy, University of Chicago Press.)

everted; the average height falls just short of 1.51 m. (five feet). The Sakai, on the whole, support the suggestion of a Negrito-Proto-Australoid ancestry.

The Ainu

Known generally as the "Hairy Ainu" because the men are allegedly characterized by the heaviest growth of facial and body hair to be found in any form of man, the Ainus have a brownish-white skin, wavy dark-brown or black hair, a short moderately broad nose, thin lips, well-developed jaws and chin, a short broad face, and a mesocephalic head (cephalic index 76.6). Average height is 1.58 m. (five feet two inches), and body build is thick-set. The Ainu were at one time thought to have constituted the original population of Japan who were driven northward by the Japanese. Archeological studies do not support this hypothesis. It is thought by some authorities (Sternberg, Komeda) that the Ainu may always have lived on Hokkaido and Sakhalin. Two possible routes of migration have been suggested: (1) through Siberia direct to Hokkaido, and (2) along the southern coasts of Asia to the Malay peninsula, Okinawa, and finally to Hokkaido. The Ainu are now confined to the northern island of Yezo (Hokkaido), and Sakhalin Island further north. The total population numbers approximately 15,000, with less than three per cent exhibiting the typical phenotypical Ainu characters.

A resemblance of the Ainu to the Australian aboriginal has often been remarked. A large proportion of Ainus show some evidences of Mongoloid admixture, but the Caucasoid types with a good hair-cut and a shave would pass unnoticed on a European street. The characters of the Australian aboriginal would appear to be those of an Ainu-like type that had been mixed with a Negroid. The resemblance of Ainu and Australian may be quite fortuitous or it may not. It is possible that the Ainus represent a fairly ancient stock, and that some early Ainu-like population after a history of intermixture with Negroid groups became the inhabitants of Australia.

In view of the fact that the Ainu type is found represented in more or less appreciable numbers throughout almost every European population—two famous men who show a superficial, though quite fortuitous, resemblance to the type are Charles Darwin and Tolstoy—it seems probable that the Ainu were once a very widespread people or else that they made very strong contributions to some of the peoples who later wandered into Europe; the former seems the more likely hypothesis, and it may be that the future will reveal that the long-neglected Ainu played a far greater part in the prehistoric settlement of Europe than is at present suspected.

The Caucasoid Major Group

This division of mankind is often called "white." The term is not an accurate one for the reason that it includes many peoples of dark skin color. The reason for giving this major group the name "Caucasoid" originates in the choice made by Blumenbach, the Father of Physical Anthropology, who in the late eighteenth century described and named the type from a female skull, whose beauty had much impressed him, which came from Georgia in the Caucasus and which seemed typical of the cranial characters of the group. Blumenbach was of the opinion that the type originated in the Caucasus, but as a matter of fact no one knows where the type did originate. Our knowledge upon this point is too weak even to warrant speculation. These facts clearly understood, the term may be retained for the major group called Caucasoid.

Head hair is usually wavy, but ranges from silky straight to various degrees of curliness. It is almost never woolly, rarely frizzly, and is seldom as coarse or as sparsely distributed as in Mongoloids. The hair on the face and over the rest of the body in males is usually well developed. Skin color varies from white to dark brown. All forms of head shape occur, but the general tendency is towards broad-headedness. The nose is comparatively narrow and projecting, being relatively high at both root and bridge, the cheek-bones are generally not prominent, and the lips tend to be thin. The face is orthognathic or straight, the palate and teeth smaller than in most other peoples, the forehead comparatively high, and the chin well developed.

There are a great number of Caucasoid ethnic groups, here again we can mention only the most representative of them. These are as follows:

        Mediterranean
        Basic Mediterranean
        Atlanto-Mediterranean
        Irano-Afghan
        "Nordic"
        Alpine
        Dinaric
        Armenoid
        Hamites
        East Baltic
        Lapps
        Indo-Dravidian
        Polynesian

Mediterranean

The various groups embraced under the term Mediterranean comprise a number of local types which may be regarded as subgroups within the Mediterranean ethnic group. The reason for giving these various groups the common name "Mediterranean" is that the type it describes, and which these groups comprise, is actually constituted by the populations which fringe the Mediterranean sea, and radiate outwards in all directions from that region as far as Northern India. Thus, Portuguese, Spaniards, Frenchmen, Italians, Greeks, Turks, North Africans of many kinds, many Arabians, Iranians, Afghans, and Indians are all peoples having physically much in common with one another.

Skin color varies all the way from tawny white to light or medium dark-brown, the predominant complexion is best described as dark brunet white or olive skinned; hair is dark brown or black, and varies from a very light wavy form to a loose curl; hair on the face and remainder of the body is moderately well developed. The head is generally long, the face generally oval and orthognathic, there being little or no protrusion of the jaws, the lips are moderately full, the chin is either weakly or moderately developed. The forehead vertical, and the nose high-bridged and generally narrow. The average height is 1.62 m. (five feet four inches).

While the Mediterranean ethnic group is remarkably homongeneous, it is convenient to recognize three sub-groups as follows:

Basic Mediterranean

This type is best seen in Portuguese, Spaniards, Italians, and in some English and Welsh; in North Africa in the Hamitic speaking peoples (discussed on p. 456) such as the ancient and modern Egyptians; in Arabia, and among the Berbers of Morocco. To this type belonged the basic Jewish population of Palestine. According to Coon the purest present day nucleus of this type is to be found in Arabia.

Average height is about 1.65 m. (five feet five inches), head dolicho- and meso-cephalic, straight narrow nose, slender and somewhat delicate build, and light brown complexion.

Atlanto-Mediterranean

This type forms the principal element in the population of North Africa, and is strongly represented in Iraq, Israel, parts of Arabia, and the eastern Balkans. It also forms the principal element, in varying degrees of mixture with Negroids, throughout the whole of East Africa, and is represented in small numbers in Portugal, Spain, and the British isles. Tall, long-headed, straight to convex-nosed, white-skinned, and rather more robustly built than the Basic Mediterranean.

Irano-Afghan Mediterranean

The principal element in the population of Iran, Afghanistan, and the Turkoman country, occurring also in parts of India, Arabia, and North Africa.

Tall, long-faced, high-headed, hook-nosed; complexion is brunet with some blondism.

The "Nordic"

The so-called "Nordic" is a Mediterranean with very light skin, fair hair, and blue or gray eyes. The conventional description of the type is as follows:

The hair may be either blond, yellow, very light brown, or reddish, and is slightly wavy to curly in form; facial and body hair is sparse. Skin is florid or pinkish-white, eyes blue or gray; the head is long but of medium breadth in relation to its length (mesocephalic 76-79), the face is long and its bones strongly developed; the nose is fairly prominent, straight and narrow. The chin is well developed and prominent. The average height is 1.72 m. (five feet eight inches). The average cranial capacity is about 1,350 c.c. or 1,400 c.c.

The "Nordic" is often said to be the characteristic type of Scandinavia, but the same type occurs in varying frequencies in Iceland, the Frisian Islands, the British Isles, Belgium, the Netherlands, and in the north central European plain, embracing Russia on the East, and Poland and Northern Germany on the west. There has been much speculation as to where this alleged racial type originated, the most favored argument being that which suggests that the elements which entered into its formation came together in the early Neolithic somewhere in north central Europe. It has been further suggested that the depigmentation of the "Nordic" represents a mutation from the Mediterranean stock, but since these characters, the white skin and lightly pigmented eyes, are well known to occur quite frequently in true Mediterraneans, the appeal to mutation is quite unnecessary. It is possible that the action of natural selection, isolation, and such factors as random variability in favor of blondism, the action of sexual and social selection have been involved in the development of the "Nordic" type, but it seems quite as, if not more, likely that the type represents a mere recombinational segregant thrown up from a highly mixed population. This is a matter upon which certainty is not at present possible, but it does seem likely that the type originated within the populations of various parts of Europe not once but several times, and that there never was at any time in the history of man a distinct "Nordic" race. In short, it is likely that the "Nordic" type is nothing but a color segregant of Mediterranean stock, its strongest affinities being with the Atlanto-Mediterranean subgroup of that stock. Certainly, the practice of arbitrarily extracting such individuals from the populations in which they occur and lumping them together in an artificially created group called "Nordic" would scarely seem to be a defensible procedure.

The recent cult of the "Nordic" in Germany, where the type occurs less frequently than in any of the other lands of its distribution, can only be regarded as an unfortunate perversion of thought, for there are no anthropological grounds whatever upon which the notion of a "superior" Nordic race could be sustained. The discussion of such matters must, however, be deferred for consideration to the next chapter.

Alpine

One of the most round-headed members of the Causasoid major group is the Alpine, the breadth of the head generally being over 85 per cent of its length. It is possible that brachycephalization was introduced into European populations by the Alpines, though it will be recalled that it was already encountered among the Mousterian Neanderthaloids of Krapina.

The Alpine stock receives its name from the fact that the type tends to be concentrated along a line extending from France eastwards along the Alps, down through the Balkans, east into the mountains of Asia Minor, and from thence north-west into Russia and Siberia. The type, however, occurs sporadically throughout Europe.

Situated as they are between Nordics to the north and Mediterraneans to the south there has been, as would be expected, a great deal of admixture with these ethnic types, so that the Alpine has taken on many of the characters of his neighbors, the only two more or less consistently associated characters remaining to him being brachycephaly and a sallow complexion.

The typical Alpine is broad and high-headed, with somewhat high curved occiput, vertical forehead, moderately to strongly developed brow-ridges, more or less roundish face, with prominent nose which has a tendency to broadness, and "blobbiness" at the tip; the face is orthognathic, there being no protrusion of the jaws, and the chin is

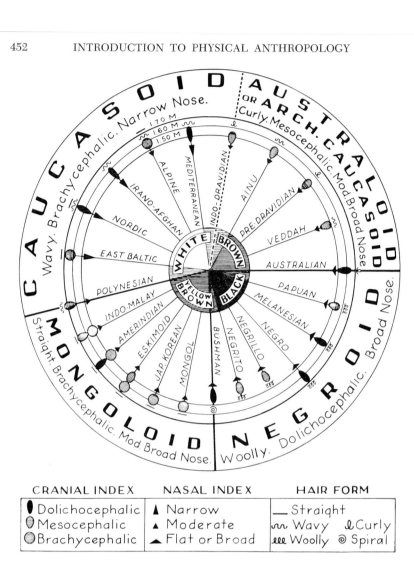

CRANIAL INDEX	NASAL INDEX	HAIR FORM
● Dolichocephalic	▲ Narrow	___ Straight
◑ Mesocephalic	▲ Moderate	∿ Wavy ℓ Curly
◐ Brachycephalic	▲ Flat or Broad	ℓℓℓ Woolly ◎ Spiral

Figure 191. Diagram showing the major and ethnic groups of man usually recognized, together with certain of their physical characters. This diagram is simply intended to provide a useful approximation to facts which are at present not capable of accurate description.

well-developed. Skin color is sallow, and not quite as dark as in Mediterraneans, hair color is chestnut-brown to black, frequently blond, and generally straight though sometimes wavy in form, hair is very abundantly distributed over the body, being especially heavy on the face. Average height is about 1.65 m. (five feet five inches), and the build tends to be sturdy rather than stocky. The popular conception of the Frenchman's appearance provides a good example of the type.

The origin of the Alpines is unknown, and in the present state of our knowledge speculation is not of much help. Some think that they originated in Asia, while Coon believes that they may represent a west European upper paleolithic survival, somewhat reduced in head and face size. What's the truth 'tis hard to say!

Dinarics and Armenoids

The Dinarics and the Armenoids as customarily classified by the physical anthropologist afford good illustrations of the kind of error into which the investigator may fall when he relies upon external characters for the criteria of his classifications. The principal character by which these two types have been distinguished from related types is the extreme flattening of the occiput (planoccipitaly) which is associated with extreme round-headedness (hyperbrachycephaly) and high-headedness (hypsicephaly). It has recently been shown that these traits are largely, probably entirely, due to the cradling habits of these peoples. It appears that planoccipitaly is due to the length of time that the infant's head has remained relatively immobile. Ewing, Ehrich, and Coon have independently shown that, in most cases at least, the occipital flattening is due to local cradling practices (tying the infant down, flat on its back, for a year or so). Ewing found that in Lebanon-born Maronites the average cephalic index was 88.3, while in American born Maronites the index was 79.4. The conclusion that the Lebanese custom of cradling was responsible for the hyperbrachycephaly of the Lebanon-born Maronites was inescapable.

Ehrich tested a series of 851 subjects almost entirely from Montenegro, and found that except for the independent variable of artificially deformed heads, the so-called Dinaric type proved to be in no way different from the rugged Atlanto-Mediterranean type. Coon subsequently arrived at the same conclusions with regard to Albanians with deformed and undeformed heads.

These findings render invalid the three major diagnostic characters upon which the recognition of distinct Dinaric and Armenoid types was based. They also illustrate the dangers involved in relying upon certain external characters which by tradition are believed to have some stability. It is today known that bones are among the most plastic of living tissues, the bones of the head being no exception (as witness the ease with which orthodontists are able to move teeth within the jaws).

Ewing, Ehrich and Coon conclude that while one cannot exclude the possibility of planoccipitaly occurring genetically, it is no longer possible to apply the names Dinaric and Armenoid, as hitherto defined, to races in the genetic sense. The terms, if they may be used at all, can only be applied to types having a certain appearance (phenotypes *not* genotypes). In this sense the Dinaric and Armenoid *types* may be described as follows:

Dinaric

The so-called Dinaric type, sometimes called the Adriatic or Illyrian occurs in a range from east Switzerland through the Austrian Tyrol, and south through Yugoslavia to Albania. The head ranges from high mesocephaly to moderate brachycephaly, the forehead runs all the way from strongly sloping to high and vertical, with well-developed brow-ridges. A remarkable feature of the Dinaric face, which is long and deep, is the long prominent, generally convex nose usually with a fleshy tip. The lips are of medium fulness, and the chin well-developed. Hair color varies from brown to black, and hair form from straight to wavy and sometimes curly, but lighter hair, skin, and eye colors are very frequent. The Dinarics are remarkably tall having an average height of 1.72 m. or five feet eight inches.

The Dinarics have undoubtedly a considerable Atlanto-Mediterranean component, an Alpine, and probably also an appreciable Irano-Afghanian one. Beyond the mountains they extend to the north-east, being found in some numbers in the Hungarian region, while to the south they are a major element in the Po Valley where, with the Alpines proper, they have introduced a considerable brachycephalic strain into Italy as a whole. Unquestioned Dinaricized types are also to be found in the dominantly brown and round-headed population of Asia Minor and Syria.

Armenoid

In Asia Minor to the east and the south-east of the Black Sea, that is in Armenia and north-eastern Turkey, is found the highest concentration of a type closely resembling the Dinaric, namely, the Armenoid. It occurs with varying frequency throughout Asia Minor.

The Armenoid head ranges from high mesocephaly to moderate brachycephaly. The nose is prominent and convex, and is remarkable for the length and fleshiness of its tip—a characteristic which occurs more frequently among the females than the males. The cheekbones are rather well developed, the lips moderately full, hair abundant and

dark brown to black in color, and slightly wavy to straight in form,
eyebrows and beard in the males are especially thick, the former often
meeting over the root of the nose. The average height is 1.67 m. or
(five feet six inches) and body-build somewhat stocky tending towards
corpulence in middle and old age.

That the Armenoid represents a blend, but possibly in different
proportions, of the same ethnic groups and sub-groups as have entered
into the composition of the Dinarics would seem probable. The difference may lie in the lesser Atlanto-Mediterranean component, and the

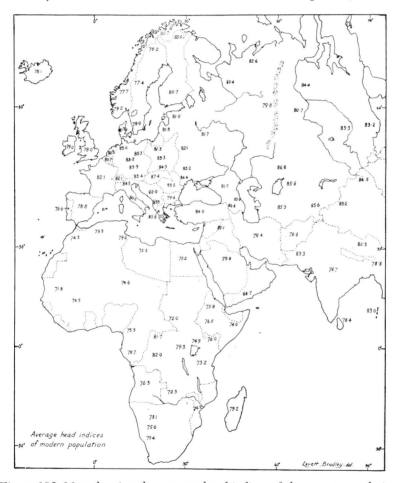

Figure 192. Map showing the average head indices of the recent populations
of Europe, Africa, and Western and Central Asia. (From Weidenreich.
Courtesy, University of Chicago Press.)

greater Irano-Afghanian element which, with some Nordic and Alpine elements, has entered into the composition of the Armenoid type.

The Hamites

The Hamites or Hamitic-speaking peoples, it has already been pointed out, are essentially Basic Mediterraneans, bound together by the Hamitic group of languages and a basic skeletal similarity. The languages are spoken over about one-fifth of Africa, with forty-seven stock languages and seventy-one dialects. The range of the Hamites is, however, more extensive than this, embracing the greater part of North Africa and a large section of East Africa. The Northern Hamites tend to be rather more Caucasoid in appearance and to form a somewhat more homogeneous type than the Eastern Hamites who have, in most cases, a greater Negroid admixture. Among both the Northern and Eastern Hamites are to be found some of the most beautiful types of humanity.

The Northern Hamites consist of the Mediterranean Berbers of Cyrenaica, Tripoliteana, Tunisia, and Algeria, together often referred to as the Libyans; the Atlantic Berbers of Morocco such as the Kabyles; the West Saharan Berbers, the Tuaregs; the Tibu of East Sahara; the Fula or Fulani of Nigeria, and the exinct Guanche of the Canary Islands.

The Eastern Hamites comprise the ancient and modern Egyptians, now much mixed with Semitic-speaking (Arabic) elements, the Nubians, Beja, Galla, Somali, Danakil, and most Ethiopians.

It has already been stated that skin color varies all the way from white to black, and head-hair from straight to frizzly. Body hair tends to be sparse. The head is dolichocephalic (cephalic index 75.0). The nose is straight, arched, or aquiline; the elongated oval face is never prognathous, the chin is pointed, the lips vary from thick to thin, but are seldom everted. Body build is slender, stature about 1.65 m. (five feet five inches).

Physically and culturally the influence of the Hamites has been considerable upon Negro Africa, Seligman saying that "the civilizations of Africa are the civilizations of the Hamites, its history the record of these peoples and of their interaction with the two other African stocks, the Negro and the Bushman."

East Baltic

In northeastern Germany, Poland, the Baltic States, and Finland, there occurs a rather variable though well-differentiated type which, from the region in which it is chiefly concentrated, is known as the East Baltic type. While there is some variation in the pigmentary factors and in other characters, the type is characterized by its feeble pigmentation of hair, skin, and eyes. The straight head-hair is best described as tow-colored, having reached the maximum degree of depigmentation—outside albinos—known in the human species; facial hair is moderately developed but body hair is usually sparse; skin color is generally a tawny white; the eyes are very gray or light blue. The head is very brachycephalic, rather flat at the back, the forehead is broad and high, the cheekbones fairly prominent, and the angles of the lower jaw rather widely separated; all these characters give the head and face a rather squarish appearance, hence the name "Square-heads" for the type. The chin is well developed, the brow ridges moderately well developed; the nose, while quite prominent, is generally broad at the wings, somewhat short at the tip, so that the roundish nostrils are directed forward, and in profile is characteristically concave. The German Junker class of East Prussia, as represented in particular by the German general von Hindenburg, is a good example of the type. It is the type which is often miscalled "Nordic" by the Germans.

The composite nature of the East Baltic type is obvious, but the ethnic elements which have entered into that composition and produced it have thus far escaped anthropological analysis. Alpine, Atlanto-Mediterranean, Lapp, and some Nordic strains have been suggested, but these are merely speculations.

The Lapps

The Lapps live in Northern Scandinavia, in the highlands of Sweden, the tundra of northern Finland, the Norwegian coastal provinces of Troms and Finnmark, and occupy a great part of the Russian Kola Peninsula. With other ethnic groups of the circumpolar zone they share many features in common. The Reindeer Lapps live in the forests and mountains, the Sedentary Lapps live along the coast and rivers. At one time the Lapps were classified with the Mongoloids. As they have become better known anthropologically it has become clear that they are, from a classificatory point of view at any rate, more dominantly Caucasoid than Mongoloid. Some anthropologists believe that the original ancestral Lapps may represent a stage in the evolution of both the Upper Paleolithic Europeans and the Mongoloids (Schreiner, Coon).

The head form tends to be brachycephalic, with an average cephalic

TABLE XLIII

AVERAGE CRANIAL CAPACITIES IN ANTHROPOIDS AND MAN. MALES

Group	Reference	Method	Cubic Capacity
Gibbon	Schultz 1933	m	97
Siamang	Schultz 1933	m	125
Chimpanzee	Hooton 1942	m	400
Orang-Utan	Hooton 1942	m	416
Gorilla	Ashton 1950	m	543
Plesianthropus	Ashton 1950	e	506
Australopithecus africanus	Broom 1946	e	600
Paranthropus robustus	Ashton 1946	e	650
Australopithecus prometheus	Ashton 1950	e	715
Pithecanthropus II	Weidenreich 1945	e	775
Telanthropus	Robinson 1953	e	850
Pithecanthropus robustus	Weidenreich 1945	mc	900
Pithecanthropus I	Weidenreich 1945	e	940
Paranthropus crassidens	Broom 1950	e	1000
Sinanthropus	Weidenreich 1945	mc	1043
Solo	Weidenreich 1945	mc	1100
Steinheim	Berckhemer 1934	c	1177
Saccopastore I	Sergi 1948	c	1300
Cape Flats	Drennan 1929	mw	1230
Baining	von Bonin 1934	c	1243
Saldanha	Singer 1954	c	1250
Australian aborigines Northern Territory	von Bonin 1934	c	1256
Tasmanians	Morant 1927	c	1264
Andamanese	Morant 1924; von Bonin 1931	m	1264
Australian aborigines Southern Australia	von Bonin 1934	c	1278
New Guinea	Hambly 1947	c	1280
Veddas	Morant 1924	m	1285
Rhodesian man	Keith 1925	mc	1305
La Quina	Patte 1955	c	1307
Talgai	Smith 1918	c	1300
Saccopastore II	Sergi 1945	c	1320
Melanesians	Hambly 1947	m	1323
Bushman	von Bonin 1934	mc	1329
Gibraltar Adult	Patte 1955	mc	1333
Hindu and Tamil	Hambly 1947	m	1335
Australian aborigines Victoria	Wunderly 1943	m	1338
African Negroes	Hambly 1947	m	1346
American Negroes	Todd 1923	mw	1350
Piltdown	Keith 1925	e	1358
Tyrolese	Frizzi 1912	m	1359
Ainu	Hambly 1947	mc	1383
London (Lloyds)	Keith 1931	e	1386
Galla and Somali	von Bonin 1934	c	1388
Galley Hill	Keith 1925	m	1400
Dayaks	von Bonin 1934	c	1403
Burmese	Tildesley 1921	m	1406
Hottentots	von Bonin 1934	c	1408
Aetas	von Bonin 1931	c	1415
Malayans	Morant 1924	m	1424
Spy II	Vallois 1957	c	1425
Châtelperron	Montagu 1950	mc	1425
Marquesans	von Luschan 1907	m	1427
Moriori	von Bonin 1934	c	1434

TABLE XLIII—(*continued*)

Group	Reference	Method	Cubic Capacity
1st to 2nd Dynasty Egyptians	von Bonin 1934	c	1435
Czechs	Morant 1928	m	1438
Fijians and Loyalty Islanders	Hambly 1947	m	1439
Combe Capelle	Keith 1925	e	1440
S. Amer. Indians	Hambly 1947	c	1442
Modern Europeans	von Bonin 1934	c	1446
Neanderthal	Keith 1925	mc	1450
Ingwavuma	Cooke *et al.* 1945	e	1450
Polynesians	Hambly 1947	m	1451
Sandwich Islands	Wagner 1937	m	1456
Swanscombe	Keith 1939	c	*1457*
"Kaffirs"	Shrubshall	m	1460
Chinese	Morant 1924	m	1467
Swiss	Morant 1928	m	1468
Fontéchevade	Vallois 1949	mc	1470
Western Eskimo	Hambly 1947	m	1473
Bury St. Edmunds	Keith 1925	e	*1474*
Japanese	von Bonin 1931	m	1475
Maoris	von Bonin 1934	c	1476
Ehringsdorf	Weidenreich 1928	e	1480
Modern English	Keith 1931	m	1480
Tahitian	von Luschan 1907	m	1487
Buriats	Woo & Morant 1932	m	1490
Koreans	Morant 1924	m	1490
E. Centr. Amerinds	von Bonin & Morant 1938	c	1495
Kalmucks	Woo & Morant 1924	m	1498
Springbok Flats	Keith 1931	e	1500
Ancient Europeans	von Bonin 1934	c	1501
Upper Paleolithic	von Bonin 1934	c	1505
Central Eskimo	Hambly 1947	c	1516
Iroquois	von Bonin 1934	c	1519
Spy I	Vallois 1957	c	1525
Chancelade	Keith 1925	c	1530
Algonkin	von Bonin 1934	c	1532
Matjes River	Keith 1934	c	1532
Galilee	Keith 1931	e	*1540*
Tepexpan	Romero 1949	mw	1540
Monte Circeo	Sergi 1939	c	1550
Mount Carmel	Keith & McCown 1939	c	1552
Early Neanderthals	Montagu 1959	mc	1553
Later Neanderthals	Montagu 1959	mc	1553
Le Moustier	Vallois 1957	c	1564
Mongols	Woo & Morant 1924	m	1573
Singa	Wells 1951	c	1575
Předmost	Keith 1925	c	1590
Keilor	Wunderly 1943	m	1593
Fish Hoek	Keith 1931	c	1600
Teshik-Tash child	Okladnikov 1946	e	1600
La Chapelle aux Saints	Keith 1931	mc	1625
LaFerrassie	Vallois 1952	mc	1641
Wadjak	Dubois 1920	c	1650
Gibraltar boy	Keith 1931	e	1650
Cro-Magnon	Keith 1925	c	1660
Elementeita	Keith 1931	c	1680
Boskop	Broom 1914	e	1700
Zitzikama	Keith 1931	c	*1925*

Capacities in *italics* indicate that 10 per cent has been added to the capacity of the female skull which is the presumed sex from which this particular type is known. Female capacities may generally be approximated by deducting 10 per cent from the male capacity. In the human species the cranial capacity is about 200 cc. more than the volume of the brain.

m = measured with seed; mc = measured and calculated; mw = measured with water c = calculated; e = estimated.

index of 84.0. The forehead is usually narrow and steep and often exhibits bilateral frontal eminences; supraorbital ridges are usually absent. A remarkably short face, with an average nasionmenton height of 112.0 mm (as compared with 125.0 mm for Norwegians and Finns), is a characteristic Lapp feature. The shortness of the face is largely due to the feeble development of the upper and lower jaws and the small teeth, there is little or no prognathism. The face is moderately broad (140.0 mm) and well within the Caucasoid range; flaring Mongoloid cheek-bones are rarely encountered, though they tend to project forward prominently. The nose is moderately broad, with a concave bridge, and a peculiar snubbed or pointed up-turned tip; the lips tend to be moderately thin. The eyes are widely separated, set in low orbits, and rarely overhung by a Mongoloid fold. In about two-thirds of Lapps skin color varies from grayish yellow to yellowish brown, and in these the hair is mostly dark brown or black and the eyes dark; in those with light hair and eyes (about a third) skin color is as light as that of any Scandinavian. Hair color is most frequently dark brown or black, and usually straight or slightly wavy, it is rarely of Mongoloid type; facial and body hair is sparse. The Lapps are a short people, average height being 1.59 m (5 feet 3 inches).

The Lapps have undoubtedly mixed to some extent with Swedes, Finns, Norwegians, East Baltics, Russians, and Samoyedes, nevertheless they remain a distinctively recognizable ethnic group.

Indo-Dravidians

Distributed very widely throughout India and Ceylon is a basically Mediterranean people who exhibit some evidences of Negritoid, and possibly proto-Australoid, admixture. The head form varies from dolicho- to brachycephalic, the cephalic index averaging 74.3; the forehead is usually rounded, the supraorbital ridges moderately developed, the face narrow and of medium length, with little or no prognathism. The nose is of moderate breadth, fairly prominent and straight in profile, somewhat depressed at the root, and the wings somewhat flaring; the lips are moderately full, but not Negroid. Stature averages 1.64 m (five feet four inches). Skin color varies from light to dark brown; hair is usually black and slightly wavy, though straight hair is quite frequent and frizzly hair also occurs; facial and body hair is sparse.

Here, too, the basic Mediterranean character of the Indo-Dravidians is brought out by the fact that the hybrids or crosses between Europeans and Indo-Dravidians, are indistinguishable from basic Mediterraneans, except in skin color, which may be a little darker than is customarily found in the latter.

A familiar offshoot of the Mediterranean Indo-Dravidians are the gypsies or Romanies. These peculiar people are descended from outcast groups who wandered westward into every corner of Europe, where they have in the last thousand years remained a foreign population in the midst of western peoples and customs. Fundamentally Indo-Dravidian Mediterraneans, they have to a certain extent been modified in physical type by admixture with western peoples. Their language basically remains a modification of Sanskrit, with many incorporations from western languages.

Polynesians

A line drawn from Hawaii in the north to the Fiji Islands in the Southwest, and thence to New Zealand, then to Easter Island in the east, and finally back to Hawaii, will embrace the whole of the vast area of Polynesia. In this area of the Pacific lives a far-flung branch of the Mediterranean stock, the tall, handsome peoples called Polynesians.

The Polynesians are predominantly brachycephalic, high-headed, with slightly sloping forehead, flattish occiput, and with long broad faces, fairly prominent cheek bones, a prominent nose somewhat broad at the wings of the nostrils, lips of moderate fullness, and chin well developed. Skin color is generally light brown, hair color dark brown to black, and head hair is slightly wavy, occasionally straight, rarely curly, and in some individuals frizzly. Body hair is very sparse. Very rarely a Mongoloid fold over the medial angle of the eye is present. The average height is about 1.72 m. or five feet eight inches; body build is muscular with a strong tendency to corpulence towards middle age.

Essentially Mediterraneans, the Polynesians would appear to have undergone some admixture both with a Negroid and a Mongoloid stock, the former may have been Melanesians, the latter possibly already much mixed Mongoloids or people with only slightly developed Mongoloid characters.

In the Hawaiian Islands admixture between the native Polynesians, Mongoloids, and Caucasoids has been proceeding apace, so that a new ethnic type is gradually emerging. This new ethnic type is seen in individuals, it is far from characteristic of the Hawaiian population as a whole, though in the course of time it may become so. A great variety of hybrid types are to be seen in Hawaii today, a part of the world in which intermixture between different physical types and different cultures is proceeding at a more rapid rate than in any other region of the earth. The results of this admixture, both physically and culturally, constitutes a living testimony to the benefits of ethnic mixture.

At this point we may appropriately turn to an account of the Mongoloid major group of man.

The Mongoloid Major Group

The skin has a yellowish tinge but is really a yellowish light brown, head hair is generally black and straight, each hair is very large in cross-section. There are fewer hairs per square centimeter of skin and face, and body hair is less developed than in any other variety of man. The head is generally brachycephalic, the average cephalic index being 85.0, but meso- and dolichocephalic groups occur, the forehead is of medium height and rounded, and the occiput projecting. The brain is among the largest in the human species, a cranial capacity of 1700 c.c. being quite frequent. The nose is flat or low at the root, the bridge is low, and the wings of the nostrils of medium spread; lips are of medium fulness, and the chin well developed. The face tends to be remarkably flattened in most groups, and the gonial angles of the lower jaw everted in some. The cheek bones are very strongly developed, projecting forwards and laterally. The incisor teeth tend to be shovel-shaped, scooped out behind like a scoop shovel; the tooth-bearing portion of the upper jaw has a marked tendency to project slightly upwards and forwards, to give the appearance in many individuals of "buck teeth." This is seen in its most extreme form in the Japanese, and is also very frequent in the Chinese. But the trait which above all others gives the typical Mongoloid his characteristic appearance is the fold of skin from the upper eyelid which lies over the inner angle (canthus) of the eye or extends over the whole of the upper eyelid, the internal epicanthic or complete so-called Mongoloid fold, a character which gives the eye its slit-like appearance (Figure 211, p. 575). Stature averages about 1.66 m. (five feet five inches).

The skeleton of the classic Mongoloid type is very delicately made, even down to the character of the sutures of the skull which, like those of the infant skull, are relatively smooth and untortuous. In fact the Mongoloid presents so many physical traits which are associated with the late fetus or young infant that he has been called a fetalized, infantilized or pedomorphic type. Those who have carefully observed young babies may recall that the root of the nose is frequently flat or low as in Mongoloids, and that an internal epicanthic fold in such instances is usually present. The smaller number of individual head hairs and the marked hairlessness of the remainder of the body are infantile traits, as are likewise the small mastoid processes, the shallow fossa into which the jawbone fits (the mandibular fossa), the rather stocky build, the large brain-pan and brain, lack of brow ridges, and quite a number of other characters. Since fetalization seems to be the process by which man has attained many of his unique characters there is reason for regarding the Mongoloids as a rather highly evolved type.

Inhabitants chiefly of northern, central, and south-eastern Asia, embracing the Philippines, Malaysia, the East Indies, and the Americas, the Mongoloids are anthropologically perhaps the least known of the varieties of man. There have been no really adequate studies on any Mongoloid group, including the American Indian. The following account of the Mongoloids is therefore deliberately brief.

Many anthropologists believe that the Mongoloid was the last great variety of man to become differentiated. Weidenreich, on the other hand, believes that the Mongoloid was probably derived from a Sinanthropoid stock; others see in the Eskimo-like characters of the paleolithic skull found at Chancelade, a possible ancestral type of the Mongoloids, but these are all speculations which arise out of the paucity of our knowledge of prehistoric Asia. When future expeditions

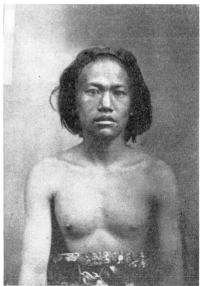

Figure 193. Young Javanese male from Bautam. (Courtesy, Musée de l'Homme, Paris.)

and researches in the field have brought in more abundant material finds we may be in a position to speak with some authority on the origin of the Mongoloids. Until then it were better to record our ignorance than to conceal it with poorly founded speculation.

Among the Mongoloids there are probably as many, if not more, ethnic groups and sub-groups as there are among the Caucasoids, but the satisfactory recognition and description of most of these awaits future research.

The Mongoloids have been subdivided into four great geographic subdivisions, as follows: (1) The central or classical Mongoloid, (2) the northern or Arctic, which we shall call Eskimoid, (3) The American Indian or Amerindian from North to South America, (4) the Southern or Indo-Malayan.

The Central or Classical Mongoloid

The central or classical Mongoloid type is found sporadically distributed in Northern China, Mongolia, and Tibet. The cephalic index averages about 85.0, and the Mongoloid fold is always present. For the remainder the classical Mongoloid's traits are as already described. The type is well seen in such tribes as the Gilyak, Koryak, Goldi, Buriats, and Kalmucks.

The Arctic Mongoloids or Eskimoids

The northern or Arctic subdivision includes peoples living in northeast Asia, the arctic coast of North America, Greenland, Labrador, and western Alaska including the Aleutian Islands. This subdivision is typically represented by the Eskimos, and like the classical Mongoloids tends to be brachycephalic. In addition to the Eskimos it includes such paleoasiatic peoples as the reindeer and coastal Chukchee, the Kamtchadales, and such neoasiatics as the Tunguses, Samoyedes, and Yakuts.

The Eskimos represent a single continuous breeding population, with their center in western Alaska, where they are brachycephalic and low headed, becoming increasingly so from north to south.

The Eastern Aleutian Eskimo has an average height of 1.62 m. (five feet four inches) and is brachycephalic (c.i. 84.6). The lower Kuskokwim Eskimo has an average height of 1.62 m. (five feet four inches) and is brachycephalic (c.i. 81.5). The Asiatic Eskimo has an average height of 1.62 m. and is brachycephalic (c.i. 80.8). The Arctic Eskimo has an average height of 1.65 m. and is mesocephalic (c.i. 78.6). The Greenland Eskimo is mesocephalic (c.i. 76.8) and has a stature of

1.62 m. The arctic Eskimos have a high gabled head. In less extreme form this gabling or keel is also present in the western Eskimos.

Eskimos as a group are characterized by large broad faces, markedly flaring cheek bones, narrow noses, high incidence of the complete Mongoloid fold, straight black hair, small hands and feet, large trunks and relatively short legs, and large amounts of blood group A, and small amounts of blood group B.

The Kamtchadales and eastern Tungus belong to the mesocephalic group (c.i. 78.3 to 80.8), the western Tungus, Chukchee, Gilyak, and Samoyedes, belong to the brachycephalic group (c.i. 83.0 to 85.6).

The migrations of peoples of this stock into Europe has resulted in much admixture, evidences of which are still recognizable in such peoples as the Baltic Finns, Esths, Livonians, Finlanders, Magyars (Hungarians), and others. This latter group of peoples is usually termed Finno-Ugrian or Uralic, a term which also defines a family of languages spoken by these peoples.

The American Indian or Amerindian

Physically among the least known groups of Mongoloids are the Indians of North, Middle, and South America. Research on the physical anthropology of the American Indian has been extremely slow in getting started. The little we know indicates that not all those who at different times migrated into the Americas were of predominantly Mongoloid stock, that, indeed, judging from their physical characters, such as the absence of shovel shaped incisors in many Indians, the shape of the nose, and the high frequencies of blood group A (50 per cent among the Blackfeet) some of these immigrants were possibly dominantly Caucasoid with some Mongoloid admixture.

The American Indians exhibit a certain basic homogeneity but at the same time are evidently characterized by an equally certain diversity of types. Owing to the lack of the necessary data it is impossible to say quite how many diverse types there may be. General impressions based on sporadically measured and photographed individuals from various groups provide an insufficient basis upon which to erect a satisfactory account of the American Indian.

The basic traits which American Indians have in common are yellow-brown to red-brown skin color; hair, black, straight, coarse, sometimes slightly wavy, very sparse on body and face, and usually entirely absent on the sides of the face. Eye color varies from medium to dark brown. A complete Mongoloid fold is rarely present, though the internal epicanthic fold is frequently seen in women and children, but very rarely in males in whom an external epicanthic fold is commonly present. The face is broad, with large flaring cheek bones, the lips vary from thin to average thickness, the chin is fairly well developed, shovel-shaped incisors are common, and the bite (of the teeth) is edge to edge.

The character gradients, as might have been expected, follow the geographic gradients. For example, the Indians of the north-west coast, the Tlingit, Haida, Tsimshian (c.i. 82.5, stature 1.68 m., five feet six inches), and the Kwakiutl (c.i. 84.5, stature 1.64 m., five feet four and a half inches) rather more resemble the Arctic Mongoloids than do the Indians east of the Rockies. The latter extending through the great Plains into the northern and eastern Woodlands area, range from brachycephaly, through mesocephaly to dolichocephaly, with the northeast predominantly dolichocephalic. In the Plateau area brachycephaly prevails, and stature tends to be somewhat shorter, and noses somewhat straighter.

In Mexico, Middle and South America it is known that every form of head shape is encountered. Eastern Brazil shows a very large proportion of mesocephalic types.

It has already been pointed out that these different waves of migrants entered North America from Siberia across the Bering Straits by way of Alaska. The Asiatic origin of the American Indians is now beyond dispute. In Tibet there are to be found types which closely resemble the Fuegians of southernmost South America; the Chukchee of Siberia closely resemble the whole Eskimo population, furthermore, in many aspects of their culture these populations are very much alike.

Indonesian-Malay

Throughout southeastern Asia fluorishes a large number of Mongoloid peoples most of whom look as if in the past they had experienced an appreciable Caucasoid, and probably Negroid, admixture. This is the Indonesian-Malay or Oceanic Mongoloid strain.

The Indonesian is slenderer and slightly shorter (1.55 m. or five feet one inch) than the stockily built Malay (1.58 m., five feet two inches); he is longer-headed (c.i. 78.5) while the Malay is usually brachycephalic (c.i. 85.0); the head hair tends to be slightly wavy, and for the rest is very sparse in both groups; in the Malay head hair is straight. In the Indonesian the nose is narrower and higher, and the internal epicanthic fold less frequent. The Mongoloid influence, indeed, seems to be less strongly marked in the Indonesians than in the Malays. In the Malay Archipelago the Indonesian type, generally

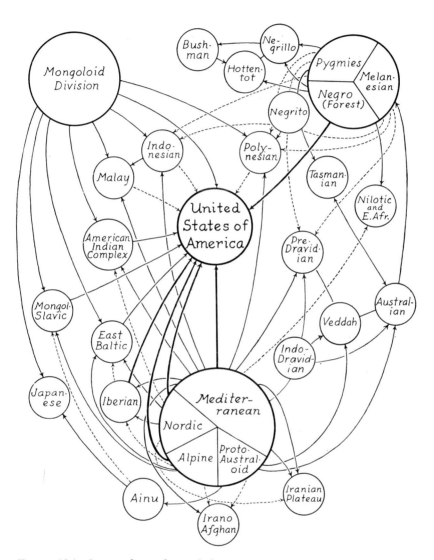

Figure 194. Some relationships of the varieties of mankind to one another, and those which have entered into the formation of the population of the United States.

speaking, occurs more frequently inland, while the Malays are the coastal peoples. The Japanese largely belong to the Malay type.

The Indonesian type is found in southern China, Indo-China, Burma, Thailand, the interior of the Malay Archipelago, while the Malay type in addition occurs in the Malay Peninsula, the Dutch East Indies, the Philippines, Japan, Okinawa, and adjacent islands.

CONCLUSION

In this chapter an attempt has been made to give an account of the principal varieties and ethnic groups of man, and we have seen that far from pursuing a completely independent course of development it is probable that all of them have at one time or another met and contributed their genes to produce new modifications of older types. Through these modifications something of the older types can sometimes be seen more or less clearly shining through, but this is not always the case, for the new made pattern is usually an harmonic one, and unless there are certain striking features such as skin color, hair form or Mongoloid fold, very refined methods of analysis are required in the not always successful attempt to discover the components which have entered into the formation of a particular type.

It is clear that there are no "pure races" in existence, and it is greatly to be doubted that there ever were any. The ethnic groups of mankind are not, and never have been, so many separate streams and tributaries flowing within well-defined banks, but currents and eddies in one great river, in which there has been a constant interchange of what each has carried.

In Figure 194 is reproduced a diagram showing some of the relationships of the major and principal ethnic groups of man, and the contribution of all these to the population of the United States. This diagram may perhaps serve to suggest the probable truth that the United States stands out in high relief as the example of what, upon a lesser scale, has occurred throughout the history of man, the mingling of peoples to produce greater strength in almost every way, to illustrate the truth that diversity of genes as well as of culture is the basis of collective achievement. When it is realized that between the years 1820 and 1950 over 39,325,000 immigrants entered the United States, something of the scale of this mingling may be understood.

The reader will have read the significance of this chapter correctly if he understands that the arrangement of the major and ethnic groups of man here listed is quite arbitrary, tentative and temporary, being a classification based upon a few characters statistically averaged for an appallingly small number of the world's peoples. It must always be remembered that the concept of a human group characterized by a certain uniformity of physical characters is a statistical concept which applies only to groups and not to individuals. So real are the transitions between one group and another, and so great the variability of almost all human groups that any individual taken at random from some such groups could, in many cases, fit into the framework of variability of almost any other. Thus, for example, there are many Caucasoids who could easily fit into a Negroid group, and *vice versa,* and the same holds true for the relationships of many Mongoloids with both these groups.

The error most commonly committed in this connection is to think in terms of a genetically wholly independent development of each of the varieties and even ethnic groups of man, and to regard them as clear cut types which are readily contrasted with one another. As we have seen, this is a very great fallacy for the good reason that no human groups have ever undergone completely independent development, that all are much mixed, and that temporary stabilization of their more or less distinctive characters has been due to the action of isolating factors, not merely of a geographic kind, upon a mixed population. This mixing of all peoples is evident in their resemblances to one another, and in the imperceptible transitions in physical characters which exist between all ethnic groups. The differences between them are due to the differences in the proportions of the ethnic elements which have entered into the composition of each group, and the action of the primary and secondary factors upon them. When these differences are considered and evaluated they are seen to be relatively few in number compared to the overwhelming number of likenesses, and they are seen to be of a nature which does not render any one of the groups concerned either biologically superior or inferior to the other The physical differences are merely expressive of a somewhat different biological history, differences for which we should be extremely grateful since, among other things, they assist us to demonstrate the essential unity—not difference—of mankind, and will enable us eventually to trace a good part of the history of that unity and differentiation. Our classificatory schemes must be regarded as nothing more than convenient devices calculated to assist us toward the achievement of such a desirable end.

The Major and Ethnic Groups of Man

Major Group: NEGROID

African Negroes

Ethnic Group: a. **The True Negro:** West Africa, Cameroons and Congo.
b. **The Half-Hamites:** East Africa and East Central Africa.
c. **Forest Negro:** Equatorial and Tropical Africa.
d. **"Bantu-Speaking Negroids:"** Central and Southern Africa.
e. **Nilotic Negro:** Eastern Sudan and Upper Nile Valley.
f. **Bushman:** Southern Angola and North-West Africa.
g. **Hottentot:** South Africa.

Oceanic Negroids

Ethnic Group: a. **Papuans:** New Guinea.
b. **Melanesians:** Melanesia.

African Pygmies or Negrillos

Ethnic Group: a. **African Pygmies or Negrillos:** Equatorial Africa.

Asiatic Pygmies or Negritos

Ethnic Group: a. **Andamanese:** Andaman Islands.
b. **Semang:** Central region of Malay Peninsula, and East Sumatra.
c. **Philippine Negritos:** Philippine Islands.

Oceanic Pygmies or Negritos

Ethnic Group: a. **New Guinea Pygmies:** New Guinea.

Major Group: CAUCASOID

Ethnic Group: a. **Basic Mediterranean:** Borderlands of the Mediterranean Basin.
b. **Atlanto-Mediterranean:** Middle East, eastern Balkins, East Africa, Portugal, Spain, British Isles.
c. **Irano-Afghan Mediterranean:** Iran, Afghanistan, parts of India, Arabia, and North Africa.
d. **Nordic:** Central Europe, Scandinavia and neighboring regions.
e. **East Baltic:** East Baltic regions.
f. **Lapps:** Northern Scandinavia, Kola Peninsula.
g. **Alpine:** France along the Alps to Russia.
h. **Dinaric:** Eastern Alps from Switzerland to Albania, Asia Minor, and Syria.
i. **Armenoids:** Asia Minor.
j. **Hamites:** North and East Africa.
k. **Indo-Dravidians:** India and Ceylon.
l. **Polynesians:** Polynesia (Central Pacific).

Sub-Division: AUSTRALOID or ARCHAIC CAUCASOID

Ethnic Group: a. **Australian:** Australia.

  b. **Veddah:** Ceylon.
  c. **Pre-Dravidian:** India.
  d. **Ainu:** Japan, Hokkaido (Yezo) and Sakhalin Islands.

MONGOLOID

Classical Mongoloids

Ethnic Group: a. An undetermined number of ethnic groups in the older populations of Tibet, Mongolia, China, Korea, Japan, and Siberia, including such tribes as the **Buriats** east and west of Lake Baikal, the **Koryak** of northern Siberia, the **Gilyak** of northernmost Sakhalin and the mainland north of the Amur estuary (who appear to have mixed with the Ainu), and the **Goldi** on the Lower Amur and Ussuri.

Arctic Mongoloids

Ethnic Group: a. **Eskimo:** Extreme northeast of Asia, Arctic coast of North America, Greenland. The type includes the **Aleuts** of the Aleutian Islands, and the Reindeer and **coastal Chukchee** of northeastern Siberia.
  b. **Evenki or true Tungus (Americanoids):** Mongolia, Siberia, Asiatic highlands north of the Himalayas.
  c. **Kamchadales:** Kamchatka.
  d. **Samoyedes:** Kola Peninsula, White Sea and Yenisei regions.

The Mongoloids of the extreme north-east of the Asiatic continent are distinguished as the *Paleoasiatics*. These are considered to be the complex of ancient populations of Asia who early migrated to this extreme peripheral region. The populations believed to have migrated later into the northeast of the Asiatic continent are known as the *Neo-asiatics*.

Paleoasiatics: Chuckchee, Koryak, Kamchadale, Gilyak, Eskimo, Aleut, Yukaghir, Chuvantzi, Ostyak of Yenisei, Ainu.
Neoasiatics: Finnic tribes, Samoyedic tribes, Turkic including Yakut, Mongolic, Tungusic.

American Indians

Ethnic Group: a. An undetermined number of ethnic groups of North, Middle, Central, and South America.

Indo-Malay

Ethnic Group: a. **Indonesian:** Southern China, Indo-China, Burma, Thailand, interior of Malay Archipelago.
  b. **Malay:** In addition to Indonesian distribution Malay Peninsula, Dutch East Indies, Philippines, Okinawa, and adjacent islands.

FOR FURTHER READING, CONSULT:

COLLINS, H. B.: The origin and antiquity of the Eskimo. *The Smithsonian Report for 1950.* Washington, D.C., Smithsonian Institution, pp. 423-467.
A most helpful discussion.

COON, C. S.: *The Races of Europe.* New York, Macmillan, 1939.
A book rich in basic materials following the conventional methods of classification, but entirely without reference to the data of genetics.

————, GARN, S. M. and BIRDSELL, J. B.: *Races: A Study of the Problems of Race Formation in Man.* Springfield, Thomas, 1950.
An interesting and suggestive volume, containing a new classification of the races of man. Particularly good on the adaptive characters of man.

DENIKER, J.: *The Races of Man.* New York, Scribners, 1900.
This is a classic and fundamental work on the races of man. Indispensable reading.

EHRICH, R. W. and COON, C. S.: Occipital flattening among the Dinarics. *Am. J. Phys. Anthropol.,* 6:181-186, 1947.
A discussion of the part played by cradling practices in determining what was at one time assumed to be a "racial" set of characters.

EWING, J. F.: Hyperbrachycephaly as influenced by cultural conditioning. *Papers Peabody Museum, Harvard University,* 23:10-99, 1950.
An important piece of research showing the influence of cradling practices upon the form of the skull.

GARN, S. M. and COON, C. S.: On the number of races of mankind. *Am. Anthropol.,* 57:996-1001, 1955.
A stimulating contribution.

HADDON, A. C.: *The Wanderings of Peoples,* New York, Macmillan, 1911.
An excellent little book on the migrations of different peoples throughout the world.

————: *The Races of Man.* New York, Cambridge University Press, 1924.
An authoritative and well-balanced little book.

HOOTON, E. A.: *Up From the Ape,* 2nd edition. New York, Macmillan, 1946. pp. 423-661.
Containing an interesting discussion of raciation and the classification of human races with which, however, no genetically minded physical anthropologist could possibly agree.

KEANE, A. H.: *Man Past and Present.* Cambridge: At the University Press, 1920.
Rewritten and revised by A. Hingston Quiggin and A. C. Haddon, this is a fundamental work on the ethnic groups of man, rich in source materials, and all sorts of out-of-the way information. A volume too often neglected.

LAUGHLIN, W. S. (editor): *Papers on the Physical Anthropology of the American Indian.* New York, The Viking Fund, 1949.
Six fundamental papers on the peopling of the Americas, Indian physical types, blood groups, teeth, and genetics.

MONTAGU, M. F. ASHLEY: *Man's Most Dangerous Myth: The Fallacy of Race,* 3rd edition. New York, Harper, 1952.
A critical examination of the concept of race.

————: *Statement on Race,* 2nd edition. New York, Schuman, 1952.
The UNESCO Statement on Race explained.

MORANT, C. G.: *The Races of Central Europe.* London, Allen & Unwin, 1939.
An invaluable little book.

SELIGMAN, C. G.: *The Races of Africa,* 3rd edition. New York, Oxford University
Press, 1957.
A small and excellent book dealing both with the physical and general cultural
characters of the peoples of Africa.

STEWARD, J. H. (editor): *Physical Anthropology, Linguistics, and Cultural Geog-*
raphy of South American Indians. Handbook of South American Indians, vol. 6,
Washington, D.C., Smithsonian Institution, 1950.
A good source for the physical anthropology of South American Indians.

————, and FARON, L. C.: *Native Peoples of South Africa.* New York, McGraw-
Hill Book Co., 1959.
The best one-volume survey of the demography and cultures of the South
American Indians.

THOMAS, E. M.: *The Harmless People.* New York, Knopf, 1959.
A charming book on the life of the Bushman, beautifully told by a field observer.

Chapter VIII

THE SIGNIFICANCE OF ISOLATE DIFFERENCES
OR THE RELATION BETWEEN BODY,
MIND, AND CULTURE

IN THE PRECEDING CHAPTER we saw something of the significance which is to be attached to the physical differences existing between the ethnic groups of man, in the present chapter we shall chiefly consider the significance of the mental and cultural differences which exist between such isolates. Since the belief is often encountered that certain physical characters are invariably associated with certain mental ones, and that membership in a particular "race" generally means that one may expect certain mental and cultural traits to be exhibited by every member of that "race," we may profitably inquire to what extent such a belief is true, and what significance is to be attached to the association, which can so easily be observed in different groups, between physical, mental, and cultural traits. Our purpose in this chapter will be to inquire into the nature of this association.

The Racist View

A typical expression of the racist viewpoint runs as follows: A "something" called "race" or "blood" is the prime determiner of all the important traits of body and soul, of character and personality, of mind and thought. This "something" is a fixed and immutable part of the germ-plasm which, differing in each people, is transmitted from generation to generation, to unfold in each people in a typical expression of personality and culture. Hence, there must exist irreconcilable differences in mind, soul, and blood between the "races" of mankind. During the last hundred years this view has found supporters in many different lands, culminating finally in the Nazi doctrine of racism, the basis of the official viewpoint of the German government of 1933-1945.

The Genetic Facts

The parents contribute a set of genes to their children which combine to form the new individual, an individual who is unlike anyone

474

who has ever lived before or who will ever live again. Since man possesses 23 pairs of chromosomes, their possible combination in a single mating amount to 8,388,608 or 2 raised to the 23rd power. The chances of exactly the same combination occurring in any two individuals are, on the basis of the number of chromosomes alone, 1 in 70,000,000,000,000, or about once in every 600,000 generations, which, is, for all practical purposes, never. This tremendous range of variation is due to the fact that the carriers of the hereditary materials are particulate more or less independent structures, the genes, carried on the 23 pairs of chromosomes of each parent, and that these can combine in a practically infinite variety of relations. That is why no two persons are ever alike.

We have seen that out of this inexhaustible reservoir of genetic materials certain combinations may be produced as the result of the action of a variety of factors, so that we find one group with white skin, another with brown, and still another with yellowish skin and so on. Even so we never find any two individuals who are ever alike, and that is in essence what we mean by the term variation. The particulate and extra-chromosomal forms of inheritance and the consequent variability are facts which lend not the slightest support to any notion that a "something" which is a fixed and immutable part of the genetic system is responsible for any irreconcilable differences between the ethnic groups of mankind. These facts are, on the other hand, quite opposed to such a view. There are no fixed and immutable parts of the genetic system, and hence it is impossible to transmit them; there are merely temporary combinations of genes which under isolate conditions will tend to remain relatively stable. They are, of course, more or less constantly in process of undergoing change, and undergo very substantial modification as soon as the conditions relative to which the gene combinations have maintained their stability are changed.

Genes do not make their own conditions of expression, but have them made for them by the environment in which they develop. Hence, it is not only new combinations and mutations of genes which are responsible for the production of novelty, but the environment as well. It is not traits or characters which are inherited, but the potentialities to develop traits or characters, and the expression of these potentialities is to a large extent determined by the environment in which they undergo development.

Thus, for example, as has been mentioned in an earlier chapter, the head-shape of children born in the United States will differ from that of their European-born siblings and parents in a manner which can only be explained as due to the effect of the new environment. A poor socio-economic environment will almost invariably exert an untoward effect upon the growing individual, so that it is safe to say that practically the whole of his body is affected, and he grows up to be somewhat different from what he might have been under more favorable conditions. Even the shade of the skin will vary in different environments, appearing darker in an area of intense sunlight than it would in the same individual in a cloudy, foggy, climate. Physiological characteristics such as the onset of first menstruation (menarche), basal metabolism, and blood pressure, will vary very significantly in association with the climates in which these functions develop (see Chapter IX).

The expression of a gene is, therefore, to a certain extent, dependent upon the environment to which it is exposed and to which it is in a very definite sense a response. The ultimate characters the genes produce will therefore tend to vary as the environment varies. The term "character" is itself an abstraction, but one which is unavoidable for descriptive purposes. As Dobzhansky points out, "Genes produce not characters but physiological states which, through interactions with the physiological states induced by all other genes of the organism and with the environmental influences, cause the development to assume a definite course and the individual to display certain characters at a given stage of the developmental process."[1]

There is nothing stable or immutable about the genetic system. Under varying conditions it will tend to vary. The delimiting physical characters of a major group will be preserved only as long as genes from another major group are excluded from the group. With the introduction of such genes the group tends to lose its former characters and to acquire new ones. Were there to exist any irreconcilable differences in the genetic structure between the members of different ethnic groups such processes could not occur or else they would exhibit themselves in disharmonic or undesirable effects in the hybrids. And this we know very definitely not to occur.

One of nature's favorite methods of producing new and better types of living forms, and strengthening old ones, is by hybridization. This is as true of man as of any other living creature.

The popular stereotype that interbreeding or crossing between different "races" results in inferior offspring and in ultimate degen-

---

[1] DOBZHANSKY, TH., and HOLZ, A. M.: A re-examination of the problem of manifold effects of genes in Drosophila melanogaster. *Genetics,* 28:301, 1943.

eration of the stock is totally without scientific foundation, and, indeed, is quite contrary to the truth.

Studies on Polynesian-White crosses carried out by Shapiro, on Australian-White crosses, by Tindale and others, by numerous investigators on crosses between Japanese, Filipinos, Koreans, Puerto Ricans, Europeans of all sorts, and Hawaiians, by Boas on Indians and whites, by Herskovits on the American Negro, by Davenport and Steggerda on the Jamaican offspring of Negro-white unions, by Fischer on Dutch-Hottentot crosses, by Lotsy and Goddijn on a great variety of crosses in South Africa between Bushmen, Basutoes, Fingoes, "Kaffirs," Zulus, Mongoloids, Indians, whites and many others, all these studies, and a great many more, prove the great value, from every possible unbiased point of view, of hybridization.

There have, however, been some writers who have concluded from their studies of "race-crossing" that the process results in neither good nor bad effects, while some have concluded that the crossing of ethnic groups does not, on the whole, result in desirable types. I do not read the evidence so.

The "half-caste" is, as his name implies, not fully accepted by either of the castes or ethnic groups with which his parents are associated, and though he tends to adhere to that group which is lower in his social scale, he tends also to be somewhat isolated, to be "outcast." In most instances the half-caste finds it extremely difficult to adjust himself to conditions which are themselves the cause of maladjustment in others. One of America's leading geneticists, Castle, has put the matter very cogently. He writes, "Since there are no biological obstacles to crossing between the most diverse human races, when such crossing does occur, it is in disregard of social conventions, race pride and race prejudice. Naturally therefore it occurs between antisocial and outcast specimens of the respective races, or else between conquerors and slaves. The social status of the children is thus bound to be low, their educational opportunities poor, their moral background bad. . . . Does the half-breed, in any community in the world in which he is numerous, have an equal chance to make a man of himself, as compared with the sons of the dominant race? I think not. Can we then fairly consider him racially inferior just because his racial attainments are less? Attainments imply opportunities as well as abilities."[2]

In the isolating factors which operate upon the half-caste we are

---

[2] CASTLE, W. E.: Biological and social consequences of race crossing. Am. J. Phys. Anthrop., 9:147, 1926.

dealing with a conspicuous example of the action of socially depressing conditions and not with the effects of biological ones. These facts are invariably overlooked by those who attribute the unfavorable effects of "race crossing" to biological factors.

At every point then, we see the enormous importance of the environmental factor, either physical or social, in conditioning what we so often misinterpret as biologically determined.

"Blood"

A very general belief, and one which has led to much serious misunderstanding of human relationships, is the prevailing popular conception of blood as the carrier of the heritable qualities of the family, "race," or nation. The term "blood-relationship," and its anglicised Latin equivalent "consanguinity," meaning the condition of being of the same "blood" or relationship by descent from a common ancestor, enshrines the belief that all biological relationships are reflected in, and are to a large extent, determined by the character of the blood. Such terms as "blue blood," "blood royal," "pure blood," "full-blood," "half-blood," and "good blood," further reflect that meaning.

All these terms reflect the belief that "blood" is equivalent to "heredity," and that blood, therefore, is that part of the organism which determines the quality of the individual. By extension it is further generally believed that the social as well as the biological status of the individual is determined by the kind of "blood" he has inherited. Supposed national and "racial" differences are recognized in such terms as "German blood," "English blood," "Negro blood," and so forth; so that today the words "race" and "blood" are often used as synonyms.

The facts of science lend no support to the conception of blood thus implied. Blood is in no way connected with the transmission of hereditary characteristics. The carriers of the hereditary potentialities which, in interaction with the environment, express themselves in characters, are the genes which lie in the chromosomes and cytoplasm of the germ cells represented in the spermatzoön of the father and in the ovum of the mother. These genes have no connection whatever with blood, except insofar as they determine its serological properties. Blood has nothing whatever to do with determining the heredity of the individual or of the group, either biologically, culturally, or in any other manner.

The belief that the blood of the mother is transmitted to the child, and hence becomes a part of the child, is an ancient but erroneous one. Scientific investigation of the processes of pregnancy has long ago made it perfectly clear that there is normally no actual passage of blood from mother to child. The developing child manufactures its own blood, and the character of its various blood cells is demonstrably different from that of either of its parents. The mother does not contribute blood to the fetus, nor is her blood continuous with that of the fetus. The placenta is a complex system of semi-permeable membranes which permits the passage only of molecules of very small size. Blood cells are too large to pass across the placental barrier, except toward the end of pregnancy, when the membranes of the villi become thinned out and permeable. Such facts should completely dispose of the false idea of a "blood-tie" between any two individuals whether they be mother and child or even identical twins. Hence any claims to kinship based on the tie of "blood" can have no scientific foundation whatever. Nor can claims of group consciousness based on "blood" be anything but spurious, since the character of the blood of all human beings is determined not by their membership in any group or nation but by the fact that they are members of the single species *Homo sapiens*.

The serological traits which we have already discussed in a previous chapter are determined by the presence or absence of certain genes in combination with one another. It is these hereditary molecules which determine the character of the blood, and not the blood which determines heredity. The frequencies of these genes vary from population to population, as do the genes for other characters. In short, the serological characters of the blood are the expression of certain gene combinations, not the cause of them.

SPIRITUAL QUALITIES, GENES, AND CULTURE

By the "soul" may, apparently, be understood many strange things. The principal Nazi "anthropologist," Hans Günther, as long ago as 1922 classified the "souls" of different "races" according to their alleged colors and stated, for example, that the soul of the Dinaric "race" seems to be dark green ("Als 'seelische Farbe' der dinarischen Rasse scheint sich ein dunkles Grün zu ergeben").

Scientists cannot presume to speak on the nature of the soul since it has never been the subject of serious investigation, but if one may make an approximation to what is generally meant by the word and suggest that it is the spiritual principle which appears to inform a person's conduct, there are several important things which a scientist can say about the "soul." He can say with some degree of assurance that the spiritual quality of a normal man's mind or conduct is not produced so much by anything inborn, by anything which he inherits in his genes, as by the influence of cultural factors upon the organization of his mind. The genes provide the necessary factors for the development of a nervous system and a mind, but the potentialities of that nervous system and its functioning as mind can never be realized in the absence of the human social stimuli which serve to organize that system to function as a human mind.

The fact that an infant ever develops into a human being is almost entirely due to the influence upon its genetic endowment of the human environment in which it is brought up. Genes alone cannot create a human being. They largely create the physical characters which we associate with individuals who are human, and they create the potentialities for the development of human behavior. Behavior which becomes human only because a suitable environment has organized such gene potentialities in a human way. Children who are brought up in solitary confinement, isolated from the socializing influence of human contacts, have no resemblance but a physical one to human beings. There is no such thing as a human mind, apart from a human socializing influence. The human mind as an entity is not so much inherited as socially produced, and it will depend, to the largest extent, upon the nature of the socializing influences which are brought to bear upon it, what the nature of that mind will be.

If it is true that genes alone cannot create a human being, it is equally true that environment alone cannot do so. However powerful the socializing influences might be, they would be powerless to create a human mind if the necessary gene potentialities were wanting. There can be no human mind without the unique gene potentialities with which every member of mankind is endowed. This is a point which cannot be too greatly stressed in view of the fact that in recent years the reaction to the extreme claims of the racists has caused the pendulum to swing in the opposite direction, and there has been a tendency to deny any relation between the biological make-up of the individual and his mental characteristics. Such a connection undoubtedly exists in every individual and it is an important one. Differences in temperament, special abilities, and in intelligence, are to a certain extent undoubtedly determined by the genetic structure of the individual, but only in interaction with the total environment of the individual.

Were it possible to expose every person to the same total environment—social, economic, climatic, geographic, and so on—persons would still differ from each other, and these differences would express the effect of the genetic factor in the assimilation of the external factors, and that is all. Biologically determined differences in mental characteristics exist between all *individuals*, but this is a very different thing from saying that such differences exist between all ethnic *groups*, or that the mental differences between individuals are biologically determined.

In pure breeds of dogs or birds differences in mental behavior are very closely associated with each breed, but human ethnic groups are not pure breeds, but are, on the other hand, very much mixed. Human groups do not in the least approach the type of genetic uniformity which one encounters among breeds of domesticated animals. Hence, any comparison between them is quite unsound since these domestic breeds are genetically relatively uniform, whereas man, in almost every group in which he may be considered, is characterized by considerable genetic diversity. The evidence indicates that from the earliest times to the present day ethnic intermixture has been the rule, evidence of such intermixture is found in the most inbred ethnic groups. Study of hereditary traits in family lines in most human populations which have thus far been investigated shows that each family line differs from every other, that the diversity in family lines is so great as to render it impossible to speak, in such a population, of hereditary traits common to the whole group.

The history of mankind would lead us to expect such a result, for that history is one of migration and mixture of group with group, again and again. In view of the tremendous diversity of genetic lines which have entered into the formation of each group of mankind such a thing as a pure breed of mankind cannot be said to exist anywhere on this earth. The claim, therefore, that any group of mankind represents a pure group different from all others, all of whose members are distinguished by the same characteristics, is quite untenable.

We must recognize, and be properly grateful for, the fact that all individuals are biologically determined to be unlike, but we must also recognize the fact that when such individuals are evaluated collectively in terms of the groups which they compose, each group seems to average up to about much the same level as every other. At any rate, science has not been able to discover that there exist any fundamental biologically determined mental differences between groups that would outweigh the influence of culture. As Boas has put it: "Our conclusion is that the claim to biologically determined mental qualities of races is not tenable. Much less have we a right to speak of biologically determined superiority of one race over another. Every race contains so many genetically distinct strains, and the social behavior is so entirely dependent upon the life experience to which every individual is exposed, that individuals of the same type when exposed to different surroundings will react quite differently, while individuals of different types when exposed to the same environment may react the same way."

We can be perfectly certain that whatever genetic differences exist between individuals or groups, genes do not and cannot make a mind or produce a "soul." It is the environmentally conditioned experiences acting upon a relatively undifferentiated variety of nervous tissues, formed by the genes, which serve to differentiate and organize those tissues into a bioneurological system which creates mind, and it is a particular history of interaction between those genes and environmental or cultural experience which determines the exact spiritual quality of a mind. As that history differs so will the quality of the mind. To a large extent every human being is culturally or spiritually the product of the society into which he is born. His thoughts, his ideas, his habits are all socially acquired. He is not born with any of these things. Individuals born and brought up in the same society will nevertheless differ from one another because however like their experience may have been it can never have been quite the same, and because of certain individual differences in genetic endowment.

When we consider the great differences in the cultural experience of persons not of the same family, economic or class group, nation, or ethnic group, we can readily see why great mental and spiritual differences may exist between them. The differences are primarily due to differences in culture and cultural experience. These differences have no known or demonstrable connection with the genetic system, although it would be unjustified to assume that they are entirely unconnected. Whatever that connection may be, it is insignificant when compared with the cultural factor.

Now, since the cultural factor is extremely variable for individuals, and even more so for social isolates, it is obvious, even apart from such differential action as the genes may exercise, that individuals and groups will differ from one another as their cultural experience varies. The very fact that cultural and spiritual differences exist between individuals and between groups is proof positive of the fact that there is nothing fixed or immutable about or irreconcilable between such differences, for if such differences were fixed then we should observe no cultural development or change of the most sub-stantial kind within a culture or a people. The inhabitants of the British Isles today would still be in a Stone Age phase of cultural develop-ment, for the population of those isles has not significantly changed during the last few thousand or more years; the various non-literate peoples of Tsarist Russia would still be non-literates instead of the westernized peoples of the U.S.S.R. who have adapted themselves with amazing rapidity to the new cultural demands which have been made upon them. The Japanese could hardly have become "western-ized," nor the Mexican Indians Hispanicized. In those parts of Africa in which an enlightened administrative policy has been followed, particularly in West Africa, there are many thousands of native Af-ricans who have never left their own land who have come most ca-pably abreast of the novel Western culture with which they have been confronted. In India, after two centuries of British rule, a great number of Indians have made British culture a part of their own.

The example of the Jews, who constitute not an ethnic group but a cultural isolate wherever they are found, is well known. The Jews carry certain kinds of historically conditioned cultural traits with them wherever they go. These are often stated to be biologically de-termined, but that this is false is proven by the fact that when Jews completely adopt the culture of the land in which they happen to live they frequently become completely indistinguishable from the non-Jewish population of that land. Such "Jews," of course, pass un-noticed, but those who retain Jewish cultural traits are easily recog-nized, *principally by virtue of their retention of certain cultural traits which have no connection whatever with biological factors*. The fact is, however, that Jews still carry an appreciable number of genes derived from their original Near Eastern ancestors.

The American Negro is another case in point. So far as he has been permitted he has acquired the cultural traits of the white popu-lations among which he lives, while the white populations have ac-quired some of his traits. This is not due to a physical intermixture but to a cultural intermixture. If the physical intermixture were re-sponsible then we should observe a blending of Negro and white cultural traits, but we observe nothing of the sort. The original cul-tures of the African Negro ancestors of the American Negro survive in Africa but have been to a large extent lost among many Negro groups in America, having been practically completely eroded by the dominant white culture. This could not have occurred had the genes been responsible for the development of either "soul" or culture.

It may, however, be argued that culturally the American Negro, after being exposed to western culture for some 250 years, is still not culturally indistinguishable from the white. This is, of course, true in precisely the same way that it is true of any social isolate. The American Negro has never been allowed to become socially or culturally indistinguishable from the white. On the other hand, distinctions have been deliberately created and maintained, barriers have been erected across which the Negro has not been permitted to pass; he has been segregated, culturally isolated. Is it any wonder then that he should exhibit certain differences in culture and behavior which distinguish him from the populations from which he is excluded? Having been excluded he has been forced to create a more or less parallel culture, and under conditions of the most difficult kind he has succeeded in doing so. Since the Negroes as a group are hardly ever given the opportunity to realize their potentialities on an equal social footing with whites, it is as unfair as it is unscientific to count the effects of the lack of such social equality against them. Were they given such an opportunity it is more than likely that the Negro average of achievement would turn out to be quite as high as that of the average white.

Another example of interest is provided by the gypsies. In spite of a certain amount of physical and cultural amalgamation with the peoples among whom they have lived the gypsies have, on the whole, successfully resisted complete assimilation. They have retained a substantial part of their original language, and culturally they have remained a foreign element in the midst of every population in which they have lived. This is obviously not because their genes have prevented them from adopting the cultural manners of their hosts, for many of them have made the change, but because they have consciously preferred to retain their own spiritual and cultural integrity.

"Changes in personality without change in heredity," writes Boas, "may be observed in the history of many peoples. The impoverished Indian who has become a laborer is the descendant of his daring, warlike ancestors. The terrorized Germans of our time are in part the same individuals, in part the direct descendants, of the fine citizens of twenty years ago; the Europeanized Japanese of our time are by heredity the same as their ancestors who closed the door to all foreign influence." To which may be added, the Jews of the towns who have in our own time become farmers and the invincible soldiers of Israel.

Thus, at every point we see that individuals and groups will or will not undergo spiritual or cultural change not for any genetic reasons but for purely cultural ones, without themselves necessarily undergoing any genetic change.

The racist assertion of the biological inheritance of spiritual and mental qualities peculiar to each "race" is, therefore, negated by the facts of science.

Relationship of Body, Mind, and Behavior. The material structures which are ultimately to subserve mental functions are to a large extent inherited precisely as are all other structures of the body. This assumption is supported by at least some sporadic investigations of the brains of near relatives, in addition to certain observational considerations of a like nature. The qualification "to a large extent" is a very necessary one since, in man, the nervous system continues to undergo structural differentiation and development long after birth, and is therefore appreciably influenced by the post-natal experience of the individual. In every part of the nervous system new connections can always be established through education. As a leading neuroanatomist, S. W. Ranson, has put it, "The neurons which make up the nervous system of an adult man are therefore arranged in a system the larger outlines of which follow an hereditary pattern, but many of the details of which have been shaped by the experiences of the individual."[3]

It is evident that experience must play a considerable rôle in the development of the *structure* of the nervous system, hence in the manner in which it functions. It should also be clear that the aspect of the nervous system which we know as *mind*, behavior, is dependent upon the interaction of several factors. These are primarily, the inherited, *incompletely developed*, structure of the nervous system, and the character of the external developing influences. Coghill's fundamental studies on the development of the nervous system in relation to behavior in the spotted salamander *Amblystoma punctatum* has demonstrated that the conditioning processes of experience are registered in the nervous system in such a way that the neural structures involved acquire functional specificity with reference to the experience. Specificity of function is established by interaction of growth and excitation, that is to say, the excitation fixes upon the growing terminals of neurones its own mode of activation. As Coghill writes when discussing the mammalian cortex, "cortical cells, beginning their function with the beginning of experience, grow as

[3] RANSON, S. W.: *The Anatomy of the Nervous System.* Philadelphia, 1943, p. 41.

experience progresses till all of the essential behaviour and conditioning processes are registered in them. Every pyramidal cell as a
growing unit may be conceived as blending, so to speak, the experience of the individual from the beginning to the end of stimulation
and response. . . . As a result of this, although the behaviour at any
moment may be dominated by some patricular phase of experience, it
cannot be utterly disconnected from any part of the whole. Only with
the retrogressive changes of senescence or with arrested development
in pathological cases does experience cease to register in a progressive
manner."[4]

The mind of man, in the sense above indicated, is a social product. It reflects the pattern of the culture in which it is conditioned.
The functional specificities thus determined when expressed in behavior can clearly only be expressed according to the pattern of the
culture in which they have been organized. The hereditary determinants of the morphological potentialities from which a mind may be
organized are what is given. It is the cultural organization of such
nervous morphological potentialities that *creates* mind. Genes do not
create mind, but they do provide every individual with a somewhat
different morphological pattern of cellular tissues; so that if it were
possible to keep all other factors constant, differences in behavior, that
is in mind would still serve to distinguish every person. Such differences would express the action of the genetic differential and nothing
else. Put in another way what we have been saying is that the genetic
potentialities are organized by the socially structured field to which
they are exposed.

There is every reason to believe that in any human population
the genetically determined nervous structure is at least as variable
as any of its other physical characters. But once this has been granted,
it must be said that there is equally good reason to believe, and this
is the important point, that the observable differences in the behavior between different individuals are to a far larger extent determined by cultural factors than by the total number of biological factors which operate from within the individual. Chief among these
biological factors are the functional capacities of the nervous system
itself, and it cannot here be too often emphasized that those functional capacities, to the most important extent, are organized by the
action, from birth to maturity, of cultural influences. Again, it cannot
be too often repeated that all the evidence indicates that it is prin-

[4] COGHILL, G. E.: *Anatomy and the Problem of Behaviour*. New York, Cambridge University Press, 1929, pp. 105-107.

cipally due to this unique plasticity that the species *Homo sapiens* owes most of those qualities which are implied in the words "human being."

The principal fact which all those who are in any way interested in human behavior must continually hold before their minds is that man, alone among the members of the animal kingdom, is a creature influenced more prominently by his cultural history than by his ancestral or individual biological history. In the meaning of this fact lies the uniqueness of man.

Are There Any Mental Differences between the Major and Ethnic Groups of Mankind?

It may be that in some different ethnic groups the nervous system differs in some of its hidden or undiscovered characters, but if this is so all attempts to demonstrate such differences have thus far failed. What seems to be quite clear is that if such differences exist then they are of the most insignificant kind. The measurable mental characters of different ethnic groups strongly suggest that so far as the average member of the group is concerned no significant mental differences exist beween such groups which may be attributed to the inherited character of the nervous system alone. Furthermore, the mental differences which exist between human groups would appear to be much less than those which are found to exist between individuals of the same group. In the light of our present knowledge, the evidence shows that within the limits of the normal, brain weight, cranial capacity, head size, or the *gross structure* and form of the brain bear no relation whatsoever to the characters of the mind, as between individuals of the same or different ethnic groups. Nor is there any necessary association between certain major group characters and certain kinds of mentality. Since mental functions are so largely dependent upon experience, upon cultural conditions, it is impossible to make any inferences as to the equivalence or non-equivalence of mental potentialities as between ethnic groups or isolates among whom the cultural conditions are not strictly comparable. In short, no statement concerning the mentality of an individual, an ethnic group or other isolate, is of any value without a specification of the conditions of the environment in which that mentality has developed. No discussion of ethnic mental characters can be countenanced which neglects a full consideration of the associated cultural variables, for it is evident that it is precisely those cultural variables which play the most significant part in producing mental differences between ethnic groups and other isolates.

It is perfectly clear that genetically determined mental differences do exist between individuals of the same and of different ethnic groups, but there is absolutely no evidence that significant mental differences which are determined by the genetic characters of the nervous system exist between any two ethnic groups. It would appear to be chiefly because of differences in cultural experiences that individuals and groups differ from one another mentally and culturally, and it is for this reason that, where the cultural experience has appreciably differed, cultural achievement alone is an exceedingly poor measure of the mental value of an individual or of a group.

It is quite probable that in a non-isolated, heterogeneous, hybridizing population, the range of variability in the genetic determination of mental potentialities is greater than it is in a relatively isolated, homogeneous, inbreeding population. This is true of physical characters, and may be true of mental potentialities, and eventually it may, in part, provide the explanation for the more frequent occurrence of individuals of genius in much mixed groups as compared with relatively less mixed or inbred groups. The average member of both groups would, however, have about the same potential mental range.

Thus far scientific investigation has been unable to demonstrate any ethnic mental differences due to hereditary differences. As Klineberg, one of the leading students of the subject, has put it, "We have the right to say that the results obtained by the use of intelligence tests have not proved the existence of racial and national differences in innate mental capacity; and also that as the social and economic environments of the two ethnic groups become more alike, so do their tests scores tend to approximate each other. We have no right to conclude that there are no racial differences in mental ability, since it is conceivable that new techniques may some day be developed which will indicate that such differences do exist. This is unlikely, however, and we may state with some degree of assurance that in all probability the range of inherited capacities in two different ethnic groups is just about identical."[5]

THE EVOLUTION OF THE MENTAL CHARACTERS
OF MANKIND

From the standpoint of the student of human evolution man's distinctive mental character is the product of mutation, selection, genetic drift, and hybridization—and something more. A narrow biologism

---

[5] KLINEBERG, OTTO: Mental testing of racial and national groups, in *Scientific Aspects of the Race Problem*. New York, Longmans, 1941, p. 283-284.

usually stops before reaching the "something more," and treats man as if he were no more than a purely biological entity. He is, however, something more, a great deal more. The specific human features of the evolutionary pattern of man cannot be ignored. Man is a unique product of evolution in that he, far more than any other creature, has escaped from the bondage of the physical and the biological into the multiform social environment. This remarkable development introduces a third dimension, a new zone of adaptation, in addition to those of the external and internal environments, a dimension or zone of adaptation which many biologists, in considering the evolution of man, tend to neglect. The most important setting of human evolution is the human social environment. A biologist approaching the problems of human evolution must never lose sight of the truth stated more than 2,000 years ago by Aristotle: "Man is by nature a political animal."

In the words of Fisher, "For rational systems of evolution, that is, for theories which make at least the most familiar facts intelligible to the reason, we must turn to those that make progressive adaptation the driving force of the process." It is evident that man by means of his reasoning abilities, by becoming a "political animal," has achieved a mastery of the world's varying environments quite unprecedented in the history of organic evolution. The system of genes which has permitted the development of the specifically human mental human capacities has thus become the foundation of and the paramount influence in all subsequent evolution of the human stock. An animal becomes adapted to its environment by evolving certain genetically determined physical and behavioral traits; the adaptation of man consists chiefly in developing his inventiveness, a quality to which his physical heredity predisposes him and which his social heredity provides him with the means of realizing. To the degree to which this is so, man is unique. As far as his physical responses to the world are concerned, he is almost wholly emancipated from dependence upon inherited biological dispositions, uniquely improving upon the latter by the process of learning that which his social heredity (culture) makes available to him. Man possesses much more efficient means of achieving immediate or long-term adaptation than any other biological species; namely, through learned responses or novel inventions and improvisations.

In general, two types of biological adaptation in evolution can be distinguished. One is genetic specialization and genetically controlled fixity of traits. The second consists in the ability to respond to a given range of environmental situations by evolving traits favorable in these particular situations; this presupposes genetically controlled plasticity of traits. It is known, for example, that the composition of the blood which is most favorable for life at high altitudes is somewhat different from that which suffices at sea level. A species which ranges from sea level to high altitudes on a mountain range may become differentiated into several altitudinal races, each having a fixed blood composition favored by natural selection at the particular altitude at which it lives; or a genotype may be selected which permits an individual to respond to changes in atmospheric pressure by definite alterations in the composition of the blood. It is well known that heredity determines in its possessor not the presence or absence of certain traits but, rather, the responses of the organisms to its environments. The responses may be more or less rigidly fixed, so that approximately the same traits develop in all environments in which life is possible. On the other hand, the responses may differ in different environments. Fixity or plasticity of a trait is therefore genetically controlled.

Whether the evolutionary adaptation in a given phyletic line will occur chiefly by way of genetically controlled plasticity of traits will depend on circumstances. In the first place, evolutionary changes are compounded of mutational steps, and consequently the kind of change that takes place is always determined by the composition of the store of mutational variability which happens to be available in the species populations. Secondly, fixity or plasticity of traits is controlled by natural selection. Having a trait fixed by heredity and hence appearing in the development of an individual regardless of environmental variations is, in general, of benefit to organisms whose milieu remains uniform and static except for rare and freakish deviations. Conversely, organisms which inhabit changeable environments are benefited by having their traits plastic and modified by each recurrent configuration of environmental agents in a way most favorable for the survival of the carrier of the trait in question.

Comparative anatomy and embryology show that a fairly general trend in organic evolution seems to be from environmental dependence toward fixation of the basic features of the bodily structure and function. The appearance of these structural features in the embryonic development of higher organisms is, in general, more nearly autonomous and independent of the environment than in lower forms. The development becomes "buffered" against environmental and genetic shocks. If, however, the mode of life of a species happens to be such that it is, of necessity, exposed to a wide range of environments, it becomes desirable to vary some structures and functions in accordance with the circumstances that confront an individual or a strain at a given time and place. Genetic structures which permit adaptive plasticity of traits become, then, obviously advantageous for survival and so are fostered by natural selection.

The social environments that human beings have created everywhere are notable not only for their extreme complexity but also for the rapid changes to which immediate adjustment is demanded. Adjustment occurs chiefly in the psychical realm and has little or nothing to do with physical traits. In view of the fact that from the very beginning of human evolution the changes in the human environment have been not only rapid but diverse and manifold, genetic fixation of behavioral traits in man would have been decidedly unfavorable for the survival of the individual as well as the species as a whole. Success of the individual in most human societies has depended and continues to depend upon his ability rapidly to evolve behavior patterns which fit him to the kaleidoscope of the conditions he encounters. He is best off if he submits to some, rebels against others, compromises with some, and escapes from still other situations. Individuals who display a relatively greater fixity of response than their fellows suffer under most forms of human society and tend to fall by the way. Suppleness, plasticity, and, most important of all, ability to profit by experience and education are required. No other species is comparable to man in its capacity to acquire new behavior patterns and discard old ones in consequence of training. Considered socially as well as biologically, man's outstanding capacity is his educability. The survival value of this capacity is manifest, and therefore the possibility of its development through natural selection is evident. Natural selection on the human level favors gene complexes which enable their possessors to adjust their behavior to any condition in the light of previous experience. In short, it favors educability.

It should be made clear at this point that the replacement of fixity of behavior by genetically controlled plasticity is not a necessary consequence of all forms of social organization. The quaint attempts to glorify insect societies as examples deserving emulation on the part of man ignore the fact that the behavior of an individual among social insects is remarkable precisely because of the rigidity of its genetic fixation. The perfection of the organized societies of ants, termites, bees, and other insects is indeed wonderful, and the activities of their members may strike an observer very forcibly by their objective purposefulness. This purposefulness is retained, however, only in environments in which the species normally lives. The ability of an ant to adjust its activities to situations not encountered in the normal habitats of its species is very limited. On the other hand, social organizations on the human level are built on the principle that an individual is able to alter his behavior to fit any situation, whether previously experienced or new.

This difference between human and insect societies is, of course, not surprising. Adaptive plasticity of behavior can develop only on the basis of a rather more complex nervous system than is sufficient for adaptive fixity. The genetic differences between human and insect societies furnish a striking illustration of the two types of evolutionary adaptations—those achieved through genetically controlled plasticity of behavioral traits and those attained through genetic specialization and fixation of behavior.

The genetically controlled plasticity of mental traits is, biologically speaking, the most typical and uniquely human characteristic. It is very probable that the survival value of this characteristic in human evolution has been considerable for a long time, as measured in terms of human historical scales. Just when this characteristic first appeared is, of course, conjectural. Here it is of interest to note that the most marked phylogenetic trend in the evolution of man has been the special development of the brain, and that the characteristic human plasticity of mental traits seems to be associated with the exceptionally large brain size. The brain, for example, of the Lower or Middle Pleistocene fossil forms of man was, grossly at least, scarcely distinguishable from that of modern man. The average Neanderthaloid brain was at least as large as that of modern man, though slightly different in shape. More important than the evidence derived from brain size is the testimony of cultural development. The Middle Acheulian handiwork of Swanscombe man of several hundred thousand years ago and the beautiful Mousterian cultural artifacts associated with Neanderthal man indicate the existence of minds of a high order of development. The cultural evidence thus suggests that the essentially human organization of the mental capacities emerged quite early in the evolution of man. However that may be, the possession of a gene system which conditions educability rather than behavioral fixity is a common property of all living mankind. In other words, educability is truly a species character of man. This does not mean that the evolutionary process has run its course and that natural selection has introduced no changes in the genetic structure of the human species since the attainment of human status. Nor is there any implication that no genetic variations in mental equipment exist at our time level. On the contrary, it seems likely that with the attainment of human status that that part of man's genetic system which is related to mental potentialities did not cease to be labile and subject to change.

This brings us once more face to face with the old problem whether significant genetic differences in the mental capacities of the various ethnic groups of mankind exist. The physical and, even more, the social environments of men who live in different countries are quite diversified. Therefore, it has often been argued, natural selection would be expected to differentiate the human species into local races differing in psychic traits. Populations of different countries may differ in skin color, head shape, and other somatic characters. Why, then, should they be alike in mental traits?

It will be through investigation rather than speculation that the problem of the possible existence of average differences in mental make-up of human populations of different geographical origins will eventually be settled. Arguments based on analogies are precarious, especially where evolutionary patterns are concerned. If ethnic groups differ in structural traits, it does not necessarily follow that they must also differ in mental ones. Ethnic group differences arise chiefly be- cause of the differential action of natural selection on geographically separated populations. In the case of man, however, the structural and mental traits are quite likely to be influenced by selection in different ways.

We have seen that ethnic differences in traits such as the blood groups may conceivably have been brought about by genetic drift in populations of limited effective size. Other ethnic traits are genetically too complex and too consistently present in populations of some large territories and absent in other territories to be accounted for by genetic drift alone. Differences in skin color, hair form, nose shape, etc., are almost certainly products of natural selection. The lack of reliable knowledge of the adaptive significance of these traits is perhaps the greatest gap in our understanding of the evolutionary biology of man. Nevertheless, it is at least a plausible working hypothesis that these and similar traits have, or at any rate had in the past, differential sur- vival values in the environments of different parts of the world.

By contrast, the survival value of a higher development of mental capacities in man is obvious. Furthermore, natural selection seemingly favors such a development everywhere. In the ordinary course of events in almost all societies those persons are likely to be favored who show wisdom, maturity of judgment, and ability to get along with people—qualities which may assume different forms in different cultures. Those are the qualities of the plastic personality, not a single trait but a general condition, and this is the condition which appears to have been at a premium in practically all human societies.

In human societies conditions have been neither rigid nor stable enough to permit the selective breeding of genetic types adapted to different statuses or forms of social organization. On the other hand, the outstanding fact about human societies is that they do change and do so more or less rapidly. The rate of change was possibly comparatively slow in earlier societies, as the rate of change in present-day non-literate societies may be, when compared to the rate characterizing occidental societies. In any event, rapid changes in behavior are demanded of the person at all levels of social organization even when the society is at its most stable. Life at any level of social development is a pretty complex business, and it is met and handled most efficiently by those who exhibit the greatest capacity for adaptability, plasticity.

It is this very plasticity of his mental traits which confers upon man the unique position which he occupies in the animal kingdom. Its acquisition freed him from the constraint of a limited range of biologically predetermined responses. He became capable of acting in a more or less regulative manner upon his physical environment instead of being largely regulated by it. The processes of natural selection in all climes and at all times have favored genotypes which permit greater and greater educability and plasticity of mental traits under the influence of the uniquely social environments to which man has been continuously exposed.

As Muller has pointed out "racial genetic differences . . . may well be insignificant in comparison with the individual ones, owing to the lack of any substantial difference in the manner of selection of most of these characters in the major part of the past history of the various human races." Whether or not we are reasonably justified in assuming that there has been little if any significant change in man's mental potentialities during the major part of his past history, this does seem to be reasonably clear, namely, that the effect of natural selection in man has probably been to render genotypic differences in mental traits, as between individuals and particularly as between ethnic groups, relatively unimportant compared to their phenotypic plasticity. Instead of having his responses genetically fixed as in other animal species, man is a species that invents its own responses, and it is out of this unique ability to invent, to improvise, his responses that his cultures are born.

Hence, we should expect to find the range of inherited capacities in all human groups "just about identical."

The Isolate Effect in Cultural Differentiation

A question often asked is: Why do the cultures of different ethnic groups frequently differ so considerably from our own? If the members of all ethnic groups are characterized by a range of inherited capacities which are about identical, why have not all ethnic groups arrived at a stage of cultural development which is about identical?

Very briefly, the answer is: Because culture is not a function of inherited capacities alone but of inherited capacities *plus* experience, and that in so far as the experience of ethnic groups has been different in so far will their cultures be different. By experience is meant anything that an individual or group of individuals, has undergone or lived, perceived or sensed. The reason why the cultures of different ethnic groups differ so much from our own is that these groups have been exposed to experiences which differ as considerably from our own as do the cultures in question.

Had the reader and the author of the present volume, with their present genetic backgrounds, been born and brought up among a group of Australian aborigines they would now be, culturally and mentally, Australian aborigines, though physically they would each remain members of their own ethnic group; for experience is determined by the place and culture in which groups and individuals live, and it is for this reason that groups and individuals belonging to different cultures will differ mentally from one another. Our physical structure would not have varied substantially from our parental ethnic type because it was genetically determined by our present parents, but our culutral equipment would have been that of an Australian aboriginal. Why? Because culture, and by culture is to be understood socially transmitted social behavior and all its products, is something one acquires by experience, unlike one's physical characters, which one acquires through the action, for the most part, of inherited genes; and the culture of individuals, as of groups, will differ according to the kind of experience which they have undergone. We have every reason to believe that the culture of different peoples, as of different individuals, is practically entirely a reflection of their past history or experience.

If this is true then it constitutes a very hopeful discovery for mankind, for we have not had much success in controlling the genes, and there is no great prospect that we shall be able to do so very much better in the immediate future, nor can we change those of individuals now alive. But we can change the cultural organization of a group or of an individual, and by this means bring about the changes we desire.

All learned activities are culturally, and not biologically, determined, whether those activities are based upon basic needs or traditional practices. The generalized urges which all human beings in common inherit continue to be present in all human beings in all cultures, but how these urges are permitted to operate, and how they are satisfied, is something which is determined by tradition, and varies not only in different cultures but in different groups within the same culture. For example, one of the fundamental urges which we all inherit is the urge to eat. Now, different human groups, to whom the same foodstuffs may, or may not, be available, not only eat different foods, but prepare them in ways peculiar to themselves, and consume them with or without implements in a variety of different styles, usually for no better reason than that it is the customary practice to do so. The potentiality of speech is genetically determined, but what language we shall speak and how we shall speak it, is determined entirely by what we hear in the culture in which we have been conditioned or culturalized. Human beings everywhere, when they are tired, experience a desire to rest, to sit down or to sleep, but the manner in which they do all these things is culturally determined by the custom of the group in which they live. Many other instances will doubtless occur to the reader's mind. The important point to grasp here is that even our fundamental biological urges are culturally controlled and regulated or culturalized, and their very form and expression, not to mention their satisfaction, molded according to the dictates of tradition.

Different cultures are really the expression of different isolate effects, differences in experience determined by limiting factors such as physical, geographic, and social barriers. Since this is so, the concept of cultural relativity applies here, that is to say, all cultures, and cultural achievements, must be judged in relation to their own cultural history, and definitely not by the arbitrary standard of any single culture such, for example, as our own.

Judged in relation to its own history each culture is seen as the resultant of the responses to the conditions which that history may or may not record. If these conditions have been many and complex in character, then so will the culture be. Culture is essentially a relation which is the product of the interaction of two correlates, the one a plastic, sensitive biological being, the other simply—experience. If we agree that mankind is everywhere plastic, adaptable, and sensitive, then the mental and cultural differences which exist between different groups of mankind can be accounted for on the basis of a difference in experience. And this, when everything is taken into consideration, seems to be a reasonably satisfactory explanation of the mental and cultural differences which exist between the ethnic groups of man. However, the possibility remains that genetic factors may play a more important role in producing such differences than we at present understand.

One or two examples of the isolate effect and of cultural relativity, as it were, in action, may be given here.

Four thousand years before the birth of Christ the peoples of Europe were living in a Mesolithic or at best Early Neolithic phase of cultural development, whereas at this period the civilization of the Egyptians, as represented by the Old Kingdom (IV-VI dynasties, 4000-3335 B.C.), had reached one of its most splendid periods. Six thousand years ago and less the peoples of these great cultures could have looked upon the Europeans as savages comparable to beasts and by nature completely incapable of civilization—and hence, better exterminated lest they pollute the blood of their superiors! Whatever sins the Europeans have since committed, they have at least shown that given a sufficient amount of time and experience they were capable of cultural development not less than that to which the peoples of the early kingdoms of Egypt attained.

Here we have an example of cultural relativity. If we use time as our framework of reference and say "The Egyptians have had a much longer time than we in which to develop as far as we have culturally—why haven't they?" the answer is that time is not a proper measure to apply to the development of culture or cultural events; it is only a convenient framework from which to observe their development. Cultural changes which, among some peoples, have taken centuries to produce, are among other peoples often produced within a few years. The rate of cultural change is dependent upon a multiplicity of different conditions, but the one indispensable and necessary condition for the production of cultural change is the irritation produced by the stimulus of new experiences. Without the irritation of such new experience cultural change is exceedingly slow. Hence, if new experience is the chief determinant of cultural change, then the yardstick by which we may most efficiently judge cultures is that of the history of the experience which has fallen to the lot of the cultures observed. In other words, to evaluate cultural events properly one must judge them by the measure of experience viewed through the framework of time. We, of the Western world, have packed more varieties of experience into the past two thousand years than has probably fallen to the lot of the Australian aborigines, and other peoples, throughout their entire history. Hence, any judgments of value we may attempt to make as between our own culture and that of other peoples will be quite invalid unless those judgments are made in terms of experience.

If, then, the essential physical differences between the ethnic groups of mankind are largely limited to adaptive characters such as skin color, hair form, and nose form, while the cultural and mental differences are due principally to differences in experience, then from the socio-biological standpoint all the ethnic groups of mankind must be adjudged as, at least, potentially more or less equal.

All normal human beings are everywhere born as culturally indifferent animals, and they become culturally differentiated according to the social group into which they happen to be born. Some of the culturally differentiating media are neither as complex nor as advanced as others; the individuals developed within them will be culturally the products of their cultural group. As individuals they can no more be blamed or praised for belonging to their particular cultural group than an individual can either be blamed or praised for being born into a particular class in the social group. Culture, the culture of any group, is more or less determined by accidental factors which the group, as a group, has usually done little to bring about. The more advanced cultures have merely been luckier in the breadth and variety of their experience, in their contacts, than the less advanced cultures. By the pure accident of geographical locality, rather than by the amount of time they have had at their disposal, and by the accidents of history, the peoples of Europe have found themselves in the very center of the maelstrom of cultural development. Experiencing the fertilizing effects of the various cross-currents of different seminal cultures to which they have been exposed, the cultures of Western Europe, for example, could hardly have avoided advancing beyond the state of development of many other cultures which have, in comparison, remained relatively isolated from such stimulating effects. Let it be remembered that man is the creature who transmutes accidents into opportunities, but that in order for him to be able to do so he must fall heir to a fair share of accidents.

Much as physical variability is limited and reduced by isolation, so is cultural variability limited and reduced by isolation, while the removal of the isolating barriers produces exactly the opposite effect.

FOR FURTHER READING, CONSULT:

BENEDICT, R.: *Race: Science and Politics.* New York, Viking, 1943.
A valuable analysis of racism.

BERRILL, N. J.: *Man's Emerging Mind.* New York, Dodd, Mead Co., 1955.
A delightful and brilliantly written book on the evolution of man, by a distinguished biologist.

BOAS, F.: *The Mind of Primitive Man.* New York, Macmillan, 1938.
A book which covers almost the whole field of anthropology in brief compass, stimulating, sound, and indispensable.

————: Racial purity. *Asia, 40*:231-234, 1940.
Possibly the best demolition of the idea of "racial purity" ever written.

————: *Race, Language and Culture.* New York, Macmillan, 1940.
Containing most of Boas's fundamental papers. A treasure-house of unequalled value.

————: *Race and Democratic Society.* New York, Augustin, 1945.
An important selection of Boas's papers on race.

DICE, L. R.: *Man's Nature and Nature's Man.* Ann Arbor, Michigan, University of Michigan Press, 1955.
A stimulating study of the interrelationship of man and his communities, of his plant and animal associates, and how they act upon one another. The dnyamics of human populations.

HARDIN, G.: *Nature and Man's Fate.* New York, Rinehart, 1959.
A brilliant book on evolutionary theory and the dynamics of human evolution.

HONIGMANN, J. J.: *Culture and Personality.* New York, Harper, 1954.
An excellent account of the manner in which culture acts to influence the development of behavior.

————: *The World of Man.* New York, Harper, 1959.
A most comprehensive and informative work on general anthropology.

KROEBER, A. L. and KLUCKHOHN, C.: Culture: A Critical Review of Concepts and Definitions. *Papers of the Peabody Museum of American Archaeology and Ethnology,* Harvard University, 47:viii-223, 1952.
An historical analysis of the development of the concept of culture. Unique and invaluable.

LINTON, R.: *The Cultural Background of Personality.* New York, 1945.
A brilliant work.

METTLER, F.: *Culture and The Structural Evolution of the Neural System.* James Arthur Lecture, New York, American Museum of Natural History, 1956.
A most stimulating study.

MONTAGU, M. F. ASHLEY: *The Direction of Human Development.* New York, Harper, 1955.
On the nature of human nature.

————: *Anthropology and Human Nature.* Boston, Porter Sargent, 1957.
See especially the essay "The young of human kind."

————: *The Biosocial Nature of Man.* New York, Grove Press, 1956.
A short book on man as "a political animal."

ROE, A. and SIMPSON, G. G. (editors): *Behavior and Evolution.* New Haven, Yale University Press, 1958.
Behavior in animals and man considered from the evolutionary standpoint.

SPUHLER, J. N. (editor): The evolution of man's capacity for culture. *Human Biology*, 31:1-73, 1959.

A stimulating symposium.

THOMAS, JR., W. L. (editor): *Man's Role in Changing the Face of the Earth.* Chicago, University of Chicago Press, 1956.

A magnificent symposium.

TURNER, R.: *The Great Cultural Traditions.* 2 vols., New York, McGraw-Hill, 1941.

Two volumes which mark a new departure in the writing of ancient history, tracing the development of culture and civilization in a manner at once both learned and readable.

WALLIS, W. D.: *Culture and Progress.* New York, Whittlesey House, 1930.

A valuable examination of the nature of culture and culture change, and the criteria of progress.

WHITE, L. A.: *The Science of Culture.* New York, Farrar, Straus & Co., 1949.

An original and provocative study of the concepts of culture.

————: *The Evolution of Culture.* New York, McGraw-Hill, 1959.

On the origin, evolution, and development of culture.

————: *The Concept of Culture.* Am. Anthropol., n.s. 61:227-251, 1959.

The best and most illuminating definition of the concept of culture.

Chapter IX

HEREDITY AND THE INFLUENCE OF THE ENVIRONMENT UPON MAN

THUS far we have considered mankind in various groups and as a whole, in the present chapter we shall consider man as a person, and we shall seek to determine what relation exists between heredity and environment in determining his physical development. We have already discussed this relation with respect to the mental and cultural development of mankind.

THE TWIN METHOD OF STUDYING THE EFFECTS OF HEREDITY AND ENVIRONMENT

Twins have been used as a favorable means of investigating the relative effects of environment and of heredity upon the physical and mental development of the individual. It was Francis Galton who first pointed out the value of this method. "Twins" he wrote "have a special claim upon our attention; it is that their history affords a means of distinguishing between the effects of tendencies received at birth and of those that were imposed by the special circumstances of their after-lives." [1]

It was Galton, in fact, who first committed the error into which many students of twins have since fallen, namely, the error of assuming that all likenesses exhibited by twins are genetically determined, while most of the differences which they exhibit are environmental in origin.

With respect to monozygotic twins, i.e., "identical twins," originating from the same ovum, there can be not the slightest doubt that the physical likenesses are due to a fundamental genetic likeness, and there can also be little doubt that many of the mental likenesses are due to the same cause. There can, however, be equally little doubt that many of the mental likenesses, as well as the differences, are due to environmental factors.

The cliché "identical twins" used as a synonym for monozygotic twins is an unsatisfactory one for the reason that monozygotic twins

---

[1] Francis Galton, *Inquiries Into Human Faculty and its Development*, London, 1883.

are rarely, if ever, identical. Prenatal differences in blood supply, position, pressure, etc., generally produce effects which in many ways serve to produce a differential effect upon each twin. As Newman, Freeman, and Holzinger write, "General biological facts suggest that . . . prenatal conditions produce differences of significant magnitude in the personal characteristics of identical twins and possibly, therefore, in the organic substrate of mental abilities and personality. For example, identical-twin embryos differ more in size than do fraternal-twin embryos, and identical twins differ as much as fraternal twins, i.e., dizygotic twins, derived from separate ova at birth. The prenatal mortality rate of identical twins is several times as high as that of fraternal twins, and very frequently one member of an identical-twin pair dies before birth, showing symptoms of injury from lack of nutrition. There is an exchange of blood supply between identical-twin fetuses which frequently produces an imbalance in blood exchange to the disadvantage of one twin. Conjoined twins (Siamese twins) show marked differences in height, weight, features, and intelligence. The differences between completely separated identical twins may have the same origin as these differences. These considerations predispose the biologist to attribute to prenatal factors the predominant share in the causation of differences between identical twins reared together."

From fertilization on, small changes may occur in the egg which will affect the development of various characters. The inner environment because of random variation may have different effects in different parts of the embryo. Indeed, as Dahlberg has pointed out, small purely accidental variations in the environment of the egg and in the embryo can have a decisive effect. The characteristics of a fully grown individual can therefore be said to depend not only on inheritance and environment, but also on pure chance.

Thus, it is seen that during prenatal development environmental factors are already producing different effects upon originally genetically identical organisms. It is therefore an error to assume that at birth monozygotic twins are "identical." The effects of prenatal environmental factors upon the operation of the genetic system in organizing indifferent tissue may be, and probably often is, considerable. Such differences not only express themselves in physical characteristics, but may also be expressed, as Newman and his co-workers suggest, in the organic substrate of mental abilities and personality. While some of the physical and mental differences between identical twins probably arise in this manner, there is reason to doubt the soundness of attributing "to prenatal factors the dominant share in the causation of differences between identical twins, reared together." This may be so in many cases but it need not be so in all.

We may accept the important rôle played by prenatal factors in producing differences between monozygotic twins reared either apart or together, but it should be quite obvious that when we find that monozygotic twins reared apart exhibit greater differences than those reared together, the greater difference is most probably due to the difference in environment. This is abundantly proven by the findings of Newman, Freeman, and Holzinger, to the effect that "educational and social changes in environment are effective in producing variations in such traits as intelligence and school achievement. Some slight change is also suggested in the case of temperament. Variations in physical environment are responsible for changes in weight and, again, to some extent in temperament." They add, "The analysis indicates that the rôle of heredity and environment in producing twin differences is a function of the type of environment. . . . From the viewpoint of the educator it is important to note that extreme differences in educational and social environment are accompanied by significant changes in intelligence and educational achievement as measured by our tests."

The organism, which is always the solution of the heredity-environment equation, will vary as the terms of this equation vary. Where one of the terms, heredity, is relatively constant, as in monozygotic twins, while the other term, environment, is variable, the differences in the result of the equation must for the most part be attributed to the environmental factors, prenatal and postnatal.

Stated very simply, the individual is the expression of five interacting and interdependent fundamental factors: (1) a system of genetic relations, (2) a system of developmental relationships influenced by the maternal uterine environment, (3) family environment, (4) general socio-economic environment, and (5) general physical environment. If, as is necessary, one is to evaluate the relative importance of these factors it can be laid down as a general principle that the environmental factors produce the most important effects upon the mentality of the organism. Whatever the action of the environmental factors may be the organism will always develop, in general, according to the basic "pattern" determined by the genetic system. But that basic structure can be taken very much for granted; what is important—and vastly more important—is the regulation and filling-in of the details of that "pattern." This is where the environmental factors play their important rôle. It may not be possible to make a silk purse out of a sow's ear, but by sufficiently depressing the quality of the environmental factors it is possible to make a sow's ear out of materials which, under the proper conditions, could have been woven into a silk purse.

In an investigation of the temperament of monozygotic twins, Cattell and Molteno found that in the factors of temperament tested, such as fluency of association, perseveration, and surgency (quickness, cleverness, wit), environment played a more important part than heredity. For fluency of association and, they presume, surgency, "environment is about eight times as efficacious as heredity in the production of the mean differences between children of the same family and five times as important in accounting for variance within the family."

These conclusions are of the first importance because hitherto even the most extreme environmentalists were ready to admit that temperament was for the most part germinally determined. One may still believe that this is so, but in the light of recent psychodynamic studies an important modification in this belief must be made, namely, that environment plays a much more important part in determining temperament than has hitherto been supposed.

Monozygotic twins are in every respect more alike than are any other kinds of siblings, and it must be assumed that in the organic substrates of mind they are similarly more alike. Evidence in support of this is, in fact, to be found in the studies of the brain waves taken with the electroencephalograph on twins; in identical twins these waves follow an almost identical course. Nevertheless, whether they are reared together or apart, monozygotic twins are always characterized by mental differences of varying magnitudes, and these differences, recent researches indicate, are to a large extent to be attributed to environmental factors. As Newman and co-workers conclude, "We feel in sympathy with Professor H. S. Jenning's dictum that what heredity can do environment can also do."

Tests on identical twins reared apart from each other indicate that country life has a less stimulating effect upon intellectual development than urban life, the urban reared twin being invariably ahead in this respect of his rural bred twin. Such studies demonstrate that educational advantages have a marked effect on the qualities of intelligence which it is possible to measure. Such findings by no means underestimate the importance of heredity. They succeed rather in clarifying the important rôle which it plays, and at the same time bring out and emphasize the significance of appreciable differences in the environment for the development of the individual's innate potentialities. As Woodworth has recently pointed out, "When individuals of identical heredity are subjected to environments differing about as much as those of the children in an ordinary community, such identical twins differ much less than the children of such a community. Therefore the differences found among the children of an ordinary community are not accounted for, except in small measure, by differences in homes and schooling."

In other words, heredity would appear to play a considerable part in determining the individual's response to his environment. We arrive then, at the conclusion that *environment provides the opportunities for the development of innate potentialities which are limited by heredity.* For all practical purposes, however, it may be said that the limits of heredity can only be reached in an environment which is itself unlimited, in the sense of affording unrestricted opportunities for development to the individual. This, in fact, has rarely occurred. As Thorndike put it many years ago, "To the real work of man for man,—the increase of achievement through improvement of the environment,—the influence of heredity offers no barrier."

The study of "foster children" again serves to emphasize the importance of the rôle played by environment in shaping the intelligence, personality, and social qualities of the subject. The limiting factors of heredity are clearly brought out in these studies, but at the same time it is demonstrated that the environment is, all things considered, a most important factor in the development of the (limited) hereditary powers.

CRIMINALITY IN TWINS

If heredity has anything whatever to do with behavior, one-egg twins should be very much alike in behavior, at least significantly more so than two-egg twins. Several investigators have recently occupied themselves with the study of the concordance of criminal behavior in one-egg twins as compared with two-egg twins. When both members of a twin pair were found to be similar with respect to the commission of one or more crimes, they were termed "concordant"; when dissimilar, that is, when one was found to have committed a crime and the other not, they were termed "discordant." In Table XLIV are summarized the findings of one American and four European investigators on such adult twins.

From this table it will be seen that of 104 pairs of one-egg twins

TABLE XLIV

CRIMINAL BEHAVIOR OF TWINS

Author	One-Egg Twins		Two-Egg Twins	
	Concordant	Discordant	Concordant	Discordant
Lange (1929)	10	3	2	15
Legras (1932)	4	0	0	5
Kranz (1936)	20	12	23	20
Stumpfl (1936)	11	7	7	12
Rosanoff (1934)	25	12	5	23
Total	70	34	37	75
Per Cent	67.3	32.7	33.0	67.0

examined, 70 were concordant and 34 were discordant. The concordant were almost exactly twice as numerous as the discordant pairs. On the other hand, the two-egg twins showed a discordance almost exactly twice as great as the concordance shown in this group of 112 pairs. These are impressive figures, but what do they mean? Newman, the latest writer on this subject, and our leading authority on twinning, believes that these figures prove "beyond question that hereditary factors bulk large among the causes of criminal behavior." This is the opinion of all the investigators mentioned, but in reality such studies do not prove, but only suggest, a connection between hereditary factors and criminal behavior. The following comment by Newman, who has perhaps observed more twins than anyone else living, is to the point here, he writes:

"The only serious criticism I have known to be aimed at the twin method of studying the factors of crime is that one-egg twins far more than two-egg twins are close companions in their social activities and are therefore more likely to encounter together such social influences as might lead to criminal behavior. This is one more instance of lack of control features in nature's scientific experiments, for it can hardly be maintained that the social environment of two-egg pairs is as closely similar as that of one-egg pairs. Therefore, environmental similarities may to some extent account for the close concordance in crime of one-egg twins, while lack of any such similarity in environment may to an equal extent account for lack of concordance in crime of two-egg twins. Undoubtedly the study of crime by means of the twin method is less simple than it seemed at the outset."

This is, of course, the crucial point. The factor of environment has been virtually completely omitted from these studies of criminal behavior in twins. Hence, the attribution of the behavior of such twins to hereditary factors may possibly be written off as yet another illustration of the fallacy of *false cause*.

Since heredity is supposed to play no significant rôle in the case of the two-egg twins, if the hereditary theory is to be consistent, the proportion of two-egg twins who are both affected should be lower than the proportion of one-egg twins where only one is affected; for one would expect the hereditary factor to be so much stronger in the one-egg twins. The actual proportions, however, are almost identical, being 33.0 per cent for two-egg concordance, and 32.7 per cent for one-egg discordance. Furthermore, as Reckless has pointed out, "If biological determination of destiny is correct, a discordant monozygotic one-egg twin set should be impossible, whereas discordant dizygotic two-egg sets should be frequent." The actual findings, however, reveal that one-third of the one-egg pairs of twins investigated were discordant. Why did not the hereditary factor for crime declare itself in the other one of the pairs of this one-third of single-egg twins? If the answer is that an environmental factor was probably operative in these cases, a factor which was absent in the case of the criminal sibling, then the theory of the hereditary cause of crime collapses beyond repair; for it then becomes obvious that it was the absence of such environmental factors, or the presence of others, that was the one indispensable condition in the causation of the criminal behavior!

It appears then, that just as it takes environmental conditions to activate, to organize, and to produce a mind, so, too, does it take environmental conditions to organize the hereditarily determined elements of the nervous system to develop and function, or not, in ways which society terms "criminal." There is not the slightest evidence which would lead one to believe that anyone ever inherits a tendency to commit criminal acts. On the other hand, the evidence points overwhelmingly to the fact that criminal acts, and crime as a whole, are largely determined by social conditions, and not by biological ones.

Suicide is, in all occidental societies, regarded as a crime, *felo de se* or self-murder. If the tendency to commit criminal acts is in any way inborn then this crime should occasionally occur in identical twins. A recent investigation by Kallman and Anastasio demonstrates, on the contrary, "that except for rare suicide pacts self-destruction does not seem to occur in both members of twin pairs, even if the twins are alike in type of personality, cultural setting, social frustration, and depressive features of a psychosis." Clearly the discordance of suicide in monozygotic twins is evidence of the preponderant influence of environmental rather than genetic factors in producing self-destruction.

CONSTITUTION AND CRIME

The late Professor E. A. Hooton was among the more recent investigators of the relation between crime and the physical characters exhibited by the individual. Hooton's findings led him to assert that "whatever the crime may be, it ordinarily arises from a deteriorated organism. . . . You may say that this is tantamount to a declaration that the primary cause of crime is biological inferiority—and that is exactly what I mean."

This, it will be recalled, was the view of the Italian school of criminologists led by Cesare Lombroso. The errors committed by this school, and by the students of criminality in twins already discussed were recommitted by Hooton. Hooton's first report was based on the examination of 4,212 native-born white prisoners of Old American stock, and 313 native white civilians. Unlike Lombroso, Hooton did not set out with any preconceived notions concerning the nature of physical marks of inferiority, but was content to allow the greater frequency with which certain physical characters occurred in his criminal series as compared with his civilian series to indicate these. Thus, he wrote, "if we find felons to manifest physical differences from civilians, we are justified in adjudging as undesirable biological characters those which are associated in the organism with anti-social behavior. . . . It is the organic complex which must be estimated inferior or superior on the basis of the type of behavior emanating from such a combination of parts functioning as a unit."

An analysis of the characters studied by Hooton in the light of the biological standards of what are generally accepted to be "advanced," "indifferent," and "primitive," human characters, yields interesting results. By such standards we find that Hooton's criminal series show, for the combined anthropometric, indicial, and morphological characters, only 4 per cent of primitive, 15.8 per cent of indifferent, and the astonishing amount of 49.5 per cent of *advanced* characters, more frequently than the non-criminal sample.

By biological standards Hooton's criminal series would, on the whole, appear to be superior to his non-criminal series! Whatever such a finding may mean, the fact is that Hooton did not draw his criminal and non-criminal series from the same local, social, economic, and occupational levels of the population, and furthermore, almost half his check sample was drawn from 146 Nashville firemen; in an occupation for which, Hooton observes, "the physical qualifications are rather stringent."

In order to make any biological test of differential behavior, it is necessary that both the criminal series and the check non-criminal series be in every respect similar except in the one condition of behavior. The two series must be drawn from the same population or populations, from the same areas, and must come from the same social, economic, and occupational levels. When these requirements have been satisfied, and a significantly higher frequency of certain physical characters is found among the criminals than among the non-criminals, it may be legitimately inferred that there is some significant *association* between criminal behavior and the presence of a high frequency of such characters in an individual or in a group. But to infer from this that such characters reflect the cause of criminal behavior is to misunderstand the nature of causation.

In his investigation Hooton did not satisfy the requirement of equating the conditions of his two groups in all but those in which they were being compared, and he did fall into the error of taking a statistical association to be a cause.

Crime is the resultant of a complex of factors which there is very good reason to believe has but little, if any, relation to genetic or constitutional factors, and every relation to social ones. It is certain kinds of social organization which make for the production of criminals, not certain kinds of genes. The genetic potentialities of all persons under certain social conditions are capable of being made to function in a criminal manner. Just as genes do not cause a majority of Chinese in the United States to become laundrymen, so genes do not cause certain individuals to become criminals, in both cases it is a special pattern of socio-economic conditions which must be regarded as the principal causative factor.

Constitution. The subject of human constitution has been of interest to men from the earliest times, and most people still tend to see in the physical appearance of the individual clues to his functional character. That there exists some relationship between the body habitus of an individual and his functional character seems probable, and in the last quarter of a century a considerable amount of work has been done in the hope of throwing some light upon the nature of this relationship.

Constitution may be defined as the sum total of the structural, functional and psychologic characters of the individual. It is in large part determined by heredity but influenced in varying degrees by environmental factors. It fluctuates in varying degrees over a wide range of normality and occasionally crosses an arbitrary boundary into abnormality or pathology.

The problem in studying constitution is to analyze and define the relations of its component parts in the individual, and its ultimate goal is the development of a constitutional typology which will allow, on the basis of certain measurements, the classification of individuals into constitutional types. This is obviously an exteremely difficult problem, and although much work has been done in this field, the study of constitution is still in its very early beginnings, while the relationships it seeks to discover and elucidate are still largely in the realm of unsolved problems.

In 1921 the German psychiatrist, Ernst Kretschmer, described three morphologic constitutional types, the *pyknic, athletic,* and *asthenic,* and discussed the relation of normal and abnormal types of mind to each of them. He found that manic-depressive psychoses were predominantly associated with the pyknic habitus (stocky, well-padded, compact), while the asthenic habitus (tall, lean) was predominantly associated with schizophrenia. In general the relation has not been confirmed by independent investigators, but the Kretschmerian method of typing is scarcely refined enough since it deals in rather extreme types. The principal fault with most constitutional typologies has been that they have approached the individual as if he were constituted of one piece. Desiring to give a description of the organism as a whole, students of constitution have erroneously assumed that the organism should be measured as a whole. This is a pre-Mendelian method of observing morphologic facts. Human structure is not transmitted as a single morphologic block but as a large variety of distinct units or components in interrelation. Interrelation of these distinct components together forms the complex whole, the morphologic habitus. Because these components are the expression of the modified action of different groups of genes on different autosomes, their varieties and combinations in forming a morphologic whole are practically unlimited. Hence, any attempt to describe morphologic types on the basis of the gross description of the organism as a whole is foredoomed to failure. Certainly the individual must be studied as a whole, but the description of that whole can satisfy scientific requirements only when the component parts which enter into its formation are analyzed and their interrelations properly understood.

The method of somatotyping developed by W. H. Sheldon during the last twenty years, though more elaborate and ambitious than previous attempts, has proved even less satisfactory than these earlier adventures in fixing the elusive relationship between body and mind. Sheldon's constitutional method turns out to resemble the phrenology of an earlier day, except that in Sheldon's somatotyping the body as a whole has its bumps, so to speak felt, rather than the head alone.

Physique and Temperament. Quantitative studies have again and again demonstrated that the relationships between physical traits and temperament which are popularly believed to exist do not, in fact, exist. Blondes and brunettes are not temperamentally distinguishable, height, weight, length or breadth, shape of skull, cranial capacity, skin color, or any other physical trait has never been shown to have any connection with temperament or intellect. It would seem that the genetic determinants of temperament are quite independently inherited of those which determine the traits of the body. This is not to say that the possession of certain physical traits may not *socially* condition the behavior of the person. Being a person of color in the United States or the Union of South Africa is an obvious association having marked effects upon behavior in such persons. In societies in which physical beauty is highly valued the homely person is likely to exhibit certain behavioral traits which are the effects of frustration and insecurity. Psychosomatic medicine has revealed the profound effects which the psyche may have upon somatic processes and *vice versa*, and that, indeed, the psyche and the soma are but different aspects of the functioning of the same thing, the organism as a whole. Let any part of the organism be affected and the whole is more or less affected, and at the same time the whole organism affects the part. Genetic, physiological, psychological, and enviornmental factors of various sorts, enter into the total pattern, and the rôle which each plays must be carefully assessed in considering the status of the organism at any one time. Temperament is a labile system of potentialities which is markedly affected by environmental conditions, and while it is possible to classify temperaments, it is another thing to understand the nature of their determinants.

Factor Analysis. Another method of approaching the problem of body form and behavior is that of factor analysis. In factor analysis the object is to simplify the description of the data by reducing the number of variables which will provide the fewest differentia covering the widest number of attributes. In factorial constitutional studies one begins with a correlation matrix, that is, a table of intercorrelations among a set of measurements, and one ends with a factor matrix, that is, a table showing the weight or loading of each of the factors in each of the measurements or group of related measurements. In this way one obtains factors for a number of traits of a person which may be directly compared with the factors similarly derived from the measurements of other persons. Most promising in this field is the work of W. W. Howells.

It is important to understand that constitution, body-type, and inheritance are not the same things. Constitution is the aggregate of characters, structural, functional, and mental of the individual, which are in part determined by genes and in part by environment. Obviously, then, constitution embraces both inheritance and body-type. Inheritance is the total genetic endowment with which the individual is born; body-type is one expression of that genetic endowment in interaction with the environment. It should be clear that useful knowledge of the relationship of constitution to temperament and to disease will require the tracking down of alleles, and that body-type short cuts will not suffice.

To conclude, then, thus far all attempts to establish an integral relationship between traits of the body and behavior have failed. The problem, however, is still in its exploratory stage of development. Success, if it is ever achieved, will undoubtedly prove to be so in a statistical sense, that is to say, that some correlations between traits may be found which will allow prediction only within fairly wide limits.

CONSTITUTION AND DISEASE

Much evidence exists which indicates that susceptibility to certain diseases is associated with constitutional factors. But the briefest of surveys of this association can be attempted here. The association is dealt with in several recent volumes fairly exhaustively.

Tuberculosis. Much evidence is now available which points to a high correlation between susceptibility to all forms of tuberculosis and the tall-thin, leptosomic, asthenic or ectomorphic habitus. Petersen has even argued that freedom from tuberculosis depends on natural resistance and not on acquired immunity. The importance of the constitutional factor is well illustrated by the practically identical course which the disease follows in monozygotic twins. It often happens, however, that tuberculosis affects only one of a pair of monozygotic twins. An important fact, since it shows that the constitutional factor is only in part associated with the development of the disease. When only one twin develops the disease the prognosis is good for the affected twin. The affected twin, it is presumed, has succumbed despite a relatively high resistance. In redheads and persons with freckles tuberculosis tends to follow a stormier course than in other complexioned individuals.

Gastro-Intestinal Disease. Most investigators have found a high correlation between the asthenic habitus and diseases of the gastro-intestinal tract. Diseases of the gall-bladder, however, appear to be closely associated with the thick, stocky build, while the ulcer type is more generally asthenic. Peptic ulcer patients have longer and thinner necks than patients with gall-ladder disease. In persons showing a mixture of feminine and masculine features (gynandromorphy) gastric ulcer appears to be conspicuously absent.

Arthritis. Osteo-arthritis appears to be significantly associated with the endomorphic pyknic habitus, while rheumatoid arthritis has a tendency to be associated with the mesomorphic athletic types.

Heart Disease. When valvular diseases of the heart follow rheumatic fever and other infectious diseases, tall thin individuals are most often the victims. For other forms of heart disease the evidence indicates a correlation with mesomorphy.

Infantile Paralysis. Draper first revealed the existence of a constitutional factor in susceptibility to infantile paralysis. Among susceptibles there is a lack of coordination between growth and development, expressed in a tendency to overgrowth and retarded development. Susceptible children often present a facial appearance, marked by the following characters: persistent epicanthic fold, excessive inter-inner canthus space, relatively flat nasal root, large central incisors and central incisor spacing, long curved eyelashes and pigment spots. These individuals are generally endomorphic mesomorphs or mesomorphic endomorphs. Addair and Snyder have recently provided suggestive evidence of the genetic susceptibility, of some family lines at any rate, to poliomyelitis. The pedigrees analysed suggest an autosomal recessive gene, showing about 70 per cent penetrance.

Diabetes. In diabetes mellitus two morphologic types have been recognized: one mostly associated with pancreatic diabetes, and the other with diabetes of pituitary origin. Persons with the former tend to be predominantly endomorphic, while those with the latter tend to fall into intermediate and linear groups.

Menstrual Disturbances. Bayer has shown that virile and hypo-feminine women are subject to amenorrhea (abnormal stoppage of the menses), hyperfeminine women tend to have disturbances in menstrual rhythm and flow, while feminine types are essentially normal.

Constitutional Factors in Gynecology and Obstetrics. "It is well known that red-haired women frequently have a postpartum hemorrhage even though the delivery was spontaneous and skillfully managed" (Gellhorn). Such observations have impressed some obstetricians with the importance of the constitutional factor in influencing the character of the various functions subserving the reproductive processes. Familial icterus (hemolytic jaundice), toxemia of pregnancy, difficult labor, infant mortality, and many other obstetric complications are suspected, in many cases, to have an underlying constitutional cause or to be associated with body type. Seibert, for example, has shown that there are certain constitutional differences between mothers who had some infant deaths (infants under one year) and mothers whose reproductive histories showed no infant deaths. In 262 cases investigated, mothers who had experienced infant mortality among their offspring were, on the average, shorter in stature and related measurements than mothers with no infant mortality. The mean girth measurements were greater than in the nonmortality group. In body habitus the former tended towards the pyknic, the latter towards the asthenic. The asthenic character in the former was especially marked in the trunk and legs.

Longevity. Possibly the most complete demonstration of the relationship of a measurable functional character to the rate and character of aging is Bernstein's proof that early onset of longsightedness (presbyopia, due to a loss of elasticity of the crystalline lens) indicates early death by senile degeneration.

Another functional characteristic, in itself complex, with which duration of life is highly correlated, is what Pearl has called the rate of living. Length of life is generally in inverse proportion to rate of living. The more rapid the pace of living, the shorter the time that life endures. To a large extent rate of living is determined by constitutional factors, but the regulation of the rate of living is to a certain degree within the power of the individual. Pearl has shown that heredity plays an important part in the determination of human longevity. The interesting question from the constitutional standpoint is whether there are any measurable morphologic or physiologic characters which in the healthy individual would indicate his probable span of life. Pearl and Moffett found, indeed, that in individuals measured when in good health who eventually died of heart or kidney diseases, average minimal chest girth on expiration and maximal chest girth on inspiration were greater in short-lived than in long-lived individuals. In all girths and in body weight, persons destined to die of diabetes on the average exceed persons in normal and most other disease groups.

Regarding body habitus, the short-lived who die of heart or kidney diseases tend to be more frequently pyknic than otherwise, while the short-lived who die of cancer and pneumonia tend to be of intermediate type in the direction of the asthenic habitus.

In all the series studied by Pearl and Moffett, including diseases of the heart and circulatory system, nephritis and other kidney affections, cancer, pneumonia (all forms), accident, and diabetes, the mean pulse rate was higher in the short-lived than in the long-lived group. Mean pulse rate (beats per minute) in the long-lived group was, in the heart group, for example, 72.85, and in the short-lived group 74.38. Pearl and Moffett remark "It is perhaps not unreasonable to suppose that the heart of the short-lived group of the heart series, for example, that had beat more than 18,246,000 times *more* in the first 41 years of its life than had the heart of the average man in the long-lived group of the same series, would not be likely to last so long thereafter. Many diverse lines of inquiry have led to the conclusion that the duration of life in general varies inversely with the rate of living. The present findings as to the comparative rate of heart beat in the long-lived and the short-lived appear to add further confirmation to this generalization."

The same investigators found in the heart series that the mean systolic (heart contraction) and diastolic (heart dilatation) blood pressures of the short-lived group (134/20) were lower than those of the long-lived group (136/46).

Basal Metabolism. Seltzer has shown that "linear" individuals and those with relatively shorter upper and lower extremities, longer torsos, flatter chest outlines and narrower hips relative to breadth of shoulders, have higher oxygen intakes in the resting state than their "lateral" counterparts. In moderate exercise, greater mechanical efficiency is shown by the laterals, while in exhausting work, greater capacity per kilogram of body weight for supplying oxygen to the tissues is shown by the linears.

Lucas and Pryor found that normal slender-built children generally have higher basal rates than broad-built children of the same age-sex group. For linears, high basal metabolic rates are the rule, and total calories per hour, calories per kilogram body weight per hour and calories per square meter body surface per hour are also higher.

SEX DIFFERENCES IN CONSTITUTION

The differences between males and females are largely determined by those processes and functions which subserve the end of reproduction. Almost all differences between the sexes stem from this primary

TABLE XLV

Mortality Rates From Each Cause by Sex. White Population of
Continental United States Fof the Year 1957
Rates Per 100,000

Cause of Death	Male	Female
Tuberculosis of respiratory system	9.5	3.1
Tuberculosis, other forms	0.5	0.3
Syphilis and its sequelae	2.5	0.9
Virus diseases	1.6	1.5
Malignant neoplasm of buccal cavity and pharynx	5.6	1.5
Malignant neoplasm of digestive organs and peritoneum	59.1	48.3
Malignant neoplasm of respiratory system	36.1	6.3
Malignant neoplasm of breast and genito-urinary organs	28.4	58.2
Malignant neoplasm of other and unspecified sites	17.6	15.0
Neoplasms of lymphatic and hematopoetic tissues	17.2	11.9
Benign neoplasm	1.0	1.6
Neoplasm of unspecified nature	1.7	1.3
Allergic disorders	5.5	2.4
Thyroid diseases	0.2	1.0
Diabetes mellitus	12.9	19.0
Other endocrine gland diseases	0.5	0.5
Avitaminoses and other metabolic diseases	0.8	0.7
Pernicious anemia	0.4	0.5
Hemophilia	0.1	0.0
Psychoses	0.7	0.6
Psychoneurotic disorders	0.0	0.1
Disorders of character, behavior and intelligence	2.1	0.5
Cerebral hemorrhage	63.6	67.9
Meningitis	1.1	0.8
Multiple sclerosis	0.8	1.0
Other diseases of central nervous system	5.4	4.2
Epilepsy	1.3	0.9
Motor neurone disease and muscular atrophy	0.8	0.5
Diseases of ear and mastoid process	0.3	0.2
Rheumatic fever	0.5	0.4
Arteriosclerotic and degenerative heart disease	292.2	242.1
Other diseases of heart	14.4	9.3
Aortic aneurysm, nonsyphilitic	6.4	2.2
Peripheral vascular disease	0.3	0.1
Thrombo-angiitis obliterans	0.2	0.1
Arterial embolism and thrombosis	0.3	0.2
Varicose veins lower extremities	0.1	0.2
Hemorrhoids	0.1	0.0
Varicose veins other sites	0.3	0.1
Influenza	4.2	3.6
Lobar pneumonia	8.8	5.2
Bronchopneumonia	18.0	13.5
Primary atypical pneumonia	2.9	2.2
Pneumonia, other and unspecified	4.0	2.9
Bronchitis	2.8	1.3
Bronchiectasis	1.9	0.9
Stomach ulcer	4.5	1.6
Duodenal ulcer	5.2	1.4
Gastrojejunal ulcer	0.3	0.1
Gastritis and duodenitis	0.2	0.1
Appendicitis	1.5	0.7
Abdominal hernia	2.3	1.9
Gastro-enteritis and colitis	2.1	2.0

TABLE XLV—(continued)

Cause of Death	Male	Female
Chronic enteritis and ulcerative colitis..............	1.7	1.7
Peritonitis..	0.4	0.4
Cirrhosis of liver..................................	15.8	7.5
Cholelithiasis......................................	1.7	2.4
Cholecystitis......................................	0.9	1.2
Other diseases of gallbladder and biliary tracts........	0.5	0.8
Diseases of pancreas...............................	1.6	1.1
Chronic nephritis..................................	6.9	5.7
Hydronephrosis....................................	0.2	0.1
Cystitis...	0.2	0.1
Rheumatoid arthritis...............................	0.4	0.7
Osteitis deformans.................................	0.1	0.0
Myasthenia gravis..................................	0.1	0.2
Inborn defect of muscle.............................	0.5	0.2
Curvature of spine.................................	0.1	0.1
Congenital malformations...........................	13.8	11.5
Intracranial and spinal injury at birth...............	2.7	1.5
Other birth injury.................................	4.9	3.4
Postnatal asphyxia and atelectasis..................	11.9	7.7
Pneumonia of newborn.............................	2.0	1.3
Other diseases peculiar to infancy...................	17.7	12.9

Based on Vital Statistics—Special Reports, National Summaries vol. 50, No. 2, 4 February 1959. U. S. Dept. Health, Education and Welfare, Public Health Service, National Office of Vital Statistics, Washington, D. C.

difference in functional organization. Sex, therefore, is one of the most important elements of constitution, and it begins to exert its effect practically from the moment of conception and continues to the moment of death.

Deaths from almost all causes are more frequent in males at all ages. This is very clearly brought out in Tables XLV and XLVI. Morbidity, the sickness rate, on the other hand, is higher among females than among males. Males are more likely to succumb to diseases from which the female tends to recover, although rates of susceptibility vary at different ages, and certain diseases affect females oftener than males (Table XLVII). It must be emphasized that such sexual differences in susceptibility to disease are markedly influenced by differences in occupation, diet, climate, social rôle and status.

In 1956 the average expectation of life of the female child of white parentage in the United States was a little over 73.7 years, for the male 67.3 years. Since the year 1900 the increase has been 23.7 years for the female and 19.11 years for the male.

In Figures 195 and 196 the life expectancy rates are shown for the 48 States and the District of Columbia of continental United States. These figures will repay study, not so much for any problems they solve, as for the questions they raise. How do such differences come

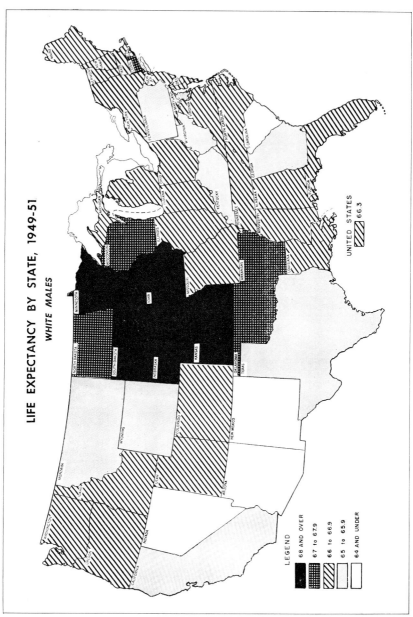

Figure 195. The life expectancy of white males in the United States. (Courtesy, U.S. Public Health Service.)

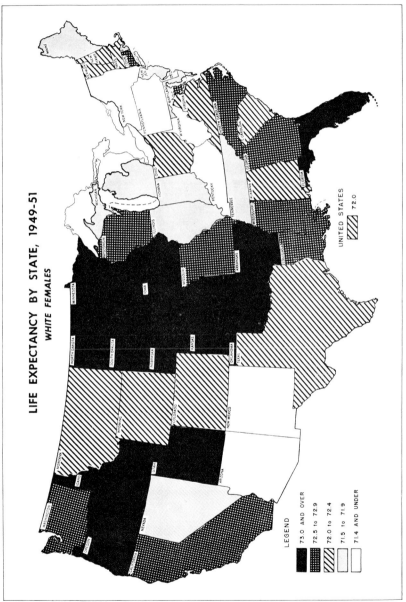

Figure 196. The life expectancy of white females in the United States. (Courtesy, U.S. Public Health Service.)

TABLE XLVI

Sex Differences in Mortality Rates, Whites, United States, 1930
(After Ciocco, 1940)

Death from Disease of Organ System	Occurred More Frequently In
Circulatory, blood	50.2% males
Respiratory	34.2% males
Nervous, sense organs	33.5% males
Alimentary tract	25.6% males
Kidney and excretory	8.9% males
Skin	1.9% males
Skeletal, muscular	0.5% males
Endocrine	13.0% females

about, and why should the differences in life expectancy rates between the sexes be so marked in different States? No one knows the answers, but some fascinating research is indicated. It will be observed that the States with the highest life expectancy rates for white males aggregate in the west north central area, but the females both extend the range and more than double the number of States in which their highest life expectancy rates occur. It would be of great interest to know the nature of the conditions entering into the production of these differences.

If women are biologically stronger and more resistant to disease than men, they are also better shock absorbers, as numerous studies testify. Hysteria occurs more frequently among men than among women. Under heavy bombardment cases of shock and neurosis are far more frequent in the civilian male than in the female population. At all ages suicide rates are much higher among males than females. Epilepsy is much more frequent in males, and stuttering has an incidence of eight males to one female.

To what extent the sexual differences cited are influenced by social factors and to what extent by genetic factors must remain an open question. We know that both types of factors are involved. In recent years it has become increasingly more evident that social factors play a much larger rôle in producing such sexual differences than was previously supposed.

SEX-LINKED, SEX-INFLUENCED, AND SEX-LIMITED GENETIC EFFECTS

The development of traits which are associated in inheritance with sex are of three kinds: (1) sex-linked; (2) sex-influenced; and, (3) sex-limited. When the association is due to a gene lying in the X-chro-

TABLE XLVII

SEXUAL DIFFERENCES IN SUSCEPTIBILITY TO DISEASE

| Males | | Females | |
Diseases	Pre-ponderance	Diseases	Pre-ponderance
Acute pancreatitis	Large majority	Acromegaly	More often
Addison's disease	More often	Arthritis deformans	4.4–1
Amebic dysentery	15–1	Carcinoma of genitalia	3–1
Alcoholism	6–1	Carcinoma of gallbladder	10–1
Angina pectoris	5–1	Cataract	More often
Arteriosclerosis	2.5–1	Chlorosis (anemia)	100%
Bronchial asthma	More often	Chorea	3–1
Cancer buccal cavity	2–1	Chronic mitral	
Cancer G. U. tract	3–1	endocarditis	2–1
Cancer head of pancreas	4.5–1	Combined sclerosis	More often
Cancer respiratory tract	8–1	Diphtheria	Slight
Cancer of skin	3–1	Gall stones	4–1
Cerebral hemorrhage	Greatly	Goiter, exophthalmic	6 or 8–1
C. S. meningitis	Slight	Hemorrhoids	Consid.
Childhood schizophrenia	3–1	Hyperthyroidism	10–1
Chronic glomerular nephritis	2–1	Influenza	2–1
Cirrhosis of liver	3–1	Migraine	6–1
Coronary insufficiency	30–1	Multiple sclerosis	More often
Coronary sclerosis	25–1	Myxedema	6–1
Duodenal ulcer	7–1	Obesity	Consid.
Erb's dystrophy	More often	Osteomalacia	9–1
Gastric ulcer	6–1	Pellagra	Slight
Gout	49–1	Purpura haemorrhagica	4 or 5–1
Heart disease	2–1	Raynaud's disease	1.5–1
Hemophilia	100%	Rheumatoid arthritis	3–1
Hernia	4–1	Rheumatic fever	Consid.
Hodgkin's disease	2–1	Tonsilitis	Slight
Hysteria	2–1	Whooping cough	2–1
Korsakoff's psychosis	2–1	Varicose veins	Consid.
Leukemia	2–1		
Mental deficiencies	2–1		
Muscular dystrophy, Ps.h.	Almost exclusively		
Myocardial degeneration	2–1		
Myocardial infarction	7–1		
Paralysis agitans	Greatly		
Pseudohermaphroditism	10–1		
Sciatica	Greatly		
Scurvy	Greatly		
Syringomyelia	2.3–1		
Tabes	10–1		
Thromboangiitis obliterans	96–1		
Pericarditis	2–1		
Pigmentary cirrhosis	20–1		
Pleurisy	3–1		
Pneumonia	3–1		
Poliomyelitis	Slight		
Progr. muscular paralysis	More often		

TABLE XLVIII

SOME HUMAN TRAITS REPORTED AS DEPENDENT UPON SEX-LINKED GENES
(After Snyder)

(Many of these traits have alternative forms dependent upon autosomal genes, and
some of them are influenced by variations in environment)

Albinism of the eyes	Megalocornea
Alopecia congenita	Microcornea
Anhidrotic ectodermal dysplasia	Microphthalmia
Coloboma iridis	Mitral stenosis
Color-blindness of the red-green type	Myopia
Day blindness	Night blindness
Defective hair follicles	Nomadism
Defective tooth enamel	Nystagmus
Distichiasis (double eyelashes)	Optic atrophy
Epidermal cysts	Peroneal atrophy
Glaucoma of the juvenile type	Pseudohypertrophic muscular dystrophy
Hemophilia	Retinal detachment
Ichthyosis	Thromboasthenia
Keratosis	White occipital lock of hair

mosome it is said to be *sex-linked*. One of man's 23 pairs of chromosomes differs from the remaining 22 pairs (autosomes) in being intimately, though not exclusively, associated with the determination of sex. In the female this pair consists of two equal-sized chromosomes called the X-chromosomes (allosomes), or sex chromosomes. In the male there is also a pair of chromosomes, but only one of these is a full chromosome, and this is an X-chromosome which is exactly the same as the X-chromosomes in the female. The male's second chromosome, however, is appreciably smaller, it is called the Y-chromosome. The Y-chromosome is one-third the size of the X-chromosome, and carries masculine determining factors. It is customary to speak of the X- and Y-chromosomes as sex chromosomes.

Sex-Linked Genes. It will be recalled that the male always receives his X-chromosome from the mother and the Y-chromosome from the father (since the mother has no Y-chromosome), whereas the female receives one X-chromosome from each parent.

Sex-linked genes can be represented on only one chromosome, the X-chromosome in males. Sex-linked genes can be represented on both X-chromosomes in females. From these facts and the fact that almost all sex-linked mutant genes are recessive, it is possible to give specific advice to families known to be carrying such genes. If the men in such a family do not exhibit the trait, and more than 30 such traits have been described (see Table XLVIII), then clearly the genes for it are not present in his X-chromosome, and he cannot therefore transmit the condition to any of his offspring. He may safely have children. An affected father can transmit his affected X-chromosome to his daughters, who will *all* be carriers; since the sons receive only his unaffected Y-chromosome *none* of them will be affected. The sons may safely marry. Some of the sisters who carry the gene in heterozygous form may have affected sons, and so may some of the apparently normal women in the family. A woman cannot be affected unless her father was affected and her mother carried the gene, unless, in other words, the gene was present on her father's X-chromosome and on at least one of her mother's X-chromosomes.

Genes that can cross over from the X- to the Y-chromosome, and vice versa, will be differentially transmitted as to sex. Such genes are known as *incompletely sex-linked*. They may be present in both sex chromosomes of both sexes. They will, therefore, behave similarly to autosomal genes in inheritance, with this difference: About half the families in which the father carries the gene will contain more affected sons and unaffected daughters than would be expected on the basis of autosomal inheritance, while the other half will contain more affected daughters and unaffected sons than would be expected.

Eight traits believed to be due to incompletely sex-linked genes have been described. These are, total color blindness (as opposed to red-green blindness), xeroderma pigmentosum (a skin disease), Oguchi's disease (a type of blindness), spastic paraplegia (a neuromuscular defect), the recessive form of epidermolysis bullosa (malignant skin blisters), the dominant form of retinitis pigmentosum, hereditary hemorrhagic diathesis (a blood abnormality), and a type of cerebral sclerosis (a mental defect).

Sex-influenced Traits. Sex-influenced traits are conditioned by genes carried in the autosomes, and hence are equally inherited and transmitted by both sexes. The gene which is dominant in one sex is recessive or intermediate in the other, and vice versa. Several sex-influenced traits have been described in man, such as one form of white forelock, some cases of absent upper lateral incisor teeth, simple ichthyosis (scaling of skin), and Heberden's nodes (enlargement of terminal joints of fingers). Though baldness has customarily been attributed to sex-influence, it is in fact an example of sex-limitation and not of sex-influence. We shall deal with baldness under sex-limited traits.

An example of a sex-limited trait is provided by a form of white forelock described by Holmes and Schofield in 1917, which appeared in four generations in a family of 32 individuals in 14 males, but was not present in 3 males nor was it present in 15 females. It could be transmitted either through the males or the females and was dominant in males and recessive in females, and hence was sex-influenced.

Sex-limited Traits. When certain traits are expressed in one sex but not in the other they are said to be *sex limited*. Sex-limited characters are conditioned by genes which are carried either on the autosomes or on the sex chromosomes. There are, therefore, many different types of sex-limited heredity. The expression of sex-limited traits depends largely upon the presence or absence of one or more sex hormones, or to put it more accurately, the amount of such hormones present within the organism. Complete sex limitation, that is, complete development of the trait in one sex and complete absence of it in the other sex is not frequent. Examples of complete sex limitation are milk production and menstruation in females but not in males. Another example of such complete sex limitation is the appearance of coarse hairs on the external ear of white men during the process of aging, and the absence of such hairs in women.

Another example, but not so complete, is the presence of a developed beard and mustache in the male and their absence in the female. It has been shown that women have exactly the same number of hairs on the face as men, but the hairs simply do not develop and grow as they do in men. However, under the proper endocrine stimulation with male hormones women are capable of growing fairly respectable beards and mustachios.

A familiar example of sex limitation is baldness. That baldness is not due to a sex linked gene is clear from the fact that bald fathers, depending upon whether they carry two or only one baldness gene, transmit their baldness to all or only half their sons, and it will be remembered that since sex-linked characters are conditioned by those carried in the X-chromosomes, a man cannot transmit X-linked genes to his sons, but only to his daughters in whom they remain recessive. Furthermore, hereditary baldness in the female is extremely rare. In the male baldness in varying degrees occurs in more than 40 per cent of those over the age of 34 years. Baldness can show up in males when neither parent shows any degree of baldness, when one or both parents contribute a baldness gene to their sons. A bald father may have some sons who become bald and some who never become bald or all the sons may become bald in varying degrees. Daughters, however, will experience thinning or partial baldness, but complete hereditary baldness of the masculine type in the female is of excessive rarity.

The difference between sex influence and sex limitation is that the same trait when it is *sex-influenced* (the genes being carried in the autosomes) can be equally frequently expressed in both sexes, but that in one sex the trait will appear to be transmitted as a dominant, while in the other it will act as if its expression were due to a recessive. Whereas in sex-limited inheritance (genes carried on both autosomes and sex chromosomes) the trait is fully expressed in one sex alone. It is not the genes that condition the expression of the trait but the sex of the individual.

Gout, for example, is an *incompletely sex-limited* trait because while the gene is dominant and is carried on the autosomes, it is expressed in about 95 per cent of males and only in 5 per cent of females. Gout occurs in females not only in a much smaller percentage of cases but in a less exacerbating form. The female constitution exercises a strikingly modifying effect not only upon the expression of certain genes, but even upon the damage that certain infective organisms will work upon her as compared with the male. For example, syphilis follows so benign a course in the female as compared with the male that it has been said to manifest itself in the female "almost as if she were of another species." This is true of many other conditions.

There is very good reason to believe that secondary sex characters in general, including not only physical traits but differential response of the nervous system, depend upon sex limited factors. The degree of secondary sexual development in the sexes is obviously differentially limited by the hormones of the glands of internal secretion, in other words, the factors of sex are in themselves genetically limited, but this limitation is to some extent under the control of the hormones.

It is important to note that in one family a trait may be due to a sex-linked dominant gene, while in another family the same trait may be due to an autosomal recessive gene, and in still another family to an autosomal dominant gene. Such cases may represent the expression of differences in translocation or position effects.

Mutant genes and linkage between such genes occur, of course, in autosomes, but their study is considerably more difficult than sex-linkage. Several such linkages have, however, been described, and it is reasonably certain that in time several others will be. Examples of claimed linkages are ear flare and finger length, finger length and eye color, ear size and ability to taste phenylthiocarbamide, hair whorl and cross eyes, cross eyes and hair color, eye color and tongue curling, hair shade and hair color, ability to taste mercapto-benzo-selenazol and ear size, ability to taste MBS and tongue curling, body-build, eye color, and freckling, and several others. However, the only well established linkage of this sort is between sickle-shaped red blood corpuscles and the MN blood type.

Penetrance, Expressivity, and Viability of Genes

Under the conditions of development genes show varying degrees of activity. They are influenced by internal and external environmental factors, and one non-allelic gene may act upon another to inhibit its action (epistasis), or may itself be inhibited by a non-allelic gene (hypostasis).

Penetrance. When a gene regularly produces the same effect as, for example, do the blood group genes, it is said to have *complete penetrance.* When the trait is not manifested in some individuals it is said to have *reduced penetrance.* Dominant genes with low penetrance may be mistaken for recessives. When the penetrance of an autosomal gene is completely reduced in one sex, the gene is sex limited. Penetrance relates, therefore, to the *either-or* state of the gene—either it is expressed in the form of a definite condition or it is not. The blood groups constitute an example of genes that show complete penetrance. Every individual inheriting a gene for a particular blood trait will exhibit that trait. On the other hand, in such a disease as diabetes insipidus (the rarer form of diabetes, the common form being diabetes mellitus) is probably due to an incompletely dominant gene which manifests itself in about 10 per cent of those carrying it. *Penetrance* is to be carefully distinguished from *expressivity.*

Expressivity. When the manifestations of a trait produced by a gene are different from individual to individual, the gene is said to have *variable expressivity.* When the manifestation of the trait is constant, the gene is said to have constant expressivity. The dominant gene for allergy shows variable expressivity, and may take such forms as asthma, eczema, "hay fever," angioneurotic edema, or urticarial rash.

Viability. Genes carried in the homozygous state which shorten the life span of the individual are known as lethal genes. Such genes are incompatible with life at various stages during the development of the individual. This means that such genes may exert their effect at fertilization and at almost any time thereafter. Most of these lethals are recessive. In Table XLIX are listed the twenty or so conditions which have been reported as due to lethal genes.

SOME SOCIAL CONSEQUENCES OF THE BIOLOGICAL DIFFERENCES BETWEEN THE SEXES

In human society the social status of the sexes is greatly influenced by the physical differences existing between them. The most important of these differences is physical strength. By virtue of the possession of this one advantage men are able to enforce their will upon the opposite sex. The greater physical power of the male is the one factor which has weighted the balance of social power in his favor. In human as in non-human primate societies social sanctions, in the ultimate analysis, rely upon force for their maintenance. The difference between human and non-human primate societies in this respect would appear to lie in the degree to which force has been converted into a power for the development and maintenance of social relations. It was Plato who said that civilization is the victory of persuasion over force. Monkey overlords use their power to gratify their immediate desires,

TABLE XLIX

Conditions Reported as Due to Lethal Genes
(After Snyder)

Recessive lethals

Acute idiopathic xanthomatosis (Niemann-Pick's disease). Great enlargement of spleen and liver with discoloration of skin.
Amaurotic idiocy
    (a) Infantile type   Impairment of vision leading to total blindness, degeneration
    (b) Juvenile type   of nervous system and idiocy.
Degeneration of the cerebral white matter
    (a) Acute infantile type
    (b) Subacute juvenile type
    (c) Convulsive type

Epidermolysis bullosa	A skin disease in which blisters form on the slightest pressure
Gargoylism	Multiple growth derangement, gargoyle-like face
Glioma retinae	Tumor of the retina
Ichthyosis fetalis	Scaling of the skin
Infantile muscular atrophy	Wasting of muscles with paralysis
Microphthalmia of the sex-linked type	Abnormally small eyes
Pseudohypertrophic muscular dystrophy	Muscular enlargement and paralysis

Semidominant lethals

Minor brachydactyly	Shortness of fingers
Pelger's anomaly	Unsegmented leucocytes
Sebaceous cysts	Cystic tumors of sebum secreting glands
Spina bifida	Congenital cleft of vertebral column
Telangiectasia	Dilatation of capillaries, particularly serious nose bleeding

TABLE L

Some Presumed Social Consequences of the Biological
Differences Between the Sexes

(Modified after Scheinfeld, *Women and Men*).

Biological Sex Differences	Functional Expression	Social Consequences
Men bigger, more powerful	Greater capacity for heavy labor	Dominance of males. Division of labor. Different roles, assigned each sex; in anticipation, different training given to each
Women bear children, nurse them	Movements impeded, kept closer to home	
Greater muscular development in male	Urge to physical exertion, greater pride in it	Greater interest of male, in sports, etc.
Male's larger size, higher metabolism, greater activity	Need for more food, more expenditure of energy	Greater drive in work, achievement
Lesser strength of female	Inability to cope with male physically	Round-about "feminine" devices to achieve ends
Pregnancy in women	Greater risk in sexual relationships, uncertainty of parernity. Bad habits may affect children	"Double standard" of conduct, stricter codes for behavior of unmarried girls and married women
Earlier puberty in girls	Ready for mating earlier	Girls permitted to marry, reach "age of consent" earlier
Differences in genitalia and body	Garments adjusted differently for comfort, utility	Differences in dress, styles
Menstruation	Effects on body, mind, consciousness of blood issue, other symptoms	Taboos on women, psychological and social restraint
Male conscious of strength	Tendency of men to treat women gently	Codes of chivalry, etiquette
Rôle in sex relationships	Women can have intercourse without desire, men cannot	Prostitution largely confined to women, rape to men
Menopause in women	Reproductive capacity ends much earlier than men's	Men's marriage chances continue beyond women's
Female biologically more resistant to disease, bodily upsets	Her life span longer, surplus of women increasing	Threat to monogamous marriage system; problems of widowhood

human overlords to fulfill both their immediate desires and their remote wants. It is a difference of degree not of kind.

The correlation, in almost every society of animals, is so complete that one may lay it down as a general law that wherever one sex is larger or physically stronger than the other, that sex will occupy a position of dominance with respect to the smaller or physically less powerful sex. The relationship between strength and sexual or social dominance in human societies has often been neglected or overlooked by those who are inclined to attribute the differences in sexual status to exclusively cultural factors. In human societies the more powerful male is able to establish a physical and social supremacy over the female, which is the starting point of that social supremacy of the male that we find in practically all human societies. From such an initial gross mammalian advantage arise the variegated ways in which the social status of the sexes is expressed.

Another important difference is the difference in reproductive functions. These functions similarly serve to put the female at a physical disadvantage in comparison with the male. But while such differences serve as a basis for rationalization or a point of departure for the recognition of differences in social capacity and status, the ascription of the different rôles and statuses is almost entirely a matter of cultural determinance. In Table L the most general social and behavioral consequences of the biological differences between the sexes are briefly listed.

THE INFLUENCE OF ENVIRONMENTAL FACTORS UPON THE STRUCTURE AND FUNCTIONS OF MAN

In the laboratory it is possible to demonstrate the effects of slight changes in temperature, amount of light, humidity, or wakefulness upon the experimental animal. Growth, development, reproductivity, and behavior may all be affected. Such experiments are easily repeated and the results checked and verified. With human beings such experiments are not easily possible, though man's own mobility has provided thousands of such unpremeditated experiments. Yet, interestingly enough, when evidence is accumulated which proves that man is in many ways as susceptible as other animals are to the physical effects of changes in environment, the proof is generally treated with the greatest incredulity. Perhaps it is that the insecurity of life in general causes men to hold fast to some fancied ideal of stability and immortality, at least physically, of their own type. The facts, however, indicate that environment is a very potent force in its action upon the organism.

Environment is a term for a very large complex of conditions, each of these conditions acting with different degrees of intensity upon the organism at different times. By environment is here understood any condition, or group of conditions, external to the organism which may in any way affect it. This includes such conditions as variations in temperature, humidity, barometric pressure, number and kinds of

TABLE LI

INCREASE (+) OR DECREASE (−) IN MEASUREMENTS OF CHILDREN OF IMMIGRANTS
BORN IN THE UNITED STATES COMPARED WITH THOSE OF IMMIGRANTS
BORN IN EUROPE (FROM BOAS)

Nationality and Sex	Length of Head mm.	Width of Head mm.	Cephalic	Width of Face mm.	Stature
Bohemians:					
Male	−0.7	−2.3	−1.0	−2.1	+2.9
Female	−0.6	−1.5	−0.6	−1.7	+2.2
Hebrews:					
Male	+2.2	−1.8	−2.0	−1.1	+1.7
Female	+1.9	−2.0	−2.0	−1.3	+1.5
Sicilians:					
Male	−2.4	+0.7	+1.3	−1.2	−0.1
Female	−3.0	+0.8	+1.8	−2.0	−0.5
Neapolitans:					
Male	−0.9	+0.9	+0.9	−1.2	+0.6
Female	−1.7	+1.0	+1.4	−0.6	−1.8

particles in the air, solar and cosmic radiation, food, water, mineral content of the soil, and all that is embraced under the terms social and economic conditions.

Since, in human societies, it is the regulative effect of the socio-economic conditions which play a dominant rôle in modifying the action of purely physical factors, it must be re-emphasized here that the importance of these regulative conditions must always be borne in mind and given proper consideration in any attempted evaluation of the effects of the environment upon the individual.

Changes in Bodily Form of the Descendants of Immigrants from One Geographic Area to Another. In 1912 Boas conclusively showed that American-born descendants of immigrants differ in type from their foreign-born parents. Table LI shows the kind and degree of differences in the measurements of children of immigrants born in the United States compared with those of immigrants born in Europe. The results set out in this table prove that the form of the head may undergo certain changes, with change in environment, without change in descent. In other words, that the pattern of the genotype may re-main unaltered but that as a result of the effects exercised by a new environment its physiological expression undergoes modification. Fur-thermore, Boas showed that the influence of environment makes itself felt with increasing intensity according to the time elapsed between the arrival of the mother and the birth of the child. This is well brought out in Figure 197.

The American-born descendants differ in head form from their parents. The differences develop in early childhood, and persist throughout life. The head index of the foreign-born is practically the same, no matter how old the individual at the time of immigration. This might be expected when the immigrants are adult or nearly mature, but even children who come to the United States when one year or a few years old develop the head index characteristic of the foreign-born. For Jews this index ranges around 83, that of the American-born changes suddenly. The value drops to about 82 for those born immediately after the immigration of their parents, and reaches 79 in the second generation, i.e., among the children of American-born offspring of immigrants. The effects of American environment makes itself felt immediately, and increases slowly with the increase of time elapsed between the immigration of the parent and the birth of the child. Observations made in 1909 and 1937 yield the same results, save that there is an appreciable increase in all measurements in the latter series.

Boas found similar modifications in the head form of the descendants of Spanish ancestry living in Puerto Rico. The average head index of Spaniards being 77 while that of their Puerto Rican descendants is 82.5.

In 1918 Guthe confirmed Boas's findings with respect to changes

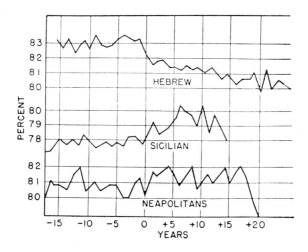

Figure 197. Head breadth taken as a per cent of head length (cephalic index) in immigrants and their descendants. (−) Those born in Europe, 5, 10, and 15 years before immigration. (+) Those born in America 5, 10, 15 and 20 years after immigration of mother (after Boas.)

in the cephalic index of the American born offspring of Russian Jews living in Boston.

Returning to Table LI it will be observed from the figures there given that there is, in general, a negative correlation between stature and cephalic index; that increase in stature is accompanied by a decrease in cephalic index. The changes in cephalic index, therefore, may at least in part be considered as functionally associated with changes in stature.

In recent years (1939) findings similar to those of Boas have been obtained by Shapiro and Hulse on the Hawaiian born children of Japanese migrating from Japan to the Hawaiian Islands. This is by far the most exhaustive study of its kind, and covers a great many more characters and conditions than Boas was able to investigate.

Shapiro and Hulse found that the changes in the first generation descendants of Japanese in Hawaii was limited principally to their quantitative characters, chiefly those of size and proportion. Here is a list of the characters principally affected:

The Hawaiian born males show significant increments over the immigrants in the following measurements:

1. Stature
2. Sitting Height
3. Trunk Height
4. Upper Arm Length
5. Lower Arm Length
6. Total Leg Length
7. Lower Leg Length
8. Shoulder Breadth
9. Head Breadth
10. Head Height
11. Inter-Ocular Width

In other words the Hawaiian born males are taller, broader in shoulders, longer in limbs, and have broader and higher heads than their Japanese born parents. But they also show significant decreases in the following measurements:

1. Chest Width
2. Chest Depth
3. Head Length
4. Total Face Height
5. Nose Breadth

The following are the significant alterations in proportions among the Hawaiian born males:

1. Lower Relative Hip Width
2. Lower Shoulder-Hip Index
3. Higher Tibio-Femoral Index
4. Lower Fronto-Parietal Index
5. Lower Cephalo-Facial Index
6. Lower Nasal Index
7. Higher Head Length-Height Index
8. Lower Nose Length-Height Index
9. Increased Cephalic Index

In a more recent investigation of the physical characters of Chinese immigrants and American-born Chinese in the eastern United States Lasker (1946) found changes in some 25 different characters.

American born Chinese males show significant increments over the immigrants in the following measurements:

Stature	Foot Length
Span	Hand Breadth
Total Arm Length	Total Facial Height
Upper Arm Length	Nasal Height
Lower Arm Length	Nasal Index
	Leg (Tibial) Length

Slight though significant increments were observed in:

Sitting-Height	Hand Length
Shoulder Width	Hand Breadth
Bi-Iliac Width	Face Breadth
Chest Width	Upper Facial Height

Significant decreases were observed in the following:

Chest Depth	Nasal Breadth

Other changes observed were

Coarser Hair	Sclera Less Frequently Pigmented
Slightly Hairier	More Prominent Nose
	Torus Palatinus More Frequent

On the basis of Shapiro and Hulse's and Lasker's studies we may say then that the typical Oriental youth born and brought up in Hawaii or the United States when compared with his ancestral stock or immigrants from his ancestral homeland, is taller, with longer arms and legs, has relatively slenderer hands and feet, and a flatter chest. His head is likely to be shorter but broader and his nose to be relatively narrower, and he has more body hair.

In a study of 2,252 Jews of eastern European origin Dornfeldt (1941) found that the cephalic index was lower for Jews born in Berlin than for those born abroad, that is to say, that the heads of children born in Berlin tend to increase in length and to decrease in breadth.

Spier (1929) in a study carried out at Seattle, found that American-born children of Japanese parents were taller at all ages than Japanese-born children from the district of southern Japan from which most of the Seattle Japanese were believed to have come. Children born six or more years after the arrival of the mother in the

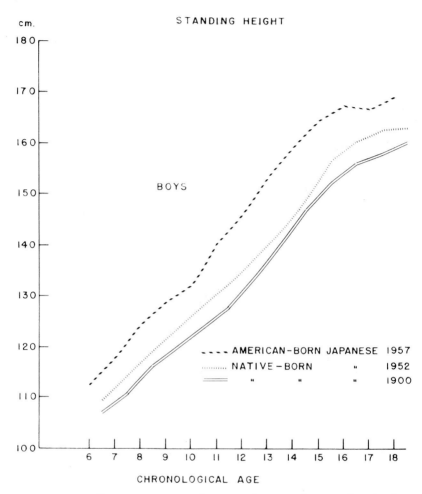

Figure 198. Differences in stature between American-born and native-born Japanese boys. (From Greulich. Courtesy, *Science.*)

United States had a greater average size. Children whose mothers migrated to the United States prior to 1909 were somewhat taller than those whose mothers migrated to the United States after 1909.

Ito (1936) found that newborn babies of Japanese parentage in the United States were far superior in physical growth at birth to those born in Japan, though the body proportions characteristic of the Japanese infant were fully retained under the new environment.

In a later study on four groups of Japanese women from 18 to 30 years of age reared under different environments, Ito (1942) found a significant increase in stature in the American-reared Japanese whether born in the United States or Japan, as compared with those reared in Japan. The figures are as follows:

Born and Reared in Japan	Born in U.S., and Reared in Japan. Returned to U.S.	Born in Japan and Reared in U.S.	Born and Reared in U.S.
149.8 cm	151.9 cm	153.9 cm	154.0 cm

Facts such as these constitute strong evidence that the increased

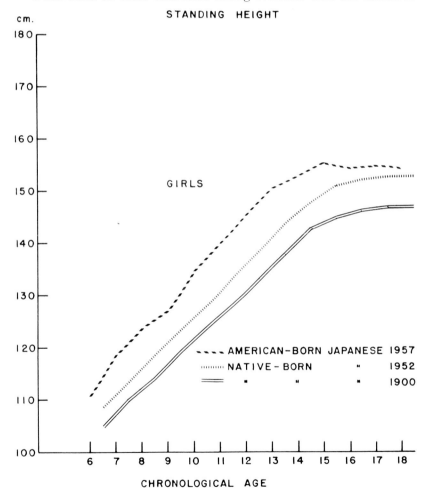

Figure 199. Differences in stature between American-born and native-born Japanese girls. (From Greulich. Courtesy, *Science*.)

stature of the American-reared women of Japanese ancestry is principally due to the effect of the more favorable American environment, and is not simply a reflection of selections, as some writers have
supposed.

Greulich (1958) has provided independent evidence that the small
stature of many Japanese is not so much genetically as environmentally
determined. Greulich compared the stature, weight, sitting-height,
and skeletal age of 898 American-born Japanese children in California
with the corresponding attributes of Japanese children of the same
age in Japan. The California children of Japanese ancestry were found
to be significantly more advanced in all the measured attributes.

Ito also found that the average age at menarche (the first menstruation) was about 20 months earlier in the Japanese women reared
in the United States than for those reared in Japan whether born in
the United States or in Japan.

In the lateral development of the body the American-reared
women are slightly superior to the Japanese-reared, except in chest
circumference which is reduced, a compensatory response, doubtless
to the markedly increased stature.

Goldstein (1943) investigated the presumed effects of the American environment on Mexican immigrants in Texas and their American-
born children. The following significant changes were found in the
sons as compared with their Mexican-born parents:

Increase in:	*Decrease in:*
Stature	Weight
Hand Length	Hand Breadth?
Ear Index	Bizygomatic Breadth
	Bigonial Breadth?
	Nose Height
	Nose Breadth
	Ear Height
	Ear Breadth
	Nasal Index

In qualitative traits the American-born sons differed from their
Mexican-born fathers in having:

More Medium Body Build	Lower Nasal Bridge Height
Less Body Fat	Shallower Nasal Root
Wavier Hair	Thicker Lips
Lighter Hair Color?	More Shovel Shaped Incisors
Darker Eye Color	Less Dental Caries

A comparison of the immigrant Mexicans with the sedentary Mexicans in the districts from which they came, revealed the fact that the immigrants differed from the "sedentes" in the direction realized by the American-born children of the former. A similar finding was made by Shapiro and Hulse on Japanese sedentes, immigrants, and their Hawaiian-born offspring.

Lasker (1952) has found that Mexicans migrating to the United States for one year or more, from the age of fifteen to over 27 years, exceed the sedentes in size in practically every measured dimension. Those who went to the United States youngest and stayed longest are the tallest of the migrants and are significantly taller than the sedentes. The later the age of migration to the United States the more closely, in their measurements, do the migrants resemble the sedentes.

The results obtained by these and many other investigators show that significant changes occur in various dimensions and proportions of the body, as well as in certain qualitative traits, following upon birth and development in a habitat not that of the parents.

What can be the cause or causes of these changes?

From the work of Shapiro and Hulse, Goldstein, and Lasker, it appears that, at least in Japanese and Mexicans, a trend to vary is already present in the immigrants. The new environment selectively stimulates these preadaptive tendencies to greater development in the generations born and bred in it. This interpretation is supported by the evidence derived from most studies thus far made on the subject.

Immigrants presenting developmental trends of different kinds entering the same environment will have offspring who are affected by the environment in different ways, owing to their original preadaptive genetic differences.

Immigrants presenting developmental trends of the same kind entering different environments may be affected in different ways owing to the differences in the action of the differing environments.

Once more we perceive the important rôle which the environment plays in the development of variations in human types. It is not, however, the environment alone which produces the changes observed in the descendants of immigrants, but the interaction between the genotype and the environment. The two can never be dissociated. As Boas puts it, "If there is any kind of environmental influence, it is obvious that we can never speak of a genetic type *per se*, but that every genetic type appears under certain environmental or physiological conditions, and that in this sense we are always dealing with the physiological form of a certain genetic type."

Climate. Man is a tropical animal capable of living under all climatic conditions. His normal body temperature is 98.6°. Man's comfort zone for external temperature is between 65° and 95°. Man seems to tolerate heat better than cold. In the United States, for example, in a typical year the death rate for the month of February is 14.6 per 1,000, while the death rate for August is 6.8 per 1,000.

The hot weather season is characterized by the lowest mortality rate. The death rate is much lower and the sickness rate is lower in the months of July, August, and September, than during the other months of the year. No wonder that man everywhere seeks out the sun.

Climatic factors exert very definite effects upon the human organism. Whole libraries have been written upon the subject, but a great part of this work suffers from the incompleteness of its scientific treatment. On the other hand, such rigorously scientific studies as have been made, in general serve to corroborate the effects of climatic changes upon man as have been experimentally demonstrated to occur in lower animals. For example, Hartman found that in the colony of macaque monkeys living at Baltimore, ovulation was inhibited during the summer months (June, July, and August) and there was a greater irregularity of the menstrual cycle, and an increase in amenorrhea. Similar findings were made by Engle and Shelesnyak on pubertal girls in New York City, the authors concluding that "The pubertal individual is a physiologically unstable organism, in which slight extrasomatic factors may profoundly influence somatic responses, so that phenomena may appear here which disappear with maturity."

The evidence strongly suggests that seasonal changes in climate continue to exert their effects upon the functions associated with the reproductive system, in both sexes, throughout the effective duration of those functions.

Some fifty years ago Engelmann showed that age at menarche (the first menstruation) in the descendants of European immigrants tended to approach the age at menarche of the aboriginal American Indians, and that the longer the American ancestry of the female the earlier was the age at menarche. Thus the mean age at menarche was about 15 years in Europe but in America it was 14.2 years, while for the American Indians it was about 13 years. Thirty years later Mills found that the average age at menarche of white females in the United States had apparently dropped to 13.55 years.

Such facts are not to be construed as meaning that climatic conditions eclipse in importance the genetic and cultural factors. They do not. Climate represents but one complex of variables in a much larger universe of variables all of which act upon the potentials of the organism to the extent to which the environing conditions make possible.

Although the influence of climatic factors upon the maturation of sexual functions has frequently been vigorously denied, the indubitable and unequivocal proof of that influence is to be seen in the fact that the breeding seasons of all animals characterized by such circumscribed periods of reproductivity are markedly affected by climatic influences. In the macaque monkeys there is a relative sterility period during the summer months, whether those months of summer fall in June, July, or August as in the Northern Hemisphere, or in November, December and January as in the Southern Hemisphere. Furthermore, the sexual functions and breeding seasons of animals can be altered by experimentally varying the climatic conditions to which they are exposed. In man there is some reason to believe that climatic factors exert their effect upon almost every aspect of his reproductive functions. Monge (1948) and others have found that removal from low to high altitudes (3,000 to 6,000 meters) in the Andes will not only produce sterility and impotence in man (as well as in animals) but in some cases actual atrophy of the gonads. In most cases these changes endure until the organism becomes adjusted to the new environment.

The migratory behavior and sexual periodicity of birds, as Rowan was the first to show, and the sexual periodicity of small mammals, as Bissonnette and others have since shown, are closely associated with the intensity and duration of the light to which they are exposed. Changes in the pituitary gland, in the sexual glands, and in hormone levels have been experimentally demonstrated as following upon variable periods of exposure to light. Rowan has shown in the case of birds that increased activity as a result of the prolonged exposure to light rather than the light itself is a determining factor.

Temperature has been experimentally shown to be associated with sexual behavior in rats, high temperature, as well as low, being associated with reduced sexual activity. Evidence has been adduced to show that temperature similarly affects man. Here, too, as in the case of light the effect is mainly indirect, the greater lassitude and reduced energy being the cause of low sexual activity rather than the direct action of temperature itself.

The direct action of light upon the human organism is known principally from its effect upon body pigments and the skin. The

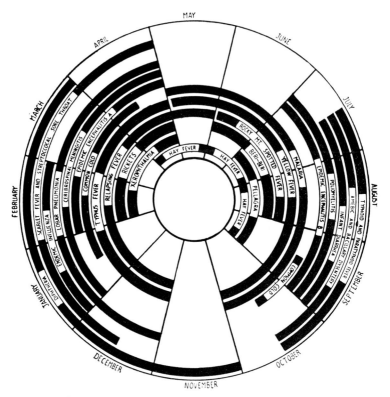

Figure 200. The seasonal incidence of some diseases. (From Perla and Marmorston. Courtesy, Williams & Wilkins.)

effects upon more general physiological activities are known but not
yet understood, even though the beneficial and disease effects of light
are fairly well known (Blum).

General Climatic Effects Upon the Individual. Growth and development, energy levels, metabolism and its pathological states, infectious diseases, body resistance, sclerosis and failure in the circulatory system, dental caries, weight, height, and intelligence, every
phase, indeed, of the life of the individual is influenced by climatic
factors. Almost everyone is aware of the fact that certain diseases
are more prevalent in winter than in summer, while others are more
common in summer than in winter; the common cold is an example
of the first kind, and hay-fever of the second. The reader will recall
many other examples of the relationship between disease, the weather,
and the seasons (see Figure 200).

Evidence is now available which indicates that the course of practically every disease is influenced not only by seasonal changes but by changes in the weather from hour to hour, while quite a number of disorders, such as sinusitis, and some joint and respiratory disorders, are actually activated by changes in humidity and barometric pressure. But we are not here concerned with the effects of climate upon disease, but rather with climatic effects upon the normal structure and functions of man.

In a study of the height and weight measurements of more than 21,000 men of the New Zealand army draft for World War II Fitt (1955) found that the tallest and the heaviest men were born in summer and the shortest and lightest were born in winter. The average difference was about one-third of an inch in height and about one-third of a pound in weight.

It has been shown that the growth of the human body proceeds at different rates during the different seasons. Thus, maximal increase in height generally occurs in the spring, while maximal increase in weight occurs during the autumn. Interestingly enough there appears to be a tendency for mental functions to be in their maximal phase when weight increase is dominant, and in their minimal phase when height increase is dominant.

Studies by many different investigators on white populations throughout the world have led to the following conclusions (Fitt, 1941):

Mental abilities are at their highest in midwinter and at their lowest during the transition period from winter to spring or in early spring.

Muscular ability is highest in midsummer, and lowest in midspring and late autumn.

Gross mortality rates are higher in the spring-summer half of the year than in the autumn-winter half.

Suicide and abortion rates are highest in summer and lowest in winter.

Conception rates are lowest in summer, and the greatest number of menstrual irregularities occur in the same season.

There exists a rather considerable amount of evidence which suggests that individuals born during the autumn-winter period tend, in many ways, to be more favored than those born during the spring-summer period. During this period the vitality of the new-born is higher, and such individuals grow to be taller, heavier, and stronger,

Figure 201. Seven cretins from the Urnatsch Almshouse, Appenzelle Canton, Switzerland. The tall man is normal, the height of the woman immediately in front of him is just 39 inches. (Courtesy, Dr. J. F. McClendon.)

and some investigators claim, also more intelligent, on the whole, than those born during the spring-summer period. Evidence of this kind suggests that seasonal factors exert a conditioning effect upon genetic development. That this is so in the case of the lower animals has been repeatedly demonstrated by experimental means, and by the detailed analysis of observations.

In these matters we may, however, be dealing not so much with the direct as with the indirect effects of climate, such, for example, as the changes in number, distribution, and virulence of disease-producing micro-organisms which may act more severely at one season than at another.

Under the general rubric of climatic conditions may be classed the foods consumed by man, since the qualities of food are determined, for the most part, by climatic conditions.

The foods consumed by man vary considerably in different parts of the world, and since there can be no question as to the importance of their effects upon the growing individual and the group, the nutritional factors must always be borne in mind in any attempt at the evaluation of differences and likenesses between individuals and groups. There is definite evidence available that the shape of the head, for example, is affected by nutritional factors. Experimentally this has been demonstrated on dogs fed on a somewhat iodine-deficient diet. The mention of iodine recalls the fact that in areas of the world in which the soils and foods are deficient in iodine very striking arrests in development may occur. In certain parts of Switzerland, in the Tyrol, and in the Pacific Northwest, there were, until very recently, large numbers of individuals whose thyroid glands functioned at a very low level because the low iodine content of the soil upon which they lived was reflected in the still lower iodine content of the water and the foods they consumed. Hence, the absence of the normal iodine intake necessary for the proper functioning of the thyroid gland resulted in such iodine-deficiency diseases as cretinism, arrested physical and mental growth, simple goiter, Graves' disease (exophthalmic goiter) and serious disturbances of metabolism (see Figure 201). The domesticated animals living in these regions were similarly affected. People who live sufficiently near the sea-coast for the evaporated sea salts to be borne inland by the winds, never suffer from deficiencies of this sort. As might have been expected exophthalmic goiter is more frequent in iodine deficient areas than elsewhere.

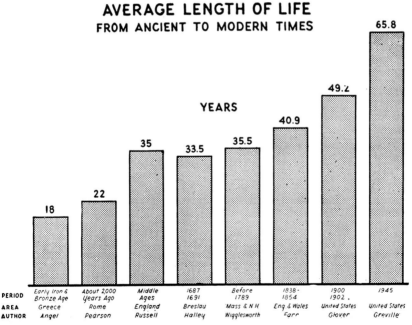

Figure 202. Average length of life from Ancient to Modern Times. (Courtesy, Metropolitan Life Insurance Company, New York.)

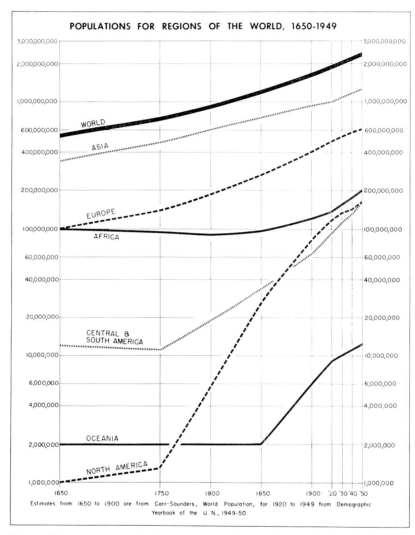

Figure 203. The Growth of Population 1650-1949. (Courtesy, U.S. Public Health Service.)

The relation of food to some of the differences exhibited by the various ethnic groups of mankind is still an almost completely unexplored field. It is one which would richly repay investigation. It is, in reality, a part of the study of human ecology, that is, the study of man in relation to his total environment.

Environmental Effects as Determined by Socio-Economic Factors.

Socio-economic factors are not generally regarded as physical environmental factors, and this is, of course, quite a proper view to take, but since these factors, for the most part, determine the kind of physical environment to which the individual shall be exposed, it is obvious that they play an important regulative rôle in the psychophysical history of the individual. This important fact is too often overlooked. The history of public health provides a very clear illustration of the influence of socio-economic factors upon the incidence of disease and mortality rates. Improved social and economic conditions have significantly served to decrease these rates. From an average expectation of life of 33.5 years in antiquity, to 35.5 years at the beginning of the 19th century, we had advanced to only 40 years by the middle of the same century; and then, as Dublin says, "Shortly before the turn of the century came what may be called the era of discovery of the basic facts with regard to the control of environment, causation of disease, and the series of practical administrative measures which have since been crystallized in the modern public health movement. As this program developed, the expectation of life at birth responded rapidly and definitely so that each new set of tables showed

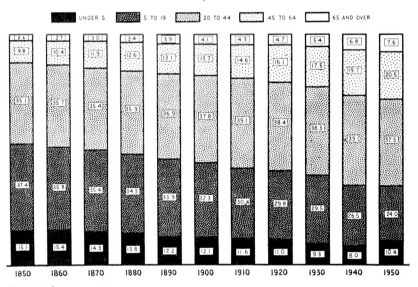

PERCENT DISTRIBUTION OF TOTAL POPULATION BY AGE
United States, 1850 to 1950*

Figure 204.

a corresponding increase in the expectation of life. By 1900, the expectation in the United States had jumped to about 50 years; by 1920, to 55 years and by 1930 to a little over 60 years." By 1959 the expectation of life was a little over 73.4 years for the female, and somewhat over 67.3 for the male.

Can it ever be too strongly emphasized that this doubling of the average expectation of life was achieved solely by *the social regulation of environmental conditions?* It is not necessary in this volume to cite the now well known facts regarding the very considerable reduction in infant mortality as well as in other mortality rates, during the last fifty years. The data for expectation of life at birth by sex is given in Table LII.

The relation between economic status, as judged, and for the most part determined, by annual income, and disability from disease, constitutes a very convincing demonstration of the influence of the economic factor upon the conditions determining the physical well-being of the individual. The figures taken from the National Health Survey, 1935-36, shown in Table LIII make this abundantly clear. As will be seen from this Table members of families on relief suffer more than two-and-one-half times the volume of disability from all diseases combined than do families with incomes of $5,000 and over. The ratio for specific diseases ranges from almost nine times for tuberculosis to 1.24 times for infectious diseases. The facts brought out in this table should at this late date be known and understood by everyone. Similar tables could be provided for almost every country in the world. It is here necessary to point out that the relation between socio-economic conditions and disease is not simply one-way, for disease tends to reduce the wage-earner to a low income group. However, the fact remains that the incidence of disease is to a very large extent a function of socio-economic factors.

The relation between occupation and physical disability of various sorts is, of course, well known and need not be dealt with here.

The effects of dietary habits, and such practices as drinking and smoking, which are all socially conditioned, are more or less well known. As Pearl and others have shown, heavy drinking and even moderate smoking are associated with reduced longevity.

Growth. Among the most striking effects of socio-economic factors upon the organism are those which express themselves in the growth of the individual. Differences in environment determined by these factors are operative from the moment of conception, if not before.

TABLE LII

Expectation of Life at Birth by Sex in Various Countries for Specified Periods

Country and Period	Total Persons	Male	Female	Country and Period	Total Persons	Male	Female
North America				Ireland			
United States				1950–52	65.8	64.5	67.1
1955	69.5	66.7	72.9	1940–42	60.0*	59.0	61.0
1939–41	63.6	61.6	65.9	Luxembourg			
1955				1946–48	63.7*	61.7	65.8
White	70.2	67.3	73.6	Netherlands			
Nonwhite	63.2	61.2	65.9	1953–55	72.5*	71.0	73.9
Canada				1931–40	66.5*	65.7	67.2
1955	70.1	67.6	73.0	Northern Ireland			
1940–42	64.6*	63.0	66.3	1950–52	67.1*	65.4	68.8
Costa Rica				1936–38	58.5*	57.8	59.2
1949–51	55.7	54.6	57.1	Norway			
El Salvador				1946–50	71.0*	69.3	72.7
1949–51	51.2*	49.9	52.4	1931–40	65.8*	64.1	67.6
Greenland				Poland			
1946–51	34.9*	32.2	37.5	1952–53	61.4*	58.6	64.2
Guatemala				1931–32	49.8	48.2	51.4
1949–51	43.7*	43.8	43.5	Portugal			
1939–41	36.5*	36.0	37.1	1949–52	58.0*	55.5	60.5
Mexico				1939–42	50.7*	48.6	52.8
1949–51	48.7	46.7	49.9	Scotland			
1940	38.9*	37.9	39.8	1956	68.6*	66.0	71.2
Puerto Rico				1930–32	57.8*	56.0	59.5
1955	68.3	66.7	70.0	Sweden			
1939–41	46.0	45.1	46.9	1951–55	72.0*	70.5	74.3
				1936–40	65.6*	64.3	66.9
South America				Switzerland			
Argentina				1948–53	68.6*	66.4	70.9
1947	59.2*	56.9	61.4	1933–37	62.7*	60.7	64.6
Brazil (Federal District)				U. S. S. R.			
1949–51	52.9	49.8	56.0	1954–55	64	61	67
1939–41	42.5*	39.7	45.2	1926–27‡	44.4	41.9	46.8
Chile				Yugoslavia			
1952	51.4	49.8	53.9	1950	56.3*	54.5	58.2
1939–42	41.8	40.7	43.1				
Ecuador (Quito)				*Africa and Asia*			
1949–51	52.0*	50.4	53.7	Belgian Congo			
Venezuela				1950–52	38.8*	37.6	40.0
1946	47.0*	45.9	48.1	Ceylon			
1941–42	46.7	45.8	47.6	1954	59.9*	60.3	59.4
				1946	42.8*	43.9	41.6
Europe				Cyprus			
Austria				1948–50	66.2*	63.6	68.8
1949–51	64.4*	61.9	67.0	India			
1930–33	56.5*	54.5	58.5	1941–50	32.1*	32.5	31.7
Belgium				1921–31	26.7*	26.9	26.6
1946–49	64.6	62.0	67.3	Israel (Jewish)			
1928–32	57.9*	56.0	59.8	1955	70.8*	69.4	72.1
Czechoslovakia				1939–41	63.5*	62.3	64.6
1949–51	63.2*	60.9	65.5	Japan			
1929–32	53.6*	51.9	55.2	1955	66.1*	63.9	68.4
Denmark				1935–36	48.3*	46.9	49.6
1946–50	68.9*	67.8	70.1	Philippines			
1936–40	64.7*	63.5	65.8	1948	51.2	48.8	53.4
England and Wales				1938	46.0*	44.8	47.2
1956	70.5*	67.8	73.3	Thailand			
1937	62.3*	60.2	64.4	1947–48	50.3*	48.7	51.9
Finland				1937–38†	40.0*	36.7	43.3
1951–55	66.6*	63.4	69.8	Union of South Africa‡			
1931–40	57.0*	54.5	59.6	1945–47	66.0*	63.8	68.3
France				1935–37	61.0*	59.0	63.1
1954–55	68.2	65.1	71.4	*Oceania*			
1933–38	58.7	55.9	61.6	Australia			
Germany				1946–48	68.4*	66.1	70.6
1952–53 (East)	67.1*	65.1	69.1	1932–34	65.3*	63.5	67.1
1949–51 (West)	66.5*	64.6	68.5	Hawaii			
1932–34	61.3*	59.9	62.8	1949–51	69.5*	67.8	71.3
Hungary				1939–41	61.0*	59.5	62.6
1955	66.7*	64.7	68.7	New Zealand‡			
1941	56.6*	54.9	58.2	1950–52	70.4*	68.3	72.4
				1934–38	67.0*	65.5	68.5

*Average of male and female.   †Bangkok municipal area.   ‡European population.
Source: Largely from United Nations Demographic Yearbooks and reports of various countries. *Statistical Bulletin*, April 1958, Metropolitan Life Insurance Company, New York.

TABLE LIII

RATIO OF ANNUAL PER CAPITA VOLUME OF DISABILITY IN THE UNITED STATES*
FOR LOW INCOME GROUPS TO THAT IN THE HIGHEST INCOME GROUPS;
1935–36 ACCORDING TO SPECIFIED DIAGNOSIS CLASSIFICATIONS†

| | INCOME STATUS OF FAMILY | | | |
Diagnosis	Relief	Under $1000 per year	$1000 to $1500 a year	$5000 and over
Tuberculosis	875	388	250	100
Orthopedic Impairments	420	283	175	100
Rheumatism	369	213	138	100
Digestive Diseases	340	180	114	100
Nervous Diseases	287	204	135	100
Degenerative Diseases	268	156	109	100
Accidents	221	173	129	100
Respiratory Diseases	189	121	91	100
Infectious Diseases	124	93	93	100
All Diagnoses	266	166	121	100
Diagnoses not elsewhere grouped	261	160	127	100

* Defined as the product of the frequency of illness and the duration of illness.

† Adjusted to the age composition of the National Health Survey total white population, 1935-36.
   Source: National Health Survey, 1935-36, Preliminary Reports, Sickness and Medical Care
Series, Bulletin No. 9, *Disability from Specific Causes in Relation to Economic Status* (Washington,
1938), p. 9.

The best discussion of the subject is to be found in Sanders' book, *Environment and Growth*.

Growth may be defined as increase in size, while by development is to be understood increase in complexity.

A detailed and rigorously critical study of the evidence shows that, regardless of area, children reared in a superior socio-economic environment are, on the average, heavier and taller than their age-mates who have been exposed to a less favorable environment. A general improvement in the environment of the child, whether introduced by increased income or by placement in an institution where his status is improved, or by more competent care, tends always to accelerate growth. Conversely, an increase in untoward conditions, disease, poverty or a general deterioration of the environment, is followed by a decline in the rate of growth.

From such findings it should be evident that no studies of human growth which fail to pay careful attention to the socio-economic factors can be regarded as satisfactory, for the evidence strongly suggests that there are few, if any, aspects of the growth process which are not affected by these factors.

These facts were well brought out in one of the earliest studies made on the relation between socio-economic factors and growth. This study, carried out in Glasgow, Scotland, during the years 1905-1906, was devoted to an investigation of the heights and weights of 70,000 school children between five and 18 years of age. The results obtained were then correlated with the types of school which the children attended, this yielded four socio-economic district school groups from A to D, where "A" were from the poorest districts of the city and "D" from the most prosperous. The results of this study are shown in Table LIV.

From Table LIV it will be seen that at practically every age, and for both sexes, a very appreciable and regular difference was shown between the children of the four graded socio-economic districts, in both height and weight, and this always in favor of the higher socio-economic groups. Thus, at age nine the average height of boys in district A was 48.8 inches, in B 49.5 inches, in C 49.9 inches, and in D 50.9 inches. At every age we observe a steady increase from group A to group D. Boys from district D at age five are between 1.7 inches and at age thirteen 2.5 inches taller than those of district B.

Later studies carried out in many different parts of the world have fully confirmed the capital importance of the environment and its

TABLE LIV

Height (inches) and Weight (pounds) in 70,000 Glasgow (Scotland) School Children, 1905–1906, by Ascending Order (from A to D) of Socioeconomic Status of School

Age:	5	6	7	8	9	10	11	12	13
Boys					*Height (Inches)*				
Group A	41.3	43.0	45.1	47.0	48.8	50.6	52.3	53.8	55.2
Group B	42.1	44.0	45.9	47.7	49.5	51.1	52.8	54.3	55.5
Group C	42.1	44.0	46.2	48.1	49.9	51.5	53.5	55.0	57.2
Group D	43.0	44.8	46.9	49.0	50.9	52.6	54.2	55.9	57.7
Girls									
Group A	41.0	42.9	44.6	46.6	48.5	50.3	52.4	54.4	55.8
Group B	42.0	43.7	45.6	47.4	49.2	51.1	53.0	55.2	57.1
Group C	41.9	43.7	45.6	47.6	49.4	51.2	53.3	55.4	57.0
Group D	42.7	44.8	46.4	48.6	50.4	52.2	54.1	56.5	58.7
Boys					*Weight (pounds)*				
Group A	40.9	44.2	48.0	52.3	56.7	61.6	66.4	71.7	75.6
Group B	42.0	45.6	49.6	53.9	58.4	62.7	67.8	72.9	77.3
Group C	42.5	45.9	50.1	54.4	59.5	63.9	69.1	75.6	82.2
Group D	43.3	46.6	51.2	56.3	61.2	66.3	70.8	76.9	83.2
Girls									
Group A	39.9	43.0	46.4	50.5	54.7	59.5	65.3	72.4	76.8
Group B	40.6	43.9	47.7	51.8	55.8	60.8	66.8	74.3	81.3
Group C	41.3	44.7	48.1	52.7	56.9	61.9	68.4	76.1	83.0
Group D	41.8	45.6	49.3	54.3	58.8	64.4	70.5	78.8	89.0

From E. M. Elderton: Height and Weight of School Children in Glasgow. *Biometrika*, 10(2/3): 288–340, 1914.

TABLE LV

PERCENTAGES OF CHILDREN, AGE 5 TO 15 YEARS, WHO ARE UNDER AVERAGE
HEIGHT, CLASSIFIED BY COUNTRY AND SOCIO-ECONOMIC STATUS

Location of School	United States	Canada	Scotland	England	Ireland
Prosperous District......	7.5	11.0	11.2	18.5	22.7
Average District.........	18.3	23.4	24.6	24.4	24.3
Poor District...........	36.4	31.6	27.3	35.1	30.7

Adapted from Cudmore and Neal, "A Height and Weight Survey of Toronto Elementary School Children 1939," Ottawa, 1942.

effect upon the processes of growth. One of the most striking of these studies, by Craven and Jokl (1946), evaluates the growth records of 1,067 physically substandard adolescent boys studied at the Physical Training Battalion in Pretoria, South Africa. It was found that within the first nine months these boys spent at the training station they grew in bulk, on the average, at a rate five times as great as they would have grown in their unsatisfactory home enviornment. Nutritional factors would seem to be those most significantly involved. In Table LV are set out the figures for five different English speaking countries with somewhat different food and other economic habits, showing the percentages of children, between the ages of five and 15 years, by socio-economic status who are under average height.

These figures tell a remarkable, and almost dramatic, story. They show how the least number of children under average height and the greatest number of children under average height occur in the land in which the greatest extremes of socio-economic welfare are to be found, in the United States. Here we find that the percentage of children from the prosperous districts who are under average height is only 7.5 while in the poor districts that percentage is as high as 36.4 per cent. Only England, with its (then) notoriously bad nutrition, comes anywhere near the figure with 35.1 per cent. On the average, however, there are less under height children in the United States than in the other four English-speaking countries. Indeed, English children from prosperous districts do not do as well as American children from average districts. On the whole these figures would point to the nutritional factor as being the one most directly involved here.

Studies carried out by Boas on institutionalized children have very impressively demonstrated the effect of nutrition upon stature. With an ill balanced diet the children were retarded in stature, when the diet was improved there were not only fewer under height children, but all those who had been retarded finally attained normal height.

In a study already cited Goldstein has shown that the descendants of Mexican immigrants in Texas are taller and better developed than Mexicans of the same generation living in Mexico. He found also that the adult children of Mexican parents in Mexico proper, as well as those born of Mexican parents in the United States were taller and better developed than their parents, the American born, however, being always superior in these respects to the Mexican born. Goldstein attributes these changes to improvement in living conditions, that is, better and more food, better housing, health, and sanitation.

From such findings it should be evident that the general environmental factors can scarcely ever be adequately separated from the factors which are broadly classified under heredity. Methodologically, there will always be good reason for attempting to separate out these factors, but while this is so there is also a sound case for bearing in mind the fact that there is such a thing as social heredity as well as biological heredity, and that strictly speaking the two can never be completely separated. The general framework of the individual is due to its genotype which is biologically inherited, but the detailed development of this framework is always more or less considerably influenced by the environment which the individual has socially inherited. Hence, strictly speaking heredity must be regarded as the blending of two inheritances, the one biological, and the other social. A great deal of much needed attention has been paid to the former, but far too little to the latter type of inheritance and its effects. It has been the principal purpose of the present chapter to draw attention to the much neglected important physical effects of the latter.

FOR FURTHER READING, CONSULT:

BEWS, J. W.: *Human Ecology.* New York, Oxford University Press, 1935.
  An introduction to the study of man in relation to his total environment.

CALHOUN, J. B.: The social aspects of population dynamics. *J. Mammal., 33:* 139-159, 1952.
  An important discussion, based largely on studies of non-human mammals, but with very significant relevance for the understanding of the dynamics of human populations.

COLLIER, K. G.: *The Science of Humanity.* New York, Nelson, 1950.
  A most readable book on the development of human nature, and human nature in action.

DAHLBERG, G.: Environment, inheritance, and random variations with special reference to investigation on twins. *Acta Genetica et Statistica Medica,* Basle, *1:1;* 104-114, 1948.
  A valuable discussion of chance and prenatal influence upon development, with a long-overdue caution with respect to inferences concerning the mechanism of heredity in man drawn from the study of so-called identical twins.

DRAPER, G., DUPERTIUS, C. W. and CAUGHEY, J. L., JR.: *Human Constitution and Clinical Medicine.* New York, Hoeber, 1944.
An important study of constitution and disease.

DUNN, H. L. (editor): *Health and Demography.* Washington, D.C., U.S. Department of Health, Education, and Welfare, 1956.
An admirable survey of population dynamics, with numerous graphs and tables.

EWING, O. R.: *The Nation's Health.* Washington, D.C., Federal Security Agency, 1948.
An illuminating report on the state of the nation's health, with recommendations for its improvement.

FITT, A. B.: *Seasonal Influence on Growth, Function and Inheritance.* London, Oxford University Press, 1941.
A useful and informative analysis.

GATES, R. R.: *Human Genetics.* 2 vols., New York, Macmillan, 1946.
An exhaustive source book. To be used with caution.

HALLIDAY, J. L.: *Psychosocial Medicine.* New York, W. W. Norton, 1948.
A brilliant application of the concepts of psychosomatic medicine to the illness of communities and social groups.

HARRIS, D. B. (editor): *The Concept of Development.* Minneapolis, University of Minnesota Press, 1957.
The concept of development interestingly examined by seventeen authorities, each dealing with his own field.

KALLMANN, F. J.: *Heredity in Health and Mental Disorder.* New York, Norton, 1953.
The standard book on the subject, short and readable.

KROGMAN, W. M. (editor): The growth of man. *Tabulae Biologicae, 20:*vi-963, 1942.
An invaluable collection of tables, graphs, and figures covering the period 1926-1938.

————: *A Guide-Outline for the Study of Physical Growth in Children.* Philadelphia Center for Research in Child Growth, Philadelphia, 1958.
A useful guide to the recent literature.

————: Changing man. *J. Am. Geriatrics Soc., 6:*242-260, 1958.
A stimulating discussion of the factors productive of change in man.

LADELL, W. S. S.: The influence of environment in arid regions on the biology of man. In UNESCO Publication, Arid Zone Research VIII, *Human and Animal Ecology.* New York, Columbia University Press, 1957, pp. 43-99.
A fundamental study with an exhaustive bibliography.

KAPLAN, B. A.: Environment and human plasticity. *Am. Anthropol., 56:*780-800, 1954.
The best available summary and discussion of most of the investigations on the effects of a changed environment upon the descendants of immigrants.

KENNEY, R. A.: Anatomical differences due to race or climate. Section contributed to Ladell's study, 83-84.
A brief and pointed discussion of man's adaptation to a desert habitat.

LESSA, W. A.: *An Appraisal of Constitutional Typologies.* American Anthropological Association, Memoir No. 62, 1943.
A well balanced critical examination of both psychological and morphological constitutional typologies.

MAY, J. M.: *The Ecology of Human Disease*. New York, M.D. Publications, 1958. The first of three volumes dealing with the relation between disease and the geographical environment in which it occurs.

MEAD, M.: *Male and Female*. New York, Morrow, 1949. A brilliant study of the sexes in a changing world, full of illuminating insights and provocative ideas.

M'GONIGLE, G. C. M. and KIRBY, J.: *Poverty and Public Health*. London, Gollancz, 1936. An impressive survey of the relation between poverty, health, and its social and biological consequences.

MERTON, R. K., and MONTAGU, M. F. ASHLEY: Crime and the anthropologist. *Am. Anthropol.*, 42:384-408, 1940. A critical examination of Hooton's work on the criminal. Reprinted in Montagu's *Anthropology and Human Nature*, pp. 264-290.

MONGE, C.: *Acclimatization in the Andes*. Baltimore, Johns Hopkins Press, 1948. An extremely interesting study of the effects of climatic conditions upon the physiological functions and survival of man, under differences of air density, temperature, and atmospheric pressure.

MONTAGU, M. F. ASHLEY: Constitutional and prenatal factors in infant and child health. In the author's *Anthropology and Human Nature*. Boston, Porter Sargent, 1957, pp. 214-239. An examination of the evidence concerning the roles played by genetic and environmental factors in the development of the fetus, and the influence of these factors upon the postnatal development of the person.

————: *The Natural Superiority of Women*. New York, Macmillan, 1953. A discussion of the evidence that females are naturally biologically superior to males.

————: *Human Heredity*. New York, World Publishing Co., 1959. Human inheritance, the genetic mechanisms and the influence of the environment. A census of hereditary disorders, their mode of inheritance and incidence is provided.

NEWBURGH, L. H. (editor): *Physiology of Heat Regulation and the Science of Clothing*. New York, Saunders, 1949. An invaluable work on man's adjustment to climate and clothing as a thermal barrier. The opening chapter by F. R. Wulsin brings together the material on adaptations to climate, among non-European peoples.

NEWMAN, H. H.: *Multiple Human Births*. New York, Doubleday, Doran, 1940. The most reliable and readable account of the subject.

————, FREEMAN, F. N. and HOLZINGER, K. J.: *Twins: A Study of Heredity and Environment*. Chicago, University Chicago Press, 1937. The most authoritative study of its kind.

PERLA, D. and MARMORSTON, J.: *Natural Resistance and Clinical Medicine*. Baltimore, Williams & Wilkins, 1941. The best and most exhaustive discussion of genetic, ethnic, environmental, climatic, and numerous other factors influencing natural resistance.

PETERSEN, W. F.: *The Patient and the Weather*. Ann Arbor, Michigan, Edwards Bros., vols. 1-4, 1934-39. A very full presentation of original observations on the relation between changes in the weather and associated changes in persons suffering from various diseases.

SANDERS, B. S.: *Environment and Growth*. Baltimore, Warwick & York, 1934.
An excellent review and analysis of the data on man.

SCHEINFELD, A.: *Women and Men*. New York, Harcourt, 1944.
An excellent discussion of the differences between the sexes.

————: The mortality of men and women. *Scientific American, 198:22-28, 1958.*
A succinct account of the differences.

SCHWESINGER, G.: *Heredity and Environment*. New York, Macmillan, 1933.
A good presentation of the problem, and a clear discussion of the data presented.

SHELDON, W. H.: *The Varieties of Human Physique*. New York, Harper & Bros., 1940.

————: *The Varieties of Human Temperament*. New York, Harper & Bros., 1942.

————: *Varieties of Delinquent Youth*. New York, Harper & Bros., 1949.

————: *Atlas of Men*. New York, Harper & Bros., 1954.
Sheldon's four works on the techniques and principles of somatotyping.

ŠKERLJ, B.: *Development of Secondary School Students of Ljubljana*. Institut za Antropologijo, Univerza V Ljubljana, Ljubljana, 1950.
A valuable study of the relationship of social factors to physical development.

SHETTLES, L. B.: Biological sex differences with special reference to disease, resistance, and longevity. *J. Obst. & Gynaec. Brit. Emp., 45:288-295, 1958.*
An informative and stimulating study.

SNYDER, L. H.: The effects of selection and domestication on man. *J. Nat. Cancer Inst., 15:759-769, 1954.*
A most stimulating study.

————: Fifty years of medical genetics. *Science, 129:7-13, 1959.*
A valuable account by a leader in the field.

SORSBY, A. (editor): *Clinical Genetics*. St. Louis, Mosby, 1953.
An invaluable gathering of 29 separate survey studies of hereditary disorders in man.

STERN, B. J.: *Society and Medical Progress*. Princeton, Princeton University Press, 1941.
An excellent, and very readable, account of the progress made in human health under improved living conditions, and the development of medical and public health measures.

TANNER, J. M.: *Growth at Adolescence*. Springfield, Thomas, 1955.
An able coverage of the subject.

THORNDIKE, E. L.: *Human Nature and the Social Order*. New York, Macmillan.
A fundamental book on the expression of human nature in the United States.

TUCKER, W. B. and LESSA, W. A.: Man: a constitutional investigation. *Quart. Rev. Biol., 15:265-289, 1940.*
A valuable survey of constitutional classifications.

WALLACE, B.: Genetic studies of population. *Eugenics. Quart., 1:10-15, 1954.*
A brilliant study of population genetics.

WATSON, E. H. and LOWREY, G. H.: *Growth and Development of Children*, 3rd Edition. Chicago, Yearbook Publishers, 1959.
A thoroughly useful book.

WOODWORTH, R. S.: *Heredity and Environment*. New York, Social Sc. Res. Council, 1942.
A critical survey of recently published material on twins and foster children.

A PRACTICAL SYNOPSIS OF METHODS OF MEASUREMENT IN PHYSICAL ANTHROPOLOGY

THE MEASUREMENT OF MAN

THE FOLLOWING account is intended to give the reader a working knowledge of some of the methods of measurement most commonly used in physical anthropology. For a more complete account the reader should refer to the works listed at the conclusion of this appendix.

In view of the fact that no two persons are ever alike in all their measurable characters, that the latter tend to undergo change in varying degrees from birth to death, in health and in disease, and since persons living under different conditions, and members of different ethnic groups and the offspring of unions between them, frequently present interesting differences in bodily form and proportions, it is desirable to have some means of giving quantitative expression to the variations which such traits exhibit. *Anthropometry* constitutes that means. It is the technique of expressing quantitatively the form of the body. Anthropometry means the measurement of man, whether living or dead, and consists primarily in the measurement of the dimensions of the body.

While the methods of measurement used in physical anthropology are numerous, there are only two which are uniquely its contribution and which are peculiar to it, these are anthropometry and anthroposcopy. Other methods have been borrowed from anatomy, medicine, physiology, biochemistry, genetics, and statistics. In fact, physical anthropology makes use of every method which is capable of throwing light upon the significant likenesses and differences existing between individuals and groups of men.

Anthroposcopy is the visual observation and description of physical traits which do not easily lend themselves to exact measurement. For example, form and character and distribution of the hair, skin color, eye color, eye folds, form of lip, of nose, and the like.

Physiometry, the measurement of the physiological functions of the body, constitutes an important adjunct of anthropometry, the methods of which are mostly borrowed from physiology and serology.

Anthropometry is conveniently subdivided as follows:

Somatometry: The measurement of the body in the living and in the cadaver.
Cephalometry: Included in somatometry, the measurement of the head and face in the living and in the cadaver and from x-ray films.
Osteometry: The measurement of the skeleton and its parts.
Craniometry: Included in osteometry, the measurement of the skull.

The techniques of anthropometry are best acquired from an experienced worker in the field or laboratory. The attainment of accuracy in anthropometry requires a good deal of practice. A fundamental rule to bear in mind is that when a problem requiring the assistance of anthropometry is presented, all those parts of the body, and only those, should be measured which are capable of throwing some light upon that problem. If the form and dimensions of the lower jaw are the subject of principal interest, it is very unlikely that the length of the forearm will cast any additional light upon the problem. The dimensions of the head would seem more likely to be of assistance, and in any event constitute relevant information for an understanding of the lower jaw in its anatomico-physiological relationships, hence it were advisable to make relationally significant measurements of the head.

On the other hand if one is interested in relative growth, rates of growth may be discovered to exist for lower jaw and for upper and lower extremities which are similar. This, indeed, has been found to be the case.[1] In studies of growth few measurements can be irrelevant.

Before a measurement is projected it is useful to ask what purpose it is designed to serve. Every measurement constitutes an answer to a question, and as Cardinal Newman once remarked, any fool can ask meaningless questions. It is well to remember that the answer obtained to a question is largely determined by the structure of the question asked. Some questions are more meaningful than others. A measurement is a reply to the question: What is the extent, quantity or size of this dimension? The answer obtained does not necessarily express any fact other than that it has been determined according to the criteria or standards used. The purposes for which measurements are made may differ considerably. If, for example, the investigator is

---

[1] Shepherd, R. H., Sholl, and Vizoso, A.: The size relationship subsisting between body length, limbs and jaws in man. *J. Anat.,* 83:296-302, 1949.

interested in total height, his method of measurement will be very different from that followed by the investigator who is interested in discovering the rate of growth of the different components that enter into the conditioning of total height. The inquirer who is interested in objectifying genetic variation will attempt measurements that are refined enough to reflect the genetic conditions. These, of course, he will at best only approximate. The investigator interested in the growth of the head will make measurements that recognize the genetic and functional individuality of the many elements that go to make up the head, and he will therefore attempt to devise measurements that will individually serve to follow the changes in these elements as they grow and develop in relation to one another and to the head as a whole.

New methods based on sound principles may always be devised by an investigator to meet the demands of his particular problem. Measurements based on genuine functional biological relations are those most to be encouraged. The development of such biologically based measurements is to be preferred to the slavish repetition of those embalmed in anthropometric manuals, not excluding the present one.

ESSENTIAL HISTORICAL DATA

The history of the person measured should always be taken, since that history is to some extent part and parcel of the body being measured. Anthropometric findings should, so far as possible, always be evaluated in the light of the historical data. The following constitute the minimum historical data to be gathered:

Name	Religion
Sex	Occupation
Age, to the nearest birthday	Social status
Birthplace	Economic status
Ethnic group	Physical environment
Birth order, 1st, 2nd, etc.	First menstruation
Brothers	First conception
Sisters	Marital status
Mother's ethnic group	Children
Father's ethnic group	Illnesses

INSTRUMENTS IN SOMATOMETRY

The following instruments are those most commonly used in somatometric as well as in osteometric studies.

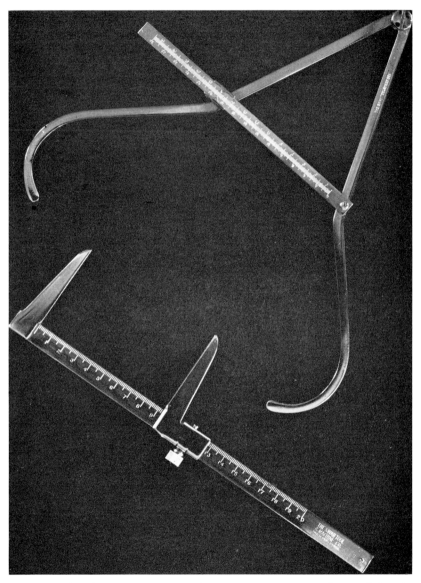

Figure 205. Sliding compass (below) and spreading calipers (above). (Photo Dr. Morris Steggerda and the Swan Tool and Machine Company, Hartford, Connecticut.)

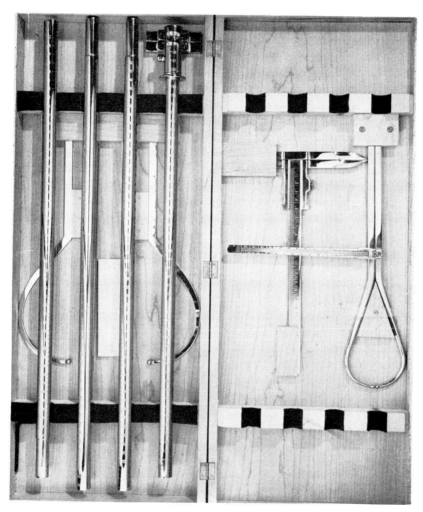

Figure 206. Case of basic anthropometric instruments. Anthropometer, sliding compass, and spreading calipers. (Courtesy of the manufacturers, Gilliland Instrument Co., Oakland, California.)

Weight Beam Scale.[2] To determine weight, preferably in grams.

Camera. Photography of subjects.

Measuring Tape. Graduated in millimeters, of good flexible steel.

Anthropometer.[3] For measuring height and various transverse diameters of the body, this convenient instrument generally consists of four hollow tubes which fit into one another to form a rigid rod of about two meters in length. Each tube is graduated in millimeters, one side reading from above and the other from below zero to two thousand millimeters. This instrument may be used for taking stature, sitting-height, and various other heights, as a caliper in taking transverse diameters, and as a pelvimeter.

Spreading Caliper.[4] For measuring such diameters of the head as the length and breadth of the head, bizygomatic diameter, etc.

Sliding Compass. For measuring shorter diameters such as those of the nose, ears, hand, etc.[5]

Head Spanner. For determining the height of the head.[6]

SOMATOMETRY

Measurement of the Dimensions of the Body

It is desirable to make most measurements with the subject in the standing position. To this rule measurements of the head and face, sitting-height, and a few others constitute the only exceptions.

Whenever possible all measurements should be made during the morning rather than the afternoon or evening, for the reason that individuals generally decrease in height from morning towards evening, and further because they tend to be more relaxed during the morning.

Where the body as a whole is being measured it is preferable that the subject be completely unclothed. When this is not possible the

---

[2] No. 66830, C. H. Stoelting & Company, Illinois, weighs up to 240 pounds, the beam is graduated in both pounds and grams. This balance scale is portable and therefore lends itself for use in field work. A remarkably light scale (total weight two pounds) is that developed by the late Dr. Morris Steggerda. This scale is capable of weighing a man of 325 pounds. It is obtainable from the Swan Tool and Manufacturing Machine Company, 30 Bartholomew Avenue, Hartford, Connecticut.

[3, 4, 5] May be inexpensively purchased from the Swan Tool and Manufacturing Machine Company, 30 Bartholomew Avenue, Hartford, Connecticut.

[6] This and all other anthropological instruments may be ordered from Siber Hegner & Co., Ltd., Talstrasse 14, Zurich, Switzerland. New York office: 183, Madison Avenue, New York 16, New York. Delivery: four to six weeks. U.S. duty: 45 per cent! Also Gilliland Instrument Co., Oakland, California.

investigator will have to make the best of the situation encountered. All measurements on the living should be made with a minimum of pressure by the instruments.

Landmarks (see Figures 207 and 208). In order that all measurements shall be comparable it is customary to take them from certain definite points, these are designated as landmarks. These landmarks will not be listed separately here but will be defined in connection with the measurements to be taken.

Measurements With Subject in Standing Position

Position of Subject. All measurements, unless otherwise indicated, should be made with the subject standing in the military position at attention, head erect, looking straight ahead, so that his visual axis is parallel to the surface of the floor. The latter is the best free approximation to the Frankfurt Plane (p. 567).

1. *Standing Height or Stature* (Anthropometer). The distance from the highest point of the top of the head in the mid-sagittal plane to the floor.

2. *Suprasternal Height* (Anthropometer). From the middle of the anterior-superior border of the manubrium sterni to the floor.

3. *Right Acromiale Height* (Anthropometer). From the most lateral projection of the lateral border of the acromion of the scapula to the floor.

4. *Right Radiale Height* (Anthropometer). From the highest point of the head of the radius (usually at the dimple of the elbow) to the floor.

5. *Right Stylion Height* (Anthropometer). From the distolateral end of the styloid process of the radius to the floor.

The *upper* and *lower arm dimensions* may be obtained by the subtraction of measurements 4 from 3 and 5 from 4, but are more accurately measured directly.

6. *Upper Arm Length* (Anthropometer). From acromiale to radiale when the arm is hanging down and the palm facing inward.

7. *Lower Arm Length* (Anthropometer). From radiale to stylion when the arm is hanging down and the palm facing inward.

8. *Total Arm Length* (Anthropometer). From acromiale to stylion when the arm is hanging down and the palm facing inward or by adding measurements 6 and 7.

9. *Total Upper Extremity Length* (Anthropometer). From acromiale to dactylion, *i.e.* the tip of the middle finger.

10. *Right Dactylon Height* (Anthropometer). From the middle of the tip of the middle finger when the fingers are removed from

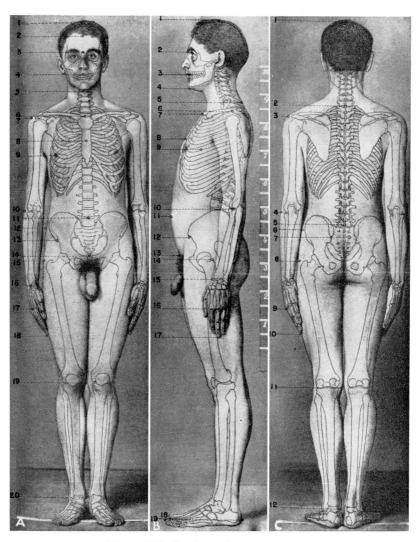

Figure 207. See legend opposite page.

contact with the thigh and are pointing perpendicularly downwards to the floor.

11. *Right Iliocristale Height* (Anthropometer). From the most laterally projecting point on the crest of the right ilium to the floor.

12. *Right Iliospinale Height* (Anthropometer). From the right anterior-superior iliac spine to the floor.

13. *Right Trochanterion Height* (Anthropometer). From the superior surface of the greater trochanter of the femur to the floor.

14. *Right Tibiale Height* (Anthropometer). From the superior surface of the medial condyle of the tibia to the floor.

15. *Right Sphyrion Height* (Anthropometer). From the inferior surface of the medial malleolus to the floor.

Transverse and Antero-Posterior Dimensions

16. *Span* (Anthropometer). The distance between the tips of the middle fingers of each hand when the arms are outstretched sidewards horizontally from the body. Measured from behind.

17. *Bi-Acromial Breadth* (Anthropometer used as sliding compass). The distance between the most lateral margins of the acromion processes of the scapula, the subject standing as he does normally.

18. *Chest Breadth or Transverse Diameter of the Thorax* (Anthropometer used as sliding compass. The transverse distance between the most lateral points on the chest. The mean of the measurements made at expiration and inspiration while the subject is breathing normally.

19. *Chest Depth or Antero-Posterior Diameter of the Thorax*

←

Figure 207. Landmarks of the body (after Martin).

Figure 207A. Landmarks on the frontal view. 1, vertex; 2, trichion; 3, nasion; 4, prosthion; 5, gnathion; 6, suprasternale; 7, akromion; 8, mesosternale; 9, thelion; 10, radiale; 11, omphalion 12, iliocristale; 13, iliospinale anterior; 14, symphysion; 15, trochanterion; 16, stylion; 17, phalangion; 18, daktylion; 19, tibiale; 20, sphyrion.

Figure 207B. Landmarks in the lateral view. 1, vertex; 2, nasion; 3, stomion; 4, gnathion; 5, cervicale; 6, akromion; 7, suprasternale; 8, mesosternale; 9, thelion; 10, radiale; 11, omphalion; 12, iliospinale anterior; 13, symphysion; 14, trochanterion; 15, stylion; 16, phalangion; 17, daktylion; 18, pternion; 19, akropodion.

Figure 207C. Landmarks in the posterior view. 1, vertex; 2, cervicale; 3, akromion; 4, radiale; 5, lumbale; 6, iliocristale; 7, iliospinale posterior; 8, trochanterion; 9, phalangion; 10, daktylion; 11, tibiale; 12, sphyrion.

(Large Spreading Caliper). At the level of the inferior angles of the scapulae. The mean of the measurements made at expiration and inspiration while the subject is breathing normally.

20. *Bi-Iliac or Pelvic Breadth* (Anthropometer used as a sliding compass). From iliocristale, the most lateral point on the crest of the ilium to iliocristale.

21. *Bi-Trochanteric or Hip Breadth* (Anthropometer used as a sliding compass). From trochanterion, the most lateral point on the great trochanter, to trochanterion.

Girths

22. *Axillary Chest Girth* (Tape). The tape applied well up in the axillary fossae. Mean reading of measurements during normal inspiration and expiration.

23. *Mesosternale Chest Girth* (Tape). At the level of the mesosternale. Mean of measurements during normal inspiration and expiration.

24. *Minimum Circumference of the Trunk-Waist Girth* (Tape). The minimum waist girth. Mean of measurements during normal inspiration and expiration.

25. *Maximum Gluteo-Pubic Circumference—Hip Girth* (Tape). The subject stands in the military position at attention. The tape is placed over the most prominent portion of the buttocks, is brought around the level of the greater trochanters to terminate anteriorly at the level determined by the buttocks and trochanters in the pubic region.

26. *Maximum Circumference of the Right Arm* (Tape). When the arm is hanging relaxed at the subject's side.

27. *Maximum Circumference of the Right Forearm* (Tape). Immediately distal to the elbow joint, with the whole extremity relaxed.

28. *Minimum Circumference of the Right Forearm—Girth of Wrist* (Tape). Slightly above the level of the styloid processes of the radius and ulna.

29. *Maximum Circumference of the Right Thigh* (Tape). Perpendicular to the long axis of the thigh, with the tape in the gluteal fold.

30. *Minimum Circumference of the Right Thigh* (Tape). Slightly proximal to the condyles of the femur.

31. *Maximum Circumference of the Right Leg—Girth of Calf* (Tape). The level of the maximum diameter above the floor should also be recorded.

32. *Minimum Circumference of the Right Leg—Girth of Ankle* (Tape). Slightly above the level of the malleoli.

Measurements With Subject in Sitting Position

Sitting Heights

A bench or box, high enough to keep the subject's feet away from the ground is placed against a wall, and the subject is instructed to take his seat in such a manner as to enable him to swing his legs freely over the front of the bench or box, while his scapular and sacral regions are resting vertically against the surface of the wall. In this position all measurements are taken from the specified landmark to the seat of the bench or box. The subject sits erectly with the head in the plane of the visual axis.

33. *Sitting Vertex Height* (Anthropometer). From the highest point, in the sagittal plane, of the head to the surface upon which the subject is seated.

34. *Sitting Suprasternale Height* (Anthropometer). From the middle of the anterior-superior border of the manubrium sterni to the floor.

By subtracting 34 from 33 the height of the head and neck is obtained.

Dimensions of the Hand and Foot

35. *Maximum Hand Length* (Sliding Compass). The hand is laid flat on a table. The distance from the mid-point of a line connecting the styloid processes of radius and ulna to the most anterior projection of the skin of the middle finger.

36. *Hand Breadth* (Sliding Compass). From the radial side of the second metacarpo-phalangeal junction to the ulnar side of the fifth metacarpo-phalangeal junction.

37. *Maximum Foot Length* (Spreading Calipers). From the most posteriorly projecting point on the heel (akropodion) to the tip of the most anteriorly projecting toe (pternion), when the subject is standing erect.

38. *Foot Breadth* (Anthropometer as Sliding Compass). From the medial margin of the head of the first metatarsal to the lateral margin of the head of the fifth metatarsal.

Dimensions of the Head

Measurements of the head are best made while the subject is comfortably seated in a chair. As for the rest of the body so in the case of the head, the measurements which the investigator will want to make upon the head will, for the most part, be determined by the nature of his problem. Below are given the measurements most generally made, but the investigator may devise others to suit the special requirements of his particular problem. Such new measurements, however, must have some morphological basis and should not begin and end, as it were, in thin air.

Before listing the measurements made to determine the various dimensions of the head it is necessary to define the landmarks from which such measurements are conventionally made. The position of these landmarks is shown in Figure 208.

Alare (al). The most lateral point on the wing of the nose.

Cheilion (ch). The most lateral point at the corner of the lips.

Ectocanthion (ex). Outer corner of the eye or palpebral opening.

Endocanthion (en). Inner corner of the eye or palpebral opening.

Euryon (eu). The most lateral point on the side of the head.

Frontotemporale (ft). The most medial (deepest) point on the incurvure of the temple, just above and lateral to the orbit (see Figure 208).

Glabella (g). The most prominent point, in the midsagittal plane, between the eyebrows.

Gnathion (gn). The lowest median point on the lower border of the mandible.

Gonion (go). The most lateral point upon the postero-inferior angle (formed by the ramus and the body) of the mandible.

Infradentale (id). The highest point on the gum between the mandibular central incisors.

Labrale inferius (li). The median point in the lower margin of the lower membranous lip.

Labrale superius (ls). The median point in the upper margin of the upper membranous lip.

Metopion (m). The median point of a line connecting the two frontal eminences.

Nasion (n). The point at which a horizontal tangential to the highest points on the superior palpebral sulci intersects the midsagittal plane (Figures 208A and 218). The subject should be looking straight ahead.

Ophryon (on). The median point of a line drawn tangent to the upper border of the eyebrows.

Opisthocranion (op). The point of most backward projection of the head, in the mid-plane.

Orbitale (or). The lowest point on the inferior orbital margin.

Otobasion inferius (obi). The lowest point at which the ear attaches to the side of the head.

Porion (po). The point 5.0 mm. above the middle of the external border of the roof of the cutaneous external auditory meatus.

Postaurale (pa). The most posterior point on the helix of the ear.

Preaurale (pra). The point at which a straight line drawn from the postaurale perpendicular to the long axis of the external ear meets the base of the external ear.

Pronasale (prn). The tip of the nose.

Prosthion (pr). The lowest point on the gum between the maxillary central incisors.

Stomion (sto). The central point in the oral fissure when the lips are closed.

Subaurale (sba). The lowest point on the inferior border of the ear lobule when the head is held in the Frankfurt Plane.

Subnasale (sn). The point at which the nasal septum, between the nostrils, merges with the upper cutaneous lip in the mid-sagittal plane.

Superaurale (sa). The highest point on the superior border of the helix.

The Frankfurt Plane or Horizontal (F.H.). The plane determined by the lowest points on the infra-orbital margins (the *orbitalia,* "or" in Figure 208B) and the tragion or tragial notch of the ear ("t" in Figure 208A). This corresponds almost exactly to the plane of the visual axis, which obtains when the individual is looking straight ahead of him.

Tragion (t). The notch immediately above the tragus of the ear.

Trichion (tr). The mid-point at the hairline on the forehead.

Tuberculare (tu). Darwin's point on the ear; the tubercle on the upper portion of the helix.

Vertex (v). The highest point of the head, in the mid-sagittal plane, when the head is held erectly or in the Frankfurt Plane.

Zygion (z). The lateralmost point on the zygomatic arch.

Cephalometry

Measurements of the Head

Maximum Head Length (Spreading Caliper). The distance between the glabella and the farthest projecting point in the mid-sagittal plane, on the back of the head (occiput). The latter point is termed the opisthocranion.

Maximum Head Breadth (Spreading Caliper). The greatest transverse diameter of the head. This is usually found at a point over each parietal bone (each point is termed the euryon).

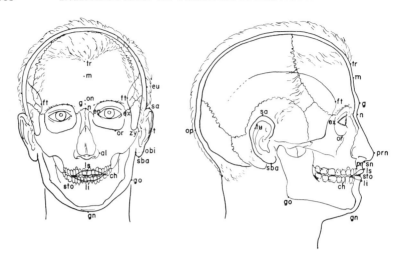

Figure 208A   Figure 208B

Figure 208. A. Landmarks in the frontal view of the head. B. Landmarks in the lateral view of the head. al, alare; ch, chelion; ex, ectocanthion; en, endocanthion; eu, euryon; ft, frontotemporale; g, glabella; gn, gnathion; go, gonion; li, labrale inferius; ls, labrale superius; m, metopion; n, nasion; on, ophryon; op, opisthocranion; or, orbitale; obi, otobasion inferius; prn, pronasale; pr, prosthion; sba, subaurale; sn, subnasale; sa, superaurale; t, tragion; tr, trichion; tu, tuberculare; zy, zygion. (From Martin, *Lehrbuch der Anthropologie*, 1928. Courtesy, Gustav Fischer, Jena.)

Head Height (Todd's Head-Spanner). The fiber-tipped movable horizontal rods are inserted into the ear-holes so that they touch the roof of the latter, the rods are then secured by screws. The orbital arm is then placed at the level of the most inferior point on the infra-orbital margin and kept there. As long as this position is maintained the head is in the Frankfurt Plane in relation to the measuring ruler. The latter is then released to the level of the top of the head, and the measurement read off. Eight mm. may be deducted from this measurement to allow for the thickness of the skin and subjacent tissues, should the height of the skull be desired. Five millimeters should then also be deducted to allow for the thickness of the tissues forming the roof of the ear-hole.

Minimum Frontal Breadth (Spreading Caliper). The shortest distance between the origins of the zygomatic processes of the frontal bones (the fronta-temporales, "ft" in Figures 208A and 208B).

Bizygomatic Breadth (Spreading Caliper). The distance between the most laterally situated points on the zygomatic arches (the zygia, "zy" in Figure 208B).

Bigonial Breadth (Spreading Caliper). The distance between the gonial points.

Physiognomic Facial Length (Sliding Compass). From trichion to gnathion.

Morphological Facial Height (Sliding Compass). From nasion to gnathion.

Total Jaw Height (Sliding Compass). From subnasale to gnathion. The jaws must be normally closed without undue pressure.

Inter-Canthic Diameter (Sliding Compass). From the medial point of the junction of the upper and lower eyelids ("en" in Figure 208A) of one side to the other.

Extra-Canthic Diameter (Sliding Compass). From the lateral point of the junction of the upper and lower eyelids ("ex" in Figure 208A) of the one side to the other.

Nasal Length (Sliding Compass). From nasion to subnasale.

Maximum Physiognomic Nasal Breadth (Sliding Compass). The maximum transverse distance between the most laterally situated points on the wings of the nose (the alare, "al" in Figure 208A).

Maximum Breadth of the Mouth (Sliding Compass). The maximum breadth of the mouth when the face is in a relaxed condition (from "ch" to "ch" in Figure 208A).

Physiognomic Ear Height (Sliding Compass). The distance between the superaurale and the subaurale ("sa" and "sba" in Figure 208B).

Physiognomic Ear Breadth (Sliding Compass). The distance between the preaurale and the postaurale. ("pra" and "pa" in Figure 208B).

Girths

39. *Maximum Circumference of the Head* (Tape). From the smooth area between eyebrows (glabella) around the maximum projection of the occiput (opisthocranion) to the glabella.

40. *Circumference of Neck* (Tape). At the level of the most prominent portion of the thyroid cartilage.

Indices

An index, as used in anthropometry, is the ratio of one measurement to another expressed as a percentage of the larger one. Thus, if it is desired to determine the proportional relation of the breadth of the head to its length, the length is equated to the value of 100, and the breadth is then expressed as a ratio of 100. This yields the cephalic index, in which breadth is to length as x is to 100, the value of x being found by multiplying the actual value of the breadth by 100 and dividing by the actual length. Thus:

$$\frac{\text{Breadth} \times 100}{\text{Length}} = \text{Cephalic Index (x).}$$

By means of indices obtained in this way, it is possible to convey an exact idea of the proportion which one measurement bears to another, and thus something of the form of the structures concerned, in a single numerical expression. For example, a cephalic index of 75 per cent means that the breadth of the head is to its length as 75 is to 100; which clearly means that the breadth of the head is equal to three-fourths of its length or is 75 per cent of its length. An index greater than 75 would mean that the head was so much broader in relation to its length, and an index below 75 would mean the opposite. Thus, an index of 100 would mean that the head was as broad as it is long, and an index of 50 that the breadth of the head was exactly equal to half its length.

The number of indices which have been devised are almost countless. A good general rule to follow is to use or devise only such indices as are absolutely necessary to the prosecution, and the presentation of the results, of an investigation.

In comparing any two measurements it is sometimes convenient to refer them to some definite standard, preferably one which is not too variable. Total stature and sitting height are as near as we can get to such standards, and any bodily measurement may be expressed as an index with reference to total height or sitting height, thus:

$$\frac{\text{any bodily measurement} \times 100}{\text{total height or stature}} = \text{stature index of measurement used}$$

$$\frac{\text{any bodily measurement} \times 100}{\text{sitting height}} = \text{sitting height index of measurement used}$$

The following represent some of the anthropometric indices most commonly used:

$$\text{Cephalic index} = \frac{\text{Maximum Head Breadth} \times 100}{\text{Maximum Head Length}}$$

Dolichocephalic $\times -75.9$
Mesocephalic $76.0-80.9$
Brachycephalic $81.0-85.4$
Hyperbrachycephalic $85.5-\times$

$$\text{Brachial Index} = \frac{\text{Length of Forearm} \times 100}{\text{Length of Upper Arm}}$$

$$\text{Forearm-Hand Index} = \frac{\text{Hand Length} \times 100}{\text{Length of Forearm}}$$

$$\text{Hand Index} = \frac{\text{Hand Breadth} \times 100}{\text{Hand Length}}$$

$$\text{Tibio-Femoral Index} = \frac{\text{Length of Lower Leg} \times 100}{\text{Length of Thigh}}$$

$$\text{Lower Leg-Foot Index} = \frac{\text{Length of Foot} \times 100}{\text{Length of Lower Leg}}$$

$$\text{Intermembral Index} = \frac{\text{Length of Entire Arm} \times 100}{\text{Length of Entire Leg}}$$

$$\text{Femero-Humeral Index} = \frac{\text{Length of Upper Arm} \times 100}{\text{Length of Thigh}}$$

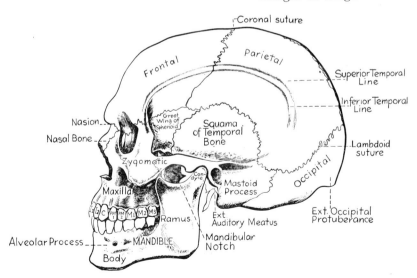

Figure 209. The Human skull.

$$\text{Tibio-Radial Index} = \frac{\text{Length of Forearm} \times 100}{\text{Length of Lower Leg}}$$

$$\text{Trunk Index} = \frac{\text{Biacromial Breadth} \times 100}{\text{Sitting Suprasternale Height}}$$

There are many more indices than these, but it is unnecessary to deal with them here. Additional lists of indices will be found in the works on anthropometry cited in the bibliography.

A large number of constitutional indices have been devised, but not one of these has yet proved satisfactory, for the reason that constitution is far too complex a thing to be expressible in terms of a single index.[7]

CRANIAL CAPACITY IN THE LIVING

This may be computed by the Lee-Pearson formula, as follows: For *males*, .000337 (cephalic length − 11) × (cephalic breadth − 11) × (ear head-height − 11) + 406.01; for *females*, .0004 (cephalic length − 11) × (cephalic breadth − 11) × (ear head-height − 11) + 206.60.

ANTHROPOSCOPIC OBSERVATIONS

In making visual observations on the subject the investigator must strive to attain the greatest precision, to eliminate the element of subjective judgment, and to obtain as objective a record as possible. The ideal at which to aim is the attainment of standards of accuracy which are as nearly quantitatively expressible as possible. Hence, methods contributing towards this end are, in all instances, to be preferred. The development of such methods is an urgent desideratum. Many anthroposcopic methods at present in use are hopelessly unreliable. Only a few of those available methods can be dealt with here which are capable of yielding relatively sound and comparable observations.

All observations should be made in good light.

Abbreviations which have been used in recording some observations are: abs = absent, undeveloped, none; sl. = slight, very small; sm. = small, submedium, few; + = average, medium, several; + + = above average, large, pronounced, many; + + + = great, very many, extraordinary development; ? = not observable.

1. *Somatotype*. Made from photographs taken in the standard positions described hereunder in direction 18, (pp. 578-579).

---

[7] For a list of constitutional indices see Tucker, W.B. and Lessa, W. A.: Man: a constitutional investigation. *Quart. Rev. Biol.*, 15:413-414, 1940.

2. *General Sex Facies or Appearance* (after establishment of puberty).

Whether the mature subject appears to deviate from normalcy; whether he is hypogonadal or gynandromorphic, infantile or juvenile, masculine or feminine (in the opposite sex), adult or senile. By "hypogonadal" is to be understood inadequate development of the secondary sexual characters. By "gynandromorphy" the degree or prominence of the secondary sexual characters of the one sex present in a member of the opposite sex. Since many groups differ from American North European white standards, the observer should take great care in arriving at his standard of the norm in such groups.

3. *Skin Color.* There is no rule as to where skin color should be taken.

The inner surface of the upper arm has been frequently used on the assumption that it is a region not too much exposed to sunlight. Whatever region is used should be used constantly in the series under investigation. Skin color should be determined by the use of some fast and easily reduplicable color standard. The best available color standards are obtainable from the non-profit Munsell Color Company (of which Mrs. B. R. Bellamy is manager), 10 East Franklin Street, Baltimore 2, Maryland. It will be found useful to cut a small square out of a piece of cardboard, and hold this over the desired area on the subject for comparison with the color squares on the Munsell charts. This eliminates the distraction of adjoining areas of skin color and speeds accurate matching of colors.

Record presence and position of any variably pigmented areas, including the so-called "blue-spot" (miscalled "Mongoloid spot") in sacral region of infants.

4. *Hair Color.* Scalp, face, and body hair, eyebrows, mustache, beard, chest, abdomen, pubes, and extremities, to be observed and recorded separately. Use Munsell color standards. Collect samples of hair and record area from which taken.

5. *Hair Form.* Usually but quite inadequately described as: Straight, low wave, medium wave, deep wave, curly, frizzly or kinky, and coiled or spiral tufts (pepper corn).

Dr. Stanley Garn has kindly supplied the following comments on hair form:

Human head hair exists in a complete range of forms, with hair that is nearly straight and hair that curls into tight spirals representing the extremes of the human distribution.

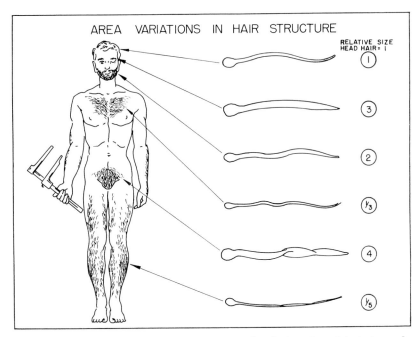

Figure 210. Area variations in structure and relative size of hair in male.
(Courtesy, Dr. S. M. Garn.)

Figure 211. Skin folds over the upper eyelid in man. →The right eye is
shown with the root of the nose, nasion, toward the middle of the page.
a, complete Mongoloid fold, b, internal epicanthic fold, c, no fold, d, external
epicanthic fold, e, median fold. a', mid-sagittal section showing the relation
of the skin fold to the upper eyelid in the Mongoloid, and c' in the non-
Mongoloid. (Modified after Hooton, *Up From the Ape,* 1946. Courtesy,
The Macmillan Co.)

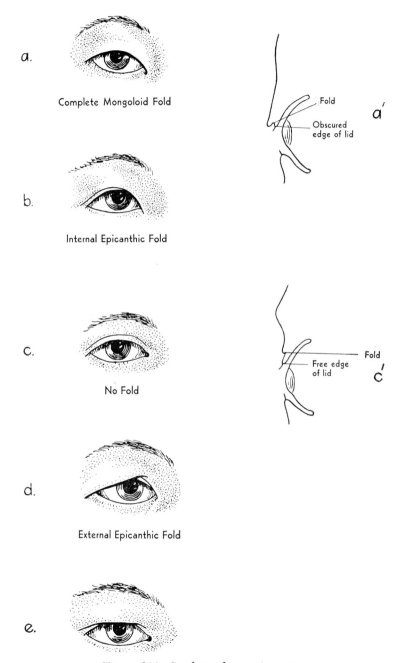

a.

Complete Mongoloid Fold

a'

Fold

Obscured
edge of lid

b.

Internal Epicanthic Fold

c.

No Fold

c'

Fold

Free edge
of lid

d.

External Epicanthic Fold

e.

Figure 211. See legend opposite page.

Actually, no human hair is completely straight, but if the radius of curvature is larger than that of the head, it appears straight when short, and hangs straight by its own weight if long. When the curvature is in one direction, the hair forms ringlets or helices. With reversing or alternating curvature the hair is "wavy," whereas very small radii of curvature, becoming progressively slightly larger, are characteristic of the spiral-tuft type. The best description of hair form is therefore not verbal, but mathematical, thus avoiding a needless series of descriptive categories.

Clearly, variations in the form of the hair are due to localized growth gradients in the follicle, with obvious synchronia among adjacent hair follicles. The form of hair that a given follicle will produce is apparently determined genetically, occasionally by a single pair of genes, but more commonly by the cumulative action of many genes. Hormonal influences also affect hair curvature, sometimes by controlling the rate of hair growth, or hair thickness.

By analogy with the propagation of light waves, one can view variations in hair form as due to oscillations within the follicle during growth. The more rapid the oscillations, the shorter is the wave-length, and, if the rotatory movement is continuous, helices and spirals are superimposed upon the growing hairs. With synchronous follicular activity, hairs in a given region, comprising a lock, have similar degrees of curvature. This is especially evident in the fur of the Karakul lamb, and in poodles, and people with helical and spiral-locks.

Where hair-straightening or hair curling is not practiced, measurements of the wavelength (distance between peaks), amplitude, radius of curvature, furnish useful genetically-meaningful data for mathematical analysis.

6. *Hair Quantity.* Number of hairs in a square centimeter of scalp; whether thick, medium, thinning, thin; degree and pattern of baldness.
7. *Eye Color.* With the subject in good light and facing a white surface the iris is matched with Munsell color samples. Record raying, zoning, and spotting of iris.
8. *Supraorbital Ridges.* Absent, slight, medium, and pronounced.
9. *Ear Form.* Degree of rolling of helix; whether lobe of ear is free or attached; Darwin's point; size; shape.

10. *Eyefolds.* The arrangements of the skin over the upper eyelids and canthi.

Described and defined as follows (see Figure 211):

    i. *Complete Mongoloid Fold:* The skin above the upper eyelid is loose and hangs down over the free margin of the eyelid.

    ii. *Internal Epicanthic Fold:* The skin hangs over the inner canthus alone.

    iii. *External Epicanthic Fold:* The skin hangs over the external canthus alone.

    iv. *No Fold:* The skin forms a gentle arch above the upper eyelid.

    v. *Median Fold:* The skin hangs down over the middle part of the margin of the upper eyelid and leaves both canthi exposed.

    vi. *Pseudo-Mongoloid Fold:* Usually present in babies but disappears within a year or two with growth; occurs often as an age change in older people, simulating the appearance of the complete Mongoloid fold.

11. *Nose Form.*

    i. *Nasal Profile:* Concave, straight, convex, concavo-convex.

    ii. *Nasal Root:* Flat, recessed, medium, prominent.

    iii. *Nasal Tip:* Narrow, medium, thick, bulbous.

12. *Nostrils.* Broad, oval, round. Angle in relation to mid-sagittal plane.

13. *Lips.*

    i. *Membranous:* Thin, medium, thick, very thick; degree of eversion.

    ii. *Integumental:* Thickness.

14. *Dentition.* A dental form showing the occlusal surfaces of the teeth of the upper and lower jaws should be used, and all observations marked, whenever possible, directly upon the teeth referred to. The S. S. White Dental Manufacturing Company supplies useful record cards for this purpose. A dental mirror will be found useful. The following details should be noted:

    i. *Occlusion or Bite:* Estimated horizontal distance between upper and lower incisors. Recorded as + when upper teeth are in advance of the lower; as — when lower teeth are in advance of the upper.

    ii. Level above gum of erupting teeth, in millimeters.

   iii. Shovel-shaped incisors.

   iv. Supernumerary teeth.

    v. Congenitally missing teeth.

   vi. Unerupted teeth.

  vii. Crowding.

 viii. Rotation.

   ix. Accessory cusps or tubercles.

    x. Wear of occlusal surfaces.

   xi. Teeth lost by extraction or otherwise.

  xii. Caries.

 xiii. Fissural patterns of occlusal surfaces of mandibular three molars, Y5, +5, Y4, or +4.

15. *Mandibular Torus.* Bony thickening, inner sides of mandible.
16. *Palatal Form.* Narrow, intermediate, broad; low, medium, high. Whether torus palatinus (a piling up of bone along the course of the palatine intermaxillary suture which may be felt and often seen at the median raphe in the living) is present.
17. *Chin Form.* Pointed, rounded, square; receding, vertical, slight, medium, marked protrusion. The observer must define his standards and consistently adhere to them.
18. *Standard Photographs.* The aim should be to obtain photographs which give as complete a view of the nude body as possible and all its outlines. This is particularly necessary for somatotyping. Full length views of the front, back, and left side are desirable. Front view and left profile photographs of the head may be taken as supplementary, or when full views in the nude are not possible. The subject should always be placed at a constant distance from the lens of the camera, the background should always be as nearly uniform as possible, and floor, wall or ground and background so arranged that they merge in the photograph, and preferably appear *white*. For purposes of standard reproduction any background may be air-brushed white. Use panchromatic film. Women should pile the hair on top of the head in a hair net, in order not to obscure the outlines of the neck and shoulders.

Frontal View

    i. Subject in normal standing position breathing normally, with lower extremities just sufficiently separated so that the inner aspects of the thighs do not touch.

ii. Eyes looking straight ahead.

iii. Arms, hands, and fingers straight. Lock olecranon process.

iv. Hands five inches out from thighs.

v. Right and left hands palm facing thigh.

Left Profile

i. Arms, hands, and fingers straight. Held flat against the body in center of body outline, so that neither elbow nor hand break the outline behind or in front.

ii. Knees and legs perfectly in line. Do not lock.

iii. Face in perfect profile, subject looking straight ahead.

Back View

i. As front. If lighting is oblique arms should be carried forward to prevent shadow on flanks.[8]

[8] For the most recent recommendations for the standardization of techniques in posing the subject see Dupertuis, C. W. and Tanner, J. M.: The pose of the subject for photogrammetric anthropometry, with especial reference to somatotyping. *Am. J. Phys. Anthropol.*, n.s. 8:27-47, 1950.

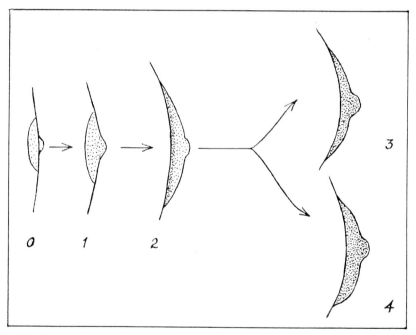

Figure 212. Four stages in areolar development of the white female. (Modified after Garn and Shamir.)

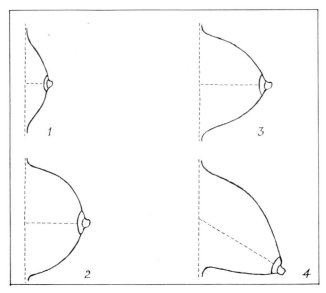

Figure 213. Schematic representation of breast shapes. 1. Bowl-shaped. 2. Hemispherical. 3. Conical. 4. Elongated.

19. *Papillae, Areolae, Breasts.* The elements of the breasts, papillae, areolae, and the fatty main body of the breasts should be carefully distinguished. Record all anomalies and asymmetries, and supernumerary elements.

> *Papillae:* Flat, infantile, everted, and their size indicated.
> *Areolae:* 0 Infantile, small, flat, lightly pigmented.
> > 1 Early-maturing, pigmentation still developing, areolae separately elevated from body of breast, papilla buried.
> > 2 Later-maturing, there is a marked ring of pigmentation at the periphery, papilla still buried.
> > 3 Mature Areolae no longer separately elevated, papilla everted.
> > 4 Mature Areolae separately elevated, papilla everted.
> *Breast Form:*
> > 1. Bowl-shaped, in which the anterior projection is less than the radius of the circumference.
> > 2. Hemispherical, in which the anterior projection is equal to the radius of the circumference.

    3. Conical, in which the anterior projection is greater than the radius.

    4. Dependent, with the papillae pointing downwards.

20. *Lumbar Curvature.* Slight, moderate, marked.

21. *Buttocks.* Flat, medium, prominent, steatopygious.

22. *External genitalia.* In the male penis may be measured from pubis to external os, in flaccid condition. In female, size of labia may be recorded.

23. *Hands and Feet.* Note any webbing of fingers or toes, or any other anomalies. Note shape of nails, as long-narrow, short-broad, etc. The relative projection of fingers and toes in relation to each of their fellows is expressible in the *digital formula.* In the hand one begins counting with the thumb as 1, the index-finger as 2, the middle finger as 3, the ring-finger as 4, and the little finger as 5. The most projecting finger is written first. For example, if the middle finger projects furthest, and the ring-finger further than the index-finger, and the index-finger further than the little finger, and the little finger further than the thumb, one writes the digital formula thus: $3 > 4 > 2 > 5 > 1$. The same procedure is followed for the toes, counting the big toe as 1 and the little toe as 5. Supernumerary digits or toes and all other possible variations and anomalies may be recorded.

FINGER, PALM, TOE, AND SOLE PRINTS

    The skin on the palmar and plantar surfaces of the human hand and foot differs in character from that covering other parts of the body. The palmar and plantar skin is corrugated into continuous ridges and lacks both hairs and sebaceous (oil) glands. Sweat glands are, however, numerous. These corrugated ridges are known as friction ridges and are present in all primates.[9] These ridges are obviously of great assistance in handling and grasping since they help to counteract slipping. Since from the time of their formation in the early fetus to the final disintegration of the skin after death the patterns which these ridges present remain unaltered [10] they are of use not only for the purpose of identification, in recognizing types of twins, but also in

---

[9] For a comprehensive study see Midlo, C. and Cummins, H.: Palmar and Plantar Dermatoglyphics in Primates. *American Anatomical Memoirs,* No. 20, Philadelphia, Wistar Inst., 1942.

[10] The ridges on the terminal digits may be so worn down as to be invisible. This is often the case in stenographers. In shoeless people (who habitually wear no shoes) the plantar and toe ridges may be similarly worn down.

studies of heredity, raciation, sex differences, growth, bodily symmetry, and comparative primatology. *Dermatoglyphics (derma, skin—glyphe, carve)* is the name given to the study of the ridge patternings of the skin of the fingers, palms, toes, and soles.

The materials necessary for making finger and palm prints, toe and sole prints are the following: A plate of lucite or bakelite 8" x 10" and ¼" thick, a tube of printer's ink, a rubber roller, and a good grade of white, *not* highly sized, paper or the standard cards customarily in use measuring 8" x 8" for finger prints.

An even film of ink is spread on the lucite or bakelite base, and each finger is then rolled firmly from the inner to the outer edge on the film, the same operation then being repeated upon the paper or cards.

A solvent should be available with which to clean fingers. Fingers for printing should be perfectly clean and dry. After the prints have been made the solvent may be used to remove the ink from the fingers.

In palm printing the inked roller is passed several times over the whole area to be printed from the base of the fingers where they join the palm to the flexion creases on the wrist. The ulnar or little finger side of the subject's palm is then laid against the paper and the hand rolled palm downward to the radial or thumb side. Appreciable pressure must be applied to the back of the hand and over the knuckles in order to obtain satisfactory impressions of the central portions of the palms and bases of the fingers. It is essential to print each tri-radius (triangular group of consolidated ridges) at the base of each finger, as well as the carpal tri-radius located at the base of the thumb.

The sole is inked and printed in the same way as the palm. Each toe is printed separately. Persons suffering from athlete's foot should not be printed even if their friction ridges are visible.

Physiometric Observations

The measurement of the physiological functions of the body will include functions which are sensibly influenced by environmental factors like pulse and even color vision, and some that are not, such as the ability to taste certain substances which is a genetically conditioned trait. A distinction between modifiable physiological functions and genetically conditioned functional traits will not be made here, though the distinction can, of course, and should for certain purposes, be made.

Ten basic observations are here listed which can be made with a reasonable degree of expedition and considerable accuracy.

The subject should always be examined alone. The presence of other persons is distracting, and the desire to imitate or look for clues in the behavior of others confusing. Among non-literate peoples special precautions and cross-checking must be instituted in order to make quite certain the instructions have been understood and the desire of the subject to please has not been too overwhelming.

1. *Physical Fitness or Step Test.* Take pulse with stop-watch. Write down the mean of four one-minute observations. The subject is then asked to step rapidly on and off a 12 inch step or platform for one minute. The exact pace is set with a metronome. Take pulse immediately after subject has completed this operation and determine how long the pulse takes to return to normal.

2. *Dynamometric Strength.* Use a physician's dynamometer with light attached. The mean of the maximum of three squeezes with the hand customarily used for squeezing.

3. *Resistance to Ulta-Violet Ray Burning.* Ethnic variations in sensitivity to skin burning as exhibited in erythema or reddening of the skin due to ultra-violet radiation is something concerning which we know very little. In view of the possibility of selective differences in the frequency of this trait as between different ethnic groups it would be of considerable interest to know whether or not such differences exist. An apparatus suitable for this purpose has been successfully used by Dr. George Levene of Massachusetts Memorial Hospitals, Boston. This consists of a small ultra-violet generator which measures 3 x 6 x 18 inches and weighs a little over seven pounds. There is a one inch square window which is applied to the surface of the skin for a predetermined period of time. The instrument is extremely critical in its radiation, with an intensity exposure of 2,537 angstrom units. The constancy of characteristic tube radiation is controlled by measuring the output from time to time with a special ultra-violet photometer. When the type of radiation varies the lamp is replaced. The degree of erythema or reddening can be measured either by determining the temperature difference between the area of erythema and non-exposed skin by means of a sensitive thermocouple, or by color comparison using the standard Munsell color charts.

This apparatus was designed by Mr. Ronald J. McKenzie of Sylvania Electric Products, Inc., 126 Washington Street, Salem, Massachusetts, who will be glad to answer inquiries concerning it.

For use in the field an electric current supply is, of course, necessary.

4. *Handedness.* Whether subject habitually uses one hand in preference to the other, or is ambidextrous.

TABLE LVI

CONCENTRATIONS OF P.T.C. SOLUTIONS

Solution No.	P.T.C. Mgm. per Liter
1	1300.00
2	650.00
3	325.00
4	162.00
5	81.25
6	40.63
7	20.31
8	10.16
9	5.08
10	2.54
11	1.27
12	0.63
13	0.32
14	0.16

5. *Ability to Taste PTC (Phenyl-Thio-Carbamide)*. The best method of testing ability to taste phenyl-thio-carbamide at various graded standard measurable concentrations is that developed by Harris and Kalmus. A solution containing 0.13% of phenyl-thio-carbamide (or phenylthiourea) is made up with boiled tap water, and serial dilutions made up as in Table LVI.

(1) Starting from the higher dilutions and working down, the subject is given a few c.c. in a glass till he says he perceives a definite taste. This gives an approximate value for his threshold.

(2) The subject is now presented with eight glasses four of which contain a few c.c. of water and four contain a few c.c. of the solution determined in stage (1). The glasses are arranged at random. The subject is told that four of them contain the substance and four contain water, and he is asked to taste them all and to separate them into the two groups of four. The quantity of fluid is not limited, and glasses are refilled during the test if desired. If the two groups of four are correctly separated the test is repeated with the next lower concentration and so on, until the subject can no longer discriminate correctly The lowest concentration at which a completely correct answer is given is taken as the threshold. If, on the other hand, the subject is unable to separate the two groups accurately, the test is repeated in the same manner with increasing concentrations till a concentration is reached when a completely correct answer is given. Since there are both sexual and age differences in the threshold ability to taste PTC, age and sex should be carefully recorded for each subject.

In the field it may not be possible to use the above method. Under such conditions the following is a useful procedure:

A slip of paper impregnated with phenyl-thio-carbamide is given to the subject and he is asked to place it upon the back of the tongue. He is then asked whether he tastes anything. If the subject is a taster he will reply in terms indicating that he tastes something bitter. If he is a non-taster he will generally indicate that he tastes nothing. Record those who are in doubt as to whether they taste anything with a question mark. In order to test the genuineness of replies each subject should be given several tests with blank strips among those offered. Some individuals detect the bitter taste almost immediately. Others have to chew the paper for some time before the taste becomes detectable to them. It is necessary to make certain that the paper used before impregnation with PTC is itself entirely free of chemicals that yield a bitter taste. Careful records should be kept to distinguish early from late tasters, for there are apparently two dominant alleles involved. A stop-watch is helpful here.

6. *Ability to Smell Hydrocyanic Acid.* THIS HIGHLY POISONOUS SUBSTANCE, potassium cyanide, in solution, cannot be smelled by a certain proportion of individuals. It is vitally important in using this test material to take every precaution against the possibility of its being erroneously taken by mouth, for one sip is likely to be fatal. Antidotes: Inhalation amyl nitrite in handkerchief held lightly over nose, meanwhile cause vomiting by giving one pint of 1 per cent sodiumthiosulfate or soapy water or mustard water by mouth. Do not give anything by mouth to unconscious subject.

7. *Ability to Roll Sides of Tongue Upward When Mouth is Open.* If the investigator is able to perform this act he should show the subject what is required. If he is unable to do so he should stick out his tongue and with his fingers press against the edges of the tongue thus rolling the sides upwards. The literate subject will not generally require any demonstration. The ability to roll the tongue into a U-shape when the mouth is open is due to a dominant gene *R*.

8. *Ability to Turn One Side of the Tongue Up, With the Mouth Open.* The subject is asked to rotate the tongue so that the left side is upward and the right remains either stationary or is lowered, and vice versa. Sides to be recorded for ability and nonability.

9. *Color Blindness.* Best tested with the *Dvorine Color Discrimination Screening Test*, obtainable from Israel Dvorine, 2328 Eutaw Place, Baltimore 17, Maryland. Tests A and B should be used.

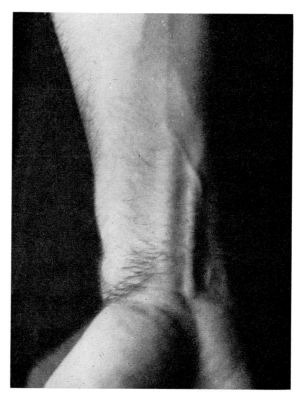

Figure 214. The palmaris longus muscle. The prominent tendon toward outer margin of this page is the palmaris longus. The right forearm is shown.

10. *Pigmentation of Iris.* A dominant gene *P* is responsible for the pigment at the front layer of the iris. The momozygous recessive genes *pp* are responsible for there being pigment particles present for the most part only in the posterior layer of the iris, thus yielding "blue" eyes. The Munsell Color Chart should be used in determining eye color (see p. 573).

11. *Interlocking Fingers and Thumb.* When the fingers are locked some individuals will invariably place the left thumb over the right thumb. This is due to a dominant gene *F*. Placing the right thumb over the left is due to a recessive gene *f*. Simply ask the individual to interlock his fingers.

12. *Palmaris Longus Muscle.* The central tendon of the forearm at the wrist which is normally visible and can be well defined when the subject's fingers are flexed upon the wrist. Three tendons are

generally visible in this region, one on the thumb side of the wrist (flexor carpi radialis) and one on the little finger side (flexor carpi ulnaris). The tendon of the palmaris longus muscle is situated between them. It is the most central tendon of the wrist. Record presence or absence. Presence is due to a pair of recessive genes *ll,* absence to a dominant gene *L.* Record condition in both wrists.

13. *Serological Traits.* A knowledge of the gene frequency distribution of the A-B-O blood groups, the blood types M, N, MN, and MNSs, and the Rh types in man is of considerable value in the study of human relationships.

If blood testing cannot conveniently be done the investigator should make complete arrangements with the scientific worker or workers within easiest reach to do the testing. Such complete arrangements will, of course, include the manner of preservation, sealing, and sending of blood samples.

If it is desired to send blood any distance or to keep it for more than a day, about 5 c.c. of blood should be taken with a sterile syringe under aseptic conditions, placed in a sterile tube with sterile stopper and allowed to clot. A suitable cell suspension can be made from this. If the blood is going to be tested promptly a sample may be taken directly into 0.9% sodium chloride solution by pricking the lobe of the ear or a finger, or in the case of infants the big toe, with a spring blood lancet. The skin and the blade of the lancet should be cleaned with alcohol or acetone, waiting for the disinfectant to evaporate before taking the blood.

Preservatives do not help a great deal. However, red cells remain agglutinable (for A, B, M, and N) for some weeks if preserved in Rous-Turner solution (3.8% sodium citrate solution 2 parts, 5.4% glucose solution 5 parts) or preferably in the ACD (citric acidcitrate-dextrose) mixture used in blood banks.

The A-B-O blood groups can often be determined from dried blood stains, mummified tissues, and even from skeletal remains of the recent period if they are in a suitable state of preservation.

Blood Typing Technique

A number of techniques are available from which each investigator may select those most suitable for his work. However, failure to follow certain practices, such as the use of positive and negative controls, has led to serious errors which have encumbered the literature and led to the formulation of fallacious theories.

A spring lancet or preferably a sterile needle [11] is used to draw blood either from an ear lobe or a finger. The ear lobe is preferable for it is easier to clean, and less liable to infection. The lobe is first swabbed with alcohol and then rubbed vigorously with cotton to stimulate circulation.[12] It is next punctured with lancet or needle and a few drops of blood are caught in a 13 x 100 mm. tube containing 1½ c.c. of physiological saline (.9%). These suspensions are centrifuged at 1200-1500 r.p.m. (revolutions per minute). The supernatant (that part of the fluid which floats on the surface) is drawn off and replaced with fresh saline, the resulting suspension of washed cells should be a 2% suspension, to be determined by visual inspection. All suspensions should be uniform, and all cells should be washed at least once.

Tests for the presence of group substances A and B, and M and N are made by placing one drop of the 2% cell suspension in a tube (10 x 75 mm.) to which is added one drop of the appropriate serum, anti-A, anti-B, anti-M, and anti-N. These tubes are then centrifuged one minute at 1000-1500 r.p.m. After all the tubes have been centrifuged and replaced in the tube rack, the rack of tubes is shaken until the cells of the known negative control are resuspended. The tubes may be read by simply holding them over a magnifying mirror. Each tube should be compared with a known positive and negative reaction included in the series being tested for control. Those specimens which give a positive reaction, i.e., clumping or agglutination of the cells, with the anti-A serum should next be tested with anti-A_1 serum. This subdivision of A is especially useful among aboriginal populations of the New World where presence of A_2 may indicate mixture with Caucasoid populations.

Tests for the presence of the A and B antigens may also be made on slides. For this kind of test the slide may be used to pick up a drop of blood directly from the ear, though it is preferable to transfer the blood with a loop or wooden applicator, so that there is no excess of blood. One drop should be placed at either end of the slide for the anti-A and the anti-B serum. After a drop of the serum, which

---

[11] Inexpensive expendable sterile needles with guards, each individually wrapped in paper, are now available for this purpose.

[12] In the rare event that it is not possible to draw blood from the ear lobe it may be taken in the same way as from the ear lobe from the tip of the middle finger. In cases in which the blood does not immediately appear a minute or so should be allowed to elapse before the attempt is made to express blood by pressure. Fear often produces a vaso-constrictor effect. This should be allowed to wear off before any attempt is made to obtain the blood.

should contain an anticoagulant, is added to the drop of blood the two are mixed with a toothpick and the slide is rotated to insure thorough mixing. The reaction should be easily visible to the eye.

Special care must be taken in using the anti-Rh sera owing to their considerably weaker reactions. A smaller tube (7 x 50 mm.) may be used in order to conserve sera and to facilitate reading the results in the tube by means of a microscope. When the tubes have been prepared, as in the A, B, M and N tests, by the addition of one drop of serum to one drop of 2% suspension of washed cells, the rack of tubes is placed in a pan of water and they are incubated for one hour at 37.5° C. Following this they are centrifuged at slow speed, 300-500 r.p.m. Before reading, each tube should be rotated or shaken gently to remove false agglutination. If the cells are not agglutinated they will be dispersed and resuspended, if they are agglutinated they will remain in clumps. These clumps of agglutinated cells vary in size with the strength of the reaction. It is useful to record the strength of each reaction as a check on the strength of various sera and as a not very reliable indication of homo- or hetero-zygosity. Care must be taken not to shake out a positive reaction. In the case of a person who is heterozygous, the reactions may be weaker with certain antisera (gene dose effect). All Rh tests should be read under the low power of a microscope as well as with the naked eye. This may be done by holding the tube directly under the objective, or by removing a drop of the suspension on a glass rod and placing it on a slide.

In the field where laboratory facilities are not available it is often necessary to use a stove for incubating the Rh tests. One practical method of maintaining the bath at the necessary uniform temperature is to place the tray containing the tubes over another pan of water so that the heat is derived from the steam of the lower pan of water rather than directly from the top of the stove which is subject to wide fluctuations in temperature.

For centrifuging the small Rh tubes corks may be dropped into each of the centrifuge tube jackets so that the small tubes can be easily removed.

No tests should be conducted without the use of both negative and positive controls. For this purpose it is desirable to type in advance all members of a field party. Reactions should be read twice. In this way those which are slow in developing will not be missed and an additional check on recording errors is provided. Sera should be permitted to come to room temperature before use, at all other times they should be kept in refrigeration. Diluted serum often declines in strength, consequently no more sera should be diluted for use than are needed for current typing.

Equipment

For field work certain eventualities must be anticipated which would otherwise retard the work. Sufficient glassware should be taken so that it is possible to work two or three days while tubes are drying. A good quality soap, such as Swan or Ivory, is adequate for washing the glassware. Precautions must be taken to be sure that the tubes are clean, dry and sterile.

Serum containers should be identified not only by labels but also by etching with a diamond pointed glass marking pencil. Even labels secured with cellulose tape will come off after exposure to moisture. This may happen when a boat carrying equipment ships water or when a refrigerator is inadvertently defrosted.

China marking pencils of different colors should be used to facilitate identification of individual tubes in tests employing different sera, thus, tests with anti-A serum may be marked with red and tests with anti-B serum marked with blue.

Four-tube hand operated centrifuges are available from such houses as Eimer and Amend, New York City.

Tuberculin syringes are useful for measuring small amounts of serum and saline. It is useful to weigh out salt in advance for preparing additional amounts of physiological saline in the field. This will obviate the need for carrying scales and save time.

A list of equipment is appended here, the appropriate numbers or amounts depend, of course, on the extent of the work to be done. Equipment List:

> laboratory microscope
> centrifuge
> 15 ml.° tubes
> 13 x 100 mm., 8 x 75 mm., and 7 x 50 mm. tubes
> ground glass slides
> glass rods
> expendable capillary pipettes
> 1 cc. tuberculin syringes and #22 needles
> laboratory thermometers
> alcohol
> test tube brushes
> cotton, absorbent and non-absorbent

° ml., milliliter, equals 1 cubic centimeter.

tube racks
expendable sterile lancets
distilled water
liter pitcher
diamond pointed glass marking pencil
magnifying mirror (shaving mirror)
colored marking pencils
beakers
soap
toothpicks
pans (for incubating and washing)
sera
corks

Collection of Bone Samples for Typing

Cancellous tissue such as that found in the bodies of the vertebrae
or in the heads of the long bones is most suitable for blood typing.
This can best be obtained by scraping with a bone curette. With care
it is possible to remove the cancellous tissue from a vertebra without
damaging its walls for measurement. The bone should be placed in
a tube and made airtight. Morphological data and cultural data concerning the skeleton should be secured. Care must be taken in the
case of incidental bones or mass burials that more than one specimen
is not taken from one individual or that several specimens taken from
one skeleton are attributed to only one.

Technique of Blood Typing Skeletons

Test for the Presence of Blood Group Substances in Skeletons

This is an absorption technique which involves the application of
serum of known strength to a specimen of pulverized bone. After a
period of incubation the supernatant serum is drawn off the specimen
and tested against fresh red cells of the appropriate group. If the
group substance, which determines the blood type, is present in the
specimen of bone, the antibodies of the serum are wholly or partially
absorbed and the strength of the serum is thereby reduced. The
consequent failure to agglutinate red cells is presumptive evidence
that agglutinins were removed from the serum and therefore that the
group substance was present in the skeleton tested.

The sera to be employed are titered by testing successively
doubled dilutions, e.g., 1:2, 1:4, 1:8, 1:16, against a 1% suspension of
fresh red cells. If 1:16 is the limiting titer, that is if it gives a $\pm$
reading whereas the next higher dilution shows no agglutination, this

is taken as the end point. Counting back three dilutions, to 1:2, gives the proper dilution to be applied to the specimen. The serum should be diluted to yield a reagent with a titer of 4 to 8 units; in the example cited the serum would be diluted 2 to 4 times. Anything with a titer of less than 4 units is too weak for reliable results. These dilutions may be made in 13 x 100 mm. tubes. From each of these tubes 0.05 cc. of the diluted serum is drawn, by means of a tuberculin syringe, and placed in a 7 x 50 mm. tube, to which is added 0.05 cc. of 1% cell suspension. These are then placed in a rack and shaken at four minute intervals for thirty-two minutes. Readings of the degree of agglutination are made with the low power of a microscope. All cell suspensions should be washed, measured, and the titration should be performed before each test.

The cancellous tissue is pulverized before each test in a mortar, and 0.25 gram placed in a 13 x 100 mm. tube. Nine-tenths of a cc. of serum is added to this and the two are thoroughly mixed by rotating the tube and with a glass rod. For each skeleton tested a separate tube is prepared for the anti-A serum and for the anti-B serum. Each tube is sealed with a cork and placed in a refrigerator at 10° C. to incubate 48 hours. The tubes should be agitated at 12 hour intervals.

At the end of two days the tubes are removed from the refrigerator and permitted to return to room temperature. They are then centrifuged and the supernatant serum drawn from each by means of a tuberculin syringe with a flat ended needle. Physiological saline is added to each specimen to equal the amount drawn off and it is titrated again in three successively doubled dilutions to duplicate the original dilutions. 0.05 cc. of each dilution is placed in a blood group tube, with 0.05 cc. of 1% fresh red cell suspension and shaken as before at four minute intervals for thirty-two minutes. The results are again read with the low power of the microscope. Failure of the supernatant to agglutinate the appropriate red cells indicates that group substance of that group was present in the specimen and absorbed the agglutinins. Agglutinins should be cleared from at least two tubes, in a number of tests, for the results to be considered positive. Controls should, of course, be employed in all tests. The technique employed in testing skeletons may be found in the following papers: "Blood-Group Tests on Stains, Mummified Tissues, and Cancellous Bone," by P. B. Candela, *Am. J. Phys. Anthrop.* 25:187-214, 1939. "Blood grouping reactions of preserved bone and muscle," by L. T. Boyd and W. C. Boyd, *Am. J. Phys. Anthrop.*, 25:421-434, 1939. "A method for reducing non-specific reactions in the typing of human skeletal material," by M. P. Gray, *Am. J. Phys. Anthrop.*, n.s., *16*:135-139, 1958.

The Determination of Hemoglobins and Haptoglobins

A simple method for determining hemoglobins and haptoglobins which can be used in the field has been described by Budtz-Olsen ("Haptoglobins and haemoglobins in Australian aborigines, with a simple method for the estimation of haptoglobins," *Med. J. Austral.*, 22 Nov. 1958, 689-692).

Hemoglobins. Hemoglobin solutions are prepared by washing the red cells in saline and hemolysing them in four volumes of water and a quarter volume of toluene. Electrophoresis of the solutions is carried out on Whatman No. 3 paper, horizontally suspended in closed tanks with barbiturate buffer, 0.05, pH 8.6. The voltage used is 10 volts per centimetre at room temperature for about six hours.

Haptoglobins. Serum is collected and enough hemoglobin solution added to give a concentration of about 200 milligrams per 100 millimeters. Following several accurate estimations of this concentration in a colorimeter, simple judgment of the color by the eye alone will generally be found to be sufficiently accurate. If any of the specimens become slightly hemolysed before separation of the serum, they should be used without the addition of hemoglobin.

The details of the electrophoresis are as follows:

Apparatus. A simple tank described by Flynn and de Mayo ("Micro-electrophoresis of protein on filter paper," *The Lancet*, 2:235, 1951) with vertically suspended Whatman No. 3 paper strips is used. Other tanks will do, but owing to the longer distance between the protein fractions obtained with the Flynn and de Mayo method, haptoglobins can be determined with greater confidence with this method.

Buffer. A barbiturate-borate buffer is used. The details of preparation are as follows: 1.85 grams of barbituric acid, 10.30 grams of barbitone, 4.809 grams of boric acid, and 0.888 grams of sodium hydroxide are dissolved in two liters of water, and four millimeters of non-ionizing detergent are added. With this buffer the a_2-globulins migrate faster than in the usual barbiturate buffer and are well separated from the β-globulins, which renders the differentiation between the different haptoglobins easy. The a_1-globulins are lost in the albumin fraction, but this is unimportant for the purpose of haptoglobin determination. The detergent sharpens the bands of the different fractions, but is not otherwise essential.

Conditions of the Run. The paper is allowed to soak in the tank until the buffer is about a centimeter from the edge; 0.04 millimeter of serum is applied to the edge; the tank is closed and left for about an hour and the current is then switched on at 130 volts for 22 hours, either in a refrigerator at 5° C. or at room temperature.

Staining. After the run the paper strips are dried in an oven at 105° C., although room temperature will do. The strips are then soaked for 10 minutes in a solution of 0.2 gram of benzidine and a small crystal of sodium nitroprusside in 15 millimeters of methanol with four drops of glacial acetic acid. This solution is washed off with a solution of one volume of 3% hydrogen peroxide, one volume of ether and two volumes of methanol, and the color is then developed with this solution for two or three minutes. The paper strips are washed in gently running tap water for about half an hour. The blue color is permanent.

The distinctions between the three haptoglobins depend entirely upon the distance moved by the particular haptoglobins. For ease of judgment a known group 2-1 should always be run with the unknown.

Anthropometric Recording Blanks

Printed blanks for the recording of anthropometric, anthropo-scopic, physiometric, and morphological measurements greatly facili-tate the processes of recording and analysis of data. Typical blanks are here reprinted through the courtesy of Dr. J. L. Angel.

Craniometry

Why Measure Skulls?

For several generations physical anthropologists measured skulls in the belief that thereby they were likely to obtain results which would enable them to trace the relationships between the races of mankind. It was believed that the form of the skull in particular re-mained constant in each race, and that different races typically showed different cranial indices. Hence, all one had to do was to measure skulls, calculate the indices, and draw the more or less "obvious" conclusions. Unfortunately for this rather naïve belief there are several crucial objections to it. In the first place the form of the head is now known to be subject to change through environ-mental influences. In the second place there are great differences in intragroup variability in all measurements and indices among the ethnic groups of mankind. In the third place closely related groups

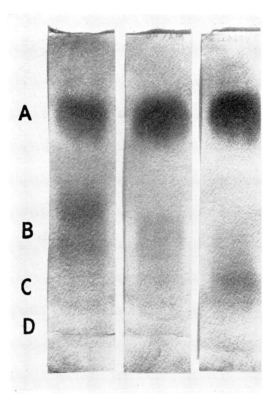

Figure 215. The three groups of haptoglobins. The group is determined by the distance moved by the haptoglobin. A, albumin; B, haptoglobins; C, position of globulins; D, point of application. (Courtesy, Dr. O. E. Budtz-Olsen.)

and individuals frequently exhibit considerable differences in cranial measurements and indices, while more distantly related groups and individuals exhibit striking likenesses (see Figures 190 & 192). Finally, the cephalic index of a whole group will change in the course of time as the trend towards brachycephalization in man abundantly shows. Why then, it may well be asked, measure skulls? The answer is: Precisely in order to obtain this kind of knowledge, and in order to be able to give as accurate a description of a skull or group of skulls as possible. In addition, in studies of the micro-evolutionary process analysis of craniometric data for neighboring populations or segments of the same population may yield valuable results.[13]

---

[13] See W. S. Laughlin and J. B. Jørgensen, Isolate variation in Greenlandic Eskimo crania. *Acta Genetica et Statistica Medica*, 6:3-12, 1956.

ANTHROPOMETRY and MORPHOLOGY

Name..
Sex............ Age........ Place................................ Birthdate................................ Examined: Date................................ Time................................ Area................................ Field number................................
Related to:................................ Observer................................
Father's name................................ Appearance................................ Occupation................................ Birthplace................................ Age if living................................ Ancestry................................ Cause of death................................ Died at age?................................
Mother's name................................ Appearance................................ Skills................................ Birthplace................................ Age if living................................ Died at age?................................ Cause of death................................
Brothers................................
Sisters................................
Stillbirths................................
Single?................ Married?................ At age?................ Divorced?................ Widowed?................ Birth rank................................
Boys................................ Childhood................................
Girls................................
Diet................................ Breakfast................................ Lunch................................ Supper................................

Occupation................................ Religion................................ Biographical................................
Social status................................ Economic status................................ Housing................................
Illnesses at age ?................................ Handedness................................
.... Film number................................
.... Recorder................................ Frames................................

Weight.. Biacromial................................ Bi-auricular breadth................................ Stature/∛ Weight................................
Bi-iliac................................ Bizygomatic breadth................................ Relative sitting height................................
Stature................................ Chest breadth................................ Bigonial breadth................................ Relative chest circumference................................
Acromion height................................ Chest depth................................ Total face height................................ Relative shoulder breadth................................
Trochanter height................................ Abdomen depth................................ Upper face height................................ Thoracic index................................
Tibiale height................................ Chest circumference................................ Chin height................................ Hand, L.-Br. index................................
Sphyrion height................................ Nose height................................
Span................................ Head circumference................................ Nose breadth................................ Cephalic index................................
Sitting height................................ Head length................................ Interorbital................................ Mean height index................................
Foot length................................ Nasion-occipital length................................ Biorbital................................ Fronto-parietal................................
Foot breadth................................ Head breadth................................ Cranio-facial................................
Humerus length................................ Auricular-vertex height................................ Mouth breadth................................ Fronto-zonial................................
Radius length................................ Auricular-nasion length................................ Ear height................................ Facial index................................
Hand length................................ Ear breadth................................ Upper facial index................................
Hand breadth................................ Minimum frontal breadth................................ Nasal index................................

arm

Pale
Pink 3
"White"
Brunet 7–9
Swarthy 10, 11
R br 12–14, 16
Lt. br. 15, 17, 18
Y. br. 19–20, 6
Md. br. 21–25
Choc. 26–29
Dk. br. 30–35
Black 36

+
++
Freckles
None
Few
+
++
Moles
None
Few
+
++

Sl.
++
Beard quantity
Ssm.
Sm.
Abs.
Sl.
+
++
Body hair
Abs.
Sl.
+
++

Low waves
Deep waves
Curly
Frizzly
Woolly
Texture
Fine
+
Coarse
Wiry
Quantity
Sm.
+
++

Head
Black 27
Dk. br. 4–5
Brown 7–9
Red br. 6, 10
Gld. br. 11–16
Ash br. 22–26
Golden 17–19
Ash 20, 21
Red 1–3
Grey, sl.
Grey, +
White
Red pigment
Abs.
Pres:

Beard

Trace
Sl.
++
Mixed eyes
+++ dark
++ dark
Even
+++ light
++ light
Pigment dots
Abs.
Pres:

Dk. brown
Dk.-lt. br.
Lt. br.
Green-br.
Grey-br.
Blue-br.
Green
Grey
Blue
Other
Unmatched

Rayed
Zoned
Scalloped
Diffuse
Spotted
Conjunctiva
Clear
Yellow
Green
Grey
Bloodshot
Orbit height
Low
+
High

Internal
Sl.
++
Median
Sl.
External
Sl.
Complete:

Palpebral slit
Down
Horiz.
Up sl.
Up +
Opening ht.
Sm.
+
++
Eyebrow thickness
Sl.
+
+++

Concurrency
Abs.
Sl.
+
+++
Temp. hair jct.
Abs.
Sl.
+
++
Browridges
Ssm.
Sm.
+
++

Nasion depr.
Trace
Sl.
+
+++
Bony profile
Straight
Concave
Wavy
Convex
Salience
Sl.
+
++

Root height
Sm.
+
+++
++
Root breadth
Ssm. (+++)
Sm.
+
++
Bridge height
Sm.
+
+++ (ssm.)

Bridge breadth
Ssm. (+++)
Sm.
+
++
Tip thickness
Ssm. (+++)
Sm.
+
++
Tip shape
Pointed
Bilobed
Angular
Rounded
Blobby
Snub

Septum tilt
Up +
Up sl.
Horiz.
Down sl.
Down +
Nostril form
Slit
Ellipse
Intermed.
Round
Visibility, lat.
None
Sl.
++

Vis., frontal
None
Sl.
++
Nostril axes
Parallel
Obl. sl.
Oblique +
Transverse
Alae
Compressed
+
Flaring
Extended

Lip thickness
V. thin (+++)
Thin
+
++
Eversion
Sl.
+
++
Lip seam
Abs.
Sl.
++

Integ. lips
Thin
+
Thick
Alv. prognathism
Abs. (+++)
Sl.
+
Chin projection
Negative
Neutral
Sl.
++

Chin type
Median
Triangle
Bilateral
Malars
Anterior proj.
Abs. (+++)
Sl.
+
++
Lateral proj.
Compr.
Sl.
+
++

Gonia eversion
Compr.
Sl.
+
+++
Ear projection
Abs.
Sl.
+
++
Helix
Flat
Sl. roll
+
++

Anti-helix
Sl.
+
++
Darwin's pt.
Abs.
Pres:
Ear sinus
Abs.
Pres:
Lobe
None
Soldered
Attached
Free
Long & free

Temp. fullness
Flat
Sl.
++
Lambd. flat.
None
Sl.
+
Occ. curve
Flat
Sl.
++

Blood type
A, B, O:
M, N:
Rh'-C:
Rho-D:
Rh''-E:

P-T-C
Taste-blind
Tastes:
Tongue-roll
Abs.
Pres:
Trilling
Abs.
Pres.
Th-sound
Abs.
Pres.

Somatotype
Temperament
Nutri. state
Menarche or Voice-change
Pulse rate

Asymmetry

Type

Pathology

Teeth wear
None
Sl.
+
++
+++

Crowding
None
Sl.
+
+++
Pyorrhea
None
Sl.
+
++
Absorption
None
Sl.
+
++

Tooth eruption
Incomplete
Complete
M₃ suppr.
Other
No. teeth lost

No. teeth carious

Palate height
Low
+
+++
Palate form
Parabolic
Elliptical
Hyperbolic V
Small U
Broad U
Palatine torus
Absent
Ridge:
Mound:
Lump:

Shovel Is.
Abs.
Sl.
++
Upper cusp no
Lower cusp no.
Teeth rotated
Central trema

Molar pattern
Plus
Dryopith.
Bite
Under
Edge
Sl. over
+ over
++ over
Accessory cusps
Teeth size

Left

Right

Dentition

8 7 6 5 4 3 2 1 | 1 2 3 4 5 6 7 8
8 7 6 5 4 3 2 1 | 1 2 3 4 5 6 7 8

X: missing   • carious   s: suppressed
m: milk tooth retained   w: worn down to roots

Figure 216. Recording blank for anthropometry and morphology of the living. (Courtesy, Dr. J. L. Angel.)

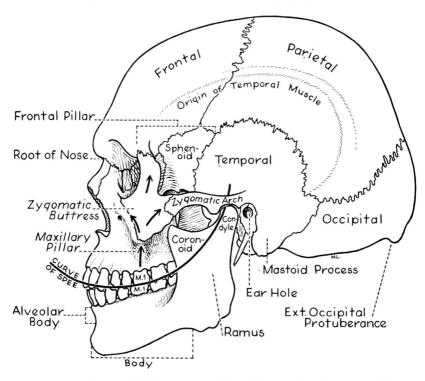

Figure 217. Showing the buttresses of the skull and the directions of distribution of the forces transmitted from the lower first through the upper first molar tooth.

The importance of craniometry in the description and analysis of the remains of fossil man and other primates is obvious; in the comparative study of the primates it is an indispensable tool, as it is in growth studies of the skull, the growth of the dental apparatus, in the study of the character and relationships of individuals and departed populations which are known mainly or solely from their cranial remains, in forensic medicine, in the identification of persons from their crania, and finally when the genetics of the skull comes to be thoroughly studied, as it must, craniometric techniques will become increasingly indispensable.

Definitions

Skull. In practice this term is commonly used with the following two interchangeable meanings, (1) the skeleton of the braincase, face, and lower jaw, (2) the skeleton of the braincase and face without the lower jaw. To this double usage there is no objection, though strictly speaking the term is by most anthropologists and anatomists defined in the first sense.

Cranium. Used with the same meanings as *skull.*

Calvarium. The skull minus the lower jaw.

Calvaria. The braincase minus facial bones and the lower jaw.

Calva or Calotte. The skull cap, i.e., the top of the braincase or calvaria minus its base.

Landmarks

There has, in the past, been a great superfluity of landmarks on the skull, most of which have rarely been used. Only those which are in most common use will be defined here. The customary abbreviations printed in parentheses.

Braincase

1. *Glabella* (gl). The most prominent point on the middle of the frontal bone between the superciliary arches (supraorbital ridges) and above the nasofrontal suture.

2. *Bregma* (br). The point of intersection of the coronal and sagittal sutures.

3. *Opisthocranion* (op). The most distant (posterior) point on the skull from the glabella in the mid-sagittal plane, excluding the external occipital protuberance or inion.

4. *Inion* (in). The base of the external occipital protuberance in the mid-sagittal plane.

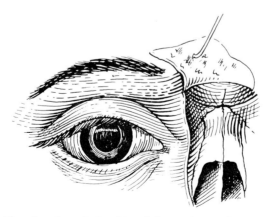

Figure 218. Showing the relationship of the nasion to the superior palpebral sulcus.

5. *Opisthion* (o). The median point on the posterior margin of the occipital foramen.

6. *Basion* (ba). The median point on the anterior margin of the occipital foramen.

7. *Porion* (po). The highest middle point on the margin of the external auditory meatus.

Facial Skeleton

8. *Nasion* (na). The mid-point of the naso-frontal suture.

9. *Nasospinale* (ns). The point at which a line tangent to the lower margins of the nasal aperture is intersected by the mid-sagittal plane. Since the base of the anterior nasal spine usually prevents actual instrumental contact with this point, it is usual to take the measurement at the level of the nasospinale somewhat to one side and deduct the two or three millimeters from the final measurement.

10. *Prosthion* (pr). The most antero-inferior point on the maxilla between the upper central incisor teeth.

11. *Maxillofrontale* (mf). The point of intersection of the anterior lacrimal crest with the frontomaxillary suture.

12. *Infradentale* (id). The most antero-superior point on the alveolar margin between the lower central incisors on the lower jaw.

13. *Gnathion* (gn). The middle point on the lower border of the mandible.

14. *Gonion* (go). The most lateral external point of junction of the horizontal and ascending rami of the lower jaw.

15. *Ectomolare* (ecm). The most lateral point on the outer surface of the alveolar margins, usually opposite the middle of the second molar tooth.

16. *Endomolare* (enm). The most lateral point on the inner surface of the lingual margins of the alveolar processes, usually opposite the middle of the lingual surfaces of the second molar teeth.

17. *Orale* (ol). The point in the bony palate where the mid-sagittal plane bisects a line drawn tangentially to the point of maximum convexity of the lingual margins of the alveoli for the two central incisor teeth.

General Comments

It should always be remembered that the best preserved of skulls is a fragile and valuable object. It should therefore always be handled with considerable care. There is something about the gaping orbits of the skull which seems universally to suggest that it be picked up by introducing the thumb in one orbit and several fingers in the other.

This is invariably fatal to the papyrus-thin bones of the medial orbital walls. Hence, all persons likely to handle skulls must be instructed never to handle a skull in this manner, and they should be similarly instructed never to lift it by the zygomatic arches. The skull is best handled with one hand at the supratemporal crests or at the occipito-parietal regions. Teeth are extremely fragile, and the enamel is easily cracked and chipped. Loose teeth should be firmly glued into the sockets in which their roots belong.

In measuring skulls a moderately soft doughnut shaped pad 1½ inches thick with an outside diameter 8½ inches, and an internal diameter of 3¼ inches will be found useful upon which to rest the skull in any desired position. A cloth bag 8 by 8 inches or more, filled with rice or sand is preferred by many workers. A puncture-proof small toy rubber tire, 7 x 1½ inches, forms an excellent rest for a skull.[14]

Instruments should be frequently checked for accuracy, and each measurement should be made in a uniform manner. It is important to record the technique used in making each measurement and to make this record an intrinsic part of the report of these measurements, whether the report is intended for publication or not.

Cranial Measurements

1. *Maximum cranial Length* (Spreading Caliper). From glabella to opisthocranion.

2. *Maximum Cranial Breadth* (Spreading Caliper). At right angles to the mid-sagittal plane wherever maximum breadth is found, above the level of the supramastoid crests or posterior roots of the zygomatic arches and the regions below.

3. *Basion-Bregma Height* (Spreading Caliper). From basion to bregma.

4. *Minimum Frontal Cranial Breadth* (Spreading Caliper). Minimum breadth between the temporal crests on the frontal bone.

5. *Maximum Bizygomatic Breadth* (Spreading Caliper). The greatest breadth between the two zygomatic arches.

6. *Total Cranial Facial Height* (Sliding Compass). From gnathion to nasion.

7. *Upper Cranial Facial Height* (Sliding Compass). From prosthion to nasion.

8. *Basion-Prosthion Line* (Sliding Compass or Spreading Caliper). From basion to prosthion.

9. *Nasal Height* (Sliding Compass). From nasion to the mean of

---

[14] The "Clipper" supplied by R.C.A. Rubber Co., Akron, Ohio.

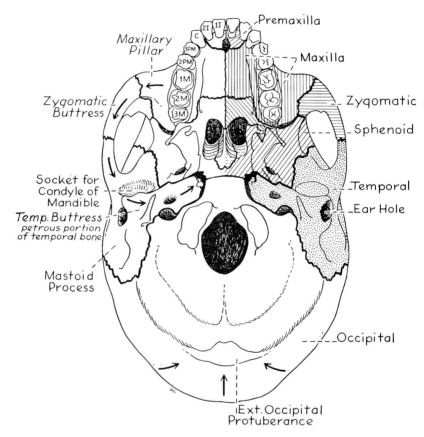

Figure 219. Basilar view of the skull showing directions in which compressive strains transmitted through the first upper molar (1M) are taken up by the zygomatic buttress, while those from the back of the skull pass down toward the external occipital protuberance.

the lowest points on the lower borders of the nasal aperture (the subnasale) on each side of the nasal spine.

10. *Nasal Breadth* (Sliding Compass). The maximum distance between the lateral margins of the nasal aperture perpendicular to the mid-sagittal plane.

11. *Upper Nasal Breadth* (Sliding Compass). The distance between the points of juncture of the naso-frontal and naso-maxillary sutures on the right and left sides.

12. *Lower Nasal Breadth* (Sliding Compass). The distance be-

tween the points at which the naso-maxillary suture terminates at the nasal aperture on the left and right sides.

13. *Orbital Breadth* (Sliding Compass). Owing to the variability in the conformation and orientation of the orbits these are conventionally treated as rectangles. The horizontal axis being determined by an imaginary line running from maxillofrontale to the middle of the lateral orbital border (ectoconchion). Right and left orbits are recorded separately.

14. *Orbital Height* (Sliding Compass). The maximum height from the upper to the lower orbital borders perpendicular to the horizontal axis of the orbit.

15. *Interorbital Breadth* (Sliding Compass). The distance between the right and left maxillofrontale.

16. *Bi-Orbital Breadth* (Sliding Compass). From the middle of one lateral orbital border (ectoconchion) to the other.

17. *Maxillo-Alveolar Length* (Sliding Compass). From prosthion to the points of bisection of a line tangent to the posterior terminal borders of the alveolar processes (maxillary tuberosities).

18. *Maxillo-Alveolar Breadth* (Sliding Compass). Maximum distance from one external lateral alveolar border to the other, usually opposite the second molar teeth. (ectomolare).

19. *Mean Diameter of Foramen Magnum* (Sliding Compass). Maximum length from basion to opisthion, and maximum transverse diameter.

20. *Bi-Condylar Width* (Sliding Compass). Distance between the most external points on the condyles of the lower jaw.

21. *Symphyseal Height* (Sliding Compass). Distance between gnathion and infradentale.

22. *Bigonial Diameter* (Sliding Compass). Distance between right and left gonion points.

23. *Height of Ascending Left Mandibular Ramus* (Measuring Board or Sliding Compass). Usually taken with a specially designed hinged measuring board from which the height of the ramus may be read directly from the base of the ramus to the highest point on the left condyle. In the absence of a measuring board, from left gonion to the highest point on the left condyle.

24. *Minimum Breadth of Left Ascending Mandibular Ramus* (Sliding Compass). Least distance between the anterior and posterior borders of the left ramus perpendicular to its height.

25. *Maximum Cranial Circumference* (Steel Tape). Above the

level of the brow ridges around the most distant projection of the occiput to the zero point anteriorly.

26. *Transverse Cranial Arc* (Steel Tape). From left porion across bregna to right porion.

27. *The Frankfurt Horizontal* (FH) *Plane.* The horizontal plane of the skull determined by the right and left porion and the lowest point on the inferior margin of, preferably, the left orbit (orbitale). The skull is usually oriented in this plane when measurements taken in a constant plane are to be made, or when craniograms, photographs, or other illustrations are to be made for comparative or illustrative purposes.

28. *Auricular Height.* This important measurement may be taken with Todd's Head Spanner or the Western Reserve Craniostat. Both instruments are provided with a simple device for determining the Frankfurt Horizontal plane. Measurements are read directly. Ranke's or Mollison's craniophor require the determination of bi-porionic breadth and the distance of each porion from the bregma. The vertical section of the triangle thus formed yields auricular height.

29. *Cranial Capacity.* Cranial capacity has been measured in a variety of ways and the results obtained are not always strictly comparable, hence it is extremely important to know when comparing figures for cranial capacity obtained from the literature what method was used. The most usual procedure is to fill the cranial cavity with some material which will easily conform to the internal irregularities and spaces of the braincase. Mustard seed or small shot is frequently used, the material being thoroughly distributed by agitating the skull either in one's hands or in an apparatus specially devised for the purpose. When the skull is securely filled the contents are then poured into a cubic centimeter measuring glass which is then agitated until it is thoroughly packed and the reading taken directly. Alternatively the mustard seed may be weighed and multiplied by a factor to give volume. Methods such as this avoid the possibility of error when the measuring glass is used. Formulae which give satisfactory results have been worked out by different investigators for several groups. The best of these formulae for determining cranial capacity are the following, where L is cranial length, H is auricular height, H′ basion-bregmatic height, and B cranial breadth. L is multiplied by B, and the product multiplied by H or H′:

$$\text{Female Capacity } .000375 \times \text{LBH} + 296.40$$

All Races: Male Capacity .000365 × LBH − 359.34   (Pearson)
Negroids: Capacity .0003849 × LBH + 96 ± 65/$\sqrt{N}$ (Isserlis)

Australoids: Capacity .000263 $\times$ LBH$'$ + 404.9 $\pm$ 35.1/$\sqrt{N}$ (von Bonin)
Caucasoids: Capacity .000366 $\times$ LBH + 198.9 (Hooke)[15]

Craniometric Indices

30. The Cranial Index

$$\frac{\text{Max Breadth} \times 100}{\text{Max. Length}}$$

Dolichocranic	$\times$—74.9
Mesocranic	75.0—79.9
Brachycranic	80.0—84.9
Hyperbrachycranic	85.0—89.9

31. Cranial Length-Height Index

$$\frac{\text{Basion-Bregma Height} \times 100}{\text{Max. Length}}$$

Chamaecranic	$\times$—69.9
Orthocranic	70.0—74.9
Hypsicranic	75.0—$\times$

32. Cranial Breadth-Height Index

$$\frac{\text{Basion-Bregma Height} \times 100}{\text{Max. Breadth}}$$

Tapeinocranic	$\times$—91.9
Metriocranic	92.0—97.9
Acrocranic	98.0—$\times$

33. Total Facial Index

$$\frac{\text{Nasion-Gnathion Height} \times 100}{\text{Bizygomatic Breadth}}$$

Hypereuryprosopic	$\times$—79.9
Euryprosopic	80.0—84.9
Mesoprosopic	85.0—89.9
Leptoprosopic	90.0—94.9
Hyperleptoprosopic	95.0—$\times$

34. Upper Facial Index

$$\frac{\text{Nasion-Prosthion Height} \times 100}{\text{Bizygomatic Breadth}}$$

Hypereuryene	$\times$—44.9
Euryene	45.0—49.9
Mesene	50.0—54.9
Leptene	55.0—59.9
Hyperleptene	60.0—$\times$

---

[15] For further details see Hambly, W. D.: Cranial capacities, A study in Methods, *Fieldiana Anthropology* (Chicago Natural History Museum), 36:25-75, 1947.

35. Nasal Index

	Max. Nasal Breadth of Nasal Aperture × 100
	Nasion-Nasospinale Height
Leptorrhine	×—46.9
Mesorrhine	47.0—50.9
Chamaerrhine	51.0—57.9
Hyperchamaerrhine	58.0—×

36. Orbital Index

	Max. Orbital Breadth × 100
	Max. Orbital Length
Chamaeconch	×—75.9
Mesoconch	76.0—84.9
Hypsiconch	85.0—×

37. Palatal Index

	Max. Palatal Breadth × 100
	Max. Palatal Length
Leptostaphyline	×—79.9
Mesostaphyline	80.0—84.9
Brachystaphyline	85.0—×

38. Maxillo-Alveolar Index

	Bi-Ectomolare Breadth × 100
	Maxillo-Alveolar Length
Dolichuranic	×—109.9
Mesuranic	110.0—114.9
Brachyuranic	115.0—×

Estimating Age of Skull

During the process of growth and development the skull shows, within broad limits, certain relatively constant changes which may be used as criteria of age. Since there is an appreciable amount of variability both in the order and time of eruption of the teeth, these features must be utilized with caution in the aging of a skull up to the age of 25 years.

Approximate Age of Tooth Eruption

Deciduous or Milk Dentition

Lower Central Incisors	5 to 12 months
Upper Incisors	6 to 14 months
Lower Lateral Incisors	8 to 20 months
First Molars	13 to 20 months

Canines	13 to 30 months
Second Molars	18 to 38 months

Permanent Dentition

First Molars	6th year
Central Incisors	7th year
Lateral Incisors	8th year
First Premolars	9th year
Second Premolars	10th year
Canines	11th to 12th year
Second Molars	12th to 13th year
Third Molars	17th to 25th year

The deciduous or milk teeth number 20 and the deciduous dental formula is written in minuscule letters i $\frac{2}{2}$, c $\frac{1}{1}$, m $\frac{2}{2}$ (incisors 2, canines 1, molars 2, on each side and in each jaw). It is to be noted that no premolars are present in the deciduous dentition. The formula for the permanent dentition is written in capital letters I $\frac{2}{2}$, C $\frac{1}{1}$, PM $\frac{2}{2}$, M $\frac{3}{3}$.

The closure or obliteration of the sutures on the external surfaces of the skull constitutes another fairly useful means of aging the skull. The standards for estimating age of the skull from suture closure have been worked out principally by Todd and Lyon on whites and Negroes in whom the pattern and time of closure appears to be much the same.[16] The variability in the closure of most of these sutures is, however, so great that too great reliance should not be based on this form of aging the skull.

The medio-frontal suture through which sutural junction between the two hemi-frontal bones is established in the infant skull usually commences to obliterate at the level of the frontal eminences during the latter half of the first year. The process of obliteration proceeds towards the bregma, and by the conclusion of the second year the greater part of the suture is obliterated. A small supra-nasal portion remains unobliterated till the sixth year, though remnants of this may persist into adult life. The whole medio-frontal suture remains unobliterated in about 8.5 per cent of Caucasoids, 1.2 per cent of Negroids, and in less than 1.0 per cent of Australoids. When the medio-frontal suture remains unobliterated *after* its normal period of closure it is known as the *metopic* suture, and the condition it thus constitutes is called *metopism*. Metopism is sometimes a familial trait, and by the unwary is occasionally mistaken as evidence of a fracture

[16] Todd, T. W. and Lyon, D. W.: Ectocranial closure in adult males of white stock. *Am. J. Phys. Anthropol.*, 8:23-46; 47-71; 149-168, 7:325-384, 1925.

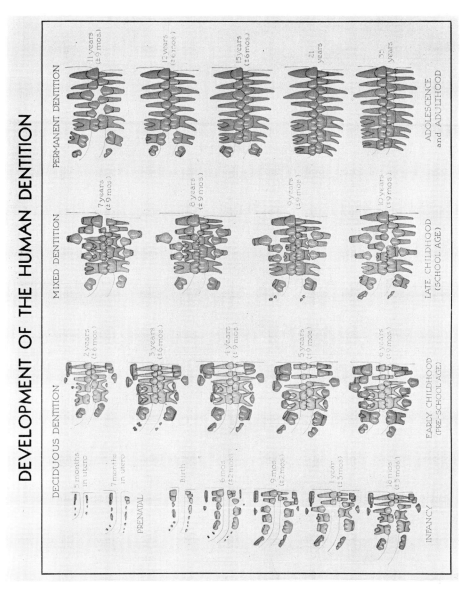

Figure 220. Development of the human dentition. (Courtesy, Drs. I. Schour and M. Massler and the American Dental Association.)

The seven unossified areas in the membrane between the bones known as fontanelles undergo closure in the following order:

Sagittal: (Situated at the obelion) At birth or before the fourth month.

Posterior: (Situated at apex of occipital bone) Two months after birth.

Antero-Lateral: (Paired. At pterion) Three months after birth.

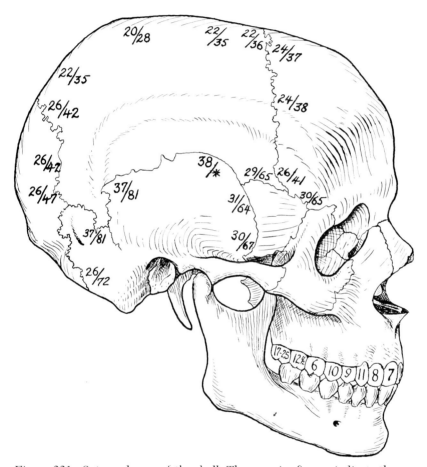

Figure 221. Suture closure of the skull. The superior figures indicate the age at which the portion of the suture commences to obliterate, the inferior figures the age at which obliteration is completed. The ° indicates that the suture never completely closes. The figures on the upper teeth give the usual ages in years of the eruption of each permanent tooth. Owing to the great variability involved these figures must be used with caution.

TABLE LVII

ECTOCRANIAL SUTURE CLOSURE IN MALES

Suture	Commencement and Course	Termina- tion or Peak	General Rate
Sagittal (s)	22	35	slows at 31 at 3.9
Spheno-frontal, lesser	22	64	slows at 30 at 3.0 final burst of activity.
Spheno-frontal, greater	22 Slow to 26		slows at 30 at 3.0 final burst of activity
Coronal (c) 1 and 2	24	38	slows at 29 at 3.4
Coronal 3	26	41	slows at 29 at 2.1
Lambdoid (L) 1 and 2	26 rapid	42	slows at 31 at 3.4
Lambdoid 3	26 to ca. 30	47	slows at 30 at 2.2
Masto-occipital 3	26	72	32–48 at 3.2, slow progress thereafter
Spheno-parietal	29	65	29–46 at 30 slow progress thereafter.
Spheno-temporal 2	30 slow at	67	at 3.9 gradual progress
Spheno-temporal 1	31 once	67	at 2.4 31–62 at 0.5 burst of activity at 63
Masto-occipital 1 and 2	30	81	32–45 at 1.25 activity between 46 and 64.
Parieto-mastoid 1 and 2	37	81	almost inactive till 50 slow progress thereafter
Squamous posterior	37 almost inactive till 62	81	burst of activity at 63 burst of activity at 79
Squamous anterior	37	81	at 3.2 burst of activity at 63 burst of activity at 79

Numbers such as 3.9, 3.0, 2.2, and the like, refer to extent of suture closure in fourths, with 0 for no suture closure, 1 for one-fourth of the total suture closure, 3 for three-fourths of the total suture closure, and 4 for complete suture closure. Age in years.

Postero-Lateral: (Paired. At posterior-inferior angle of parietal bone) End of the first year.

Bregmatic: (Situated at bregma) During the second year.

During the second year the halves of the mandible unite at the symphysis, and the mastoid process appears.

At birth the occipital bone consists of four parts: an upper or squamous portion, two lateral portions, and a basilar part. The squama unites with the lateral parts between the third and fifth years; the lateral parts with the basi-occipital during the fourth or fifth years. The basi-occipital is united to the basi-sphenoid by a strip of cartilage. The area it occupies is known as the basilar suture. This undergoes obliteration between the age of 18 and 25 years.

External or ectocranial suture closure exhibits much variability, but taken together with other features of the skull it provides a useful additional means of arriving at an age estimate of the skull. In Figure

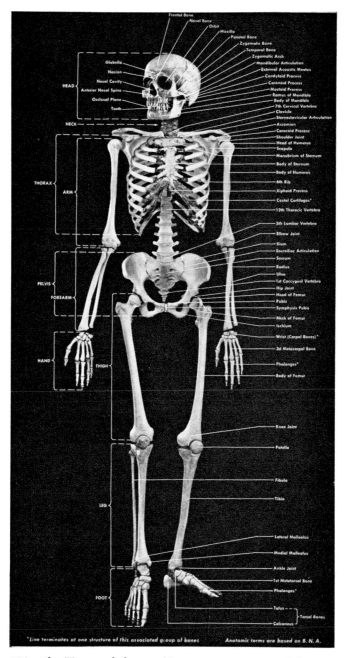

Figure 222. The Human skeleton. (Courtesy, Eastman Kodak Co., Rochester, New York.)

CRANIAL MEASUREMENTS and MORPHOLOGICAL OBSERVATIONS

Field number..................... Sex.................... Date.................... Observer....................
Area............................. Site................... Group................... Period......................
Age.............................. Muscularity............ Weight.................. Sex criteria................
Description...................... Condition.............. Anomalies............... Type........................

Glabello-occipital length........ Optic foramen-nasion..... Frontal angle........... Left orbital index..........
Nasion-occipital................. Optic foramen-basion..... Forehead slope angle.... External palatal............
Basion-bregma height............. Sphenobasion-nasion...... Nasalia profile angle...
Forehead height.................. Sphenobasion-basion...... Facial angle............ Cranial capacity............
Nasion-bregma chord.............. Sphenobasion-alveolon.... Alveolar angle.......... Skull module................
Bregma-lambda chord.............. External palate length... Orbit sagittal angle.... Vault module................
Lambda-opisthion chord........... External palate breadth.. Orbit droop angle.......
Lambda-inion chord............... Palate height (M₁–M₂).... Orbit a-p axis angle.... Stature.....................
Inion-opisthion chord,........... Orbit height, L–R........ Nasal floor angle....... Asymmetry or Deformation....
Frontal arc...................... Orbit breadth, L–R....... Alveolar plane angle.... Kind........................
Parietal arc..................... Biorbital breadth........ Mandibular plane angle.. Degree......................
Occipital arc.................... Interorbital breadth..... Chin profile angle...... Cause.......................
Sagittal arc..................... Dakryon-nasion salient... Opisthion-lambda angle.. Vault.......................
Horizontal circumference......... Upper nasalia breadth.... Foramen magnum angle....   Ill-filled................
Transverse arc................... Lower nasalia breadth.... Basi-occipital angle....   Medium.....................
Porion-temporal lines............ Nose breadth............. Auricular-vertex height.   Well-filled................
Maximum vault breadth............ Nose height.............. Auricular-bregma height. Norma verticalis............
Maximum frontal breadth.......... Nasalia length........... Auricular-nasion length.   Spheroid...................
Minimum frontal breadth.......... Nasion-prosthion height.. Auricular-infraorbitale.   Ellipsoid..................
Bi-mastoid breadth............... Nasion-menton height..... Auricular-basion height.   Ovoid......................
Bi-auricular breadth............. Incisor height........... Cranial index...........   Byrsoid....................
Bizygomatic breadth.............. Incisor overlap (vertical) Mean auricular height index Sphenoid..................
Bi-stylomastoid breadth.......... Incisor overshoot (horiz.) Fronto-parietal index...   Square.....................
Least bi-sphenoid................ Chin height.............. Bi-auricular-parietal index Rhomboid..................
Foramen magnum, L. & Br.......... Bicondylar breadth....... Basal length-breadth index Pentagonoid................
Left carotid foramen a-p......... Bigonial breadth.........   Norma Lateralis.............
Left parietal thickness.......... Bi-mental breadth........   Ellipsoid..................
Porion-mastoid height............ Gonion-symphysion length. Cranio-facial index.....   Ovoid......................
Zygoma thickness................. Direct ramus height...... Zygo-frontal index......   Pentagonoid................
Articular eminence salient....... Minimum ramus breadth.... Fronto-gonial index.....   Round......................
Articular eminence a-p........... Corpus thickness (M₁).... Zygo-gonial index.......   Square.....................
Basion-nasion length............. Molar length............. Facial index............   Sphenoid...................
Basion-prosthion length.......... Mandibular angle......... Upper facial index...... Norma occipitalis...........
                                                              Nasal index.............   Spheroid...................
                                                                                          Rounded....................
                                                                                          Gabled.....................
                                                                                          Hausform...................
                                                                                          Hayrick....................
                                                                                          Barrel-vault...............
                                                                                          Ellipsoid..................
                                                                                        Norma facialis..............
                                                                                          Rounded....................
                                                                                          Heart......................
                                                                                          Pentagonoid................
                                                                                          Squat hexagon..............
                                                                                          Long hexagon...............
                                                                                          Square.....................
                                                                                          Rectangular................
                                                                                          Trapezoid..................
                                                                                          Triangular.................

Median
Divided
Continuous
Browridge size
 Sm.
 Trace +
 ++
Metopism
 Traces
 Complete
Frontal grooves
 Trace – sl.
 + – ++

Frontal bosses
 Sm.
 +
 ++
Median crest
 Sm.
 +
PARIETAL
Postcoronal depr.
 Sl.
 +

Pterion type Left Right
 H H
 K K
 X X
 Retourné Retourné

Sl. – +
Sl. +
TEMPORAL
Fullness
 Flat
 Sl.
 +
 ++
Mastoids
 Sm.
 +
 ++
 +++
Supramastoid crest

Open
Begin
 ++
 Complete
Sagittal
 Open
 Begin
 +
 Complete
Mound
 Complete
Squamous
 Open
 +
 Complete

Crest size
 Trace
 Sm.
 +
 ++
Crest shape
 Ridge
 Mound
SUTURE SERRATION
 Coronal
 Sagittal
 Lambdoid

Suborbital fossa
 None
 Sl.
 +
Malar size
 Sm.
 +
 ++
 +++
Lateral projection
 Compressed
 Sl.
 +
 ++

Lambdoid
 Open
 Begin
 +
 Complete
Masto-occipital
 Open
 +
 Complete
Inca bone
Wormian bones
 Lambdoid
 Sagittal
 Coronal
 Other

BASE
Condyle projection
 Sl.
 +
 ++
Pharyngeal tubercle
 Sm.
 +
Pharyngeal fossa
 Sm.
 +
Petrous depression
 Sl.
 +
 ++

Styloid size
 Sm.
 +
 ++
Tympanic plate
 Thin
 +
 Thick
Postglenoid process
 Short
 +
Eminence slope
 Sl.
 +

Auditory meatus
 Round
 Oval
 Ellipse
 Slit
Angular spine
 Sm.
 +
Ext. pterygoid plate
 Short
 +
 Long
 Sl.
 +
Pterygo-spinous for.

Cerebellar bulge
 Sl.
 +
 ++
Transverse suture:

Postnatal spine
 Sm.
 +
Orbit shape
 Ellipsoid
 Square
 Rectangular
 Rhomboid
Lacrimal foramen
 Sm.
 +
Infraorbital suture
 Absent
 Present:

FACE
Palate shape
 Parabolic
 Elliptical
 Hyperbolic (V)
 Small U
 Large U
Palatine torus
 None
 Sm.
 +
Pal. torus form
 Ridge
 Mound
 Lump
Palate height:

Mylo-hyoid ridge
 Sm.
 +
Pterygoid insertion
 Sl.
 +
Gonia eversion
 None
 Sl.
 +
Mandibular torus
 Absent
 Present:

Chin form
 Median
 Triangular
 Bilateral
Chin projection
 Negative
 Neutral
 Sl.
 +
Genial tubercles
 None
 Pit
 Sm.
 +

Alveolar prognathism Maxilla Mandible
 None None
 Sl. Sl.
 + +
 ++ ++
 +++ +++
Mouth region form
 Linear
 Tilted
 Angular
 Civilized
 Infantile
 Squat
 Primitive
 Other

Nasal sills
 None
 Dull
 Sharp
Submasal grooves
 None
 Sl.
 +
Prognathism (total)
 None
 Sl.
 +
 ++
 +++

Nose profile
 Straight
 Concave
 Wavy
 Convex
 "Classical profile"
Nasal spine
 Absent
 Present
Nasal spine size
 Absent
 Sm.
 +
Nasal spine form
 Pointed
 Spatulate
 Downturned

Nose root breadth
 V. narrow
 Narrow
 +
 Wide
 V. wide
Bridge height
 V. low
 Low
 +
 High
 V. high
Bridge breadth
 Narrow
 +

Anterior projection
 Sl.
 +
Marginal process
 Sm.
 +
Nose root height
 V. low
 Low
 +
 High
 V. high
Nasion depression

Shovel incisors
 Absent
 Sl.
 +
 ++
Bite
 Under
 Edge
 Sl. over
 + over
 ++ over
Central trema
 Absent
 Sl.
 +
 ++

Teeth quality
 V. poor
 Poor
 +
 Good
 Excellent
Molar cusps (number)
 Upper
 Lower
Molar cusp pattern
 Plus
 Dryopithecus
Accessory cusps
 None
 Present:

Abscess size
 Sm.
 +
Teeth wear
 None
 Sl.
 +
 ++
 +++
Crowding
 None
 Sl.
 +

No. alveolae present
No. teeth lost p.m.
No. teeth lost a.m.
No. teeth carious
No. abscesses

Tooth eruption
Incomplete:
Complete
Suppr. all M3s
Suppr.:
Other
Alveolar absorption
 None
 Sl.
 +
 ++
Pyorrhea
 None
 Sl.
 +
 ++

Dentition   Right

8 7 6 5 4 3 2 1 1 2 3 4 5 6 7 8

Left

/ : alveolus missing   m: milk tooth
= : lost post mortem   retained
X : lost ante mortem   w: worn to roots
• : carious
a : abscess
s : suppr.

Crown L. & Br.: M₁   M₁
Upper
Lower

Figure 223—Continued

221 the age at which various parts of the cranial sutures commence to obliterate and the course and direction of the obliterative process is also shown.

In old age the skull bones are usually somewhat thinner, and the skull tends to be appreciably lighter and more fragile owing to the absorption of spongious bone and the associated extension and enlargement of the sinuses.

The state of closure of the following ectocranial sutures yield a *rough* assessment of age.

I. Vault sutures

    1. Coronal (bregmatic, complicated, and pteric portions)
    2. Sagittal (bregmatic, vertex, obelion, and lambdoid portions)
    3. Lambdoid (lambdoid, medial, and asterionic portions)

II. Circum-meatul sutures

    1. Squamous (anterior and posterior parts)
    2. Parieto-mastoid (superior and inferior parts)
    3. Masto-occipital (posterior, middle, and anterior parts)
    4. Spheno-temporal
    5. Spheno-frontal (greater and lesser wings)

Sutures on the exterior of the skull (ectocranial sutures) will not alone serve to give a reliable estimate of age. Sutures on the inner surface (endocranial) of the skull tend to incomplete closure, such incomplete closure is known as lapsed union. Suture closure is scored as 0 when there is no union, 1 when one-fourth of the suture has closed, 2 when one-half has closed, 3 when three-fourths of the suture is closed, and 4 when the suture is completely closed. There are no significant ethnic group or race differences in suture closure, though in prehistoric representatives of man the endocranial sutures tended to undergo closure at an earlier age.

A good rule to remember is that closure begins in S (sagittal) at 22 years, C (coronal) 24 years, L (lambdoid) 26 years; closure ends S 35 years, C 42 years, L 47 years. It is also well to remember that aging a skull by means of suture closure alone is a hazardous procedure, one may be as much as 20 years off in certain cases! Usually one can get within six years of actual age. Wherever feasible as many other characteristics as possible should be used in arriving at an estimate of age.

The Sex of the Skull

It is not possible with any degree of reliability to determine the sex of the skull until after puberty. In general the female skull is smaller and lighter than the male skull. It presents a more infantile appearance, the bones are smoother, more gracile, and more delicately fashioned. The supraorbital and temporal ridges are little if at all developed, the mastoid processes are small and the supramastoid crests scarcely developed, while the occipital muscle markings are weakly developed. The facial skeleton, teeth, mandible, zygomatic arches and cheekbones are smaller and more delicate, and the margins of the orbits are sharper in the female.[17]

Cranial Recording Blanks

Recording blanks for registering measurements and observations made on the skull will be found indispensable. A typical blank of this sort is reprinted here through the courtesy of Dr. J. L. Angel.

Cephalic and Cranial Deformation

Distorted or deformed crania are due to:

1. *Synostotic deformation:* consequent upon irregularities of cranial development, accompanied by precocious union of the cranial bones.

2. *Artificial deformation:* consequent upon pressure or compression applied during infancy.

3. *Pathological deformation:* the result of disease.

4. *Posthumous deformation:* consequent upon pressure exerted by the soil surrounding a skull.

The deformations considered:

1. *Synostotic deformation.* Synostosis of the cranial sutures may be either precocious or retarded. In premature synostosis, some deviation from the normal cranial form is very common, and a general rule (formulated by Rudolf Virchow) is that premature synostosis is followed by restricted growth in a direction perpendicular to that of the synostosed suture. Thus, if a longitudinally directed suture be closed by premature synostosis, the skull-growth in the transverse or coronal direction will be checked. Should the coronal suture or other trans-

---

[17] For the most recent study see Keen, J. A.: A study of the differences between male and female skulls. *Am. J. Phys. Anthropol.,* n.s. 8:65-78, 1950.

versely directed suture be obliterated, restriction of growth in the sagittal direction will ensue.

Forms of synostotic deformation

A. *Scaphocephaly:* Probably the commonest deformation associated with premature synostosis. There may be an appearance of annular constriction, and the specimens are always dolichocephalic, the narrowness being due to restricted growth transversely, in accordance with the law formulated above, following upon closure of the sagittal suture.

B. *Klinocephaly:* When the fore part of the sagittal suture is closed prematurely and at the same time the parieto-sphenoidal suture undergoes synostosis, the growth of the skull is arrested locally, at the sides and the top; this results in the production of a depression encircling the skull as though a band had been tightly applied.

C. *Trigonocephaly:* When the medio-frontal or metopic suture closes prematurely, localized arrest of transverse growth may follow; the frontal region will then remain narrow and stunted in growth, while the posterior parts of the cranium expand normally. The result is the production of a skull which, viewed from above, presents a perked or rostrated appearance, which has been described as triangular or trigonocephalic.

D. *Plagiocephaly:* The skull is asymmetrical. In typical cases there is closure of the coronal suture at a premature stage. The arrest in growth is then unilateral and the skull becomes flattened on one side, while in compensation the opposite side projects. Slight degrees of deformation of this kind may possibly be produced in childhood, if the infant lies habitually on one side rather than on the other.

E. *Acrocephaly:* The bones of the cranial vault are upraised, so that the height of the skull is much increased. These crania are usually very brachycephalic, and the coronal suture is often closed, while part of the sagittal suture near the bregma, and the basilar (basi-occipital) suture may partake in the synostotic processes.

Artificial Deformations

In artificial deformation of the head pressure is artificially applied in various ways and to various regions of the head.[18] The pressure may be:

I. *Frontal:* Exercised by means of a board or other object against the forehead.

---

[18] A useful work is E. J. Dingwall, *Artificial Cranial Deformation.* London, John Bale, Sons & Danielsson, Ltd., 1931.

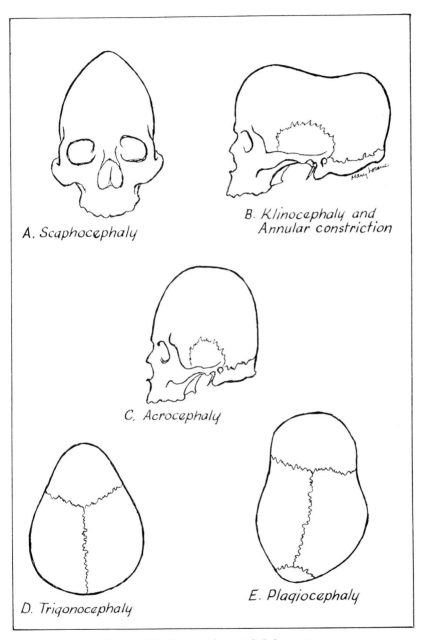

Figure 224. Types of cranial deformation.

II. *Fronto-Occipital* (Flat-head): Produced by means of pressure at the front and back of the head. There are bi-lobed and tri-lobed varieties, in which a rod is substituted for a flat surface, thus indenting the young head to which it is applied.

III. *Annular* (Aymara): Produced by tightly tying a bandage around the head.

IV. *Occipital:* Pressure applied to the back of the head.

V. *Plagiocephalic:* The compression is unequally exerted and the deformation is asymmetrical.

VI. *Platybasia:* The deformation in which the basis cranii appears to be thrust up into the cranial cavity.

Artificial cranial deformation does not affect the functioning of the brain in any way.

Pathological Deformation

I. *Hydrocephalus:* Excessive and even expansion of the constituents of the cranial walls. The sutures become separated as a result of the expansion leaving gaps which are rapidly filled by the formation of wormian bones, of which many scores may be present. The ventricles of the brain, and sometimes the sub-arachnoid spaces, are distended with fluid. The varieties of hydrocephalus have been classified according to the causes of the accumulation of the fluid.

II. *Microcephalus:* Premature arrest of the growth of the skull by early synostosis or union at sutures, with resulting diminutive size of skull.

III. *Rachitis* (or Rickets): The frontal bone is unusually prominent in its upper portion.

IV. *Sickle-Cell Anemia:* This disorder is associated with a remarkable bossing of the frontal bones.

V. Other bone diseases producing characteristic deformations are arthritis, acromegaly, congenital syphilis, leontiasis ossia, osteomalacia, Paget's disease, spondylitis deformans, and tuberculosis, being perhaps among the most important.

Postcranial Osteometry

The purposes for which the postcranial skeleton may be measured are varied. But whatever the purpose, measurements should always be adapted to throw the maximum light upon the problem under investigation. The investigator should always know *why* he is making

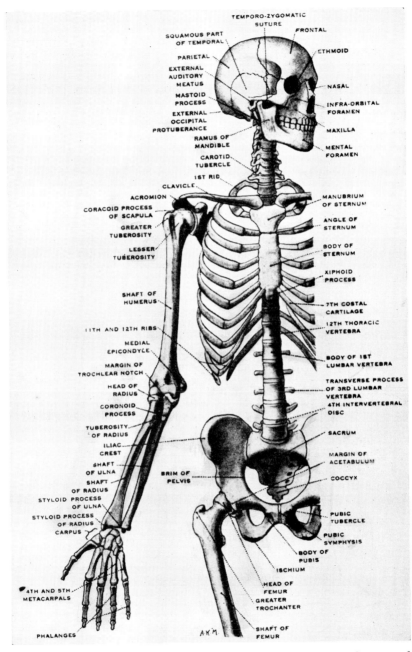

Figure 225. The Human skeleton (anterior view). (From Appleton *et al.*
Courtesy, Williams & Wilkins.)

a particular measurement. Well constructed measurements can help to solve difficult problems.

Instruments. In addition to the instruments already described, larger versions of the sliding compass and spreading calipers are used, and the anthropometer sometimes used to serve the purposes of both, that is, as a rod compass and as a sliding caliper or pelvimeter. For the measurement of long bones an osteometric board is commonly used. The *osteometric board* is a flat, seasoned block of wood, some 23 inches long by 12 inches wide, and about one inch thick. Firmly and immovably attached to one end at an exact right angle is a wooden upright of some 8 inches. Inlaid or attached metric scales run the length of the board (preferably one on each side and one down the middle of the board). A free L-shaped wooden upright completes the instrument. To measure, one end of the bone is placed against the fixed upright and the movable upright against the other, so that the bone is enclosed between the two uprights. The length is then read off the scale at the edge of the movable upright. A satisfactory osteometric board can easily be made by using a 50 cm. square sheet of graduated millimeter graph paper.

Measurements
Upper Extremity and Scapula
Humerus Radius and Ulna

1. *Maximum length* (osteometric board): Between the most proximal and most distal points, the bone being held parallel to the long axis of the board.

2. *Maximum diameter of head* (sliding compass).

3. *Antero-posterior middle shaft diameter* (sliding compass): At middle of shaft.

4. *Medio-lateral middle shaft diameter* (sliding compass): At middle of shaft.

5. *Maximum medio-lateral distal diameter* (sliding compass): At the epiphyseal end of the bone immediately above its associated processes.

6. *Radio-Humeral Index* $\dfrac{\textbf{Maximum Length Radius} \times 100}{\textbf{Maximum Length Humerus}}$

Scapula

7. *Morphological breadth* (sliding compass): From the highest point of the superior angle to the lowest point of the inferior angle.

8. *Morphological length* (spreading calipers): From the middle

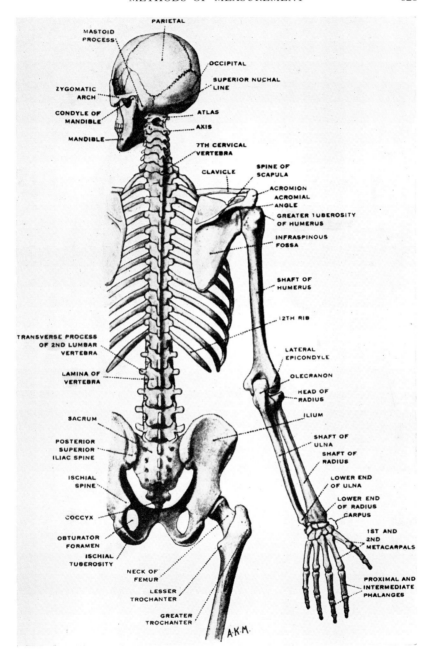

Figure 226. The Human skeleton (posterior view). (From Appleton *et al.* Courtesy, Williams & Wilkins.)

of the glenoid fossa to the point on the vertebral border midway between the two ridges terminating the scapular spine; this point is here called the vertebrion.

9. *Breadth of infraspinous fossa* (sliding compass): From the inferior angle to the vertebrion.

10. *Breadth of suprasinous fossa* (sliding compass): From the superior angle to the vertebrion.

11. *Scapular Index*
$$\frac{\text{Morphological Length} \times 100}{\text{Morphological Breadth}}$$

12a. *Infraspinous Index*
$$\frac{\text{Breadth of infraspinous fossa} \times 100}{\text{Morphological Length}}$$

12b. *Supraspinous Index*
$$\frac{\text{Breadth of supraspinous fossa} \times 100}{\text{Morphological Length}}$$

Observations

Form of vertebral border, from superior angle: Convex, straight, concave, or any combination of these.

Scapular notch: Absent, slight, medium, deep, foramen.

Age changes: Lipping of margins of glenoid fossa, atrophic patches or rarefaction of scapular fossae.

Lower Extremity and Pelvis
Femur

13. *Maximum length:* Between the internal condyle and the head. To find this measurement it is necessary to move the bone slightly up and down and from side to side between the two uprights.

14. *Bicondylar length:* The two condyles rest up against the fixed upright and the moveable upright is brought against the femoral head, so that the whole femur rests naturally between the two uprights.

15. *Maximum diameter of head* (sliding compass).

16. *Subtrochanteric antero-posterior diameter* (sliding compass): Immediately below the lesser trochanter in the sagittal plane.

17. *Subtrochanteric medio-lateral diameter* (sliding compass): From the medial to the lateral surfaces at the level of the preceding measurements.

18. *Platymeric Index*
$$\frac{\text{Antero-posterior diameter} \times 100}{\text{Medio-lateral diameter}}$$

Hyperplatymeric $\times$—74.9

Platymeric	75.0—84.9
Eurymeric	85.0—99.9
Stenomeric	100.0—×

The platymeric index may reflect and thus indicate differences in ethnic, occupational, pathological conditions, and also in such habits as sitting and squatting.

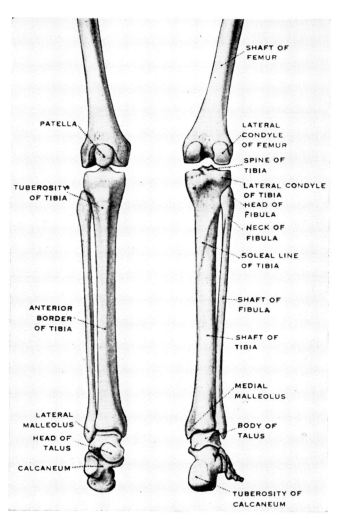

Figure 227. Skeleton of the leg. (On left) anterior aspect with bones of foot removed except talus and calcaneum; (on right) posterior aspect. (From Appleton *et al.* Courtesy, Williams & Wilkins.)

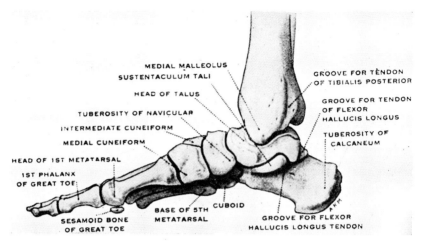

Figure 228. Skeleton of foot. Medial aspect. (From Appleton *et al.* Courtesy, Williams & Wilkins.)

19. *Antero-posterior diameter of middle of shaft* (sliding compass).

20. *Medio-lateral diameter of middle of shaft* (sliding compass): At same level as preceding.

Pilastric Index

$$\frac{\text{Antero-posterior diameter of middle of shaft} \times 100}{\text{Medio-lateral diameter of middle of shaft}}$$

Angles

21. *Collo-diaphyseal angle* (protactor): The angle made by the axis of the head and neck with that of the shaft.

22. *Angle of torsion* (protactor): The angle of the axis of the head projected upon the axis of the posterior surface of the condyles.

Tibia

23. *Maximum length* (osteometric board): The bone resting on its dorsal surface with the medial malleolus resting against the fixed upright. The movable upright is brought into contact with the antero-superior surface of the lateral condyle. The tibia must be parallel to the long axis of the board.

24. *Antero-posterior diameter middle of shaft* (sliding compass).

25. *Medio-lateral diameter of middle of shaft* (sliding compass).

26. *Antero-posterior nutrient foramen diameter* (sliding compass): Diameter of shaft at level of nutrient foramen.

27. *Medio-lateral nutrient foramen diameter* (sliding compass).

28. *Platycnemic Index* $$\frac{\text{Medio-lateral nutrient diameter} \times 100}{\text{Antero-posterior nutrient diameter}}$$

Hyperplatycnemic	×—54.9
Platycnemic	55.0—62.9
Mesocnemic	63.0—69.9
Eurycnemic	70.0—×

Observations

Lateral condyle: Concave or convex.

Squatting facets: Note whether there are any extensions of the inferior articular surface above the anterior lip or medially at the distal end of tibia.

Vertebrae

29. *Anterior height of centrum* (sliding compass): From the middle of the antero-superior lip to the middle of the antero-inferior lip of the body.

30. *Posterior height of centrum* (sliding compass): From the middle of the postero-superior border to the middle of the postero-inferior border of the body.

Pelvis and Sacrum

31. *Maximum pelvic height* (rod compass): From the highest point on the iliac crest to the lowest point on the ischial tuberosity.

32. *Maximum pelvic or cristal breadth* (rod compass): Greatest diameter between the external lips of the right and left iliac crests.

33. *Pelvic Breadth-Height Index* $$\frac{\text{Maximum Pelvic height} \times 100}{\text{Maximum pelvic breadth}}$$

34. *Interspinous diameter* (sliding compass): The maximum diameter between the antero-lateral margins of the antero-superior iliac spines.

35. *External Conjugate diameter* (pelvimeter): From the inferior tip of the 5th lumbar spine to the antero-inferior margin of the pubic symphysis.

36. *Diagonal conjugate diameter* (pelvimeter): From the mid-sagittal point on the antero-superior margin of the sacral promontory to the postero-inferior margin of the pubic symphysis.

37. *Normal conjugate diameter* (sliding compass): From the

postero-superior margin of the symphysis pubis to the deepest point of the third sacral vertebra.

38. *Sagittal diameter of pelvic inlet* (sliding compass): From the postero-superior border of the pubic symphysis to the center of the sacral promontory.

39. *Transverse diameter of pelvic inlet* (sliding compass): Maximum diameter between arcuate lines.

40. *Pelvic Inlet Index* $$\frac{\text{Sagittal diameter of pelvic inlet} \times 100}{\text{Transverse diameter of pelvic inlet}}$$

Platypellic	$\times$—89.9
Mesatipellic	90.0—94.9
Dolichopellic	95.0—$\times$

In a study, by roentgen pelvimetry of 686 living white women, and 107 girls from five to 15 years of age, Greulich and Thoms found the following distribution of pelvic inlet indices:

	Platy-pellic per cent	Mesati-pellic per cent	Doli-chopellic per cent
582 primiparous clinic women (lower socio-economic classes)	35.2	27.5	37.3
104 nulliparous student nurses (higher socio-economic classes)	13.5	13.5	73.0
107 children	8.4	35.2	82.2

Of the 686 women studied 68.1 per cent had a pelvic inlet index of 90 or more. Only 31.9 per cent were of the platypellic type which the textbooks generally describe as typical.

In 69 male medical students at Yale the same authors found the pelvic inlet index to vary between 77.0 to 121.0, with an average index of 100.5. The frequencies were 7.2 per cent platypellic, 14.5 mesatipellic, and 78.2 dolichopellic.

41. *Inferior antero-posterior diameter* (sliding compass): From the postero-inferior border of the pubic symphysis to the postero-inferior border of the sacrum.

42. *Distance between ischial spines* (sliding compass): Minimum.

43. *Intertuberous diameter* (sliding compass): Minimum diameter between the postero-medial margins of the ischial tuberosities.

44. *True pelvic height* (sliding compass): From the lowest point on the medial margin of the ischial tuberosity to the arcuate line anterior to ileopectineal eminence.

Sacrum

45. *Anterior sacral length* (sliding compass): From the middle of sacral promontory to the middle of the antero-inferior margin of the last sacral vertebra.

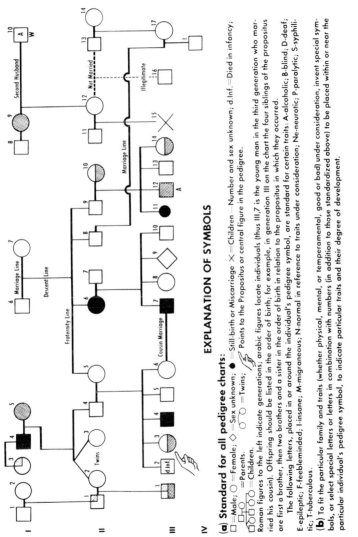

Figure 229. Sample genetic pedigree chart. (From Ashley Montagu. Courtesy, World Publishing Co.)

46. *Anterior sacral breadth* (sliding compass): At junction with arcuate lines.

47. *Length-Breadth Sacral Index* $\dfrac{\text{Anterior sacral breadth} \times 100}{\text{Anterior sacral length}}$

Dolichohieric	$\times$— 99.9
Subplatyhieric	100.0—105.9
Platyhieric	106.0—$\times$

Sexual Characters of the Pelvis

It is possible to determine the sex of the skeleton in a large percentage of cases from the characters of the pelvis. Variability is, however, very considerable. Each sex may exhibit the typical pelvic characters of the opposite sex. One can, therefore, never be quite certain that sex has been accurately determined from the characters of the pelvis. Below is given a list of 21 characters in which the female pelvis and sacrum generally differs from that of the male.

Pelvic Characters	*In the Female*
Cristal breadth	Less
Iliac crest	Less rugged
Tubercles of iliac crest	Much less marked
Anterior and posterior slopes iliac crest	Less steep
Iliac blades or bones	More vertical
Iliac part of ileopectineal line	Greater
Sagittal diameter of pelvic inlet	Greater
Transverse diameter of pelvic inlet	Greater
Symphysis pubis	Broader and lower
Symphyseal height	Less
Ischial portion of pubic bone	Lipped outward, constricted just below symphysis
Subpubic angle	Greater
Intertuberous breadth	Greater
Acetabulum	Lighter
Diameter between ischial spines	Greater
Greater sciatic notch	Broader and more shallow
Preauricular sulci or grooves	Present and well developed
Sacrum	Broader and shorter
Sacral curve	Less
Lower portion of sacrum	Bent backward and upward

Washburn has devised an ischium-pubis index which will accurately sex, according to him, over 90% of skeletons. Length of ischium is measured from the point at which ischium, pubic, and ilium meet in the acetabulum. In the adult this point can be approximately identified because: (1) there is often an irregularity present both in acetabulum and inside the pelvis, (2) holding the bone up to a light will reveal a change in thickness, and (3) there is frequently a notch in the border of the articular surface of the acetabulum. In making measurements hold calipers parallel to long axis of each bone. It is, of course, understood that sexing will be carried out on skeletons belonging to a single division of mankind. The pubic bone is absolutely and relatively larger in females than in males.

$$\frac{\text{Pubis Length} \times 100}{\text{Ischium Length}} = \text{Ischium-Pubis Index}$$

The ischium-pubis index averages 15% higher in females than in males. The mean index in white males was found to be 83.6 (range 73-94) ± 4.0, for white females 99.5 (range 91-115) ± 5.1. In Negro males the comparable figures were 79.9 (range 71-88) ± 4.0, and in Negro females 95.0 (range 84-106) ± 4.6. Only 5 white males were found to fall within the range of female variation. More overlapping occurs among Negroes, probably due to ethnic mixture.

PEDIGREES FOR GENETIC STUDIES

Figure 229 shows a sample pedigree chart together with an explanation of the symbols. For the traits listed any others may be substituted at the convenience of the investigator.

WORKS ON ANTHROPOMETRY AND ANTHROPOSCOPY

BRUES, A. M.: Identification of skeletal remains. *J. Crim. Law, Criminol. & Police Sci.*, 48:551-563, 1958.
A good general discussion.

GARN, S. M.: The measurement of skin temperature. *Am. J. Phys. Anthropol.*, n.s., 12:1-4, 1954.
A review and practically oriented discussion of the necessity and reason for taking skin temperature in anthropometric studies.

———— and SHAMIR, Z.: *Methods for Research in Human Growth.* Springfield, Thomas, 1958.
A useful work oriented to studies and growth.

GAVAN, J. A., WASHBURN, S. L. and LEWIS, P. H.: Photography: an anthropometric tool. *Am. J. Phys. Anthropol.*, n.s., 10:331-353, 1952.
A method of taking standardized photographs of the human body, from which accurate anthropometric measurements may be secured.

GODYCKI, M.: Sur la certitude de détermination du sexe d'après le fémur, le cubitus, et l'humérus. *Bull. et Mém. de la Soc. d' Anthrop. Paris*, 8:405-410, 1957.
A valuable analysis of methods of determining sex from the long bones.

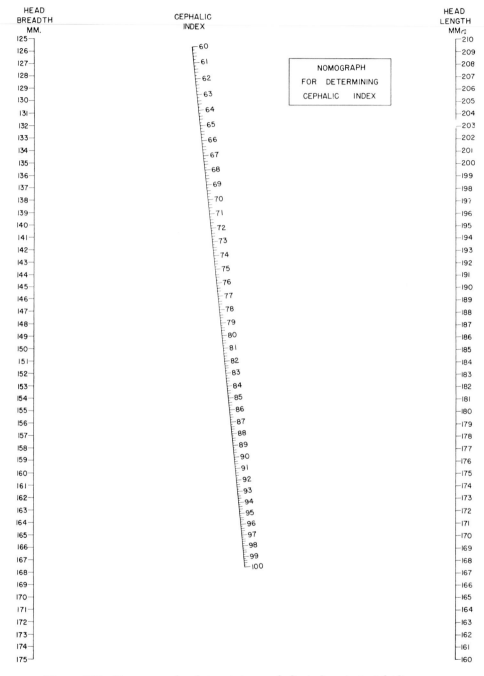

Figure 230. Nomogram for determining cephalic index. A straight line passing from the measurement for head breadth to the measurement for head length will yield the correct reading for cephalic index in the middle column. (From the *Yearbook of Physical Anthropology for 1949*. Courtesy, Dr. G. W. Lasker and the Wenner-Gren Foundation for Anthropological Research, New York.)

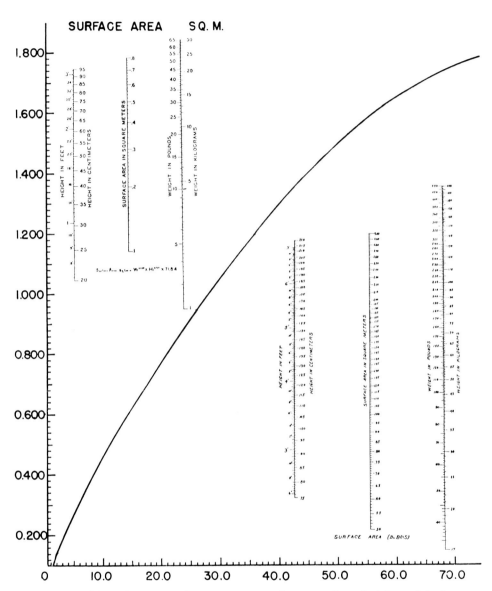

Figure 231. Nomogram for estimating surface area from height and body weight. (Surface area, Sq. Cm. $= Wt.^{0.425} \times Ht.^{0.725} \times 71.84$). The subject's surface area is found by drawing a straight line between the point representing his weight and the point representing his height. (From J. D. Crawford *et al.* Courtesy, *Pediatrics.*)

GEOGHEGAN, B.: The determination of body measurements, surface area and body volume by photography. *Am. J. Phys. Anthropol.*, n.s., *11*:97-119, 1953.
A system of photogrammetric anthropometry by means of which a wide range of measurements may be obtained from photographs of subjects in certain postures, including specific gravity when body weight is known.

HERTZBERG, H. T. E., DUPERTUIS, C. W., and EMANUEL, I.: Stereophotogrammetry as an anthropometric tool. *Photogrammetric Engineering, 23*:942-947, 1957.
A method of measuring body contours in three dimensions from photograph to drawing.

HERTZBERG, H. T. E. (editor): Annotated bibliography of applied physical anthropology in human engineering. Aero Medical Laboratory, Wright-Patterson Air Force Base, Ohio, 1958, 301 pp.
A most valuable compendium of the results of applied anthropometry and biomechanics.

HOOTON, E. A.: Elementary Anthropometry, in *Up From the Ape*, 2nd edition, New York, Macmillan, 1946, p. 715-769.
An excellent introduction to general anthropometry on the skeleton and the living subject.

HRDLIČKA, A.: *Practical Anthropometry*, 4th edition (edited by T. D. Stewart). Philadelphia, Wistar Inst., 1957.
Especially useful as a reference book to the decisions of various congresses.

KROGMAN, W. M.: A Handbook of the Measurement and Interpretation of Height and Weight in the Growing Child. *Monographs of the Society for Research in Child Development, 8*:1-68, 1950.
A simply written work telling how to measure, what errors to avoid, and how to put height and weight together in the form of an index, on a growth chart, or on the Wetzel Grid.

MARTIN, R.: *Lehrbuch Der Anthropologie*, 2nd edition, 3 vols., Jena, Fischer, 1928.
The standard work on anthropometry and anthropometric methods, though somewhat out of date, and therefore to be used with caution. The third volume is entirely devoted to the literature of physical anthropology, and is an indispensable reference work. A third edition edited by Karl Saller is in process of publication.

MERRITT, E. L.: *Analytical Photogrammetry*. New York, Pitman, 1958.
A general introduction to measurement by photography.

OLIVIER, G. and PINEAU, H.: Détermination du sexe par le poids des os. *Bull. et Mém. de la Soc. d'Anthrop. Paris, 9*:329-339, 1958.
On determining sex from the weight of the individual bones of the skeleton. There are significant differences, the bones of the forearm yield perhaps the most significant of the sex differences in weight.

SUNDERMAN, F. W. and BOERNER, F.: *Normal Values in Clinical Medicine*. Philadelphia, Saunders, 1949.
A practical compendium of normal values and standards relating to the physiological functions of the human organism, with especial reference to the needs of the doctor, but of great value to the anthropologist.

SULLIVAN, L. R.: *Essentials of Anthropometry. A Handbook for Explorers and Museum Collectors.* (Revised by H. L. Shapiro.) New York, American Museum of Natural History, 1928.

A useful pocketbook devoted to the anthropometry and anthroposcopy of the living; somewhat out of date.

WILDER, H. H.: *A Laboratory Manual of Anthropometry.* Philadelphia, Blakiston, 1920.

A very useful book on the anthropometry of the skeletal and living subject, but somewhat out of date.

WORKS ON STATISTICS

ARKIN, H. and COLTON, R. R.: *Statistical Methods,* 4th edition. New York, Barnes & Noble; 1956.

A most useful distillation of the essence of statistical methods.

CHAMBERS, E. G.: *Statistical Calculation for Beginners.* New York, Cambridge University Press, 1948.

An excellent introduction, on a very elementary level.

DAHLBERG, G.: *Statistical Methods for Medical and Biological Students.* New York, Norton, 1948.

An excellent book, assuming an elementary knowledge of mathematics.

FISHER, R. A.: *Statistics for Research Workers,* 10th edition. Edinburgh, Oliver & Boyd, 1948.

The most widely used practical treatise.

FRANZBLAU, A. N.: *A Primer of Statistics for Non-Statisticians.* New York, Harcourt, Brace, 1958.

A genuinely helpful practical introduction for the non-mathematical reader.

HILL, A. B.: *Principles of Medical Statistics,* 6th edition. New York, Oxford University Press, 1955.

A first-rate elementary introduction.

KURTZ, A. K. and EDGERTON, H. A.: *Statistical Dictionary of Terms and Symbols.* New York, Wiley, 1939.

An authoritative dictionary of clear and accurate definitions of statistical terms and symbols.

LI, C. T.: *Population Genetics.* Chicago, University of Chicago Press, 1955.

A fundamental book.

————: *Introduction to Statistical Inference.* Ann Arbor, Michigan, 1957.

A non-mathematical exposition.

MAINLAND, D.: *Elementary Medical Statistics.* Philadelphia, Saunders, 1952.

MORONEY, M. G.: *Facts from Figures.* Baltimore, Penguin Books, 1951.

A helpful introduction.

PEARL, R.: *Introduction to Medical Biometry and Statistics,* 3rd edition. Philadelphia, Saunders, 1940.

A standard and invaluable work, especially useful to physical anthropologists and medical men.

RAO, C. R.: *Advanced Statistical Methods in Biometrical Research.* New York, Wiley, 1957.

A valuable work, for the mathematically more sophisticated student. The problems and illustrative examples are mainly based on the materials of physical anthropology.

SIMPSON, G. G., ROE, A., and LEWONTIN, R. C.: *Quantitative Zoology.* New York, McGraw-Hill, 1960.

A work on the methodology of zoology, constituting a most attractively written introduction to the use and methodology of statistics.

SNEDECOR, G. W.: *Statistical Methods*, 4th edition. Ames, Iowa, Collegiate Press, 1948.

An excellent introduction.

YULE, G. U. and KENDALL, M. G.: *An Introduction to the Theory of Statistics*, 13th edition. New York, Hafner, 1950.

A standard work, and the most commonly used by physical anthropologists, many of whom were brought up on the earlier editions of this admirable work.

WORKS ON ARCHAEOLOGY

CHILDE, V. G.: *A Short Introduction to Archaeology.* London, Muller, 1956.

An excellent elementary introduction to archaeology, prehistoric and recent, by one of the most distinguished archaeologists of our time.

CLARK, J. G. D.: *Prehistoric Europe.* New York, Philosophical Library, 1952.

A great book on the ways in which early man maintained himself in Europe since the end of the Pleistocene Ice Age.

————: *Excavations at Starr Carr.* New York, Cambridge University Press, 1954.

A model account of an early mesolithic site in Yorkshire which, among other things, conveys not only the facts but also the feeling of what life was like in mesolithic Europe.

————: *Archaeology and Society.* Cambridge, Massachusetts, Harvard University Press, 1957.

An excellent introduction to the aims and methods of archaeology, and the reconstruction of prehistoric societies.

CORNWALL, I. W.: *Bones for the Archaeologist.* London, Phoenix House, 1956. Designed to help the archaeologist make preliminary identification of bony material. The sixteen chapters cover the identification, reconstruction, measurement, cleaning, and interpretation of bones.

CORNWALL, I. W.: *Soils for the Archaeologist.* London, Phoenix House, New York, Macmillan, 1958.

A most useful work on the identification and analysis of the soils in which fossil remains and artifacts may be found.

DANIEL, G. E.: *A Hundred Years of Archaeology.* New York, Macmillan, 1950.

A highly readable and informative history.

DE LAET, S. J.: *Archaeology and its Problems.* New York, Macmillan, 1957.

An utterly delightful and indispensable introduction to the aims and methods of archaeology. There is not an aspect of the subject that is not covered.

DE MORGAN, J.: *Prehistoric Man.* New York, Knopf, 1925.

An invaluable work on the evolution of man's industries, arts, and cultures.

HEIZER, R. F. (editor). *The Archaeologist at Work.* New York, Harper, 1959.

A most instructive work.

MACALISTER, R. A. S.: *A Textbook of European Archaeology.* Vol. I. *The Palaeolithic Period.* Cambridge: at the University Press, 1921.

Admirable even though somewhat dated. This, alas, was the only one of the projected volumes published.

MACCURDY, G. G.: *Human Origins: A Manual of Prehistory.* 2 vols. New York, Appleton, 1924.

A very complete and still useful work.

MEWHINNEY, H.: *A Manual for Neanderthals.* Austin, University of Texas Press, 1957.

The best book on how Stone Age man made his tools available. As the title implies it also instructs the reader how to make similar tools.

OAKLEY, K. P.: *Man the Tool Maker,* 4th edition. London, British Museum (Natural History), also Chicago, University of Chicago Press, 1958.

An admirable short work.

PIGGOTT, S.: *Approach to Archaeology.* London, Black, 1959.

A stimulating discussion of the aims and purposes of archaeology.

WILLEY, G. R.: *Method and Theory in American Archaeology.* Chicago, University of Chicago Press, 1957.

An invaluable synthesis of New World archaeology.

WORMINGTON, H. M.: *Ancient Man in North America.* 4th ed. Denver Museum of Natural History, 1957.

The best work on the archeology of North America.

ZEUNER, F. E.: *Dating the Past.* 4th ed. New York, Longmans, 1957.

The basic work on geochronology with especial reference to archeology.

FILM-MAKING FOR FIELD WORKERS AND OTHERS

For the details of technique, equipment, care, and handling of film see N. G. Dyhrenfurth, "Film making for scientific field workers," *Amer. Anthropol., 54:* 147-152, 1952.

RADIOCARBON DATING SERVICES

A publication devoted largely to the publication of radiocarbon date lists from various parts of the world, is published separately under the title *Radiocarbon Supplement,* by the *American Journal of Science,* Box 1905A, Yale Station, New Haven, Connecticut. Published annually. Subscription $2.50.

Radiocarbon Dates Association, Inc., Peabody Foundation, Box 71, Andover, Massachusetts, supplies subscribers with edge-punched cards recording specimens assayed and their radiocarbon dates.

Radiocarbon dating service is provided, on a commercial basis, by Isotopes, Inc., 123 Woodland Avenue, Westwood, New Jersey.

TABLE OF WEIGHTS AND MEASURES

1 Micron (μ) = 1 thousandth of a millimeter (mm)
1 Millimeter = 1 thousandth of a meter
10 millimeters = 1 centimeter (cm)   1 meter = { 10 decimeters / 100 centimeters / 1000 millimeters }
10 centimeters = 1 decimeter (dm)
10 decimeters = 1 meter (m)
1 inch = 25.4 millimeters
1 foot = 30.5 centimeters (approximately), or 0.3048 meter
5½ inches = 14.0 centimeters
1 yard = 0.9144 meter
1 centimeter = .3937 inch
1 meter = 39.37 inches
1 mile = 1.6093 kilometers
Volume = Length x Breadth x Thickness
Area = Length x Breadth
1 cubic inch = 16.387 cubic centimeters
1 cubic centimeter (c.c. or cc) = 0.061 cubic inch

1 cubic centimeter of water at 4° C. weighs 1 gram
1 liter of water at 4° C. weighs 1000 grams and is called a kilogram
1 decigram = 1/10 gram (dgm)
1 centigram = 1/100 gram (cgm)
1 milligram = 1/1000 gram (mgm)
1 cubic decimeter (cd) = (1000 cubic centimeters) = 61.024 cubic inches
1 cubic meter (100 cubic decimeters) = 35.3148 cubic feet
1 cubic decimeter = 1 liter
1 liter = 1.81 pints
4 liters = 7 pints or 112 ounces
1 pint = 16 ounces
1 ounce = 28.350 grams
1 gram = about ½₈ ounce
1 kilogram = 2 pounds 3¼ ounces
16 ounces = 1 pound
3.527 ounces = 100 grams
1 pound = 453.592 grams

DRY MEASURE

Pints	Quarts	Gallons	Cubic Inches	Metric
1	0.5	0.125	33.600	550.599 cu. millimeters
2	1.0	0.25	67.201	1.101 liters
8	4.0	1.0	268.803	4.405 liters
16	8.0	2.0	537.605	8.809 liters
64	32.0	8.0	2150.42	35.238 liters

Specific Gravity = The number of times a body or substance is heavier or lighter than an equal volume of water (or some other substance taken as a standard), under specified conditions of temperature and pressure.

APPENDIX B

THE MEASUREMENT OF BODY COMPOSITION [*]

HISTORICAL PERSPECTIVE

TRADITIONALLY physical anthropologists have been interested in the skeleton. Osteometry covered a large part of the *globus anthropologicus*. Skeletal remains were plentiful and anthropologists were busy and happy. Insofar as measurements were involved, rather than qualitative descriptions and classifications of the color of skin, shape of the nose, or texture of the hair, anthropologists compared the living representatives of the races of mankind again in terms of skeletal dimensions. The techniques of physical anthropology were designed to render as negligible as possible the individual differences in fat and muscle.

The result was that anthropologists got, for the most part, what they asked for: data on the skeleton only.[1] Man, the professed subject matter of anthropology's inquiry, was squeezed out. The portion of the human body between the skin and the bone was a "no-man's-land," lying fallow. The realization was slow in coming that soft tissues *were* the anthropologist's business and that body composition is, in fact, the very key to human physique.

Body weight was measured, though more frequently by pediatricians, internists, including medical life-insurance examiners, and teachers than by those whose business was to study man's physique, *ex officio*. What has been wrong with body weight, anthropologically speaking, was the way it was used. As length determines in part body weight, a variety of height-weight indexes were devised. They had a common fault: at best, they yielded a gross measure of underweight-overweight, lumping together factors that should be kept initially apart.

In the adult individual, at a given height the body weight increases 1) with the increase in lateral dimensions of the skeletal frame; such an increase is accounted for, in a small measure, by the

[*] By Josef Brožek, Lehigh University, Bethlehem, Pennsylvania; Research Associate and formerly Professor, Laboratory of Physiological Hygiene, School of Public Health, University of Minnesota, Minneapolis, Minnesota.

637

weight of the "extra" skeletal structures and, more importantly, by increased amounts of the supporting musculature and by the increased size of the organs filling the spaces defined by the bony structures, 2) with increase in musculature, resulting from physical exercise, and with increase in adipose tissue, resulting from excessive food intake and/or underexercise.

These factors, of quite different biological significance, are hopelessly scrambled in height-weight indexes and allied concepts, such as the relative body weight (100 A/S, where A = actual weight, S = weight standard for age, sex and height). How can we partition the gross body weight?

The basic information regarding body composition is obtained on the basis of direct analysis of the human body. Because of man's size and a variety of other considerations, quantitative analyses of whole adult bodies using anatomical or chemical methods have been few and far between. There was a long gap between the work of the older German anatomists (Bischoff 1863, Volkmann 1874) and the modern data published in America by Mitchell (1945, 1953) and in England by McCance (1951) and their respective collaborators. Their work, though limited in the number and selection of the bodies, represents a significant advance. Clearly, the direct analyses provide the final calibration and validation for the indirect methods.

Individual differences in soft-tissues, specifically in subcutaneous fat, have not escaped the measurers' eyes. P. Richer, a Frenchman, reported on "the function of fat in the external form of the human body" as far back as 1890. But the roots of modern anthropological study of body composition, utilizing available anatomical information and focussed on the analysis of body weight based on external body measurements, may be traced to the work of the Czech anthropologist J. Matiegka. His important paper [2] was published in 1921 under the cryptic title "The testing of physical efficiency" in the *American Journal of Physical Anthropology*. Much interested in the functional significance of individual differences in human physique, Matiegka outlined a technique for a quantitative appraisal of the mass of the main body compartments accessible to somatometric approach. The writer has expressed the opinion, and still holds it, that it was a major loss for students of human physique that Matiegka's approach, providing physical anthropology with its vital "fourth dimension" remained, for years, unnoticed.

In subsequent years the studies of the composition of the human body continued to receive impetus through a variety of developments. At Minnesota R. E. Scammon, quantitatively oriented anatomist, portrayed in the early twenties the markedly varying rates at which different organs grow,[3] with special emphasis on the fetal period. The layer of subcutaneous fat grows precipitously between about the 28th and 40th week of menstrual age (term). Equations were provided for predicting from crown-heel length the weight of the anatomically separated subcutaneous adipose tissue and of the chemically extracted fat.[4]

R. E. Moulton, concerned with growth and development of farm animals, formulated in 1923 the concept of "chemical maturity," defined as a state in which the composition of the fat-free mass (analyzed in terms of water, protein, and minerals) approximates constancy.[5] While the species differences cannot be neglected, animal studies provide a welcome opportunity for the validation of indirect techniques.[5a]

Methodologically, an important advance in animal studies on body composition was made by J. Hammond. His complete-dissection method (1932) involves anatomical separation of the total body into its component organs and tissues. The weight of each component is recorded and expressed as percentage of total weight or, preferably, in terms of a reference organ or part (such as brain-plus-eyes). Hammond and his co-workers applied this technique to a systematic analysis of developmental changes in different anatomical regions and in the major organs and tissues of the body.[6]

The strongest stimulus to the study of body composition in man came from the work of A. R. Behnke, initially an outgrowth of his physiological studies pertaining to deep sea diving.[7, 8] Under his guidance formulae were developed for the analysis of weight of the living human body into its "fat" and "lean" fraction on the basis of the ratio of body weight to body volume[9] and of total body water.[10, 11]

In the context of nutritional researches Icie G. Macy and her co-workers began their studies on chemical growth during childhood. The first volume of their reports was published in 1942.[12] Later, they labelled the field "chemical anthropology." A large amount of valuable data was recorded and analyzed in regard to the storage of nutrients in the body of the growing child. Food intake was meticulously measured and the detailed chemical analysis of meals was combined with the collection and chemical analysis of excreta. The balance studies, involving determinations of the cumulative differences between nutrient intake and losses in urine and feces, were made for as long as 225 days—a truly Herculean labor! The metabolic balances provided detailed information on the storage of nitrogen, considered as evidence of the growth of "protoplasmic mass," and of minerals. A variety of anthropometric, physiological and other biochemical data were collected to document the complex changes constituting growth. The subsequent attempt to synthesize the simpler body measurements with the more complex biophysical and biochemical approaches to the analysis of body composition—an important task for physical anthropology—cannot be regarded as successful.[13, 13a]

The concepts and tools for the study of body composition were reviewed systematically in the comprehensive framework of human biology, as practiced at Minnesota.[14] The methodological contributions of the Minnesota group included some technical improvements (direct measurement of "residual air" in determinations of body volume by underwater weighing), the concept of normal young man as the "reference body," information on density of human fat and on the composition of mass gained by overeating ("obesity tissue"), and prediction of total fat from skinfolds and from roentgenograms of the extremities.

The technique of soft-tissue roentgenography has been utilized intensively for measuring the amounts of subcutaneous fat (plus skin), muscle and bone in several research centers concerned with growth and development.[15, 16, 17]

The concept of body composition, together with the availability of new tools for the measurement of body compartments, stimulated in recent years a substantial amount of research. Physical anthropology was brought into livelier contact with the "dynamic" problems of nutrition, of growth and aging, of physical exercise. The need for a fundamental rethinking of one of the pillars of physical anthropology of the living man, that of body build, emerged clearly.

METHODS—BASIC CONSIDERATIONS

The components into which the total body mass is separated depend on the investigator's frame of reference—anatomical, chemical, and biochemical (see Table 1). The anatomist thinks in terms of dissected organs and tissues, of mechanically separable components that can be measured in regard to their size and weighed. The organic chemist, analyzing a whole cadaver or its anatomical parts, operates with compartments defined in terms of chemical procedures. And the biochemist and physiologist, dealing with a living organism will operate with a set of body components that will again differ, at least in part, from those of the organic chemist. The biochemical approach and breakdown of body weight is guided by metabolic and functional considerations, and results in a system in which some components are defined in strictly chemical terms (e.g., body water), others (e.g., cell mass) are "histochemical" constructs, i.e., tissue (*histos*) masses defined on the basis of biochemical operations and concepts.

The physical anthropologist is closer to the anatomist than to the chemist, whether he is making anthroposcopic ratings, using direct body measurements or measuring the width of tissues in a soft-tissue roentgenogram of the leg. His "fat" is the adipose tissue of the anatomist and his measurements of "muscles" or "bones" refer to anatomical entities. Yet, prediction equations can be established for the assessment of body composition, on the basis of appropriate body measurements, in terms of anatomically, chemically or biochemically defined components.

Prior to the discussion of individual methods, an overall review of the basic data used in studies of body composition *in vivo* may be useful. These are indicated in Table 2. A variety of other techniques was developed for the study of body composition, including determinations of body fat by the use of fat-soluble indicators, such as the gases nitrogen and cyclopropane, and the estimations of the fat-free fraction of the body from creatinine excretion and basal oxygen consumption. These methods will not be described here. The densitometric and the hydrometric method will be discussed only in regard to the basic ideas.

TABLE 1

BASIC FRAMES OF REFERENCE AND THE RESULTING BODY COMPONENTS

Frames of Reference		
Anatomical	*Chemical* (Direct analysis of cadavers)	*Biochemical* (Indirect analysis *in vivo*)
Adipose tissue	Fat (ether extract)	Fat estimate (equivalent of ether extract)
	Total body water (by desiccation)	Total body water and its fractions (by dilution)
Muscle Mass, Viscera	Protein (6.25 × nitrogen)	Cell mass (estimate)
Skeletal mass	Total and bone mineral (ash)	Bone mineral (estimate)

TABLE 2

Basic Data Used in Different Approaches to Body Composition In Vivo

"Surface" Anthropometry	Roentgenogram- metry	Densitometry	Hydrometry
Height, Weight Relative Weight (Actual, as % of standard)	(Body weight)	Body weight	Body weight
Skinfolds	Width of skin plus subcutaneous tissues	Body density $(D = Mass/Volume)$	Total body water
Circumferences and diameters (especially in limbs, preferably corrected for subcutaneous fat)	Width of muscle layer (in limbs)	(Extracellular fluid)	Extracellular fluid
Bony diameters	Bony widths		
	(Degree of bone mineralization)		

The emphasis will be placed on those techniques that belong in the physical anthropologist's tool box. This is, however, a metaphor. It is easy enough to pack and carry around a box containing a couple of flexible steel tapes, a suitable L-shaped object for defining the level of the top of the head, large spreading calipers for measuring the width of shoulders and of the pelvis, smaller spreading calipers for determination of biepicondylar diameters of the extremities, and skinfold calipers. The x-ray machine is less readily transportable. Yet, in the last two decades soft-tissue roentgenography has been an important tool allowing the anthropologist to make a significant contribution to the fund of knowledge on the body composition of the living man. This tool has been applied especially to the study of growth and development while the densitometric technique was applied almost solely and the hydrometric technique largely to adults. In this presentation, we shall be also concerned primarily with the adult man (and, on occasion, the adult woman). Methods for research on growth were described recently by Garn and Shamir.[18]

METHODS: DISSECTION AND CHEMICAL ANALYSIS

For well over 100 years parts of dissected human bodies have been diligently weighed and some analyzed chemically. Nevertheless, information on the total composition of the body, in anatomical or chemical terms, is surprisingly meager. Most of the modern data were obtained since 1945.

The data resulting from the dissection of two cadavers into the various organs and tissues are given in Table 3. The 35-year-old man died from a heart attack.[19] The death of the 46-year-old man was due to a skull fracture as a result of a fall.[20] Both were thin, below standard weight (with relative weights of 88 and 74, respectively; "normal" = 100). The authors reported the weights for 18 components. For our purposes the separation of body weight into that of skeleton, skin, adipose tissue, striated muscles, and a remainder will suffice.

For the purposes of integrating the direct analyses with the indirect methods applicable to the living man it is essential to characterize the composition of the body in chemical terms. Some very detailed chemical analyses have been reported.[21] The best available data regarding moisture (total water), total fat (ether extract), protein ($6.25 \times$ nitrogen), and ash (bone mineral plus non-osseous body minerals) are summarized in Table 4.

We are far from having satisfactory information in regard to the variations in body composition within the range of "normality," associated with such basic biological variables as age and sex.

METHODS: BODY MEASUREMENTS (SOMATOMETRY)

How do the traditional body measurements fit into the conceptual framework of body composition? The fact is that most of them do not fit it or at least do not fit it very effectively. The classical handbooks are brief or silent on the subject.[22]

Here we shall consider

a) linear measures of the development of subcutaneous adipose tissue and of muscularity, and
b) deviations of body weight from the "norm,"
c) estimation of principal tissue masses from body measurements.

TABLE 3

ANATOMICAL BODY COMPOSITION OF BODIES OF 2 WHITE MEN [19,20]

Age, years	35	46
	Weights as % of total body weight	
Skeleton	14.8	17.6
Skin	7.8	6.3
Adipose tissue	13.6	11.4
Striated muscle	31.6	39.8
Remainder	32.2	24.9

TABLE 4

Body Composition Resulting from Chemical Analysis

Reference	(21)	(19)	(21)	(20)
Age, years	42	35	25	46
Sex	F	M	M	M
Weight, kg.	45.1	70.6	71.8	55.7

Weight of Components Expressed as % of Total Body Weight

Fat	23.6	12.5	14.9	19.7
Water	56.0	67.9	61.8	55.7
Protein	14.4	14.4	16.6	18.8
Ash	5.8	4.8	6.4	5.5
Unaccounted for	0.2	0.4	0.3	0.3

Weight of Components Expressed as % of Fat-free Body Weight

Water	73.3	77.6	72.6	69.3
Protein	18.8	16.5	19.5	23.4
Ash	7.6	5.5	7.5	6.8
Unaccounted for	0.3	0.4	0.4	0.5

Linear Measures of Fatness and Muscularity

Skinfolds

In man about one-half of the total fat deposits is present as the subcutaneous adipose tissue. In various parts of the body surface the skin, together with the subcutaneous layer, can be readily lifted ("folded"). As the thickness of the skin itself is relatively uniform, the differences in the thickness of the skinfolds measured at different *sites* in a given individual or at a given site in different *individuals,* reflect largely the differences in the amount of subcutaneous fat.

The number of sites at which skinfold measurements can be made is large. The number and location of sites that should actually be measured will depend on the investigator's aim and circumstances under which the measurements are to be done.

Over the last dozen years several skinfold calipers have been designed.[23] A model developed by Doctor K. O. Lange, in consultation with the present writer, is pictured in Figure 1. It is fortunate that, in spite of the existing differences in construction, the caliper pressure at the contact surfaces was kept at the standard value of 10 gm/mm^2. The contact area should be small so that it remains in full contact with the skin and the caliper pressure is well defined. Depending somewhat on the shape (circular, square, rectangular), the recommended size of the contact surfaces lies roughly between 20 and 40 mm^2.

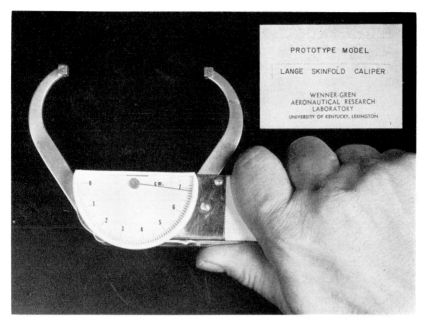

Figure 1. Lange Skinfold Caliper.°

Several other features must be standardized in order to assure comparability of skinfold measurements made by different investigators. Thus the "skin" should be lifted by grasping firmly the fold between the thumb and the forefinger. A firm grip, not exceeding the pain threshold, eliminates or at least substantially reduces the variations in the apparent thickness of skinfold that would result from wide differences in the pulling force of the fingers.

The width of the skin that is enclosed between the fingers is an important factor. It cannot be standardized, in its absolute size, for all the sites of the body. With a thick subcutaneous layer a wider segment of the skin must be "pinched" in order to form a fold than when the adipose tissue is poorly developed, as it is on the dorsum of the hand. For a given site the width of the skin should be *minimal,* still yielding a well defined fold.

The depth of the skinfold at which the calipers are placed on the fold also requires comment. The two sides of the fold are not likely to be parallel, when the skin is lifted by one hand, being narrower near the crest and larger toward the base. When the calipers are

° Available from the Wenner-Gren Aeronautical Research Laboratory, University of Kentucky, Lexington, Kentucky.

placed at the base, the resulting measurement is too large. Here, again, the correct distance from the crest is defined as the *minimal* distance from the crest at which a true fold, with surfaces approximately parallel to each other and to the contact surfaces of the calipers, is obtained upon the application of the calipers to the skin.

Some caliper models only approximate but do not actually achieve the parallelism of the contact surfaces. However, such parallelism is a desirable feature of the calipers. In very obese individuals at some sites no true skinfolds, as defined above, can be obtained. The measurements are still useful as indicators of fatness but the "skinfold" measurements are then larger than a double value of skin plus the subcutaneous layer, taking into account the compression of the tissues by the calipers. It is recommended to lift the skinfold at a distance of about 1 cm. from the site at which the calipers are to be placed and the skinfold measured.

Because of fairly rapid changes in the layer of the subcutaneous fat over relatively small distances at certain areas of the body surface, the sites should be clearly defined and carefully identified prior to measuring skinfolds in a given individual.

The selection of the location of the sites depends on several criteria, such as accessibility, the precision with which the location can be identified and reproduced, relative homogeneity of the layer of subcutaneous fat in a given region, and the validity of skinfold measurements at specified sites as an index of total body fat.

Taking into consideration all these criteria, clearcut superiority cannot be claimed for any one site. At present there is a fairly unanimous agreement on two sites which should be included in the minimum battery of somatic measurements gathered for purposes of anthropometric characterization of body composition: the dorsal skinfold on the upper-arm and the subscapular skinfold.[24]

The upper-arm site is readily accessible in individuals of both sexes in most cultures. The skinfold is located on the dorsum of the right upper-arm (over the triceps), at the level midway between the lateral margin of the acromial process of the scapula and the tip of the elbow. The level is located with the arm flexed at 90°. In making the skinfold measurement, the arm should hang freely. The crest of the skinfold is parallel to the long axis of the arm. As the changes in the thickness of subcutaneous fat from the elbow toward the shoulder are substantial, the level at which the skinfold is measured should be located rather precisely.

The subscapular skinfold is measured below the tip of the right scapula, with the subject standing but relaxed. Usually the skin is lifted most readily along a line at about 45° from the horizontal level, going medially upward (and laterally downward). One of the advantages of this site is that the thickness of the subcutaneous adipose layer is fairly homogeneous in this area and small differences in locating the site are less important than is true for the upper arm or the abdomen and chest.

A variety of other sites have been examined. The site along the mid-axillary line, at the level of the xiphoid process, appears advantageous as a predictor of total body fat.

When it is desirable to combine several skinfolds, 3 procedures can be used: 1) the skinfold thicknesses may be simply added—a least satisfactory method which is, nevertheless, justified for some purposes; 2) a measure of the "general fat-factor" may be derived on the basis of the statistical analysis of relations between the skinfolds, and 3) the skinfolds can be combined in a multivariate estimating equation so as to predict most effectively the total body fat, obtained by the densitometric or the hydrometric methods.

Limb Diameters (Muscle and Bone)

In the general population the differences in muscular development account for a lesser portion of variation in total body weight, at a given height, than does the size of the fat deposits. Nevertheless, quantitative characterization of musculature is of interest, especially to physical anthropologists concerned with the effects of exercise and physical work on man's physique.

Unfortunately, only the musculature of the extremities is readily accessible to anthropometric appraisal. When the required equipment and trained personnel are available, the size of the muscles can best be characterized in terms of the breadths (or calculated cross-sectional surfaces) of the muscular segments on the soft-tissue roentgenograms of the limbs. This method is referred to later in the text. When direct (somatometric) measurements must be relied upon, the muscular development of an individual can be characterized on the basis of limb circumferences, provided the thickness of the subcutaneous fat is measured at the same level as the limb circumference.

For the purposes of calculation, the limb is regarded as a cylinder. From the circumference (c), which is measured, we can calculate the total diameter ($c = \pi \; d; \; d = c/\pi$). The corrected diameter is obtained by subtracting the thickness of skin-plus-subcutaneous layer. On the upper arm one may measure the dorsal (S_1, over triceps) and ventral (S_2, over biceps) skinfold and use these figures for correction of the total diameter. As the skinfolds represent 2 thicknesses of the adipose layer, only one-half of the skinfold thickness is subtracted:

$$d = c/\pi - \frac{S_1}{2} - \frac{S_2}{2}$$

In practice one usually measures only the dorsal skinfold and obtains the corrected diameter as

$$d = c/\pi - S_1$$

The upper arm circumference should be taken with the arm hanging freely. It should be measured at a right angle to the long axis of the arm, at the same level as the arm skinfold (midway between acromion and the olecranon, as indicated above). The flexible steel tape should be applied lightly to the skin in order to avoid deforming the contour of the skin.[24]

The calculated calf diameter is a useful indicator of the muscular development of the lower extremities. The circumference is measured at the level of the maximal cross-sectional area, preferably with the leg placed on a chair and bent at a 90° angle. Medial skinfold is used for purposes of correction.

A more "dynamic" measure of muscularity is represented by the circumference of the upper arm, flexed under tension in order to produce maximal bulging of the triceps.

Deviations from Standard Weight

Weight Predicted from Height

The deviation of body weight from the "standard" for height (and sex and age) may serve as a gross indicator of under- or overdevelopment of soft tissues (adipose tissue, musculature, and viscera). In pathological situations other body components, such as the body fluids accumulated in patients with "hunger edema," can complicate the interpretation of the biological significance of deviations from standard in such a manner as to make body weight useless even as a very gross indicator of soft-tissue development.

Athletes performing certain types of physical exercise, notably weight-lifting, develop large muscles. In such cases the muscle mass will account for a larger fraction of body weight than would be true for the average man. In "normal" adults of a given height the adipose tissue accounts for a large fraction of the individual differences in body weight.

The standard weight is usually defined as the average weight of individuals of a given sex, height, and age. In the United States the basic tables of standard weights are those developed in the course of medico-actuarial investigations.[23a] These tables were reprinted many times, with or without essentially arbitrary corrections for the height of shoes and the weight of shoes and clothes worn by the life insurance applicants on whom the data were based.

When the number of persons measured is very large, the standard weights can be obtained by averaging the weights of men and of women of a given age and height and tabulating them, separately for the two sexes. Even then some "smoothing" of the curves portraying the age trends is usually desirable, especially for the very tall and very short individuals who are in short supply.

For a given age we can calculate the predicted weight (the "standard") from a linear equation

$$S = a + bH$$

where a is an absolute value (a weight, in kg. or lb.), b is a regression coefficient (a number), and H is standing height (in cm. or in in.).

When a more general prediction equation is desired, the age factor (Y, in years) may be included. Then the equation assumes the form

$$S = a + b_1H + b_2Y$$

In order to compare different individuals, the deviation of the actual weight (A) from the standard (S), d = A-S, may be related to the standard weight:

$$d\% = 100\ \frac{A\text{-}S}{S}$$

More frequently, the Relative Weight is computed by relating not the deviation but the actual weight to the standard

$$\text{Relative Weight} = 100\ \frac{A}{S}$$

In the population of the U.S. the weight of adults tends to increase during the period of maturity and the tables of standard weights take this fact into account. Thus the relative weight of individuals of average weight (for height, sex and age), at all ages, is 100. These are the so-called age-corrected standards. They are useful for some comparisons of individuals differing in age. Specifically, they allow us to identify groups of individuals of different ages but of the same degree of relative underweight or overweight.

From the point of view of body composition studies, the use of a single standard, such as the average weight of individuals 25 years of age, of a given sex and height, makes good sense. Deviations from such a standard provide a better estimate of leanness-fatness while the relative weight is an appropriate measure of underweight-overweight. It is essential to specify which standard is being used in a given study and to interpret the deviations from the standard accordingly.

From the statistical point of view the severe limitation of height-weight tables lies in the fact that the frequency of occurrence of a given value of relative body weight is not given. How many individuals have a Relative Weight greater than 110 or smaller than 90? This information is important for the appraisal of the biological significance of the weight deviations from standard.

The weight distributions are typically skewed toward the higher values. Consequently, the arithmetical averages (means) are larger than the "typical," most frequent values (mode) or the mid-points of the weight distributions (median, a value dividing the distribution into two equal halves). For some purposes attempts to remove the non-normality of the weight distributions by means of transformation (e.g. by using logarithms of body weights rather than the weights themselves) may be called for.

Weight Standards Taking Into Account Skeletal Frame and Muscularity

In the common height-weight standards only the height (and age) is taken into account as the point of reference: the variations in "body build" are not considered. The vertical partitioning of the body into head plus trunk versus the leg length appear to be less relevant than the consideration of the lateral bony dimensions. The measures of laterality should not be affected by the overlaying adipose tissue (or musculature). The Committee on Nutritional Anthropometry (1956) recommended two measures as indicators of the laterality of the skeletal frame: 1) the bicristal (biiliac) and 2) the biacromial diameter.[24]

The bicristal diameter, a measure of the width of the pelvic girdle, is obtained as the greatest distance between the lateral margins of the iliac crests. In well "padded" individuals it is necessary to exert strong pressure on the contact surfaces of the calipers in order to minimize the amount of soft tissues which would be otherwise included in this measurement. The failure to do so would result in a spuriously large "standard" weight, in the calculation of which the two diameters (and height) are included, and thus an underestimate of relative weight.

The biacromial diameter, a measure of the width of the shoulder girdle, is defined as the distance between the most lateral margins of the acromial processes of the scapulae. The subjects should stand erect but with the shoulders relaxed. This point is important and the failure to standardize the posture so as to obtain the maximal value, for a given individual, will introduce sizable errors.

When we wish to obtain a purer estimate of fatness, we should incorporate one or more criteria of muscular development into the prediction equation. The upper arm diameter, corrected for the thickness of the layer of subcutaneous fat may serve as such a criterion.

An equation for estimating "standard" weight on the basis of 5 predictors is given, as an example, in Table 5. The equation was derived on the basis of data obtained for 238 Minneapolis firemen.[25]

On the basis of statistical tests, 2 additional dimensions used initially as predictors of weight were eliminated: the iliocristal height, a measure of "leg length," and the biepicondylar diameter of the humerus, a measure of the "ruggedness" of the bones of the extremities. Each of the remaining 5 variables contributes significantly to the precision with which we can predict the body weight.

Deviations from a weight standard so defined may be interpreted as representing largely the amounts of adipose tissue by which an individual differs from the average man of given body proportions (and age).

TABLE 5

EQUATION FOR PREDICTING BODY WEIGHT ($\hat{Y}$) FROM HEIGHT (X_1), 2 MEASURES OF LATERALITY (BICRISTAL DIAMETER, X_2, AND BIACROMIAL DIAMETER, X_3), AN INDICATOR OF MUSCULAR DEVELOPMENT (UPPER ARM DIAMETER, CORRECTED FOR SUBCUTANEOUS FAT, X_4) AND AGE (X_5). ALL MEASUREMENTS ARE IN CM., AGE IN YEARS

$$\hat{Y} = +0.411\ X_1$$
$$+1.204\ X_2$$
$$+0.885\ X_3$$
$$+7.342\ X_4$$
$$+0.220\ X_5$$
$$-135.510$$

Anatomical Body Compartments Predicted from Body Measurements

In 1921, J. Matiegka proposed an original and potentially useful system for the estimation of certain tissue masses on the basis of body measurements.[2] He felt, with justification, that traditional anthropometry did not yield a satisfactory description of human physique. Clearly, it would be erroneous to assign too great an importance to any single body dimension as an indicator of "fitness." Thus tallness, as judged by stature, is not necessarily an indication of overall physical superiority as it may be associated with a poorly developed musculature. Similarly, large body weight may indicate an unhealthy obesity rather than a powerful physique. The traditional combinations of two or more anthropometric dimensions in the form of an index also did not yield the answer, the principal reason being that the initial measurements, such as body weight or chest circumference, were complex data in which size and tissue composition were hopelessly scrambled.

Matiegka was interested in a functionally oriented, "dynamic" anthropometry and his goal was to devise a system for an analytical, quantitative description of human physique, a system that would be adequate for the evaluation of the somatic facet of fitness ("physical efficiency") for purposes of vocational guidance, choice of athletic pursuits or life insurance examinations. He was anxious to place physical anthropology of the living man into a wider framework of human biology and visualized the somatometric evaluation of physique as a component of a broader study of man's health and work capacity. Such a comprehensive evaluation would include, in addition to body measurements, a general clinical examination, physiological assessment of principal body functions, and the psychological (psychometric) evaluation of an individual. In fact the term "somatotechnic" methods appealed to him as a parallel to the "psychotechnic" procedures of applied psychology. His goal was to enhance the biological significance of body measurements and to increase the utility of physical anthropology, measured in terms of medical and social criteria.

In Matiegka's system the gross body weight (w) was divided into four components:

$$w = O + D + M + R$$

where O = the weight of the skeleton ("*ossa*," bones),
    D = skin ("*derma*") plus subcutaneous adipose tissue

M = skeletal muscles, and
R = remainder.

The first three components, defined in terms of anatomical entities, can be estimated on the basis of body measurement (Table 6).

The estimation equations were derived on the basis of the author's experience and such data as were available in the literature, and were regarded by the author simply as first approximations. He was aware of the tentative nature and deficiencies of his approach, and in the original communication (1921) he pointed out several times the need for empirical validation and refinement. Refinement and better standardization was called for in regard to some of the basic measurements. Thus skinfolds were measured with a sliding compass with blunt points exerting only a mild pressure so that the skinfold would slip out of the branches of the calipers when not held by the fingers. This is not a very precise definition of pressure and the use of calipers with a constant tension is preferable.

While Matiegka was concerned with strengthening the practical usefulness of anthropological measurements, his ideas were of fundamental importance for quantitative human morphology in that he

TABLE 6

Matiegka's Formulae for the Calculation of the Weight, in Grams, of the Skeleton (O), Skin Plus Subcutaneous Adipose Tissue (D) and Muscles (M)

$$O = o^2 \times L \times k_1 \qquad D = d \times S \times k_2 \qquad M = r^2 \times L \times k_3$$

where $k_1 = 1.2$, $k_2 = 0.13$, and $k_3 = 6.5$,

  L = stature, in cm., S = body surface, in cm.^{2}

$$o = \frac{o_1 + o_2 + o_3 + o_4}{4}$$, with o_1 to o_4 representing the maximum transverse diameters of humeral and femoral condyles, wrist and ankle, in cm.

$$d = 1/2 \frac{d_1 + d_2 \ldots + d_6}{6}$$, with d_1 to d_6 referring to the thickness of the skinfold at the following sites: upper arm, above the biceps; the forearm, plantar side at maximum breadth; thigh, above quadriceps muscle, halfway between inguinal fold and the knee; calf of the leg; thorax, on costal margin, halfway between mammae and the umbilicus; and abdomen, halfway between the navel and the anterior superior iliac spine.

$$r = \frac{r_1 + r_2 + r_3 + r_4}{4}$$, with r_1 to r_4 representing the radii calculated from the circumferences of the arm, flexed, measured above the belly of the biceps; forearm, maximum; thigh, halfway between the trochanter and the lateral epicondyle; and leg, maximum circumference of the calf. The values were corrected for thickness of the subcutaneous tissue plus the skin.

pointed to a new way for the synthesis of individual body measurements in a meaningful biological frame of reference and emphasized the fundamental role of body composition in describing man's physique.

Quantitatively oriented anatomists and physical anthropologists, in and out of his native Bohemia, owe Matiegka a debt of hard labor, still largely unpaid. Additional research is needed in order to replace Matiegka's approximative constants by rigorously derived estimation equations, especially for the total amounts of muscle in the body. Matiegka's ideas for the estimation of the weight of the skeleton on the basis of stature and transverse bony diameters of the extremities were taken up, tested, and further developed by Mildred Trotter and her co-workers in the Department of Anatomy, Washington University, St. Louis, Missouri.[26] The diameters recommended by Matiegka for the living were measured on skeletons (not on cadavers) and the weight of each skeleton was estimated according to Matiegka's formula. This estimate was not more precise, unfortunately, than the estimate that could be obtained from stature alone. Better results could have been, perhaps, obtained by using the bony measurements and height as predictors in a multivariate estimating equation.

The following additional variables were measured for the femur: weight, length, and area of photographic projection of the total femur. The middle half of each femur was x-rayed and the area of the shadows corresponding to the compact bone was determined with the planimeter. The area of compact bone proved to be the best single predictor of skeletal weight. This is important as the value can be obtained also for the living man. Adding stature to compact-bone area improved substantially the precision of predicting total skeletal weight but the addition of transverse diameters did not yield a further gain in the precision with which the weight of the skeleton could be predicted. In the final report 5 variables (stature, femur, length, area of shaft, area of compact bone, and age) were related to skeleton on weight.[26a]

METHODS: SOFT-TISSUE ROENTGENOGRAPHY

Light roentgenograms of the extremities, obtained with appropriate combinations of exposure time and peak voltage,* provide useful means for measuring the relative amounts of bone, muscle, and skin-plus-subcutaneous adipose tissue. The need for precise, standardized

---

* Garn specifies 10 to 20 milliampere seconds and peak voltages varying from 35 to 75 kilovolts, depending on the thickness of the part to be x-rayed [18, p. 66].

positioning can hardly be overemphasized. The distance between x-ray tube and film should be large (6 ft.) so as to minimize the distortion due to the fact that the x-rays are not strictly parallel. J. M. Tanner eliminates the differences in the magnification effect present in x-raying parts that vary in thickness by keeping constant the distance between the medial plane of the limb and the film (see also [26b]).

For purposes of examining the relations of roentgenographic limb measurements to body density, roentgenograms were obtained of the upper arm and forearm, of thigh and leg.[27] The technique of measuring soft-tissue roentgenograms is illustrated in Figure 2. Three sites are presented: 1) Upper arm, in anteroposterior projection; of special interest is the thickness of subcutaneous fat, measured at the point of deltoid indentation along the line vertical to the skin (see also [28]). 2) Leg, in anteroposterior projection. All measurements were taken perpendicularly to the long axis of the limb, defined as the line connecting the midpoints of the upper and lower edges of the section of the limb, at the level of maximal width. 3) Mid-upper arm, in mediolateral projection, at a level half-way between acromion and olecranon; the measurements of the adipose and muscle layers were made along the line perpendicular to the long axis of the limb. The bone width was measured perpendicularly to the long axis of the bone.

The measurements were taken with a micrometer provided with sharp points and reading to 0.1 mm. In addition to linear measurements, the projected areas corresponding to the different tissues have been determined by some authors and cross-sectional areas of "fat," muscle and bone were calculated.

The x-ray technique is especially useful for determining the thickness of subcutaneous fat in those areas in which skinfolds cannot be measured and which exhibit, at the same time, marked individual differences. Garn's iliac and mid-trochanteric sites are outstanding examples of such sites ([18, p. 66]). On the leg only the medial skinfold can be readily measured, and only in men.

DENSITOMETRY

In a physical system consisting of two components (M_1, M_2) of known densities (d_1, d_2), determination of the density of the system (D) allows the calculation of the proportional masses of the 2 components (m_1, m_2; $m_1 + m_2 = 1$). The general formula may be written as follows:

$$m_1 = \frac{1}{D} \frac{d_1 \times d_2}{(d_2 - d_1)} - \frac{d_1}{(d_2 - 1)}$$

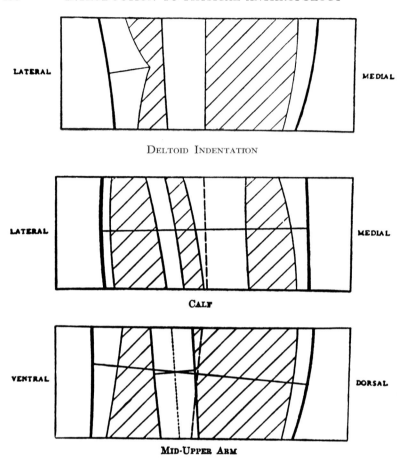

DELTOID INDENTATION

CALF

MID-UPPER ARM

Figure 2. Illustrative examples of measurements made on soft-tissue roentgenograms. Next to the skin is the white area of subcutaneous fat. Shaded areas indicate muscles, the white areas between the muscular layers represent bones. Limb axes are indicated by long dashes, bone axis of the mid-upper arm by short dashes. The lines along which the measurements are made are solid.

where m_1 is the mass of the first component (M_1) expressed as a fraction of the total body mass, M; $m_1 = M_1/M$. The body volume, needed in calculations of body density (D = Mass/Volume) can be determined by underwater weighing, making correction for the air remaining in the lungs and respiratory passages,[29] or on the principle of inert-gas (helium) dilution.[30] But what are the two components, M_1 and M_2, into which the body can be divided?

In the Minnesota system [14] these two components are 1) the body of a "reference man" (R) defined as a 25-year old individual whose actual weight is identical with the tabular standard and whose intensity was determined empirically as $d_R = 1.0629$ gm./cc.[31] and 2) the tissue gained (G) as a result of simple overeating for a period of six months, with a $d_G = 0.948$.[32]

Using these densities in the general densitometric equation, we can calculate the amount (as fraction of body weight) of tissue similar to "G" that is present in an individual for whom the density was determined:

$$g = \frac{1}{D} 8.753 - 8.235$$

"G" is not a pure fat, as defined chemically (having a density of 0.9007; [32a]), but an equivalent of a generalized adipose ("obesity") tissue. It was estimated that fat constitutes only about 62 per cent of the total weight gain. The fat by which a given individual differs from the reference man (ΔF; $\Delta F = 0.62G$) can be calculated from the formula

$$\triangle f = \frac{1}{D} 5.427 - 5.106$$

For some purposes we wish to estimate not only the difference from the reference body but the total fat. Assuming that the body of the reference man contains 14 per cent of "fat" (as ether extract), the amount of total fat in a given body can be calculated, as fraction of body weight, as follows:

$$f = \frac{1}{D} 4.201 - 3.813$$

The derivations of the formulae have been presented in detail.[14, 33] Behnke [34] operates with the concept of the "fat-free body" ($d = 1.0939$) and uses the value of 0.9018 as the density of fat. For these quantitative assumptions

$$f = \frac{1}{D} 5.135 - 4.694$$

METHODS—HYDROMETRY

Clearly, the technical complexities of determining total body water and separating it into two fractions, the extracellular and intracellular, are beyond the level of an introductory presentation. Yet, the basic ideas and facts are simple.

The water "spaces" are measured on the principle of dilution. Various substances have been used for determination of total body water (antipyrine, urea, heavy water—deuterium, water labelled with radioactive hydrogen—tritium) and of its extracellular component (thiocyanate, correcting the resulting space by a factor of 0.7 to obtain the "true" extracellular space). The intracellular water is computed by difference, Total-Extracellular. Advances in methods make it possible to administer orally a test solute (tritium) for the determination of total body water and to use urine rather than blood serum as a sample of body fluids in which the substance was dissolved. This makes the hydrometric analysis of body composition more applicable to problems in which the physical anthropologist, working as a member of a research team, is likely to be interested.

In the first approximation, the body mass (M) can be considered as a two-component system:

$$M = F + N,$$

where $F =$ fat, $N =$ non-fat. Regarding the N-component as a body mass of relatively constant composition, we can calculate its amount knowing the fraction (c) of the non-fat portion of the body accounted for by water and having determined the total body water (T) of a given body. Then

$$T = cN, \text{ and}$$

$$N = \frac{T}{c}$$

Denoting the reciprocal of c, $\frac{1}{c} = k$, we may write $N = kT$.

Fat is derived by difference, $F = M - N$.

Expressing both components as fractions of body weight ($f + n = 1$) and using the value of the non-fat component calculated from total body water, we obtain

$$f = 1 - kt$$

The values of c as applied to adult man by various authors varied between 0.71 and 0.73, yielding k values of 1.41 and 1.37, respectively.

In a more comprehensive system, involving a larger number of numerical assumptions, the total body mass (M) may be separated into fat (F), water (T), and two types of non-fat solids: the dry cell residue (S) and the bone minerals (B)

With M = 1,
$$M = F + T + S + B$$
$$f = 1 - t - s - b$$

In addition to total body water (T), the extracellular water (E) is determined, and I, the intracellular water computed (I = T — E). The values of the bone minerals (B) and the non-fat non-water component of the cells (S) are estimated, using the intracellular water—a measure of the cell mass—as the reference point: $S = k_1I$; $B = k_2I$. In the Minnesota system [14, p. 290] the constants were estimated as $k_1 = 0.429$, $k_2 = 0.134$.

With I = T — E,
$$f = 1 - t - 0.429 (t-e) - 0.134 (t-e),$$ so that in a

simplified form, $f = 1 - 1.563t + 0.563e$

where t = total body water and e = extracellular fluid, both being expressed as fractions of body weight:

$$t = \frac{T}{M}, \quad e = \frac{E}{M}$$

METHODS: PREDICTION OF TOTAL BODY FAT
FROM ANTHROPOMETRIC DATA

The linear somatic and roentgenographic measurements or areas and volumes calculated from them yield only a relative degree of leanness-fatness of a given individual. For some purposes we may wish to know the total amount of fat. This can be done, within the limits of uncertainties inherent in the underlying assumptions (and in methods of measurement), by relating the anthropometric data to the total body fat. This independent criterion can be provided by the densitometric or the hydrometric method. As the numerical interpretations of body density are open to modification, it is preferable to establish the equations for predicting density and only in the last step to convert the density values into "total fat."

Skinfolds as Predictors of Density

Equations have been provided, for young and middle-aged men, with skinfold measurements as predictors and body density as criterion of leanness-fatness.[35] The study was repeated for young men [36] taking into account subsequent refinements in techniques for measuring both skinfold thicknesses and body density. Skinfold measurements were made at a variety of sites. Body volume, used for calculation of body density, was determined by underwater weighing. Using only those skinfolds which contributed significantly to the efficiency of prediction, the following multiple regression equation was derived:

$$\hat{Y} = 1.088468 - .0007123X_1 - .0004832X_2 - .0005513X_3$$

where $\hat{Y}$ is the estimated body density (to be converted into the fat content of the body), X are the skinfold thicknesses in millimeters taken, respectively, at the chest in the midaxillary line at the level of the xiphoid (X_1), at the chest in the juxta-nipple position (X_2), and on the dorsum of the upper arm at the midpoint between the acromion and the olecranon. The values of density should be rounded, following the arithmetical manipulations, to 3 decimal places. Prediction equations based on single skinfolds were also provided. The subjects used in this study averaged 22 years in age (range 17 to 25). At ages widely differing from that of the sample from which they were derived, the prediction equations will not be strictly valid.

Roentgenographic Predictors of Density

A similar approach was followed in converting roentgenographic measurements of subcutaneous fat into density and, finally, into total body fat.[27] Equations for predicting body density were calculated for the thickness of the skin-plus-subcutaneous layer measured at single sites and for the combined lateral-plus-medial or ventral-plus-dorsal thicknesses, when available. It was noted that in this sample of middle-aged men the precision with which the density could be predicted was not improved when the width of the subcutaneous fat was related to stature, to the bone width of the limb measured on the roentgenograms, or to the width of the bone-plus-muscle segment. For 4 locations the cross-sectional area of the adipose tissue was calculated and expressed as percentage the cross-sectional area of the nonadipose (lean) tissues of the limbs, again without increasing the precision with which the density (and thus total fat) could be estimated.

According to the available evidence, admittedly limited, measurements of the layer of skin with its adjoining adipose tissue made on roentgenograms of the extremities do not appear to be more effective indicators of the overall leanness-fatness than the direct (skinfold) measurements. However, a systematic appraisal in terms of prediction of total fat remains to be carried out. A comprehensive analysis of the value of roentgenographic measurements of body fat should include also sites on the trunk, not accessible to the skinfold-caliper technique. In setting up the prediction equations proper attention should be given to factors of age and sex.

Roentgenographic Appraisal of Adipose Tissue

Garn took the roentgenogrammetric bull by the horns and attempted to arrive in simpler ways at the total amount of body "fat." [37] For these purposes he considered, in Behnke's footsteps, the body mass (M) as consisting of "fat" (A) and "fat free" weight (L):

$$M = A + L$$

The symbols were supplied by the present writer in the hope of making the matters clearer. Garn's "fat" is not the fat defined as ether extract and, consequently, all comparisons with the results of densitometric and hydrometric analyses, operating with chemically defined fat, are out of order. The symbol A indicates that we deal principally with the anatomist's adipose tissue. L stands for "lean body mass," a concept more appropriate than "fat-free mass" for Garn's purposes. The basic step is the derivation of a simple equation for predicting total body weight (M) from roentgenographic thicknesses (X) of the layer of skin plus subcutaneous adipose tissue:

$$\hat{M} = a + bX$$

The value "a" defines body mass, $\hat{M}$, for X = 0, that is the "lean body mass" (L) of the group. The constant "b" is the slope of the line of the best fit and bX_i defines the amount of roentgenographic "fat" in a given individual ($\hat{F} = bX_i$). In other words, Garn obtains an estimate of the weight of "fat," in kilograms, for an individual by multiplying the roentgenographic measurement (X_i) by the constant b.

He uses the value of calculated fat ($\hat{F}$) in conjunction with the actual body weight of an individual (M), where

$$M = \hat{F} + L$$

and defines

$$L = M - \hat{F}$$

Garn uses as predictors of weight the thickness of the iliac-crest "fat" for females and of the mid-trochanteric "fat" for males. A de-

TABLE 7

ABSOLUTE VALUES OF BODY SIZE AND BODY COMPONENTS IN
FOUR TYPES OF SUBJECTS (FROM [2])

	Trade Apprentices	A Gymnast	Emaciated Woman	Obese Woman
Height, cm.	166.9	169.3	160.2	158.0
Body weight, kg.	57.3	72.0	39.5	90.0
Skeleton, kg.	10.4	13.0	8.4	8.0
Muscles, kg.	24.5	34.6	12.7	18.8
Skin and fat, kg.	10.9	9.5	2.7	47.7
Remainder, kg.	11.5	14.9	15.6	15.4

tailed appraisal of Garn's approach and its limitations is beyond the scope of this presentation. Perhaps the really important point is the theoretical possibility of providing estimates of body composition (in terms of adipose tissue, muscle and skeleton or fat, protein, and bone mineral) on the basis of suitable roentgenograms, especially when considered in conjunction with methods allowing us to separate the total body weight into its principal components.

SOME APPLICATIONS

Because of space limitations, only illustrative findings will be cited in a limited range of topics: body build, age and sex, and nutrition.

Body Build

Human physique has several aspects—size, form, and composition. Differences in size are obvious and biologically as well as socially important, so obvious, indeed, that they have been completely left out of some of the typological systems that achieved wide popularity. Body form, a characteristic that attracted most attention, is the resultant of skeletal proportions and of the amount and distribuion of soft tissues, especially of muscles and subcutaneous adipose tissue. It has been the perennial plague of this sector of physical anthropology that typological "systems" were springing, ready-made, out of the heads of their creators. A facile synthesis tended to precede a solid analysis. Flashes of genius were more conspicuous than hard, biologically sound exploration of the basic variables and their interrelations.

When one looks at a camel and at Nilotic (Sanga) cattle one can readily observe that both have a "hump." This is as far as one can go, somatoscopically. Yet, these similarities are grossly deceptive: in one case we are looking at a fat-storing hump, in the other case at a

TABLE 8

BODY COMPONENTS, AS PERCENTAGE OF GROSS BODY WEIGHT

	Trade Apprentices	A Gymnast	Emaciated Woman	Obese Woman
Skeleton	18.1	18.1	21.3	9.0
Muscles	42.8	48.0	32.2	20.9
Skin and fat	19.0	13.1	6.9	52.9
Remainder	20.1	20.8	39.6	17.2

purely muscular thickening in the cervicothoracic region. This brief excursion into the zoological realm should encourage us to pause and to evaluate more rigorously the validity of somatoscopic ratings in man.

Somatometric Estimates of Body Components

In Matiegka's (1921) system the human physique was characterized in terms of the masses of the principal compartments, anatomically defined (skeleton, muscles, skin plus subcutaneous fat) and estimated on the basis of body measurements.[2] This represents a fundamentally sound, though not exhaustive, approach to the complex problem of body build, emphasizing body composition as its crucial facet. It may be of interest to present a sample of the data obtained by Matiegka for a group of 12 apprentices, a gymnast, an emaciated and an obese woman. The absolute values of the estimated body components are given in Table 7. For purposes of comparison, the components may be expressed as percentages of body weight (Table 8), or, preferably, in terms of the weight of the skeleton as the reference point (Table 9).

Relative Development of Adipose Tissue and Musculature

Matiegka's approach was "on the books" but it largely remained there. McCloy (1936) was aware of Matiegka's efforts to evaluate the amount of the various components making up the body but cited him as a measurer of skinfolds [38, p. 66]. Significant impetus to the measurement of subcutaneous fat in children was given by Fran-

TABLE 9

BODY COMPONENTS, AS PERCENTAGE OF SKELETAL WEIGHT

	Trade Apprentices	A Gymnast	Emaciated Woman	Obese Woman
Muscles	236	265	151	233
Skin and fat	105	72	33	591
Remainder	111	114	186	191

zen [38a] and a series of studies on subcutaneous tissue was undertaken at the Iowa Child Welfare Research Station in the thirties. "Total fat" was obtained as the sum of skinfold thicknesses measured at various sites. In one study the skinfold measurements were averaged and the individual deviations from the norm were multiplied by the computed surface area of the body in order to obtain a rough measure of the volume of fat over or under the norm. The matter of norms was considered in the second volume of McCloy's treatise on the appraisal of physical status.[39] The development of the musculature was assessed in two ways, in terms of the relative limb girths (without correction for subcutaneous fat) and of performance on strength tests. The norms covered childhood and adolescence (4 to 17 years) and were extended to college men and women.

Visual Appraisal of Body Types

The system of "body typing" that was most influential in the last two decades was developed by W. C. Sheldon.[40] Man's physique is characterized in terms of 3 "components" rated at a scale from 1 (minimum) to 7 (maximum): endomorphy, mesomorphy and ectomorphy. These components were derived from the study of photographs, conceptually far from the anatomist's dissection table. Sheldon strives for an assessment of an individual's "somatotype" which would closely approach the "morphogenotype" and, by definition, would represent a permanent characteristic of an individual. He would object to defining "endomorphy" simply as an anthropomorphic estimate of the amount of fat. The fact remains, and it is an important fact, that variations in endomorphy ratings are associated with individual differences in the density of the human body, a measure of the total fat content.

At the Laboratory of Physiological Hygiene, University of Minnesota, a group of young men were measured and photographed under control conditions and after losing one-fourth of their body weight. Two independent sets of ratings of the somatotype were obtained.[41] Combining all the available information (2 sets of ratings for the 2 conditions), an equation for predicting density (and thus total body fat) from ratings of endomorphy was calculated.[42] The data relating endomorphy ratings to density and body fat are given in Table 10.

Sheldon would probably criticize the authors of the ratings in that they have not taken into account adequately the "nutritional status" of the subjects. To us the fact is important that "endomorphy" ratings, made by competent investigators (including Sheldon's long-time associates, especially Dupertuis,[43]) correlate with the densitometric estimates of the fat content. This raises hopes that it will be possible to turn the tables and to develop a system of somatoscopic ratings and of measurements made on standardized photographs which will be based on and validated by methods yielding independent criteria of adipose, muscular, and skeletal masses or at least linear indicators of such masses.

Parnell's scheme, representing a combination of physical anthropology and photography, is a step in this direction.[43a] The use of somatometric data should help to provide a more precise definition of the "components" and add objectivity that is lacking when photoscopy is used alone. The body measurements include height, weight, a height-weight ratio (height/r^3⁻weight), biepicondylar measurements of humerus and femur as indicators of lateral bony dimensions of the extremities, two limb girths—upper arm and calf, 3 skinfolds (subscapular, suprailiac, on the back of the upper arm) and their total, and 4 trunk measurements (biacromial and bi-iliac width, chest width and chest depth).

The author aims to approach as closely as possible Sheldon's estimates of somatotypes but he has replaced the terms endomorphy, mesomorphy and ectomorphy by Fat, Muscularity and Linearity.

Lindegård's Differential Somatology

In Sweden, Lindegård [44] developed a system to which he refers as "differential somatology" (differential morphology) and which is sound in principle though the details, including the selection of the actual measurements and definition of body-build "factors," may be open to discussion. The system operates with variables chosen to reflect the individual variation in 4 aspects of physique: 1) body length (length of radius and tibia), 2) skeletal sturdiness (bicondylar breadths), 3) muscular development (from dynamometric data on grip strength, shoulder thrust and shoulder pull) and 4) adiposity, evaluated as a deviation of the actual from the predicted value of body weight or extremital girths, keeping other relevant features of body-build constant, or, more recently, from skinfolds. The basic

TABLE 10

ENDOMORPHY RATINGS OF YOUNG MEN AND THE ASSOCIATED VALUES OF BODY DENSITY AND ESTIMATED BODY FAT

Endomorphy	1	2	3	4	5	6	7
Density	1.0871	1.0790	1.0710	1.0629	1.0549	1.0468	1.0388
Body fat, %	5	8	11	14	17	20	23

variables ("factors") are presented in the form of a "body-build diagram," with group means as reference points and standard deviations as units of measurement.

The combination of functional criteria (performance on tests of strength), used in assessment of "muscularity," in conjunction with morphological criteria on the basis of which the other body-build variables are defined, is undesirable, and, most likely, unnecessary. Measurements of the circumference of the extremities, together with skinfolds determined at the same level (perhaps with bicondylar diameters and a length factor added for a good measure) provide usable morphological indicators of muscular development, at least for the extremities.

Lindegård and his co-workers investigated the variables going into the system of classifying physiques and related the somatic individual differences to a variety of morphological, endocrinological and behavioral characteristics.[44a] They studied the distribution of subcutaneous fat and confirmed, using skinfolds measured at 10 sites, the presence of a continuum of interindividual differences in the proportion of the deposits of subcutaneous fat in the trunk and extremities (cf. B. Škerlj's Truncic-Extremital Vector).[45] Muscularity, assessed on the basis of dynamometric recordings, was examined in reference to physical activity and relations between body build and selected male sex characteristics, such as genital size and trunk hair, were studied.

Body Build and Body Functions

It is not feasible to present here in detail the data on the co-variation of body build, with its description anchored in body composition, with other somatic, biochemical, and behavioral characteristics. One or two examples must suffice.

In comparing individuals, we wish at times to eliminate the effect of absolute body size. In physiological and biochemical studies, the surface area of the body was found to be a useful point of reference. Behnke,[46] at the very outset of modern investigations on body composition, expressed the hope that "lean body mass" would be a better reference for such biologically important functions as basal oxygen consumption (basal metabolism) or blood volume. This possibility was confirmed in a study on cardiac function and body composition.[47] Thus differences in "lean body mass" accounted for about twice as much (55%) of the individual variation in cardiac output as body weight (25%), body surface being intermediate in this respect (36%).

Patterns of Soft-Tissue Distribution

In addition to the *amount* of body fat (and muscles), anthropologists have been interested in *patterns of the distribution* of soft tissues. The distribution may refer to the separation of the total into the subcutaneous and the inner fraction. There are some indications [45] that these two fractions do not remain constant throughout the life span. In the process of aging the "internal" fat, contained in the various fat depots (perirenal, pericardial, mesenteric, omental), and within the muscles, appears to increase not only absolutely, as does the subcutaneous fat, but also relatively.

From the point of view of characterizing body build, the pattern of the distribution of the subcutaneous fat over the body surface is important.[48] In order to portray this component of body form, the number of sites should be larger than when we are concerned with the overall leanness-fatness. For this purpose it is desirable to supplement skinfold measurements by soft-tissue roentgenograms of those regions, such as the trochanteric region or the thigh, which are not suitable for skinfold measurements but which show marked individual differences. It is of some interest that the pattern of thicknesses of subcutaneous fat remains fairly stable when the total size of the fat stores in the body changes.[49, 50]

Age and Sex

At least during certain phases of the life cycle, age and sex "interact": the changes in body composition with age are divergent, not parallel, for the male and female of the human species.

This was shown [51] on the basis of roentgenographic measurements of the thickness of subcutaneous adipose tissue. The "outer fat" was measured on the lower thorax. The age trends, using median rather than average values because of the marked skewness of the fat-distributions, are indicated in Figure 3.

At the age of 6 years the fat layer is somewhat thicker in girls. This difference of about 1 mm. is maintained, on the absolute basis, from the 6th to the 11th year, a period in which there is a parallel increase in fat on the lower thorax in both sexes. From the 11th to the 18th year the fat on the lower thorax continued to increase in girls, up to a value of 9 mm., while in boys the fat thickness became stabilized during this period at about 4.5 mm.

Suggestive evidence of the substantial differences in the fat content of adult men and women was provided by a co-worker of R. E.

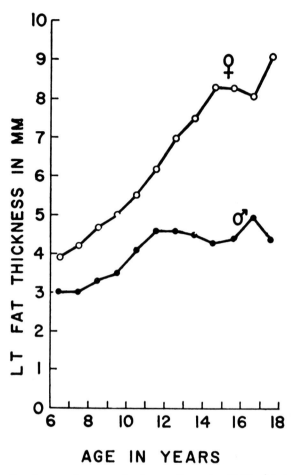

Figure 3. Continuous increase in lower thoracic (LT) fat in girls and parallel increase in boys, terminating at 11.5 years. By 14.5 years the adult female/male ratio of 180 per cent has been attained.[51]

Scammon at Minnesota.[52] The data are given in Table 11. The weight of the skin is somewhat larger in men than in women, as would be expected. When the skin weight is used as the reference point, it becomes clearly evident that women have substantially larger deposits of subcutaneous adipose tissue than men. In view of the small number of observations these data would be of little relevance were they not confirmed by much other evidence (see, e.g., [53]).

Densitometric studies indicate that both men [54] and women [55] ex-

TABLE 11

Weight of Skin and of the Subcutaneous Tissue (Tela Subcutanea) in Adult Men and Women (from [52])

	Men	Women	Women/Men
Number	13	2	
Mean age, years	37	39	
Mean skin weight, kg.	3.290	3.000	0.91
Mean weight of tela subcutanea, kg.	6.604	11.897	1.80
$100 \dfrac{\text{tela subcutanea}}{\text{skin weight}}$	201	397	1.98

hibit a marked increase in the fat content with age. The striking sex difference is maintained throughout the period of maturity. The data are summarized in Table 12.

The downward age trends in the density of both sexes are unmistakable and are due, to a very large degree, to the accumulation of body fat. The numerical interpretation of this trend in terms of the fat content is somewhat uncertain, especially as far as the calculation of fat percentages for women is concerned. Nevertheless, the existence of substantial sex differences in fatness and the presence of fat gains in the process of aging, at least in the U.S., may be regarded as well established.

Nutrition

The potential impact of diet on physique has been brought out

TABLE 12

Age, Sex, Density and Estimated Fat Content, as Per Cent of Body Weight ([54], [55])

	Men				
N	21	25	29	44	34
Age range	18–22	23–29	45–47	48–52	53–57
Mean age, years	20.3	25.2	46.0	50.0	54.6
Relative body weight, %	100.0	99.9	100.2	99.9	100.2
Density	1.072	1.063	1.047	1.044	1.041
Fat, %	11	14	20	21	22
	Women				
N		23	19	20	
Age range		18–30	31–45	46–67	
Mean age, years		24.2	39.1	56.0	
Relative body weight, %		95.3	97.3	95.3	
Density		1.040	1.027	1.016	
Fat, %		23	28	32	

TABLE 13

CALORIC EQUIVALENTS OF WEIGHT LOSSES (CAL./KG) AT DIFFERENT
INTERVALS OF CALORIC RESTRICTION

Experiment	Caloric intake, Cal./day	1–3	4–7	Period, Days 7–12	11–13	22–24
'53	580	2996	4260	5616		
'54	1010	2596			7043	8700

dramatically by animal studies: Different "planes of nutrition" not only produce animals of greatly different weights at the same age, but also of vastly different conformation and composition.[56] This fact is of basic importance for a reassessment of the concept of "genetically determined body build" and brings out its limitations. The matter is so important, even though we admittedly deal with extremes rarely if ever found in human nutrition, that the findings should be cited in full: "In general, cattle reared on a low plane of nutrition retain juvenile form; they are leggy, narrow and shallow in the body, especially in the hind quarters, with long, large heads, as compared with animals of the same breed, even identical twins, which are reared on a high plane of nutrition. As in sheep, limited nutritive supply largely inhibits the normal development of secondary sexual characters" [56, p. 498]. The principal tissues as well as the various internal organs are affected to a different degree by the restriction of the nutritive supply, fat depots being affected most, the central nervous system least.

When studied over a period of time, the adult human body—its weight and its composition—will reflect the supply of nutrients relative to the physiological requirements. Consequently, gross body composition may be used as a measure, partial and incomplete, to be sure, of "nutritional status." When the food intake exceeds the caloric needs, the excess calories are stored in the body in the form of body fat. When the caloric requirements exceed the supply, the body must cover the deficit from its own stores. Actually, under these conditions, the changes in body composition are quite complex, depending on the rate and duration of the positive or negative energy "balance," and on the availability of other nutrients which affect food utilization or water storage.

Composition of Rapid Weight Loss or Weight Gain

Dramatic changes in the composition of tissues lost when normal young men performed work on low calorie carbohydrate diets are portrayed in Table 13. These data were obtained in the course of 2 studies during which 6 men were maintained for 12 days on 580 calories per day and 13 men were given daily 1010 calories for a total of 24 days. The actual daily caloric expenditure was about 3200 cal./day.[57]

The caloric deficit was defined as the difference between the caloric equivalent of the food eaten and the energy expended over a specified period. The ratio of the caloric deficit to the weight lost, indicating the caloric value of the weight loss, changes progressively in the course of caloric restriction. The daily negative energy balance (caloric deficit) decreased only moderately, from about 1860 cal. on the sixth day of the '54 experiment to 1420 on the 24th day. In the first days of restriction the weight losses were relatively large, so that the calorie equivalents (Δ calories/Δ weight) were low. This clearly indicates a large proportion of materials, principally water, that were present in the weight loss but yielded relatively little or no energy. As restriction progressed, larger and larger proportions of the weight loss corresponded to materials yielding large amounts of energy per unit of weight, principally fat (Table 13). Oxidation of fat alone would be expected to yield about 9450 calories per kilogram of fat oxidized.

During refeeding the trend was reversed. A large part of the early gain was again made up of water. Toward the end of the recovery period it appears that fat and protein must have been stored in the body in spite of the fact that no net gain in body weight was observed at that time. It is probable that during this period the actual gain of fat (and protein), reflecting the clearly established positive energy (and nitrogen) balance, was masked by a concurrent loss of body water.

There is no doubt about the qualitative character of the changes

TABLE 14

Composition of Mean Daily Weight Losses at Different Periods of the '54 Experiment [57] Estimated by Combining Data on Weight Losses with Determinations of Energy Balance and Urinary Nitrogen Excretion (Used for Computation of the Amount of Protein that was Oxidized)

	Period of Caloric Restriction, Days		
	1 to 3	11 to 13	22 to 24
Weight loss/day, kg.	0.800	0.233	0.167
Fat	25	69	85
Protein	5	12	15
Water	70	19	0

TABLE 15

Mean Body Weight, in kg., and Body Density in the Minnesota Experiment on Prolonged Caloric Restriction (S) and Nutritional Rehabilitation (R). The Numbers Following the Period Symbols (e.g., S12) Indicate the Approximate Week During Which the Measurements Were Made. N = 32 Men

Period	Control	S12	S24	R12
Weight	69.34	57.77	53.63	59.76
Density	1.067	1.080	1.085	1.074

in the composition of the weight loss, computed on the basis of figures for energy expenditure and food intake. Is it possible to estimate the actual composition of the weight loss?

The results of such an analysis are presented in Table 14. The weight loss per day decreased by the 24th day to less than one-fourth of the initial daily weight decrement. At the same time, the composition changed profoundly, especially as far as the proportions of water and fat are concerned.

These results are presented here for three reasons:

1) To indicate the complexity of what might appear as a simple problem of rapid weight loss or weight gain.
2) To point out the changing composition of the weight gained or lost at different periods of caloric restriction or refeeding.
3) To stress the occasional necessity, without going into the details of methodology, of combining anthropometric data with information obtained by the physiologist (energy expenditure) and the biochemist (amount of protein oxidized), i.e. the necessity of interdisciplinary (team) research.

Effects of Prolonged Caloric Restriction and Refeeding

Profound changes in body weight, in physical appearance, external dimensions, and in body composition were observed in 32 young men, all volunteers, in the course of 24 weeks of caloric restriction, resulting in the loss of about one-quarter of the control body weight.[58] The period of follow-up studies during refeeding extended, for different individuals, from 12 to 58 weeks.

The values of body weight, in kg., and of body density during the control period (C), after 12 and 24 weeks of caloric restriction (S), and 12 weeks of refeeding (R) are given for the group of 32 subjects in Table 15. The trends noted during restriction (decrease in weight, rise in body density) are reversed during nutritional rehabilitation. The tabular values were not corrected either for increased hydration (expansion of the extracellular fluid), manifest in a large number of subjects as a clinically recognizable edema, or for the relative increase in the bony mass. The numerical interpretation of density in terms of body fat under these conditions is anything but a straightforward matter.[59] However, the trends in density are in agreement with the body measurements.

Photographs, taken under the direction of the present writer, were measured by G. Lasker [60] and somatotyped by inspection at the Harvard Anthropometric Laboratory in cooperation with James M. Andrews IV. Both sets of ratings confirm the decrement in "roundedness" (endomorphy) and increase in "linearity" (ectomorphy) (Table 16).

The body dimensions that showed substantial changes as a result of caloric restriction are presented in Table 17 for a typical subject.[61] They indicate the rapid growth of soft-tissues, principally the subcutaneous fat, during the 12th to 20th week of refeeding (R12 to R20) when all imposed restrictions on caloric intake were removed. At R16 the abdominal circumference exceeded the control value although the weight barely reached the control level. Changes in abdominal circumference paralleled the alterations in body fat estimated from density. The weight (and the abdominal circumference) continued to increase and by R33 body weight exceeded the control level by almost 10 kg.

Data for subjects measured at R58 indicated a tendency toward return to pre-experimental values of body weight and body composition, even though the fat content was still somewhat elevated. The overall trend of changes in body fat, expressed as percentages of the

TABLE 16

AVERAGE CHANGES IN SHELDON'S "COMPONENTS" OF HUMAN PHYSIQUE
RESULTING FROM PROLONGED CALORIC DEFICIT

Period	Ratings Based on Measurements of Photographs		
	Endomorphy	Mesomorphy	Ectomorphy
Before (C)	3.38	3.78	3.28
After (S24)	1.66	2.05	5.98
Difference	−1.72	−1.73	+2.70
	Ratings Based on Somatoscopic Appraisal		
	Endomorphy	Mesomorphy	Ectomorphy
Before (C)	3.47	3.94	3.42
After (S24)	1.82	2.81	5.71
Difference	−1.65	−1.13	+2.29

TABLE 17

WEIGHT AND BODY DIMENSIONS, IN CM., OF A TYPICAL SUBJECT [61]. C = CONTROL, S = WEEKS OF CALORIC DEFICIENCY, R = WEEKS OF REFEEDING

	C	S12	S24	R12	R16	R20	R33
Weight	64.7	55.8	52.1	54.2	64.5	68.9	74.1
Bideltoid diameter	43.2	40.0	39.0	40.0	43.4	44.8	
Circumferences:							
Chest	87.1	80.6	79.1				
Abdomen	75.4	70.5	70.8*	73.5	81.0	82.3	
Upper Arm	28.6	24.0	21.5	22.8	27.3	28.6	
Thigh	45.7	40.6	38.8	39.2	45.4	47.4	
Calf	37.5	35.1	34.0	34.5	37.8	38.2	

*"Bloated"

control value, is summarized in Table 18. The fat percentages represent only approximate values.

Who is Fat?

The fat content of the human body varies widely, although the full range is not well known. There are the habitually very thin individuals who sink readily ("swim like the bricklayer's chip," to use a Czech saying), with body densities exceeding 1.09, and skinfolds not much thicker than the double-thickness of the skin itself. On the other extreme there are the grossly obese individuals, with stores of adipose tissue approaching or exceeding the "lean" body weight, and effortlessly floating in water.

As to the procedures, all the approaches reviewed in the section on Methods are relevant, and others might be readily added (such as measurements of the depth of skin plus subcutaneous tissue in cadavers on cuts made to the underlying bony or muscular tissues). What is needed is 1) provision of adequate norms and 2) appraisal of the significance of the deviations—positive and negative, large and small, at different ages—from the norm.

TABLE 18

APPROXIMATIVE RELATIVE VALUES OF DENSITOMETRICALLY ESTIMATED BODY FAT, AS PERCENTAGE OF THE CONTROL VALUE. S = WEEKS OF CALORIC RESTRICTION, R = WEEKS OF REFEEDING. THE VALUES ARE BASED ON THE MAXIMUM NUMBER OF SUBJECTS AVAILABLE DURING A GIVEN PERIOD

Period	C	S12	S24	R12	R16	R20	R33	R58
N	32	32	32	32	12	12	6	8
Fat, as % of control	100	46	31	65	126	152	139	110

The mortality experience of the insurance companies, based on body weight and height (see, e.g., 62) will be supplemented, in time, by data on morbidity obtained in cross-sectional investigations and in a handful of important longitudinal studies that are underway. The clarification of the relations between various criteria of health and the deviations from weight norms (obtained with due regard to skeletal body build), body composition (assessed on the basis of somatic and roentgenographic measures) and other aspects of body build is one of the major challenges to physical anthropologists of the years 1960 plus.

REFERENCES

1. HOWELLS, W. W.: Introduction (to a symposium on "nutritional anthropometry"). *Human Biol.*, 28:109, 1956.

2. MATIEGKA, J.: The testing of physical efficiency. *Am. J. Phys. Anthropol.*, 4: 223-230, 1921.

3. SCAMMON, R. E.: The measurement of the body in childhood, Ch. IV in *The Measurement of Man.* Minneapolis, U. of Minn. Press, 1930, p. 173-215.

4. BOYD, E.: *Table 2 in Outline of Physical Growth and Development.* Minneapolis, Burgess Pub. Co., 1941.

5. MOULTON, R. E.: Age and chemical development in mammals. *J. Biol. Chem.*, 57:79-97, 1923.

5a. KRAYBILL, H. F., HANKINS, O. G., and FARNSWORTH, V. M.: Adaptation of anthropometric and roentgenologic measurements for appraisement of the percentage of bone in cattle. *J. Appl. Physiol.*, 7:13-18, 1954.

6. PÁLSSON, H.: Conformation and body composition, in *Progress in the Physiology of Farm Animals.* London, Butterworths, Vol. 2, 1955, p. 430-542.

7. BEHNKE, A. R.: Physiologic studies pertaining to deep sea diving and aviation, especially in relation to the fat content and composition of the human body. *Harvey Lectures*, 37:198-226, 1941-42.

8. BEHNKE, A. R., FEEN, B. G., and WELHAM, W. C.: Specific gravity of healthy men: Body weight ÷ body volume as an index of obesity. *J. Amer. Med. Assoc.*, 118:495-498, 1942.

9. RATHBUN, E. N. and PACE, N.: Studies in body composition: I. Determination of body fat by means of the body specific gravity. *J. Biol. Chem.*, 158: 667-676, 1945.

10. PACE, N. and RATHBUN, E. N.: Studies on body composition: III. The body water and chemically combined nitrogen content in relation to fat content. *J. Biol. Chem.*, 158:685-691, 1945.

11. PACE, N., KLINE, L., SCHACHMAN, H. K., and HARFENIST, M.: Studies on body composition: IV. Use of radioactive hydrogen for measurement in vivo of total body water. *J. Biol. Chem.*, 168:459-469, 1947.

12. MACY, ICIE G.: *Nutrition and Chemical Growth in Childhood.* Springfield, Ill., Thomas, 1942, 1946, 1951.

13. MACY, ICIE G. and KELLY, HARRIET J.: *Chemical Anthropology: A New Approach to Growth in Children.* Chicago, University of Chicago Press, 1957.

13a. BROŽEK, J.: Book review of *Chemical Anthropology. Am. J. Phys. Anthropol.,* n.s. *16:*489-493, 1958.

14. KEYS, A. and BROŽEK, J.: Body fat in adult man. *Physiol. Rev.,* 33:245-325, 1953.

15. STUART, H. C., HILL, P. and SHAW, C.: Growth of bone, muscle and overlying tissues as revealed by studies of roentgenograms of the leg area. Monogr. Soc. Research Child Develop. No. 26, 1940.

16. REYNOLDS, E. L.: Distribution of subcutaneous fat in childhood and adolescence. Monogr. Soc. Research Child Develop. No. 50, 1951.

17. TANNER, J. M.: *Growth at Adolescence.* Springfield, Ill., Thomas, 1955.

18. GARN, S. M. and SHAMIR, Z.: *Methods for Research on Human Growth.* Springfield, Ill., Thomas, 1958.

19. MITCHELL, H. H., HAMILTON, T. S., STEGGERDA, F. R., and BEAN, H. W.: Chemical composition of the adult human body and its bearing on the biochemistry of growth. *J. Biol. Chem., 158:*625-637, 1945.

20. FORBES, R. M., COOPER, A. R., and MITCHELL, H. H.: The composition of the adult human body as determined by chemical analysis. *J. Biol. Chem., 203:*359-366, 1953.

21. WIDDOWSON, E. M., McCANCE, R. A., and SPRAY, C. M.: Chemical composition of the human body. *Clin. Sci., 10:*113-125, 1951.

22. STEWART, T. D., ed.: *Hrdlička's Practical Anthropometry,* 4th edition. Philadelphia, Wistar Institute, 1952.

23. TANNER, J. M. and WHITEHOUSE, R. H.: The Harpenden skinfold caliper. *Am. J. Phys. Anthropol.,* n.s. *13:*743-746, 1955.

23a. Association of Life Insurance Medical Directors and Actuarial Society of America: *Medico-Actuarial Investigations,* Vol. 1, 1912.

24. Committee on Nutritional Anthropometry Food and Nutrition Board, National Research Council: Recommendations concerning body measurements for the characterization of nutritional status. *Human Biol., 28:*115-123, 1956.

25. BROŽEK, J.: Physique and nutritional status of adult men. *Human Biol., 28:* 124-140, 1956.

26. TROTTER, M.: A preliminary study of estimation of the weight of the skeleton. *Am. J. Phys. Anthropol.,* n.s. *12:*537-552, 1954.

26a. MERZ, A. L., TROTTER, M., and PETERSON, R. R.: Estimation of skeletal weight in the living. *Am. J. Phys. Anthropol.,* n.s. *14:*589-609, 1956.

26b. FALKNER, F. and WISDOM, S.: Measurement of tissue components radiologically. *Brit. Med. J.,* 2:1240, 1952.

27. BROŽEK, J. and MORI H.: Some interrelations between somatic, roentgenographic and densitometric criteria of fatness. *Human Biol., 30:*322-336, 1958.

28. GARN, S. M.: Fat patterning and fat intercorrelations in the adult male. *Human Biol., 26:*59-69, 1954.

29. BROŽEK, J., HENSCHEL, A., and KEYS, A.: Effect of submersion in water on the volume of residual air in man. *J. Appl. Physiol.,* 2:240-246, 1949.

30. SIRI, W. E.: Apparatus for measuring human body volume. *Rev. Sci. Instruments,* 27:729-738, 1956.

31. BROŽEK, J.: Changes in body composition in man during maturity and their nutritional implications. *Federation Proc.,* 11:784-793, 1952.

32. KEYS, A., ANDERSON, J. T., and BROŽEK, J.: Weight gain from simple overeating. I. Character of the tissue gained. *Metabolism,* 4:427-432, 1955.

32a. FIDANZA, F., KEYS, A., and ANDERSON, J. T.: Density of body fat in man and other mammals. *J. Appl. Physiol.,* 6:252-256, 1953.

33. BROŽEK, J.: Measurement of body compartments in nutritional research: Comment on selected methods, in *Methods for Evaluation of Nutritional Adequacy and Status.* Washington, Nat. Acad. Sci.-Nat. Res. Council, 1954, p. 265-279.

34. BEHNKE, A. R.: Body composition, in *Methods for Evaluation of Nutritional Adequacy and Status.* Washington, Nat. Acad. Sci.-Nat. Res. Council, 1954, p. 294-310.

35. BROŽEK, J. and KEYS, A.: The evaluation of leanness-fatness in man: Norms and interrelationships. *Brit. J. Nutr.,* 5:194-206, 1951.

36. PASCALE, L. R., GROSSMAN, M. L., SLOANE, H. S., and FRANKEL, T.: Correlations between thickness of skinfolds and body density in 88 soldiers. *Human Biol.,* 28:165-176, 1956.

37. GARN, S. M.: Roentgenogrammetric determinations of body composition. *Human Biol.,* 29:337-353, 1957.

38. McCLOY, C. H.: *Appraising Physical Status: The Selection of Measurements.* Iowa City, Iowa, University of Iowa, 1936.

38a. FRANZEN, R.: *Physical Measures of Growth and Nutrition.* New York, American Child Health Association, 1927.

39. McCLOY, C. H.: *Appraising Physical Status: Methods and Norms.* Iowa City, Iowa, University of Iowa, 1938.

40. SHELDON, W. C.: *Varieties of Human Physique.* New York, Harper, 1940.

41. LASKER, G. W.: Effects of partial starvation on somatotypes. *Am. J. Phys. Anthropology,* n.s. 5:323-341, 1947.

42. BROŽEK, J.: Role of anthropometry in the study of body composition: Toward a synthesis of methods. *Ann. N.Y. Acad. Sci.,* 63, Art. 4:491-504, 1955.

43. DUPERTUIS, C. W., PITTS, G. C., OSSERMAN, E. F., WELHAM, W. C., and BEHNKE, A. R.: Relation of specific gravity to body build in a group of healthy men. *J. Appl. Physiol.,* 3:676-680, 1951.

43a. PARNELL, R. W.: *Behaviour and Physique: An Introduction to Practical and Applied Somatometry.* London, E. Arnold, 1958.

44. LINDEGÅRD, B.: *Variations in Human Body-Build.* Copenhagen, Munksgaard, Acta Psychiatr. Neurol., Suppl. 96, 1953.

44a. LINDEGÅRD, B., ed.: *Body-Build, Body-Function, and Personality.* Lund, Lunds Universitets et Årsskrift, 1955.

45. ŠKERLJ, B., BROŽEK, J., and HUNT, E. E., JR.: Subcutaneous fat and age changes in body build and body form in women. *Am. J. Phys. Anthropol.,* n.s. 11:577-600, 1953.

46. BEHNKE, A. R.: Physiologic studies pertaining to deep sea diving and aviation, especially in relation to the fat content and composition of the human body. *Harvey Lect.,* 37:198-226, 1941-42.

47. TAYLOR, H. L., BROŽEK, J., and KEYS, A.: Basal cardiac function and body composition, with special reference to obesity. *J. Clin. Investigation, 31:* 976-983, 1952.

48. GARN, S. M.: Relative fat patterning: An individual characteristic. *Human Biol.,* 27:75-89, 1955.

49. GARN, S. M.: Applications of pattern analysis to anthropometric data. *Annals N.Y. Acad. Sci., 63:*537-552, 1955.

50. GARN, S. M. and BROŽEK, J.: Fat changes during weight loss. *Science, 124:* 682, 1956.

51. GARN, S. M. and HASKELL, JOAN, A.: Fat changes during adolescence. *Science, 126:*1615-1616, 1959.

52. WILMER, H. A.: Quantitative growth of skin and subcutaneous tissue in relation to human surface area. *Proc. Soc. Exper. Biol. Med., 43:*386-388, 1940.

53. REYNOLDS, E. L. and GROTE, P.: Sex differences in the distribution of tissue components in the human leg from birth to maturity. *Anat. Record, 102:* 45-53, 1948.

54. BROŽEK, J.: Changes of body composition in man during maturity and their nutritional implications. *Federation Proc., 11:*788-793, 1952.

55. BROŽEK, J., CHEN, K. P., CARLSON, W., and BRONCZYK, F.: Age and sex differences in man's fat content during maturity. *Federation Proc., 12:* 21-22, 1953.

56. PÁLSSON, H.: Conformation and body composition, in *Progress in the Physiology of Farm Animals,* Vol. 2. London, Butterworths, 1955, p. 430-542.

57. BROŽEK, J., GRANDE, F., TAYLOR, H. L., ANDERSON, J. T., BUSKIRK, E. R., and KEYS, A.: Changes in body weight and body dimensions in men performing work on a low calorie carbohydrate diet. *J. Appl. Physiol., 10:*412-420, 1957.

58. KEYS, A., BROŽEK, J., HENSCHEL, A., MICKELSEN, O., and TAYLOR, H. L.: *The Biology of Human Starvation.* Minneapolis, University of Minnesota Press, 1950.

59. BROŽEK, J.: Changes in specific gravity and body fat of young men under conditions of experimental semi-starvation. *Federation Proc., 5:*13, 1946.

60. LASKER, G.: Effects of partial starvation on somatotype. *Am. J. Phys. Anthropol., n.s. 5:*323-341, 1947.

61. BROŽEK, J.: Starvation and nutritional rehabilitation: A quantitative case study. *J. Amer. Diet. Assoc., 28:*917-926, 1952.

62. MARKS, H. H.: Body weight: Facts from life insurance records. *Human Biol.,* 28:217-231, 1956.

FOR FURTHER READING, CONSULT:

BROŽEK, J.: Measuring nutriture. *Am. J. Phys. Anthropol., n.s. 11:*147-180, 1953.
Clarifies the role of anthropometry in the assessment of "nutritional status" and the far-reaching implications of "nutritional anthropometry" for physical anthropology. The consideration of nutrition (and activity) injects into physical anthropology concern for *interpretation* of body dimensions, their etiology and biomedical significance.

BROŽEK, J., ed.: *Body Measurements and Human Nutrition.* Detroit, Wayne State University Press, 1956.
Contains recommendations concerning anthropometric assessment of nutritional status, plus 11 papers on obesity and body composition. Constitutes the final report of the Committee on Nutritional Anthropometry (Food and Nutrition Board, National Research Council).

BROŽEK, J. and HENSCHEL, A., eds.: *Body Composition: Appraisal of Methods* (in press). Detroit, Wayne State University Press, 1960.
Proceedings of symposium, held under the sponsorship of the Advisory Board on Quartermaster Research and Development, National Academy of Sciences—National Research Council in January, 1959. An up-to-date, comprehensive assessment of the complex methodology.

CURETON, T. K.: *Physical Fitness of Champion Athletes.* Urbana, University of Illinois Press, 1951, esp. p. 13-27.
The Cureton Modified Somatotype System reduces Sheldon's scheme to a two-dimensional system of thinness-fatness (linearity vs. ponderosity) as one variable (based on measurements of skinfolds, girths, weight/height ratio or vital capacity) and strength, as the other variable. Considerations of body build in reference to physical exercise represent an important area of applied physical anthropology.

EPPRIGHT, E. S., SWANSON, P., and IVERSON, C. A., eds.: *Weight Control.* Ames, Iowa State College Press, 1955.
A collection of papers on different aspects of weight control, including appraisal of obesity and its significance as a health hazard.

SPECTOR, H., PETERSON, M. S., and FRIEDEMANN, T. E., eds.: *Methods for Evaluation of Nutritional Adequacy and Status.* Washington, National Academy of Sciences—National Research Council, 1954.
In the section dealing with body composition (pp. 265-313) the quantitative assumptions in the densitometric and hydrometric system of body composition analysis are spelled out in detail.

FORSSMAN, O. and LINDEGÅRD, B.: The post-coronary patient: A multi-disciplinary investigation of middle-aged Swedish males. *J. Psychosomat. Res.,* 3:89-169, 1958.
Application of Lindegård's system of quantitative description of body build in terms of 4 "factors" (length, sturdiness, muscularity, fatness), in a biomedical context.

DIRECTORIES

International Directory of Anthropological Institutions

Published in 1953 by the Wenner-Gren Foundation for Anthropological Research, New York, and obtainable from the American Anthropological Association, William Godfrey, Jr., Executive Secretary, Logan Museum, Beloit College, Beloit, Wisconsin. Price $12.50.

International Directory of Anthropologists

Obtainable from the Secretary, Division of Anthropology and Psychology, National Research Council, 2101 Constitution Avenue, Washington 21, D.C. Price $3.00.

Yearbook of Anthropology 1955

Published by the Wenner-Gren Foundation for Anthropological Research, 14 East 71st Street, New York 21, New York. Containing a world coverage of anthropology, with data on dissertations, awards, and professional organizations.

SOME CURRENT ANTHROPOLOGICAL PERIODICALS EITHER WHOLLY OR IN PART DEVOTED TO PHYSICAL ANTHROPOLOGY

Acta Geneticae Medicae et Gemellogiae

Published quarterly, an international journal devoted to the publication of research in human genetics and multiple births. Instituto Gregorio Mendel di Roma, Largo Dell'Amba, Aradam 1, Roma. Annual subscription Lire 7,000 ($18.00).

Actas y Memorias de la Sociedad Española de Antropologia, Etnografia y Prehistoria

Published irregularly by the Sociedad Española de Antropología, Etnografia y Prehistoria, Paseo de Atocha 11, Madrid, Spain.

Acta Genetica et Statistica Medica

Published quarterly by S. Karger Ltd. Holbeinstrasse 22, Basel, Switzerland. Annual subscription 44 Swiss francs.

American Anthropologist

Published six times a year by the American Anthropological Association. Executive Secretary, William S. Godfrey, Jr., Logan Museum, Beloit College, Beloit, Wisconsin. Annual subscription by membership in the Association $8.50.

American Antiquity

Published quarterly by the Society for American Archeology. David A. Barreis, Sterling Hall, University of Wisconsin, Madison 6, Wisconsin. Annual subscription, $8.00.

American Journal of Human Genetics

Published quarterly by the American Society of Human Genetics, Mount Royal and Guilford Avenues, Baltimore 2, Maryland. Annual subscription $10.00.

American Journal of Physical Anthropology

Published quarterly by the Wistar Institute of Anatomy and Biology, Philadelphia, Pennsylvania. Organ of the American Association of Physical Anthropologists. Annual subscription $7.50.

Annals of Human Genetics

Formerly *Annals of Eugenics.* A journal of human genetics of considerable anthropological interest. Published quarterly by the Galton Laboratory, University College, Gower Street, London, W.C. 1., England. Subscription per volume £5 ($17.50).

Anthropological Quarterly

A journal of general anthropology edited by the Department of Anthropology, and published by the Catholic University of America, Washington, D.C. Annual subscription $3.00.

Anthropologie Différentielle et Sciences de Types Constitutionnels.

Published by the Bureau International d'Anthropologie Différentielle, Geneva, Switzerland.

L'Anthropologie

Published bi-monthly by the Société d'Anthropologie de Paris through Masson et cie., 120, Boulevard Saint-Germain, Paris Vle, France. Francs 6,000 ($17.00).

Anthropologischer Anzeiger

Published quarterly by the E. Schweitzerbart'sche Verlagsbuchhandlung, Johannerstrass 3/1, Stuttgart W, Germany. A review of the biological-anthropological literature. Subscription per volume 54DM ($12.00).

The Anthropologist

Published quarterly by the Department of Anthropology, Delhi University, Delhi, India.

Antropologia y Etnographia

Published quarterly by the Instituto Bernardino de Sahagùn de Antropologia y Etnografia, Madrid, Spain.

Anthropos

International review of ethnology and linguistics. Published irregularly with the support of the University of Freibourg, Poisieux-Froideville, Ct. de Freibourg, Switzerland. Each issue separately priced.

Antiquity

A quarterly review of archeology, published by H. W. Edwards, Ashmore Green, Newbury, Berks, England. Annual subscription 30s ($5.00).

Archiv der Julius Klaus-Stiftung für Vererbungsforschung, Sozialanthropologie und Rassenhygiene

Published quarterly by the Kuratorium der Julius Kalus Stiftung, Gemindestrasse 5, Zürich 7, Switzerland.

Archives Suisses d'Anthropologie Générale

Published bi-annually by the Institut d'Anthropologie de l'Université de Genève, 44c rue de Maraîchers, Geneva, Switzerland. 20 Swiss francs an issue.

Arquivo de Anatomia e Antropologia

Published irregularly by the Instituto de Anatomia de Lisbon, Lisbon, Portugal.

Archivo per l'Antropologia e la Etnologia

Published by the Società Italiana di Anthropologia e Etnolgia, Via del Proconsolo 12, Firenze, Italy.

Archivo Iberoamericano de Historia de la Medicina y Antropologia Medica

Published quarterly by the Instituto "Arnaldo de Vilanova" de Historia de la Medicina, Duque de Midinaceli, 4, Madrid, Spain. Annual subscription 140 pesettas ($4.00).

Biological Abstracts. Section H—Human Biology

Published monthly during the months January to May, October and November; bi-monthly June to September; semi-monthly in December, by Biological Abstracts, Executive Office, University of Pennsylvania, Philadelphia 4, Pennsylvania. Annual subscription $7.50.

Biometrika

Published bi-annually by the Biometrika Office, Galton Laboratory, University College, Gower Street, London, W.C.1, England. Annual subscription 54s. ($8.00).

Biotypologie

Published quarterly by the Société de Biotypologie, Laboratoire de Biometrie, 41, rue Gay Lussac, Paris, 5ᵉ. Annual subscription 1000 francs ($3.50).

Boletin Bibliografico de Antropologia Americana

Published annually by the Instituto Panamericano de Geografia e Historia, Avenida del Oservatorio Num. 192, Tacubaya, D. F. Republica Mexicana.

British Journal of Preventive and Social Medicine

Published quarterly by the British Medical Association, Tavistock Square, London, W.C. 1. Annual subscription 25s. ($4.00).

Bulletin de la Société Préhistorique Française

Published bi-monthly by the Société Préhistorique Française, Siège Social, 250, rue Saint-Jacques, Paris-Ve, France. Annual subscription 200 francs.

Bulletins et Mémoires de la Société d'Anthropologie de Paris

Published quarterly by the *Société d'Anthropologie de Paris* through Masson et Cie., 120, Boulevard Saint-Germain, 120, Paris-VIe, France. ($2.50).

Child Development Abstracts and Bibliography

Issued three times a year by the Society for Research in Child Development, Inc., at Child Development Publications, Purdue University, Lafayette, Indiana. Annual subscription $6.00.

Current Anthropology

Published six times a year. A world journal of the sciences of man. Office, Department of Anthropology, University of Chicago, 1159 East 26th Street, Chicago 37, Illinois. Annual subscription $10.00. Special rates to students and anthropologists.

The Eastern Anthropologist

A journal founded in 1948 devoted to the study of the physical and cultural anthropology of the peoples of India. Published quarterly by the Ethnographic and Folk Culture Society, Lucknow, India. Distributed by the Biotechnic Press, Ltd., BCM/Biotechnic, London, W.C. 1, England. Annual subscription 20s ($2.80).

The Eugenics Quarterly

Published quarterly by the American Eugenics Society, 230 Park Avenue, New York 17, New York. Annual subscription $5.00.

The Eugenics Review

Organ of the Eugenics Society. Published quarterly by The Eugenics Society, 69 Eccleston Square, London, W. 1, England. Annual subscription 20s ($3.00).

Evolution

Published quarterly by The Society for the Study of Evolution. Business office at Prince and Lemon Street, Lancaster, Pennsylvania. Annual subscription $6.00.

Excerpta Medica

Fifteen sections abstracting the whole field of medicine are published. Section 1 deals with anatomy, and anthropology, embryology, and histology. Published monthly. Excerpta Medica Foundation, 2 East 103rd Street, New York 29, New York. Annual subscription $22.50.

The Florida Anthropologist

Published quarterly by the Florida Anthropological Society, Ripley P. Bullen, Treasurer, 103 Seagle Building, Gainesville, Florida. Annual subscription. $3.00.

Homo

Devoted to the comparative study of man and human biology. Organ of the Deutschen Gesellschaft für Anthropologie. Published quarterly by the Ferdinand Enke Verlag, Stuttgart, Germany. Annual subscription RM 30.

Human Biology

Published quarterly by the Wayne State University Press, Detroit 2, Michigan. Annual subscription, $5.00.

Human Organization (formerly *Applied Anthropology*)

Published quarterly by the Society for Applied Anthropology. New York State

School of Industrial and Labor Relations, Cornell University, New York. Annual subscription $6.00.

Journal de Génétique Humaine

A quarterly founded in 1953, published by the Editions Medicine et Hygiene, Geneva, Switzerland. Annual subscription 3,000 French francs ($10.00).

Journal of Forensic Medicine

Published quarterly by Juta & Co., Ltd. P.O. Box 30, Cape Town, South Africa. Annual subscription 42s ($6.00).

The Journal of Heredity

Published monthly by the American Genetic Association, 32nd Street and Elm Avenue, Baltimore 11, Maryland and 1507 M St., Washington, D.C. Annual subscription $7.00.

Journal of the Royal Anthropological Institute

Published quarterly by the Royal Anthropological Institute, 21, Bedford Square, London, W.C. 1, England. Annual subscription 63s. ($9.50).

Man

A record of anthropological science, published monthly by the Royal Anthropological Institute, 21, Bedford Square, London, W.C. 1, England. Annual subscription 30s. ($5.00).

Mankind

Official journal of the anthropological societies of Australia. Published irregularly by the Anthropological Society of New South Wales, Sydney Municipal Library, George Street, Sydney, New South Wales, Australia. Annual subscription 7s 6d. ($1.75).

Man in India

A quarterly founded in 1921, 18, Church Road, Ranchi, E. Ry. Bihar, India. Annual subscription 25s ($4.00).

Mitteilungen der Anthropologischen Gesellschaft in Wien

One to three numbers per volume per annum. Published by Anthropologischer Gesellschaft in Wien, Wien 1, Burgring 7, Austria. Annual subscription 75 schillung.

Monographs of the Society for Research in Child Development

Published irregularly by the Society for Research in Child Development. Child Development Publications, Purdue University, Lafayette, Indiana. Annual subscription $6.00.

Oceania

A journal devoted to the study of the native peoples of Australia, New Guinea and the islands of the Pacific Ocean. Published quarterly by the University of Sydney, New South Wales, Australia. Annual subscription 40s. ($6.00).

Praehistorische Zeitschrift

Published at intervals annually by Walter de Gryter & Co., Berlin W 35, Germany.

Quaternaria

Published quarterly. Via Caccini, Rome, Italy. Annual subscription 5000 lire ($8.25).

Revista Colombiana de Antropología

Published by the Instituto Colombiana de Antropología, Bogotá.

Revista de Antropologia

Published quarterly by the Universidad de São Paulo, Brazil.

Rivista di Antropologia

Published irregularly by the Instituto Italiano di Antropologia, Città Universitaria, Roma, Italia.

Revista Colombiana de Antropologia

Published annually by Instituto Colombiana de Antropologia, Apartado Nal. 407. Bogotá, Colombia. Distributed without charge.

Revue Anthropologique

Published irregularly by the Institut International D'Anthropologie. Libraire Jouve, 15 Rue Racine Paris 6ᵉ, France.

La Revue de Géographie Humaine et d'Ethnologie

A quarterly containing much valuable material of interest to the physical anthropologist. Office of publication: 5, rue Sébastien-Bottin, Paris VII, France. Annual subscription 1,740 francs ($5.50).

Runa, Archivo para Las Cienias d Hombre

A quarterly covering the whole field of anthropology. Office of publication: calle Reconquista 572 Buenos Aires, Brazil. Annual subscription $6.00.

Southwestern Journal of Anthropology

Published quarterly by the University of New Mexico Press, Albuquerque, New Mexico. Annual subscription $4.00.

S.A.S. (Bulletin du Comité International pour la Standardisation Anthropologique Synthetique)

Sovetskaia Antropologiia

A quarterly first published in 1958 by the Institute of Anthropology of Moscow State University. Obtainable through Collet's Russian Bookshop, 45 Museum Street, London, W.C.1, England. Annual subscription $6.02.

Statistical Bulletin

Published monthly by the Metropolitan Life Insurance Company, 1, Madison Avenue, New York 10, New York. Obtainable upon request.

Trabajos del Instituto Bernardino de Sahgún, de Antropologia y Etnologia

Published by the Consejo Superior de Investigaciones Cientificas, Instituto Bernardino de Sahagun, Paseo de Atocha, 11, Madrid, Spain.

Trabalhos de Antropologia e Etnologia

Published irregularly by the Instituto de Antropologia. Faculdade de Ciéncias. Oporto, Portugal.

Zeitschrift für Menschliche-Vererbungs-und Konstitutionslehre

Published quarterly by Springer-Verlag, Heidelberg, Germany. Annual subscription DM 88.40.

Zeitschrift für Morphologie und Anthropologie

Published quarterly by E. Schweitzerbart'sche Verlagsbuchhandlung, Stuttgart, Germany. Each number differently priced. Annual cost varies from $30 to $40.

List of Anthropological Periodicals, Serial, and Monograph Publications

An exhaustive, though not entirely complete, list of the many university, public, private, and museum publications of this sort will be found in *The Journal of the Royal Anthropological Institute,* Vol. 76, 1946, pp. 189-210. This list is published as from June *1949.*

APPENDIX C
GENE AND GENOTYPE EQUILIBRIA, POPULA-
TIONS AND GENES, THE HARDY-
WEINBERG LAW

ONE BRANCH of genetics studies the distribution and movement of genes (gene flow) in populations. Here the geneticist and physical anthropologist have similar interests and problems. The population geneticist is concerned with all those conditions that govern gene distributions and their changes. The "conditions" refer to such factors as size of population, degree of isolation from other populations, forms of mating or marriage-regulations, differential migration (emigration and immigration), mutation, selection, and hybridization.

In the course of the history of virtually every population all these factors tend to be operative, and as we have seen in Chapter VI it is highly probable that every one of these factors, to varying extents, has contributed to the differences in gene frequencies which exist for some traits in different populations.

In the absence of the modifying conditions mentioned above, and frequently in their presence, the genetic structure of a population, that is to say the frequency distribution of its genes, tends to remain stable. The same proportions of the same genes tend to reappear generation after generation. Such a genetically stable population is said to be in *equilibrium*.

In large populations mating is usually random in respect of any particular gene, and this is what is meant when we speak of random mating—and *not* that individuals choose their mates at random, a condition that applies in no human society. The technical term for random mating is *panmixia*, a random mating population is said to be *panmictic*.

In a large panmictic population in which the pressures of mutation and selection, or other factors having similar effects upon gene frequencies, are absent or low, genotype frequencies, after the first generation of random mating, will remain indefinitely unchanged. This phenomenon is known as the Hardy-Weinberg Law (or Hardy-Weinberg Equilibrium), a law independently worked out in 1908 by the English mathematician G. H. Hardy and the German physician W. Weinberg.

In spite of three somewhat unreal assumptions, namely, infinite populations, low mutation, and little selection, the Hardy-Weinberg Law is found to work with remarkable precision in real finite populations. Not only this, it is a tool of considerable heuristic value, for when it is found not to work it may at once be suspected that we are dealing with a population in which special conditions prevail, such as isolating barriers between segments of the population which prevent free interbreeding within it. With the removal of such reproductively isolating barriers the Hardy-Weinberg Law would be found to hold true.

We shall take as a simple example of the manner in which the Hardy-Weinberg Law works a population in which there is random mating in respect of two autosomal alleles A and a. The frequencies of these alleles is 50 per cent each. Remembering that it is not phenotypes that are so much involved as the gametes, that is, the eggs and sperms, half of the eggs will carry A and half a, and so will the sperms. The results of the random combination of such eggs and sperms in the zygotes may be determined from Table LVIII. From this will be seen that the frequencies of the alleles A and a remain unchanged at 50 per cent each, $\frac{1}{4}$th of the individuals will be AA, $\frac{1}{2}$ Aa, and another $\frac{1}{4}$th aa.

$\frac{SPERMS}{EGGS}$	A p	a q
A p	AA p^2	Aa pq
a q	Aa pq	aa q^2

$$= p^2AA + 2pqAa + q^2aa,$$
or, in the example given in the text,
$$= \frac{1}{4} AA + \frac{1}{2} Aa + \frac{1}{2} aa$$

Table LVIII. The maintenance of genotype equilibrium. The Hardy-Weinberg Law.

Matings at random between the members of this population, and the offspring of such marriages, with respect to the genes A and a, will yield 9 possible matings, and precisely the same proportions of genotypes as existed in the parental population, as shown in Table LIX.

With special exceptions the Hardy-Weinberg Law applies to all populations, however unequal the frequencies of certain genes may be. It can, therefore, be generalized in the binomial $(p + q)^2$, where p equals the frequency of A, and q equals the frequency of its allele a, and $p + q = 1$. The genotype frequencies in each generation equal

9 Possible Matings	*Offspring of 9 Matings*		
$\frac{1}{16} AA \times AA$	$\frac{1}{16} AA$		
$\frac{1}{8} AA \times Aa$	$\frac{1}{16} AA$	$\frac{1}{16} Aa$	
$\frac{1}{8} Aa \times AA$	$\frac{1}{16} AA$	$\frac{1}{16} Aa$	
$\frac{1}{16} AA \times aa$		$\frac{1}{16} Aa$	
$\frac{1}{4} Aa \times Aa$	$\frac{1}{16} AA$	$\frac{1}{8} Aa$	$\frac{1}{16} aa$
$\frac{1}{16} aa \times AA$		$\frac{1}{16} Aa$	
$\frac{1}{8} Aa \times aa$		$\frac{1}{16} Aa$	$\frac{1}{16} aa$
$\frac{1}{8} aa \times Aa$		$\frac{1}{16} Aa$	$\frac{1}{16} aa$
$\frac{1}{16} aa \times aa$			$\frac{1}{16} aa$

Proportion of same genotypes $\frac{1}{4} AA + \frac{1}{2} Aa + \frac{1}{4} aa$

Table LIX. The proportions of genotypes in 9 possible matings of individuals with genes A and a.

$(pA + qa)^2 = p^2AA + 2pqAa + q^2aa$, which is precisely what we found in Tables LVIII and LIX for the special case of $p = q = \frac{1}{2}$. A similar formula may be derived for loci with more than two alleles.

The Hardy-Weinberg Law explains how it comes about that the genotypic frequencies for such traits as brown eyes and blue eyes, for tasting and non-tasting, the blood groups, and all similar traits dependent upon contrasting alleles are likely to be maintained in the same proportions generation after generation.

It should at once be evident then, why statements to the effect that brown eyes being dominant over blue, the former must eventually swamp the latter, or that the higher frequency of brachycephaly in certain populations is due to the dominance of the alleles for this trait, are erroneous. The error committed is the assumption that the numerical frequency of any trait in a population represents a reflection of the number of dominant alleles conditioning the trait.

The fact, however, is that phenotypic frequency has no necessary relation to either the dominance or the recessiveness of alleles. Dominance and recessiveness refer only to the expression of the alleles in individuals possessing them. The frequency of any phenotype in a *population* is related to the frequency of the allele controlling it, regardless of that allele's dominance or recessiveness. There are numerous conditions in man which are due to a dominant allele, but those conditions are rare in man, simply because the dominant gene is much less frequent than its normal alternative. Examples are partial albinism, the sickle-cell trait, achondroplasia, and parietal foramina of the abnormal type.[*]

In the case of the alleles for tasting and non-tasting, we have already seen in Chapter VI that tasting is dependent upon a single

[*] For other examples see Ashley Montagu, *Human Heredity*, pp.328-346.

dominant gene *T*, and non-tasting upon two recessive genes *tt*. The distribution of these genes in any population will invariably be found to follow the Hardy-Weinberg Law.

Dominant alleles in any population do not tend to replace recessive alleles. The frequency of an allele in a population is not determined by its being either dominant or recessive, but largely by the fact of its being of greater or lesser selective value.

The Hardy-Weinberg Law states that regardless of past history, random mating for one generation yields genotypic frequencies in the proportions $p^2 : 2pq : q^2$.

Gene frequency can be at equilibrium in the sense that p does not change from generation to generation in a number of circumstances, such, for example, as the following:

1. *No selection. Mutation in opposite directions.* In the absence of selection the frequency of a gene will depend upon relative rates of mutation in favorable and unfavorable directions.

2. *Selection in opposite direction from mutation.* A gene may be in process of elimination from a population, but persists within that population because the rate of elimination of the gene by selection is equal to the rate at which the gene is being reintroduced into the population by mutation.

3. *Heterozygote superior to both homozygotes.* This is well illustrated by the case of the sickle-cell trait in which the heterozygote AS is superior to the normal homozygote AA and the sickle cell anemia homozygote SS (see p. 374).

4. *Diversity of niches or environments.* If the environment is not uniform over the area occupied by a population, different genotypes may have different fitnesses in each phase of the environment. In which case polymorphism (gene equilibrium) may be preserved provided the heterozygotes are more efficient over a wider range of environments than the homozygotes.

5. *Compensation effect: more children born in families with defectives.* Where the homozygote recessive is defective, there appears to be a tendency in the families involved to have more children than normal, and more of these tend to be heterozygotes than are produced in the general population, a balanced polymorphism can be thus maintained.

6. *Dependence of fitness upon gene frequency.* When the attractiveness of blondes depends upon their rarity in the population they are at a selective advantage, and therefore increase in number. Should

blondes increase to be as common as the air, then Phoebe ceases to be esteemed fair, and is then at a selective disadvantage, and tends to decrease in frequency. At some point in this process genetic equilibrium is reached.

As another illustration of the operation of this factor reference may be made to disease. In a large population of susceptible individuals an epidemic will spread quite rapidly, and the susceptibles will be at a selective disadvantage compared to the immune individuals. However, if most of the population is immune the disease will not spread readily, and the minority (the susceptibles) will be protected by the high frequency of immunes, and equilibrium will thus be maintained.

7. *Sex differences.* If selection is different in the two sexes gene equilibrium may be achieved. For example, in a population in which fat women are preferred to svelte ones, and lithe men are preferred to somewhat over-upholstered ones, a balanced polymorphism for both sexes will be reached.

APPENDIX D

"ETHNIC GROUP" AND "RACE"

In the Unesco Statement on Race paragraph 6 reads as follows: "National, religious, geographic, linguistic and cultural groups do not necessarily coincide with racial groups; and the cultural traits of such groups have no demonstrated connection with racial traits. Because serious errors of this kind are habitually committed when the term 'race' is used in popular parlance, it would be better when speaking of human races to drop the term 'race' altogether and speak of *ethnic groups.*" It should be noted that there is a clear acknowledgment of the existence of human races in this paragraph, and that the emphasis is on popular parlance. It is recommended that in the universe of popular parlance the term "race" be dropped altogether and that we speak of "ethnic groups." Since races in various biological senses of the word can be conceived to exist in man, it would seem unnecessary to drop this long-established term in favor of some other. The truth, however, is that there are so many different senses in which even biologists use the term, that many leading members of that profession prefer not to use it at all. Huxley a biologist and Haddon a physical anthropologist repudiated the term in 1936.[1] Calman recommended that the term "variety" should be avoided altogether and suggested that "Other terms such as 'geographical race,' 'form,' 'phase,' and so forth, may be useful in particular instances but are better not used until some measure of agreement is reached as to their precise meaning."[2] Kalmus writes: "A very important term which was originally used in systematics is 'race.' Nowadays, however, its use is avoided as far as possible in genetics."[3] In a more recent work Kalmus writes, "It is customary to discuss the local varieties of humanity in terms of 'race.' However, it is unnecessary to use this greatly debased word, since it is easy to describe populations without it."[3a] G. S. Carter, in his book on *Animal Evolution*, writes that

---

[1] Huxley and Haddon, *We Europeans*, pp. 82-83.

[2] Calman, *The Classification of Animals*, p. 14.

[3] Kalmus, *Genetics*, p. 45.

[3a] Kalmus, *Heredity and Variation*, p. 30.

the terms "'race,' 'variety,' and 'form' are used so loosely and in so many senses that it is advisable to avoid using them as infraspecific categories."[4] Professor Ernst Hanhart denies that there are any "true races" in man,[5] and Professor L. S. Penrose, in a review of Dunn and Dobzhansky's little book *Heredity, Race and Society*, writes that he is unable to "see the necessity for the rather apologetic retention of the obsolete term 'race,' when what is meant is simply a given population differentiated by some social, geographical or genetical character, or . . . merely by a gene frequency peculiarity. The use of the almost mystical concept of race makes the presentation of the facts about the geographical and linguistic groups . . . unnecessarily complicated."[6]

In spite of these strictures many biologists will continue to use the term, and if they can use it in an adequately defined manner so that their meaning can be clearly understood by other scientists, erroneous though that usage may be, it will be all the more easy for the critic to direct attention to the sources of the error. It cannot be too frequently emphasized that definitions are not to be achieved at the beginning of an inquiry but only at the end of one. Such inquiries have not yet been completed to the satisfaction of most scientists who have paid considered attention to the subject of 'race.' The term, therefore, at best is at the present time not really allowable on any score in man. One may or may not be of the opinion that the term "race" ought to be dropped altogether from the vocabulary, because it is so prematurely defined and confusing and because biologists and other scientists are frequently guilty of using it incorrectly, and that therefore it would be better if they did not lend the aura of their authority to the use of so confusing a word. The term "subspecies" has been used as the equivalent of the term "race," but this suffers from the same disadvantages, and has been as misused as its equivalent.[7] The term "race" is so embarrassed by confused and mystical meanings, and has so many blots upon its escutcheon, that a discouragement of its use would constitute an encouragement to clearer thinking.

In opposition to this view a number of objections have been expressed. One doesn't change anything by changing names. It's an artful dodge. Why not meet the problem head-on? If, in popular

---

[4] Carter, *Animal Evolution,* p. 163.

[5] Hanhart, in A. Sorsby, *Clinical Genetics,* p. 545.

[6] Penrose, *Annals of Eugenics, 17:*252, 1952.

[7] Hall, Zoological subspecies of man at the peace table. *J. Mammal.,* 27:358-364, 1946.

usage, the term "race" has been befogged and befouled, why not cleanse it of the smog and foulness and restore it to its pristine condition? Re-education should be attempted by establishing the true meaning of "race," not by denying its existence. One cannot combat racism by enclosing the word in quotes. It is not the word that requires changing but people's ideas about it. It is a common failing to argue from the abuse of an idea to its total exclusion. And so on.

It was Francis Bacon who remarked that truth grows more readily out of error than it does out of confusion. The time may come when it may be possible for most men to use the term "race" in a legitimate scientific sense, with clarity and with reason. But that time is not yet. It does not appear to be generally realized that while high walls do not a prison make, scientific terms are capable of doing so. Until people are soundly educated to understand the muddlement of ideas which is represented by such terms as "race" they will continue to believe in absurdities. And as Voltaire so acutely remarked, "As long as people believe in absurdities they will continue to commit atrocities." Words are what men breathe into them. Men have a strong tendency to use words and phrases which cloak the unknown in the undefined or undefinable. As Housman put it, "calling in ambiguity of language to promote confusion of thought." [8]

The layman's conception of "race" is so confused and emotionally muddled that any attempt to modify it would seem to be met by the greatest obstacle of all, the term "race" itself. This is another reason why the attempt to retain the term "race" in popular parlance must fail. The term is a trigger word; utter it and a whole series of emotionally conditioned responses follow. The phrase "ethnic group" suffers from no such defect. If we are to clarify the minds of those who think in terms of "race" we must cease using the word primarily because in the layman's mind the term defines conditions which do not in fact exist. There is no such thing as the kind of "race" in which the layman believes. If we are to re-educate him in a sound conception of the meaning of that population or somatological or genetic group which we prefer to designate by the general and non-committal phrase *ethnic group,* then it would seem far more reasonable to convey to him the temporariness of the situation with a general rather than with a particular term. This is particularly desirable when it is sought to remove a prevailing erroneous conception and substitute one that clarifies without solidifying. Professor Henry Sigerist has well said that "it is never sound to continue the use of terminology with

---

[8] Housman, *The Name and Nature of Poetry,* p. 31.

which the minds of millions of people have been poisoned even when the old terms are given new meanings."[9] And Professor George Gaylord Simpson has written, "A word for which everyone has a different definition, usually unstated, ceases to serve the function of communication and its use results in futile arguments about nothing. There is also a sort of Gresham's Law for words; redefine them as we will, their worst or most extreme meaning is almost certain to remain current and to tend to drive out the meaning we might prefer."[10] Bertrand Russell has suggested that for words that have strong emotional overtones we should substitute in our arguments the letters of the alphabet.

The biologist who has been largely concerned with the study of animal populations will be likely to take an oversimplified view of the problems here involved and to dismiss such attempts at re-education of the layman as unsatisfactory. By substituting one term for another, he will say, one solves nothing. It it quite as possible to feel "ethnic group prejudice" as it is to feel "race prejudice." Perhaps. But this kind of comment indicates that the real point has been missed. The phrase "ethnic group" is *not* a substitute for the term "race." The grounds upon which it is suggested constitute a fundamental difference in viewpoint which significantly differentiates what the phrase stands for from what the term stands for. It is not a question of changing names, and there is no question of resorting to devices or artful dodges—the imputation would be silly. If what the phrase "ethnic group" means is clearly understood and accepted, "ethnic group prejudice" would hardly require to be taken seriously. There have been some who have felt that the use of the phrase "ethnic group" was an avoidance of the main issue. On the other hand, most students of human nature would take the view that such a usage constitutes a more realistic and more promising approach to the problem of lay thinking on this subject than the method of attempting to put new meaning into the old bottle of "race." I agree with Korzybski that "because of the great semantic influence of the structure of language on the masses of mankind, leading, as it does, through lack of better understanding and *evaluation* to *speculation on terms*, it seems advisable to abandon completely terms which imply to the *many* the suggested elementalism, although these terms are used in a proper non-elementalistic way by the few."[11]

---

[9] Sigerist, *A History of Medicine,* p. 101.

[10] Simpson, *The Major Features of Evolution,* p. 268.

[11] Korzybski, *Science and Sanity,* p. 31.

The ground on which the phrase "ethnic group" is principally suggested is that it is easier to re-educate people by introducing a new conception with a new distinctive term, particularly, I repeat, when it is desired to remove a prevailing erroneous conception and introduce a new and more correct one. Those who do not understand that the greatest obstacle to the process of re-education would be the retention of the old term "race," a term which enshrines the errors it is desired to remove, do not understand the deep implicit meanings which this word has inescapably come to possess for so many of its users. The question may, then, be asked: Will the phrase "ethnic group" be sufficient to cause such persons to alter their ideas? The answer is for some "No," for others, "It will help"; and for still others, "Yes." No one should be so naïve as to suppose that by this means alone one is going to solve the "race" problem! The suggestions here made are calculated to help; they can do no more at best. Each time one uses the term "race" most individuals believe they understand what is meant, when in fact the chances are that what they understand by the term is largely false. "Race" is something so familiar that in speaking of it one takes one's private meaning completely for granted and one never thinks to question it. On the other hand, when one uses the phrase "ethnic group" wherever "race" would have been used, the question is generally asked: "What do you mean by 'ethnic group'?" And that at once affords the opportunity to discuss the facts and explain their meaning as well as the falsities of the prevailing conception of "race." This, it seems to me, is one of the greatest educational advantages of the phrase "ethnic group" over the term "race." Another advantage of the phrase is that it leaves all question of definition open, it refers specifically to human populations which are believed to exhibit a certain degree, amount, or frequency of undetermined physical likenesses or homogeneity. An ethnic group has already been described as one of a number of populations, which populations together comprise the species *Homo sapiens,* and which individually maintain their differences, physical and cultural, by means of isolating mechanisms such as geographic and social barriers. These differences vary as the power of the geographic and social barriers vary. Where these barriers are of high power, such ethnic groups will tend to remain distinct from each other geographically or ecologically.

English and English write as follows, "Ethnic group is an intentionally vague or general term used to avoid some of the difficulties of *race.* The ethnic group may be a nation, a people (such as the Jews), a language group (the Dakota Indians), a sociologically defined so-called race (the American Negro), or a group bound together in a coherent cultural entity by a religion (the Amish)."[12] To which one may add that the group may be characterized by a certain unity of genetic or physical traits.

Yet another advantage of the phrase "ethnic group" is that it avoids the reductionist or "nothing but" fallacy, that is to say, the notion that men are nothing but the resultant of their biological heredity, that they are what they are because of their genes. The phrase "ethnic group" is calculated to provide the necessary corrective to this erroneous viewpoint by eliminating the question-begging emphases of the biologistic bias on purely physical factors and differences, and demanding that the question of definition be left open until the necessary scientific research and answers are available. The emphasis is shifted to the fact that man is a uniquely cultural creature as well as a physical organism, and that under the influence of human culture the plasticity of man, both mentally and physically, is greatly increased—indeed, to such an extent as to lead anthropologists to the creation of races upon the basis of physical traits which were subsequently discovered to be due to cultural factors, as, for example, the head forms of the so-called Armenoid and Dinaric "races."

Here, too, reply may be made to those who may object that the phrase "ethnic group" is too reminiscent of the cultural. But this is precisely why the phrase is so well found. The Greek word *ethnos* originally meant a number of people living together, and subsequently came to be used in the sense of a tribe, group, nation, or people. In modern times the term "ethnic" has occasionally been used to refer to a group identified by ties both of race and of nationality. This is pretty much what the phrase "ethnic group" ought to be taken to mean in the sense given in our description of an "ethnic group."

If it be said that what the student of man's variety is interested in is the way in which human groups came to be what they are, and that for this reason it is the biological facts and mechanisms in which he must be chiefly interested, the answer must be made that anyone who believes this must be disabused of his belief as quickly as possible. For it must be emphasized again that man is not merely a physical organism but a *human* being who as a member of a cultural group has been greatly influenced by his culture. Human populations have had a remarkable assortment of marriage or breeding regulations, for

---

[12] English and English, *A Comprehensive Dictionary of Psychological and Psychoanalytical Terms*, 189.

instance, varying standards of sexual selection, different kinds of social barriers, mobility, and similar variables, all of which have probably played an appreciable part in the evolution of ethnic differences. These are the very kinds of factors which are most neglected by those who come to the study of man with a biologistic bias. It would for such students of man, especially those who come in from the nonhuman biological fields, as well as for the layman, be a great advantage to be required to look at the problem of human variety from the viewpoint of the "ethnic group" rather than from that of "race." Where man is concerned the biologist, like the layman, needs to add a cultural dimension to his horizons. This is what the phrase "ethnic group" will help him to do.

The conception of an "ethnic group" is quite different from that which is associated with the term "race." The phrase "ethnic group" represents a different way of looking at populations, an open, nonquestion-begging way, a tentative, noncommittal, experimental way, based on the new understanding which the sciences of genetics and anthropology have made possible. A term is discontinued, retired, but another is not merely substituted for it; rather a new conception of human populations is introduced replacing the old one, which is now dropped, and a term or phrase suitable to this new conception is suggested. The old conception is *not* retained and a new name given to it, but a new conception is introduced under its own name. That is a very different thing from a mere change in names. It is important to be quite clear upon this point, for the *new conception* embraced in the phrase "ethnic group" renders the possibility of the development of "ethnic group prejudice" quite impossible, for as soon as the nature of this conception is understood it cancels the possibility of any such development. It is a noncontaminating neutral concept.

Perhaps the greatest advantage of the phrase "ethnic group" is that it is noncommittal and somewhat flexible. It may be applied to any group concerning which physical and cultural traits are so identified that it is given a certain distinctiveness which appears to separate it from other groups. The phrase may also be used as embracing the definition of race in the biological sense, and particularly groups which are less clearly defined, which may or may not be races and hence should not be called races in the absence of the necessary scientific demonstration. All that we say when we use the phrase "ethnic group" is that here is a group of people who physically, and perhaps in other additional ways, may be regarded as a more or less distinct group. Until we know what it really is, and until we understand thoroughly what we are talking about with respect to this and all other groups, let us call all such groups "ethnic groups." In other words, the concept of "ethnic group" implies a question mark, *not* a period. It implies that many questions remain to be asked, and that many answers will have to be given before we can say precisely what any particular ethnic group represents.

To conclude and summarize: The advantages of the phrase "ethnic group" are: first, while emphasizing the fact that one is dealing with a distinguishable group, this noncommittal phrase leaves the whole question of the precise status of the group on physical and other grounds open for further discussion and research; second, it recognizes the fact that it is a group which has been subject to the action of cultural influences; and third, it eliminates all obfuscating emotional implications.

As for the suggested dropping or the restricted or suspended use of the term "race," there are many parallels for this in science. Possibly the most striking one in recent years is the dropping of the term "instinct" by psychologists for similar reasons to those which make the term "race" undesirable.[13] Similarly, in anthropology the term "savage" has been completely dropped, while the term "primitive" as referring to living peoples is largely being abandoned in favor of the term "nonliterate" for much the same reason, namely, the inaccuracy of the earlier terms, and hence their unsuitability. In biology the term "unit character" as erroneously referring to single genes as determining single characters or traits, has been for ever banished from the scientific vocabulary. Retardative concepts like "phlogiston" of eighteenth-century chemistry have been dropped never to be re-adopted. It may be that the terms "instinct" and "race" may some-day be shown to have more than a merely verbal validity, but until that time it would be more in accordance with the scientific spirit to declare a moratorium on the use of the term "race."

The phrase "ethnic group" serves as a challenge to thought and as a stimulus to rethink the foundations of one's beliefs. It encourages the passage from ignorant certainty to thoughtful uncertainty. For the layman, as for others, the term "race" closes the door on his understanding; the phrase "ethnic group" opens it.

---

[13] See Bernard, *Instinct: A Study in Social Psychology.*

APPENDIX E

The UNESCO Statements on Race

Two STATEMENTS on Race were issued by UNESCO. The first was largely the work of a group of social scientists, the second was the product of a group of physical anthropologists and geneticists. The first statement was published on 18 July 1950 under the title "The UNESCO Statement by Experts on Race Problems," and the second was published July 15, 1952 under the title "Statement on the Nature of Race and Race Differences—by Physical Anthropologists and Geneticists, September 1952." In conversation one would refer to the first as "The Statement on Race" and to the second as "Statement on the Nature of Race." As the reader will perceive, there is marked agreement between the social and the natural scientists.

Most of the members on the first committee would, I believe, now replace the term "Division" in the first Statement with the term "Major Group" from the second Statement.

UNESCO Statement on Race—By Social Scientists, July 1950

1. Scientists have reached general agreement in recognizing that mankind is one: that all men belong to the same species, *Homo sapiens*. It is further generally agreed among scientists that all men are probably derived from the same common stock; and that such differences as exist between different groups of mankind are due to the operation of evolutionary factors of differentiation such as isolation, the drift and random fixation of the material particles which control heredity (the genes), changes in the structure of these particles, hybridization, and natural selection. In these ways groups have arisen of varying stability and degree of differentiation which have been classified in different ways for different purposes.

2. From the biological standpoint, the species *Homo sapiens* is made up of a number of populations, each one of which differs from the others in the frequency of one or more genes. Such genes, responsible for the hereditary differences between men, are always few when compared to the whole genetic constitution of man and to the vast number of genes common to all human beings regardless of the

population to which they belong. This means that the likenesses among men are far greater than their differences.

3. A race, from the biological standpoint, may therefore be defined as one of the group of populations constituting the species *Homo sapiens*. These populations are capable of inter-breeding with one another but, by virtue of the isolating barriers which in the past kept them more or less separated, exhibit certain physical differences as a result of their somewhat different biological histories. These represent variations, as it were, on a common theme.

4. In short, the term "race" designates a group or population characterized by some concentrations, relative as to frequency and distribution, of hereditary particles (genes) or physical characters, which appear, fluctuate, and often disappear in the course of time by reason of geographic and/or cultural isolation. The varying manifestations of these traits in different populations are perceived in different ways by each group. What is perceived is largely preconceived, so that each group arbitrarily tends to misinterpret the variability which occurs as a fundamental difference which separates that group from all others.

5. These are the scientific facts. Unfortunately, however, when most people use the term "race" they do not do so in the sense above defined. To most people, a race is any group of people whom they choose to describe as a race. Thus, many national, religious, geographic, linguistic or cultural groups have, in such loose usage, been called a "race," when obviously Americans are not a race, nor are Englishmen, nor Frenchmen, nor any other national group. Catholics, Protestants, Moslems, and Jews are not races, nor are groups who speak English or any other language thereby definable as a race, people who live in Iceland or England or India are not races; nor are people who are culturally Turkish or Chinese, or the like thereby describable as races.

6. National, religious, geographic, linguistic and cultural groups do not necessarily coincide with racial groups; and the cultural traits of such groups have no demonstrated genetic connection with racial traits. Because serious errors of this kind are habitually committed when the term "race" is used in popular parlance, it would be better when speaking of human races to drop the term "race" altogether and speak of *ethnic groups*.

7. Now what has the scientist to say about the groups of mankind which may be recognized at the present time? Human races can be

and have been differently classified by different anthropologists, but at the present time most anthropologists agree in classifying the greater part of present-day mankind into three major divisions, as follows:

The Mongoloid Division
The Negroid Division
The Caucasoid Division

The biological processes which the classifier has here embalmed, as it were, are dynamic, not static. These divisions were not the same in the past as they are at present, and there is every reason to believe that they will change in the future.

8. Many sub-groups or ethnic groups within these divisions have been described. There is no general agreement upon their number, and in any event most ethnic groups have not yet been either studied or described by the physical anthropologists.

9. Whatever classification the anthropologist makes of man, he never includes mental characteristics as part of those classifications. It is now generally recognized that intelligence tests do not in themselves enable us to differentiate safely between what is due to innate capacity and what is the result of environmental influences, training and education. Wherever it has been possible to make allowances for differences in environmental opportunities, the tests have shown essential similarity in mental characters among all human groups. In short, given similar degrees of cultural opportunity to realize their potentialities, the average achievement of the members of each ethnic group is about the same. The scientific investigations of recent years fully support the dictum of Confucius (551-478 B.C.) "Men's natures are alike; it is their habits that carry them far apart."

10. The scientific material available to us at present does not justify the conclusion that inherited genetic differences are a major factor in producing the differences between the cultures and cultural achievements of different peoples or groups. It does indicate, however, that the history of the cultural experience which each group has undergone is the major factor in explaining such differences. The one trait which above all others has been at a premium in the evolution of men's mental characters has been educability, plasticity. This is a trait which all human beings possess. It is indeed, a species character of *Homo sapiens*.

11. So far as temperament is concerned, there is no definite evidence that there exist inborn differences between human groups. There is evidence that whatever group differences of the kind there might

be are greatly over-ridden by the individual differences, and by the differences springing from environmental factors.

12. As for personality and character, these may be considered raceless. In every human group a rich variety of personality and character types will be found, and there is no reason for believing that any human group is richer than any other in these respects.

13. With respect to race-mixture, the evidence points unequivocally to the fact that this has been going on from the earliest times. Indeed, one of the chief processes of race-formation and race-extinction or absorption is by means of hybridization between races or ethnic groups. Furthermore, no convincing evidence has been adduced that race-mixture of itself produces biologically bad effects. Statements that human hybrids frequently show undesirable traits, both physically and mentally, physical disharmonies and mental degeneracies, are not supported by the facts. There is, therefore, no *biological* justification for prohibiting intermarriage between persons of different ethnic groups.

14. The biological fact of race and the myth of "race" should be distinguished, for all practical social purposes "race" is not so much a biological phenomenon as a social myth. The myth of "race" has created an enormous amount of human and social damage. In recent years it has taken a heavy toll in human lives and caused untold suffering. It still prevents the normal development of millions of human beings and deprives civilization of the effective co-operation of productive minds. The biological differences between ethnic groups should be disregarded from the standpoint of social acceptance and social action. The unity of mankind from both the biological and social viewpoints is the main thing. To recognize this and to act accordingly is the first requirement of modern man. It is but to recognize what a great biologist wrote in 1875: "As man advances in civilization, and small tribes are united into larger communities, the simplest reason would tell each individual that he ought to extend his social instincts and sympathies to all the members of the same nation, though personally unknown to him. This point being once reached, there is only an artificial barrier to prevent his sympathies extending to the men of all nations and races." These are the words of Charles Darwin in *The Descent of Man* (2nd ed., 1875, pp. 187-188). And, indeed, the whole of human history shows that a co-operative spirit is not only natural to men, but more deeply rooted than any self-seeking tendencies. If this were not so we should not see the growth of integration and organization of his communities which the centuries and the millennia plainly exhibit.

15. We now have to consider the bearing of these statements on the problem of human equality. It must be asserted with the utmost emphasis that equality as an ethical principle in no way depends upon the assertion that human beings are in fact equal in endowment. Obviously individuals in all ethnic groups vary greatly among themselves in endowment. Nevertheless, the characteristics in which human groups differ from one another are often exaggerated and used as a basis for questioning the validity of equality in the ethical sense. For this purpose we have thought it worth while to set out in a formal manner what is at present scientifically established concerning individual and group differences.

(1) In matters of race, the only characteristics which anthropologists can effectively use as a basis for classifications are physical and physiological.

(2) According to present knowledge there is no proof that the groups of mankind differ in their innate mental characteristics, whether in respect to intelligence or temperament. The scientific evidence indicates that the range of mental capacities in all ethnic groups is much the same.

(3) Historical and sociological studies support the view that genetic differences are not of importance in determining the social and cultural differences between different groups of *Homo sapiens,* and that the social and cultural *changes* in different groups have, in the main, been independent of *changes* in inborn constitution. Vast social changes have occurred which were not in any way connected with changes in racial type.

(4) There is no evidence that race mixture as such produces bad results from the biological point of view. The social results of race mixture whether for good or ill are to be traced to social factors.

(5) All normal human beings are capable of learning to share in a common life, to understand the nature of mutual service and reciprocity, and to respect social obligations and contracts. Such biological differences as exist between members of different ethnic groups have no relevance to problems of social and political organization, moral life and communication between human beings.

Lastly, biological studies lend support to the ethic of universal brotherhood; for man is born with drives toward co-operation, and unless those drives are satisfied, men and nations alike fall ill. Man is born a social being who can reach his fullest development only through interaction with his fellows. The denial at any point of this social bond between men and man brings with it disintegration.

In this sense, every man is his brother's keeper. For every man is a piece of the continent, a part of the main, because he is involved in mankind.

Original statement drafted at Unesco House, Paris, by the following experts:

> Professor Ernest Beaglehole, *New Zealand*.
> Professor Juan Comas, *Mexico*.
> Professor L. A. Costa Pinto, *Brazil*.
> Professor Franklin Frazier, *United States*.
> Professor Morris Ginsberg, *United Kingdom*.
> Dr. Humayun Kabir, *India*.
> Professor Claude Levi-Strauss, *France*.
> Professor Ashley Montagu, *United States* (Rapporteur).

Text revised by Professor Ashley Montagu, after criticisms submitted by Professors Hadley Cantril, E. G. Conklin, Gunnar Dahlberg, Theodosius Dobzhansky, L. C. Dunn, Donald Hager, Julian S. Huxley, Otto Klineberg, Wilbert Moore, H. J. Muller, Gunnar Myrdal, Joseph Needham.

Statement on the Nature of Race and Race Differences by Physical Anthropologists and Geneticists September 1952

1. Scientists are generally agreed that all men living today belong to a single species, *Homo sapiens,* and are derived from a common stock, even though there is some dispute as to when and how different human groups diverged from this common stock.

The concept of race is unanimously regarded by anthropologists as a classificatory device providing a zoological frame within which the various groups of mankind may be arranged and by means of which studies of evolutionary processes can be facilitated. In its anthropological sense, the word "race" should be reserved for groups of mankind possessing well-developed and primarily heritable physical differences from other groups. Many populations can be so classified but, because of the complexity of human history, there are also many populations which cannot easily be fitted into a racial classification.

2. Some of the physical differences between human groups are due to differences in hereditary constitution and some to differences in the environments in which they have been brought up. In most cases, both influences have been at work. The science of genetics suggests that the hereditary differences among populations of a single

species are the results of the action of two sets of processes. On the one hand, the genetic composition of isolated populations is constantly but gradually being altered by natural selection and by occasional changes (mutations) in the material particles (genes) which control heredity. Populations are also affected by fortuitous changes in gene frequency and by marriage customs. On the other hand, crossing is constantly breaking down the differentiations so set up. The new mixed populations, in so far as they, in turn, become isolated, are subject to the same processes, and these may lead to further changes. Existing races are merely the result, considered at a particular moment in time, of the total effect of such processes on the human species. The hereditary characters to be used in the classification of human groups, the limits of their variation within these groups, and thus the extent of the classificatory sub-divisions adopted may legitimately differ according to the scientific purpose in view.

3. National, religious, geographical, linguistic and cultural groups do not necessarily coincide with racial groups; and the cultural traits of such groups have no demonstrated connection with racial traits. Americans are not a race, nor are Frenchmen, nor Germans; nor *ipso facto* is any other national group. Moslems and Jews are no more races than are Roman Catholics and Protestants; nor are people who live in Iceland or Britain or India, or who speak English or any other language, or who are culturally Turkish or Chinese and the like, thereby describable as races. The use of the term "race" in speaking of such groups may be a serious error, but is one which is habitually committed.

4. Human races can be, and have been classified in different ways by different anthropologists. Most of them agree in classifying the greater part of existing mankind into at least three large units, which may be called major groups (in French *grand races,* in German *Hauptrassen*). Such a classification does not depend on any single physical character, nor does, for example, skin colour by itself necessarily distinguish one major group from another. Furthermore, so far as it has been possible to analyze them, the differences in physical structure which distinguish one major group from another give no support to popular notions of any general "superiority" or "inferiority" which are sometimes implied in referring to these groups.

Broadly speaking, individuals belonging to different major groups of mankind are distinguishable by virtue of their physical characters, but individual members, or small groups, belonging to different races within the same major group are usually not so distinguishable. Even the major groups grade into each other, and the physical traits by which they and the races within them are characterized overlap considerably. With respect to most, if not all, measurable characters, the differences among individuals belonging to the same race are greater than the differences that occur between the observed averages for two or more races within the same major group.

5. Most anthropologists do not include mental characteristics in their classification of human races. Studies within a single race have shown that both innate capacity and environmental opportunity determine the results of tests of intelligence and temperament, though their relative importance is disputed.

When intelligence tests, even non-verbal, are made on a group of non-literate people, their scores are usually lower than those of more civilized people. It has been recorded that different groups of the same race occupying similarly high levels of civilization may yield considerable differences in intelligence tests. When, however, the two groups have been brought up from childhood in similar environments, the differences are usually very slight. Moreover, there is good evidence that, given similar opportunities, the average performance (that is to say, the performance of the individual who is representative because he is surpassed by as many as he surpasses), and the variation round it, do not differ appreciably from one race to another.

Even those psychologists who claim to have found the greatest differences in intelligence between groups of different racial origin, and have contended that they are hereditary, always report that some members of the group of inferior performance surpass not merely the lowest ranking member of the superior group, but also the average of its members. In any case, it has never been possible to separate members of two groups on the basis of mental capacity, as they can often be separated on a basis of religion, skin colour, hair form or language. It is possible, though not proved, that some types of innate capacity for intellectual and emotional responses are commoner in one human group than in another, but it is certain that, within a single group, innate capacities vary as much as, if not more than, they do between different groups.

The study of the heredity of psychological characteristics is beset with difficulties. We know that certain mental diseases and defects are transmitted from one generation to the next, but we are less familiar with the part played by heredity in the mental life of normal individuals. The normal individual, irrespective of race, is essentially educable. It follows that his intellectual and moral life is largely conditioned by his training and by his physical and social environment.

It often happens that a national group may appear to be characterized by particular psychological attributes. The superficial view would be that this is due to race. Scientifically, however, we realize that any common psychological attribute is more likely to be due to a common historical and social background, and that such attributes may obscure the fact that, within different populations consisting of many human types, one will find approximately the same range of temperament and intelligence.

6. The scientific material available to us at present does not justify the conclusion that inherited genetic differences are a major factor in producing the differences between the cultures and cultural achievements of different peoples or groups. It does indicate, on the contrary, that a major factor in explaining such differences is the cultural experience which each group has undergone.

7. There is no evidence for the existence of so-called "pure" races. Skeletal remains provide the basis of our limited knowledge about earlier races. In regard to race mixture, the evidence points to the fact that human hybridization has been going on for an indefinite but considerable time. Indeed, one of the processes of race formation and race extinction or absorption is by means of hybridization between races. As there is no reliable evidence that disadvantageous effects are produced thereby, no biological justification exists for prohibiting intermarriage between persons of different races.

8. We now have to consider the bearing of these statements on the problem of human equality. We wish to emphasize that equality of opportunity and equality in law in no way depend, as ethical principles, upon the assertion that human beings are in fact equal in endowment.

9. We have thought it worth while to set out in a formal manner what is at present scientifically established concerning individual and group differences.

(1) In matters of race, the only characteristics which anthropologists have so far been able to use effectively as a basis for classification are physical (anatomical and physiological).

(2) Available scientific knowledge provides no basis for believing that the groups of mankind differ in their innate capacity for intellectual and emotional development.

(3) Some biological differences between human beings within a single race may be as great or greater than the same biological differences between races.

(4) Vast social changes have occurred that have not been connected in any way with changes in racial type. Historical and sociological studies thus support the view that genetic differences are of little significance in determining the social and cultural differences between different groups of men.

(5) There is no evidence that race mixture produces disadvantageous results from a biological point of view. The social results of race mixture whether for good or ill, can generally be traced to social factors.

(Text drafted, at Unesco House, Paris, on June 8, 1951, by: Professor R. A. M. Bergman, Royal Tropical Institute, Netherlands Anthropological Society, Amsterdam; Professor Gunnar Dahlberg, Director, State Institute for Human Genetics and Race Biology, University of Uppsala; Professor L. C. Dunn, Department of Zoology, Columbia University, New York; Professor J. B. S. Haldane, Head, Department of Biometry, University College, London; Professor M. F. Ashley Montagu, Chairman, Department of Anthropology, Rutgers University, New Brunswick, N.J.; Dr. A. E. Mourant, Director, Blood Group Reference Laboratory, Lister Institute, London; Professor Hans Nachtsheim, Director, Institut für Genetik, Freie Universität, Berlin; Dr. Eugène Schreider, Directeur adjoint du Laboratoire d'Anthropologie Physique de l'Ecole des Hautes Etudes, Paris; Professor Harry L. Shapiro, Chairman, Department of Anthropology, American Museum of Natural History, New York; Dr. J. C. Trevor, Faculty of Archaeology and Anthropology, University of Cambridge; Dr. Henri V. Vallois, Professeur au Museum d'Histoire Naturelle, Directeur du Musée, de l'Homme, Paris; Professor S. Zuckerman, Head, Department of Anatomy, Medical School, University of Birmingham. Professor Th. Dobzhansky, Department of Zoology, Columbia University, New York, and Dr. Julian Huxley contributed to the final wording.)

BIBLIOGRAPHY

ABBIE, A. A.: A new approach to the problem of human evolution. *Trans. Roy. Soc. S. Australia*, 75:70-88, 1952.

A new outlook on physical anthropology. *N.Z. Assoc. Adv. Sci.*, 28:52-63, 1951.

————: The Australian aborigine. *Oceania*, 22:91-100, 1951.

————: The original Australians. *The Leech*, 28:120-130, 1958.

————: Timing in human evolution. *Proc. Linn. Soc. New S. Wales*, 83:197-213, 1958.

ALIMEN, H.: *The Prehistory of Africa*. London, Hutchinson, 1959.

ALLEE, WARDER C.: Biology and international relations. *The New Republic*, 112:816-817, 1945.

————: *Cooperation Among Animals*. New York, Schuman, 1951.

————: Where angels fear to tread. A contribution from General Sociology to Human Ethics. *Science*, 97:518-525, 1943.

————: *Animal Aggregations*. Chicago, Univ. Chicago Press, 1931.

————, PARK, O., EMERSON, A. E., PARK, T. and SCHMIDT, K. P.: *Principles of Animal Ecology*. Philadelphia, Saunders, 1949.

ALLEN, F.: Inheritance of the Diego (Di^a) blood group factor. *Am. J. Hum. Genetics*, 10:64-67, 1958.

ALLISON, A. C.: Protection afforded by the sickle-cell trait against subtertian malarial infection. *Brit. M. J.*, I:290-294, 1954.

———— and NEVANLINNA, H. R.: Taste deficiency in Lappish and Finnish populations. *Ann. Eug.*, 17:113-114, 1952.

ALLISON, A. C., BLUMBERG, B. S. and W. A. REES: Haptoglobin types in British, Spanish Basque and Nigerian African populations. *Nature*, 181:824, 1958.

ANDREWARTHA, H. G. and BIRCH, L. C.: *The Distribution and Abundance of Animals*. Univ. Chicago Press, 1954.

ANGEL, J. L.: Constitution in female obesity. *Am. J. Phys. Anthropol.*, n.s. 7:433-471, 1949.

ARAMBOURG, C.: A recent discovery in human paleontology: Atlanthropus of Ternifine (Algeria). *Am. J. Phys. Anthropol.*, n.s. 13:191-201, 1955.

———— and BIBERSON, P.: The fossil human remains from the paleolithic of Sidi Abderrahman (Morocco). *Am. J. Phys. Anthropol.*, n.s. 14:467-489, 1956.

ARKIN, H. and COLTON, R. R.: Statistical Methods, 4th edition. New York, Barnes & Noble, 1956.

BARNES, H. E. and TEETERS, N. K.: *New Horizons in Criminology*. New York, Prentice-Hall, 1943.

BARNICOT, N. A.: Taste deficiency for phenythiourea in African Negroes and Chinese. *Ann. Eug.*, 15:248-254, 1950.

————: Human Pigmentation. *Man*, No. 144, 1957, 1-7.

————: Genetics and human races. *The New Scientist*, January 8, 1959.

BARTH, F.: On the relationships of early primates. *Am. J. Phys. Anthropol.*, n.s. 8:139-149, 1950.

BARTHOLOMEW, G. A. and BIRDSELL, J. B.: Ecology and the protohominids. *Am. Anthropol.*, 55:481-498, 1953.

BATTAGLIA, R.: Osso occipitale umano rinvenuto nel giacimento pleistocenico di Quinzano nel Comune di Verona. *Palaeontographica Italica*, 42:1-31, 1948.

BENDER, M. A., and METTLER, L. E.: Chromosome studies on primates. *Science*, 128:186-190, 1958.

BENDYSHE, T: The history of anthropology. *Mem. Anthropol. Soc. London*, 1:335, 1863; 1864.

BENEDICT, R.: *Race: Science and Politics*. New York, Viking Press, 1959.

BERRILL, N. J.: *Man's Emerging Mind*. New York, Dodd Mead, 1955.

BEWS, J. W.: *Human Ecology*. New York, Oxford, 1935.

BINGHAM, H. C.: *Gorillas in a Native Habitat*. Washington, D.C., Carnegie Inst., Pub. No. 426, 1932.

BIRD, G. W. G., et al.: The blood groups and hemoglobin of the Ghorkhas of Nepal. *Am. J. Phys. Anthropol.*, n.s. 15:163-169, 1957.

BIRD, J.: Antiquity and migrations of the early inhabitants of Patagonia. *Geographical Rev.*, 28:250-275, 1938.

————: Before Magellan. *Natur. Hist.*, 41:16-28, 1938.

BIRDSELL, J. B.: Some environmental and cultural factors influencing the structuring of Australian aboriginal populations. *Am. Naturalist*, 87:171-207, 1953.

————: Some population problems involving Pleistocene man. *Cold Spring Harbor Symposia on Quantitative Biology*, 22:47-69, 1957.

BIRKET-SMITH, K.: *The Eskimos*, 2nd ed. London, Methuen, 1959.

BISSONNETTE, T. H.: Sexual photoperiodism. *Quart. Rev. Biol.*, 11:371-386, 1936.

BLACK, D.: Asia and the dispersal of the primates. *Bull. Geol. Soc. Am.*, 4: 1925.

BLUM, H. H.: *Photodynamic Action and Diseases Caused by Light*. New York, Reinhold, 1941.

BLUMENBACH, J. F.: *On the Natural Variety of Mankind* (translated by Bendyshe, T.), *The Anthropological Treatises of Johann Friedrich Blumenbach*. London, Anthropological Society, 1865.

BOAS, F.: *Changes in Bodily Form of Descendants of Immigrants*. (*Final Report.*) Washington, Government Printing Office, 1911 (61st Congress, 2nd Session, Senate Document 208), Reprinted, New York, Columbia Univ. Press, 1912.

————: *Anthropology and Modern Life*, 2nd ed. New York, Norton, 1932.

————: *The Mind of Primitive Man*, 2nd ed. New York, Macmillan, 1938.

————: Racial purity. *Asia*, 40:231-234, 1940.

————: *Race, Language, and Culture*. New York, Macmillan, 1940.

————: *Race and Democratic Society*. New York, Augustin, 1945.

BOETTGER, C. R.: *Die Haustiere Afrikas*. Jena, Fischer, 1958.

BOLK, L.: *Das Problem der Menschwerdung*. Jena, Fischer, 1926.

————: Origin of racial characteristics in man. *Amer. J. Phys. Anthropol.*, 13: 1-28, 1929.

BONIN, G. VON: On the size of man's brain, as indicated by skull capacity. *J. Comp. Neurol.*, 59:1-28, 1934.

BOULE, M. and VALLOIS, H. V.: *Fossil Man*. New York, Dryden Press, 1957.

BOULENGER, E. G.: *Apes and Monkeys*. London, Harrap, 1936.

BOYD, W. C.: Blood groups. *Tabulae Biologicae,* 17:111-240, 1939.

———: Rh blood factors; an orientation review. *Arch. Path.,* 40:114-127, 1945.

———: Critique of methods of classifying mankind. *Am. J. Phys. Anthropol.,* 27:333-364, 1940.

———: Gene frequencies and race mixture. *Am. J. Phys. Anthropol.,* n.s. 7:587-593, 1949.

———: *Genetics and the Races of Man.* Boston, Little, Brown, 1950.

———: *Genetics and the Races of Man.* Boston, Boston Univ. Press, 1958.

———: Has statistics retarded the progress of physical anthropology? *Am. J. Phys. Anthropol.,* n.s. 16:481-484, 1959.

BRAIDWOOD, R. J.: *Prehistoric Men,* 3rd Ed. Chicago, Chicago Natural History Museum, 1957, Popular Series, No. 37.

———: Near Eastern Prehistory. *Science,* 127:1419-1430, 1958.

———, and REED, C. E.: The achievement and early consequences of food production: a consideration of the archaeological and Natural-Historical Evidence. *Cold Spring Harbor Symposia on Quantitative Biology,* 22:19-31, 1957.

BRANSBY, E. R. and GELLING, J. W.: Variations in and the effect of weather on the growth of children. *Medical Officer,* 75:213-217, 1946.

BRASH, J. C., McKEAG, H. T. A. and SCOTT, J. H.: *The Aetiology of Irregularity and Malocclusion of the Teeth,* 2nd Ed. London, Dental Board of the United Kingdom, 1956.

BREUIL, H. and LANTIER, R.: *Les Hommes De La Pierre Ancienne (Paléolithique et Mésolithique).* Paris, 1959.

BRIGGS, L. C.: The Stone Age Races of North Africa. American School of Prehistoric Research, Peabody Museum, Harvard University, Bulletin No. 18, Cambridge, Mass., 1955.

———: The Living Races of the Sahara Desert. *Papers of the Peabody Museum of Archaeology and Ethnology, Harvard University,* 28:xii+217, 1958.

BROOM, R.: *Finding the Missing Link.* London, Watts, 1950.

———: The genera and species of the South African fossil ape-men. *Am. J. Phys. Anthropol.,* n.s. 8:1-13, 1950.

——— and ROBINSON, J. T.: *Swartkrans Ape-Man: Paranthropus crassidens.* Pretoria, Transvaal Museum Memoir No. 6, 1952.

——— and SCHEPERS, G. W. H.: *The South African Fossil Ape-Men.* Pretoria, Transvaal Museum Memoir No. 2, 1946.

——— and ROBINSON, J. T. and SCHEPERS, G. W. H.: *Sterkfontein Ape-Men: Plesianthropus.* Pretoria, Transvall Museum Memoir No. 4, 1950.

BROWN, F. M.: The microscopy of mammalian hair for anthropologists. *Proc. Amer. Phil. Soc.,* 85:250-274, 1942.

BRUES, A. M.: Identification of skeletal remains. *J. Crim. Law Criminol. & Police Science,* 48:551-563, 1958.

———: Regional differences in the physical characteristics of an American population. *Am. J. Phys. Anthropol.,* n.s. 4:463-482, 1946.

BRZEZINSKI, J., GUREVITCH, J., HERMONI, D. and MANDEL, G.: Bloodgroups in Jews from Yemen. *Ann. Eugenics,* 16:331-33, 1951.

BUDTZ-OLSEN, O. E.: Haptoglobins and hemoglobins in Australian aborigines, with a simple method for the estimation of haptoglobins. *Med. J. Australia,* pp. 689-692, Nov. 22, 1958.

BUETTNER-JANUSCH, J.: Natural selection in man: The ABO(H) blood group system. *Am. Anthropol.*, 61:437-456, 1959.

BULLEN, A. K. (editor): Development of high civilizations in hot climates. *Florida Anthropologist*, 4:101-149, 1953.

CAIN, A. J.: Possible significance of secretor. *The Lancet*, 1:212-213, 1957.

CALHOUN, J. B.: The social aspects of population dynamics. *J. Mammal.*, 33:139-159, 1952.

CALMAN, W. T.: *The Classification of Animals.* New York, Wiley, 1949.

CANDELA, P. B.: The introduction of blood-group B into Europe. *Human Biol.*, 14:413-443, 1942.

—— and Goss, L. J.: Blood-group factors in the blood organs, and secretions of primates. *J. Immunol.*, 45:229-235, 1942.

CARPENTER, C. R.: A field study of the behavior and social relations of howling monkeys. *Compt. Psychol. Monogr.*, 10:1-167, 1934, Serial no. 48.

——: A field study in Siam of the behavior and social relations of the gibbon (*Hylobates lar*). *Compt. Psychol. Monogr.*, 16:1-212, 1940, Serial no. 84.

CARTER, G. F.: *Pleistocene Man at San Diego.* Baltimore, Johns Hopkins Press, 1957.

CASSIRER, E.: *An Essay on Man.* New Haven, Yale University Press, 1944.

CASSON, S.: *The Discovery of Man.* New York, Harper, 1940.

CASTLE, W. E.: Biological and social consequences of race crossing. *Am. J. Phys. Anthropol.*, 9:145-156, 1926.

——: Race mixture and physical disharmonies. *Science*, 71:603-606, 1930.

CATTELL, R. B. and MOLTENO, V.: Contributions concerning mental inheritance. II. Temperament. *J. Genet. Psychol.*, 57:31-42, 1940.

CAVE, A. J. E.: Report on a human calvaria of upper paleolithic type. *Archaeologia*, 92:117-119, 1947.

CAWLEY, R. H., McKEOWN, T. and RECORD, R. G.: Influence of pre-natal environment on post-natal growth. *Br. J. Prev. Soc. Med.*, 8:66-69, 1954.

CAZIER, M. A. and BACON, A. L.: Introduction to quantitative systematics. *Bull. Amer. Mus. Nat. Hist.*, 93:347-388, 1949.

CEPPELINI, R.: The usefulness of blood factors in racial anthropology. *Am. J. Phys. Anthropol.*, 13:389, 1955.

CHALMERS, J. N. M., IKIN, E. W. and A. E. MOURANT: The ABO, MN and Rh blood groups of the Basque people. *Am. J. Phys. Anthropol.*, n.s., 7:529-544, 1949.

—— and LAWLER, S. D.: Data on linkage in man: elliptocytosis and blood groups. II. Families 1 and 2, *Ann. Eugenics*, 17:267-271, 1953.

CHAMBERS, E. G.: *Statistical Calculation for Beginners.* New York: Cambridge University Press, 1948.

CHARD, C. S.: New World migration routes. Anthrop. Papers Univ. Alaska, 1:23-26, 1959.

CHILDE, V. G.: *Man Makes Himself.* New York, New American Library, 1946.

——: *What Happened in History.* New York, New American Library, 1946.

——: *The Dawn of European Civilization,* 6th ed. New York, Knopf, 1958.

——: *A Short Introduction to Archaeology.* London, Muller, 1956.

CHOWN, B.: Problems in blood group analysis. *Am. Anthropol.*, 59:885-888, 1957.

CHU, E. H. Y. and GILES, N. H.: A study of primate chromosome complements. *Amer. Nat.*, 91:273-282, 1957.

————: Human chromosome complements in normal somatic cells in culture. *Am. J. Hum. Genetics*, 11:63-79, 1958.

CLARK, J. D.: *The Prehistory of Southern Africa.* New York, Harper, 1959.

————, OAKLEY, K. P., WELLS, L. H. and McCLELLAND: New studies on Rhodesian man. *J. Roy. Anthropol. Inst.*, 77:7-32, 1947.

CLARK, J. G. D.: *Prehistoric Europe.* London, Methuen, New York, Philosophical Library, 1952.

————: *Excavations at Starr Carr.* Cambridge: at the University Press, New York, Cambridge Univ. Press, 1954.

————: *Archaeology and Society.* Cambridge, Mass., Harvard Univ. Press, 1957.

CLARK, W. E. LE GROS: *Early Forerunners of Man.* Baltimore, Wood, 1934.

————: Pithecanthropus in Peking. *Antiquity,* 19:1-5, 1945.

————: *History of Primates,* 6th ed. London, British Museum (Natural History), 1958.

————: New palaeontological evidence bearing on the evolution of the Hominoidea. *Quart. J. Geol. Soc.,* (London), 105:225-264, 1949.

————: *The Fossil Evidence for Human Evolution.* Chicago, Univ. Chicago Press, 1955.

————: Bones of contention. *J. Roy. Anthropol. Inst.,* 88:1-15, 1958.

————: *The Antecedents of Man.* Edinburgh, University of Edinburgh Press, 1959.

CLARKE, C. A., *et al.*: ABO groups and secretor character in duodenal ulcer. Population and sibship studies. *Brit. Med. J.,* 2:725-731, 1956.

CLARKE, C. A., *et al.*: Secretion of blood group antigens and peptic ulcer. *Brit. Med. J.,* 1:603-607, 1959.

COBB, W. M.: The physical constitution of the American Negro. *J. Negro Education,* 3:340-388, 1934.

COLBERT, E. A.: Some paleontological principles significant in human evolution. In *Early Man in the Far East* (edited by W. W. Howells), p. 103-147.

————: *Evolution of the Vertebrates.* New York, Wiley, 1955.

COLE, S.: *The Prehistory of East Africa.* Baltimore, Penguin Books, 1954.

COLIN, E. C.: *Elements of Genetics,* 3rd ed. New York, McGraw-Hill, 1956.

COLLIER, K. G.: *The Science of Humanity.* New York, Nelson, 1950.

COMAS, J.: *Manual of Physical Anthropology.* Springfield, Ill., C C Thomas, 1960.

CONKLIN, E. G.: *Heredity and Environment.* Princeton Univ. Press, 1939.

————: *Man: Real and Ideal.* New York, Scribner's, 1943.

COOKE, H. B. S., MALAN, B. D., and WELLS, L. H.: Fossil man in the Lebombo Mountains, South Africa: The 'Border Cave.' *Man,* 45:6-13, 1945.

COON, C. S.: *The Races of Europe.* New York, Macmillan, 1939.

————: *The Story of Man.* New York, Knopf, 1954.

————: Some problems of human variability and natural selection in climate and culture. *Amer. Nat.,* 89:257-280, 1955.

————: *The Seven Caves.* New York, Knopf, 1957.

————: Climate and race. In Harlow Shapley (editor): *Climatic Change.* Harvard Univ. Press, 1954, 13-34.

————, GARN, S. M., and BIRDSELL, J. B.: *Races.* Springfield, Thomas, 1950.

CORNER, G. W.: *Ourselves Unborn.* New Haven, Yale Univ. Press, 1944.

CORNWALL, I. W.: *Bones for the Archaeologist.* New York, Macmillan, 1956.

————: *Soils for the Archaeologist.* New York, Macmillan, 1958.

COWLES, R. B.: The black skin and human protective coloration. *J. Entomol. & Zoology*, 42:1-4, 1950.

CRAVEN, B. and JOKL, E.: A note on the effect of training on the physique of adolescent boys. *Clin. Proc. J. Cape Town Post-Graduate Med. A.*, 5:18-19, 1946.

CRICK, F. H. C.: Nucleic acids. *Scientific Amer.*, 197:188-200, 1958.

CUDMORE, S. A. and NEAL, N. A.: *A Height and Weight Survey of Toronto Elementary School Children 1939.* Ottawa, Ministry of Trade and Commerce, 1942.

CUENOT, L.: L'homme ce néoténique. *Bull. L'Acad. Roy. Belg.*, 31: 1945.

————: *L'Evolution Biologique.* Paris, Masson, 1951.

CUMMINS, H. and MIDLO, C.: *Finger Prints, Palms and Soles: An Introduction to Dermatoglyphics.* Philadelphia, Blakiston, 1943.

DAHLBERG, G.: An analysis of the conception of race and a new method of distinguishing races. *Human Biol.*, 14:372-385, 1942.

————: *Race, Reason and Rubbish: a Primer of Race Biology.* New York, Columbia Univ. Press, 1942.

————: Environment, inheritance and random variations with special reference to investigations on twins. *Acta Genet. et Statistica Medica, Basle*, 1: 1; 104-114, 1948.

————: *Statistical Methods for Medical and Biological Students.* New York, Norton, 1948.

DANSEREAU, P.: *A Universal System for Recording Vegetation.* Institut Botanique de L'Université de Montréal, Montreal, 1958.

DARLINGTON, C. D. and HAQUE, A.: Chromosomes of monkeys and men, *Nature*, 175:32, 1955.

————: The origin of Darwinism. *Scientific Amer.*, 200:60-66, 1959.

DART, R. A.: Taungs and its significance. *Natural History*, 26:315-327, 1926.

————: The Makapansgat proto-human Australopithecus prometheus. *Am. J. Phys. Anthropol.*, n.s. 6:391-411, 1948.

————: The predatory implemental technique of Australopithecus. *Am. J. Phys. Anthropol.*, n.s. 7:1-38, 1949.

————: Innominate fragments of Australopithecus prometheus. *Am. J. Phys. Anthropol.*, n.s. 7:301-333, 1949.

————: A second adult palate of Australopithecus prometheus. *Am. J. Phys. Anthropol.*, n.s. 7:335-338, 1949.

————: The cranio-facial fragment of Australopithecus prometheus. *Am. J. Phys. Anthropol.*, n.s. 7:187-214, 1949.

————: The second, or adult, female mandible of Australopithecus prometheus. *Am. J. Phys. Anthropol.*, n.s. 12:313-344, 1954.

————: The first Australopithecine fragment from the Makapansgat pebble culture stratum. *Nature*, 176:170, 1955.

————: The minimal bone-breccia content of Makapansgat and the australopithecine habit. *Am. Anthropol.*, 60:923-931, 1958.

————: An 'Australopithecine' scoop from Herefordshire. *Nature*, 183:844, 1959.

————: A further adolescent australopithecine ilium from Makapansgat. *Am. J. Phys. Anthropol.*, n.s., 16:473-479, 1959.

———— and CRAIG, D.: *Adventures with the Missing Link.* New York, Harper, 1959.

DAS, S. R.: A contribution to the heredity of the P.T.C. taste character based on a study of 845 sib pairs. *Ann. Hum. Genetics, 20*:334-343, 1956.

DARWIN, C.: *The Descent of Man.* London, Murray, 1871.

————: *The Origin of Species.* London, Murray, 1859.

DAVENPORT, C.: Heredity of hair form in man. *Am. Naturalist, 42*:341, 1908.

————: *The Heredity of Skin Color in Negro-White Crosses.* Washington, Carnegie Inst., 1913, publication 188.

————: *Guide to Physical Anthropometry and Anthroposcopy.* Cold Spring Harbor, New York, Eugenics Research Association, 1927.

———— and STEGGERDA, M.: *Race Crossing in Jamaica.* Washington, Carnegie Inst., 1929.

DAVIS, A.: The distribution of the blood-groups and its bearing on the concept of race. In *Political Arithmetic* (edited by Hogben, L.), New York, Macmillan, 1941.

DAY, C. B.: *A Study of Some Negro-White Families in the United States.* Cambridge, Peabody Museum, Harvard University, 1932.

DE BEER, G.: *Embryos and Ancestors.* New York, Oxford Univ. Press, 1958.

DE CHARDIN, T.: *The Phenomenon of Man.* New York, Harper, 1959.

DE LAET, S. J.: *Archaeology and its Problems.* New York, Macmillan, 1957.

DE RODRÍGUEZ, M. L. G., and ARENDS, T.: Distribution of haptoglobins in native Venezuelans. *Nature, 183*:1465-1466, 1959.

DE TERRA, H.: Geology and climate as factors of human evolution in Asia. In *Early Man in the Far East* (edited by W. W. Howells), p. 7-15, Philadelphia, The Wistar Institute, 1949.

————: New approach to the problem of man's origin. *Science, 124*:1282-1285, 1956.

————, ROMERO, J. and STEWART, T. D.: *Tepexpan Man. Viking Fund Publications in Anthropology,* No. 11. New York, Viking Fund, 1949.

DE VRIES, H., and OAKLEY, K. P.: Radiocarbon dating of the Piltdown skull and jaw. *Nature, 184*:224-226, 1959.

DHYRENFURTH, N. G.: Film making for scientific field workers. *Amer. Anthropol., 54*:147-152, 1952.

DICE, L. R.: *Man's Nature and Nature's Man.* Ann Arbor, Univ. Michigan Press, 1955.

DINGWALL, E. J.: *Artificial Cranial Deformation.* London, John Bale, 1931.

DOBZHANSKY, TH.: *Genetics and the Origin of Species,* 3rd edition. New York, Columbia Univ. Press, 1951.

————: On species and races of living and fossil man. *Am. J. Phys. Anthropol.,* n.s. 2. 251-265, 1944.

————: Genetics and human affairs. *The Teaching Biologist, 12*:97-106, 1943.

————: The genetic basis of evolution. *Scientific American, 182*:32-41.

————: Human diversity and adaptation. In *Cold Spring Harbor Symposia on Quantitative Biology.* Long Island, New York, 1950, pp. 385-400.

————: *Evolution, Genetics, and Man.* New York, Wiley, 1957.

————: *The Biological Basis of Human Freedom.* New York, Columbia Univ. Press, 1956.

———— and HOLZ, A. M.: A re-examination of the problem of manifold effects of genes in *Drosophila melanogaster. Genetics, 28*:301, 1943.

—— and MONTAGU, M. F. ASHLEY: Natural selection and the mental capacities of mankind. *Science*, 105:587-590, 1947.

—— and WALLACE, B.: The problem of adaptive differences in human populations. *Amer. J. Hum. Genetics*, 6:199-206, 1954.

DORNFELDT, W.: Studien uber Schädelform und Schädelveränderung von Berliner Ostjuden und ihren Kindern. *Ztschr. Morphol. u. Anthropol.*, 39:290-372, 1941.

DRAPER, G., DUPERTUIS, C. W. and CAUGHEY, J. L., JR.: *Human Constitution and Clinical Medicine*. New York, Hoeber, 1944.

DRENNAN, M. R.: A note on the morphological status of the Swanscombe and Fontéchevade skulls. *Am. J. Phys. Anthropol.*, n.s. 14:73-83, 1956.

——: The special features and status of the Saldanha skull. *Am. J. Anthropol.*, n.s. 13:625-634, 1955.

——: Pedomorphism in the pre-Bushman skull. *Am. J. Phys. Anthropol.*, 16:203-210, 1931.

——: The role of sex in human evolution. *S. Afr. Med. J.*, 32:1175-1178, 1958.

—— and SINGER, R.: A mandibular fragment probably of the Saldanha skull. *Nature*, 1: 1955.

DUBRUL, E. L.: *Evolution of the Speech Apparatus*. Springfield, Thomas, 1958.

DUNN, L. C.: *Heredity and Evolution in Human Populations*. Cambridge, Harvard Univ. Press. 1959.

—— and DOBZHANSKY, TH.: *Heredity, Race and Society*. New York, New American Library, 1952.

DUNSFORD, I. and BOWLEY, C. C.: *Techniques in Blood-Grouping*. Springfield, Thomas, 1956.

DUPERTUIS, C. W. and TANNER, J. M.: The pose of the subject for photogrammetric anthropometry, with especial reference to somatotyping. *Am. J. Phys. Anthropol.*, n.s. 8:27-44, 1950.

EAST, E. M. and JONES, D. F.: *Inbreeding and Outbreeding*. Philadelphia, Lippincott, 1919.

EDWARDS, E. A. and DUNTLEY, S. Q.: The pigments and color of living skin. *Am. J. Anatomy*, 45:1-33, 1939.

EHRICH, R. W. and COON, C. S.: Occipital flattening among the Dinarics. *Am. J. Phys. Anthropol.*, n.s., 6:181-186, 1947.

ELDERTON, E. M.: Height and weight of school children in Glasgow. *Biometrika*, 10:288-340, 1914.

ELLIOT, D. G.: *A Review of the Primates*, 3 vols., New York, Am. Museum of Natur. Hist., 1913.

EMILIANI, C.: Note on absolute chronology of human evolution. *Science*, 123: 924-926, 1956.

ENGELMANN, G. J.: Age of first menstruation on the North American continent. *Tr. Am. Gynec. Soc.*, 26:77-101, 1901.

ETCHEVERRY, M. A.: El factor rhesus, su genetica e importancia clinica. *Dia Med.*, 17:1237-1251, 1945.

——: El factor rhesus en Personas de Ascendencia Iberica residentes en la Argentina. *Semana Méd.*, Nov. 25:500, 1947.

EVANS, F. G.: The names of fossil men. *Science*, 102:16-17, 1945.

EVANS, R. D.: Quantitative inferences concerning the genetic effects of radiation on human beings. *Science*, 109:299-304, 1949.

EVERNDEN, J. F., CURTIS, G. H., and KISTLER, R.: Potassium-argon dating of pleistocene volcanoes. *Quaternaria*, 4:13-17, 1957.

FALCONER, D. S.: Sensory threshold for solutions of Phenyl-Thio-Carbamide. *Ann. Eugen., 13*:211-222, 1947.

FINKELSTEIN, L. (editor): *The Jews,* 2 vols. New York, Harper, 1950.

FISCHER, E.: *Die Rehobother Bastards und das Bastardierungs-problem beim Menschen.* Jena, 1913.

FISHBERG, M.: *The Jews.* New York, Scribners, 1911.

FISHER, R. A.: *The Genetical Theory of Natural Selection.* Oxford, Clarendon Press, 1930.

————: *Statistical Methods for Research Workers,* 10th edition. Edinburgh, Oliver & Boyd, 1948.

———— and TAYLOR, G. L.: Scandinavian influence in Scottish Ethnology. *Nature, 145*:590, 1940.

————, FORD, E. B. and HUXLEY, J. S.: Taste-testing the anthropoid apes. *Nature, 144*:750, 1939.

FITT, A. B.: *Seasonal Influence on Growth, Function and Inheritance.* London, Oxford, 1941.

————: The heights and weights of men according to month of birth. *Human Biology, 27*:138-142, 1955.

FLYNN, F. V. and DeMAYO, P.: Micro-electrophoresis of protein on filter paper. *The Lancet, 2*:235, 1951.

FORBES, H. O.: *Monkeys,* 2 vols. London, Shaw, 1894.

FOX, A. L.: The relationship between chemical constitution and taste. *Proc. Nat. Acad. Sc., 18*:115-120, 1932.

FRANZBLAU, A. N.: *A Primer of Statistics for Non-Statisticians.* New York, Harcourt, Brace, 1958.

FYLEMAN, R.: *Monkeys.* New York, Nelson, 1936.

GALATIUS-JENSEN, F.: Further investigations of the genetic mechanism of the haptoglobins. *Acta Genet., 7*:549, 1957.

————: On the genetics of the haptoglobins. *Acta Genetica et Statistica Medica, 8*:232-247, 1958.

GALLOWAY, A.: Man in Africa in the light of recent discoveries. *South African J. Sc., 34*:89-120, 1937.

————: Physical Anthropology in South and East Africa. *Yearbook of Physical Anthropology, 4*:40-46, 1949.

GALTON, D. A. G. (editor): *Haematology.* Brit. Med. Bull., *15*:1-88, 1959.

GALTON, F.: *Inquiries Into the Human Faculty and its Development.* London, Macmillan, 1883.

GARN, S. M.: Types and replacement of hair volume. *Ann. N. Y. Acad. Sc., 53*: 498-527, 1951.

————: The measurement of skin temperature. *Am. J. Phys. Anthropol.,* n.s. *12*:1-4, 1954.

———— and COON, C. S.: On the number of races of mankind. *Amer. Anthropol., 57*:996-1001, 1955.

———— and LEWIS, A. B.: Tooth size, and "giant" fossil man. *Amer. Anthropol., 60*:874-880, 1958.

———— and SHAMIR, Z.: *Methods For Research in Human Growth.* Springfield, Thomas, 1958.

GATES, R. R.: *Human Genetics,* 2 vols. New York, Macmillan, 1946.

————: The African Pygmies. *Acta Gen. Med. et Gemell., 8*:159-218, 1958.

GAVAN, J. A., WASHBURN, S. L. and LEWIS, P. H.: Photography: an anthropometric tool. *Am. J. Phys. Anthropol.*, n.s., *10*:331-353, 1952.

GAZIN, C. L.: A review of the middle and upper Eocene primates of North America. *Smithsonian Miscellaneous Collections*, *136*:1-112, 1958.

GENET-VARCIN, E.: *Les Négritos de l'Isle de Luçon (Philippines).* Paris, Masson et Cie., 1951.

GENOVÉS, S.: The problem of the sex of certain fossil hominids, with special reference to the Neanderthal skeletons from Spy. *J. Roy. Anthropol. Inst.*, *84:* 131-144, 1954.

GEOGEGAN, B.: The determination of body measurement, surface area and body volume by photography. *Am. J. Phys. Anthrop.*, n.s., *11*:97-119, 1943.

GERASIMOV, M. M.: Vosstanovlenie litsa po cherepu. *Izdatel'stvo Akademii Nauk SSSR*, Moscow, 1955. (Reconstruction of the features on the skull).

GIBLETT, E. R.: Haptoglobin types in American Negroes. *Nature*, *183*:192-193, 1959.

————: Js, a new blood group antigen found in Negroes. *Nature*, *181*:1221-1222, 1958.

———— and CHASE, J.: Js^a, a "new" red-cell antigen found in Negroes; evidence for an eleventh blood group system. *Brit. J. Haemat.*, *5*:319-326, 1959.

GILL, E. D.: Radiocarbon dates for Australian archaeological and geological samples. *Austral. J. Sc.*, *18*:49, 1955.

GILLIN, J. (editor): *For A Science of Social Man.* New York, Macmillan, 1954.

GLASS, B.: On the evidence of random genetic drift in human populations. *Amer. J. Phys. Anthropol.*, n.s., *14*:541-555.

————: Genetic changes in human populations, especially those due to gene flow and genetic drift. *Advances in Genetics*, *6*:95-139, 1954.

————, SACKS, M. S., JAHN, E. F. and HESS, C.: Genetic drift in a religious isolate: an analysis of the causes of variation in blood group and other gene frequencies in a small population. *Amer. Nat.*, *86*:145-160, 1952.

GODLEY, E. J.: Blood group frequencies in New Zealand and Maori soldiers. *Ann. Eugenics*, *13*:211-222, 1947.

GODYCKI, M.: Sur la certitude de détermination du sexe d'après le fémur, le cubitus, et l'humérus. *Bull. et Mém. de la Soc. d'Anthrop. Paris*, *8*:405-410, 1957.

GOLDSMITH, K. L. G. (editor): Blood Groups. *Brit. Med. Bull.*, *15*:89-174, 1959.

GOLDSTEIN, M. S.: *Demographic and Bodily Changes in Descendants of Mexican Immigrants.* Austin, Texas, Inst. Latin-American Stud., 1943.

————: Theory of survival of the unfit. *J. Nat. Med. A.*, *47*:223-226, 1955.

GRAUBARD, M.: *Man, the Slave and Master.* New York, Covici-Friede, 1938.

GRAY, M. P.: A method for reducing non-specific reactions in the typing of human skeletal material. *Am. J. Phys. Anthropol.*, n.s., *16*:135-139, 1958.

GREENBERG, J. H.: Current trends in linguistics. *Science*, *130*:1165-1174, 1959.

GREGORY, W. K.: Studies on the evolution of the primates. *Bull. Am. Museum Natur. Hist.*, *35*:239-255, 1916.

————: *The Origin and Evolution of the Human Dentition.* Baltimore, Williams & Wilkins, 1922.

————: *Our Face From Fish to Man.* New York, Putnam, 1929.

————: *Man's Place Among the Anthropoids.* New York, Oxford Univ. Press, 1934.

————: The bearing of the Australopithecinae upon the problem of man's place in nature. *Am. J. Phys. Anthropol.*, n.s. *7*:485-512, 1949.

————— and HELLMAN, M.: The dentition of Dryopithecus and the origin of man. *Anthrop. Papers, Amer. Mus. Nat. Hist.*, 28:1-123, 1926.

—————: The dentition of the extinct South African Man-Ape *Australopithecus* (*Plesianthropus*) *transvaalensis* Broom. A comparative and phylogenetic study. *Ann. Transvaal Mus.*, 19:359-373, 1939.

GREULICH, W. W.: Growth of children of the same race under different environmental conditions. *Science*, 127:515-516, 1958.

—————: A comparison of the physical growth and development of American-born and native Japanese children. *Am. J. Phys. Anthropol.*, n.s. 15:489-515, 1957.

————— and PYLE, S. I.: *Radiographic Atlas of Skeletal Development of the Hand and Wrist.* Stanford, Stanford Univ. Press, 1959.

Growth and Development of the Child. Part II. Anatomy and Physiology. New York, Century Co., 1933.

GRIMM, H.: Altern, lebensdauer, krankheit und tod bei vorgesdrichtlichen und frühgeschichtlichen bevölkerungsgruppen. *Wissensch. Ann.*, 3:171-180, 1956.

GROSS, H.: Mastodon, mammoth and man in America. *Bull. Texas Archeol. & Paleontol. Soc.*, 22:101-131, 1951.

GRÜNEBERG, H.: *Animal Genetics and Medicine.* London, Hamish Hamilton, 1947.

GUREVITCH, J., HERMONI, D. and POLISHUK, Z.: *Rh* blood types in Jerusalem "Jews." *Ann. Eugenics*, 16:129-130, 1951.

GUTHE, G. E.: Notes on the cephalic index of Russian Jews in Boston. *Am. J. Phys. Anthropol.*, 1:213-223, 1918.

HADDON, A. C.: *The Wanderings of Peoples.* New York, Macmillan, 1911.

—————: *History of Anthropology.* London, Watts, 1934.

—————: *The Races of Man.* New York, Cambridge Univ. Press, 1924.

HALDANE, J. B. S.: *The Causes of Evolution.* New York, Longmans, 1935.

—————: *Heredity and Politics.* New York, Norton, 1938.

—————: The blood-group frequencies of European peoples, and racial origins. *Human Biol.*, 12:457-480, 1940.

—————: *New Paths in Genetics.* New York, Harper, 1942.

—————: Disease and evolution. Symposium sui Fattori Ecologici e Genetici della Speciazioni negli Animali. *La Ricerca Scientifica*, 19:1-11, 1949.

—————: The argument from animals to men. *J. Roy. Anthropol. Inst.*, 86:1-14, 1956.

HALLIDAY, J. L.: *Psychosocial Medicine.* New York, W. W. Norton, 1948.

HALLOWELL, A. I.: Personality structure and evolution. *Amer. Anthropol.*, 52:159-173, 1950.

—————: The structural and functional dimensions of a human existence. *Quart. Rev. Biol.*, 31:88-101, 1957.

HAMBLY, W. D.: Cranial capacity, a study in methods. *Fieldiana Anthropol.* (Chicago Natural History Museum), 36:25-75, 1947.

HAMMOND, W. H.: The status of physical types. *Hum. Biol.*, 29:223-241, 1957.

HANKINS, F. H.: *The Racial Basis of Civilization.* New York, Knopf, 1931.

HARRINGTON, M. R.: Man's oldest date in America. *Natural History*, 64:512-517, 1955.

HARRIS, D. B. (editor): *The Concept of Development.* Minneapolis, Univ. Minnesota Press, 1957.

HARRIS, H.: *Human Biochemical Genetics.* London and New York, Cambridge University Press, 1959.

———— and KALMUS, H.: The measurement of taste sensitivity to phenylthiouria (P.T.C.). *Ann. Eugenics, 15:*24-31, 1949.

HARRISON, R. J.: *Man the Peculiar Animal.* Baltimore, Penguin Books, 1958.

HECHST, B.: Über einen Fall von Mikroencephalie ohne Geistigen Defekt. *Arch. f. Psych. u. Nervenkr.,* 97:64-76, 1932.

HEIZER, R. F. (editor): *The Archaeologist at Work.* New York, Harper, 1959.

HERSKOVITS, M. J.: *The American Negro.* New York, Knopf, 1928.

HERTZBERG, H. T. E., DUPERTUIS, C. W. and EMANUEL, I.: Stereophotogrammetry as an anthropometric tool. *Photogrammetric Engineering,* 23:942-947, 1957.

HERTZBERG, H. T. E. (editor): Annotated bibliography of applied physical anthropology in human engineering. Aero Medical Laboratory, Wright-Patterson Air Force Base, Ohio, 1958.

HIBBEN, F. C.: *Prehistoric Man in Europe.* Norman, Oklahoma, Univ. Oklahoma Press, 1958.

————: Specimens from Sandia Cave and their possible significance. *Science, 122:*688-689, 1955.

HIERNAUX, J.: Physical anthropology and the frequency of genes with a selective value: the sickle cell gene. *Am. J. Phys. Anthropol.,* n.s. *13:*455-472, 1955.

HILL, A. B.: *Principles of Medical Statistics,* 6th ed. New York, Oxford Univ. Press, 1955.

HILL, W. C. OSMAN: *Man's Ancestry.* Springfield, Thomas, 1954.

————: *Primates: Comparative Anatomy and Taxonomy.* I. *Strepsirhini.* II. *Haplorhini.* III. *Pithecoidea.* New York, Interscience Publishers, 1953, 1955, 1957.

HOFER, H., SCHULTZ, A. H. and STARK, D. (editors): *Primatologia,* 3 vols. Basel, S. Karger A. G., 1956, 1959.

HOGBEN, L.: The concept of race. In *Genetic Principles in Medicine and Social Science.* New York, Knopf, 1932, p. 122-144.

————: *Genetic Principles in Medicine and Social Science.* New York, Knopf, 1932.

———— (editor): *Political Arithmetic.* New York, Macmillan, 1938.

HONIGMANN, J. J.: *Culture and Personality.* New York, 1954.

HOOTON, E. A.: The making and mixing of human races. In *Twilight of Man.* New York, Putnam, 1939, p. 60-192.

————: *Crime and the Man.* Cambridge, Harvard Univ. Press, 1939.

————: *The American Criminal.* Cambridge, Harvard Univ. Press, 1939.

————: *Man's Poor Relations.* New York, Doubleday, Doran, 1942.

————: *Up From the Ape,* 2nd edition. New York, Macmillan, 1946.

HOPWOOD, A. T.: Miocene primates from Kenya. *J. Linnaean Soc. London,* (Zoology), 37:437-464, 1933.

HOWARD, E. G.: Evidence of early man in North America. *The Museum Journal* (University of Pennsylvania), 24:53-171, 1935.

HOWELL, E. C.: The place of Neanderthal man in human evolution. *Amer. J. Phys. Anthropol.,* n.s. 9:379-416.

————: Pleistocene glacial ecology and the evolution of "classic Neanderthal" man. *Southwest. J. Anthropol.,* 8:377-410, 1952.

————: The evolutionary significance of variation and varieties of "Neanderthal" man. *Quart. Rev. Biol.,* 32:330-347, 1957.

————: Upper Pleistocene men of the southwest Asian Mousterian. *Trans. Int. Neanderthal Cent. Congress*, Utrecht, Kemink en Zn, 1958, pp. 185-198.

————: Upper Pleistocene stratigraphy and early man in the Levant. *Proc. Amer. Phil. Soc., 103*:1-65, 1959.

HOWELLS, W. W.: *Mankind in The Making*, 2nd ed. New York, Doubleday, 1959.

———— (editor): Early Man in the Far East. *Studies in Physical Anthropology*, No. 1, Philadelphia, Wistar Inst., 1949.

————: *Variation of External Body Form in the Individual*. Peabody Museum Cambridge, Mass., 1957.

————: *Back of History*. New York, Doubleday, 1954.

HOYLE, L. E.: Physical anthropology and its instruments: an historical study. *Southwest. J. Anthropol., 9*:408-430, 1953.

HRDLIČKA, A.: *Early Man in South America*. Smithsonian Institution, Bureau of Ethnology, Bulletin, 52, 1912.

————: *The Skeletal Remains of Early Man*. Washington, Smithsonian Miscellaneous Collections, vol. 83, 1930.

————: *The Old Americans*. Baltimore, Williams and Wilkins, 1925.

————: *Practical Anthropometry* 3rd edition (edited by Stewart, T. D.), Philadelphia, Wistar Inst., 1947.

HUE, E.: *Crânes paleolithiques. Bibliographie*. In Congrès Prehistorique de France, XIIe Session, Toulouse-Foix, 1936, pp. 113-285. Paris, Société Prehistorique Française, 1937.

HUNT, JR., E. E.: Anthropometry, genetics, and racial history. *Am. Anthropol., 61*:64-87, 1959.

HUNTINGTON, E.: *Mainsprings of Civilization*. New York, Wiley, 1945.

HÜRZELER, J.: Zur systematischen Stellung von Oreopithecus. *Verh. Naturf. Ges. Basel, 65*:88-95, 1954.

————: Oreopithecus, un point de repere pour l'histoire de l'humanite a l'ere tertaire. *Colloque Internat*. No. 60, Centre National de la Recherche Scientifique, Paris, 1956, 115-121.

————: Oreopithecus bambolii Gervais. *Ver. Naturf. Ges. Basel, 69*:1-48, 1958.

HUXLEY, J. S.: *Evolution; the Modern Synthesis*. New York, Harper, 1942.

————: *Man Stands Alone*. New York, Harper, 1941.

————: *Evolution in Action*. New York, Harper, 1953.

————: *New Bottles For New Wine*. New York, Harper, 1957.

———— and HADDON, A. C.: *We Europeans*. New York, Harper, 1936.

HUXLEY, T. H. and HUXLEY, J.: *Touchstone For Ethics*. New York, Harper, 1947.

————: *Evidence as to Man's Place in Nature*. London, William & Norgate, 1863.

INGRAM, V. M.: How do genes act? *Scientific Amer., 198*:68-74, 1958.

————: Separation of the peptide chains of human globin. *Nature, 183*:1795-1798, 1959.

ITO, P. K.: Anthropometric study of new-born infants of Japanese parents in America. *Am. J. Dis. Child., 52*:321-330, 1936.

————: Comparative biometrical study of physique of Japanese women born and reared under different environments. *Human Biol., 14*:279-351, 1942.

JACOBS, M. and STERN, B. J.: *Outline of Anthropology*. New York, Barnes & Noble, 1947.

JENNESS, D. (editor): *The American Aborigines, Their Origin and Antiquity*. Toronto, Univ. Toronto Press, 1933.

JENNINGS, H. S.: *The Biological Basis of Human Nature*. New York, Norton, 1930.

————: *Genetics*. New York, Norton, 1935.

JEPSON, G. L., MAYR, E. and SIMPSON, G. G. (editors): *Genetics, Paleontology, and Evolution*, Princeton Univ. Press, 1949.

JERISON, H. J.: Brain to body ratios and the evolution of intelligence. *Science, 121*:447-449, 1955.

JOHNSON, L. H.: Men and elephants in America. *Scientific Monthly, 75*:215-221, 1952.

JONES, F. WOODS *Man's Place Among the Mammals*. New York, Longman's, 1929.

JONSON, B.: The main frequencies of blood group genes in Sweden with special regard to the Rh genes. *Acta Gen. Med. et Gemell., 8*:135-146, 1959.

JONXIS, J. H. P., and DELAFRESNAYE, T. F. (editors): *Abnormal Haemoglobins*. Springfield, Thomas, 1959.

JONXIS, J. H. P., and HUISMAN, T. H. J.: *A Laboratory Manual on Abnormal Haemoglobins*. Springfield, Thomas, 1959.

KABAT, E. A.: *Blood Group Substances*. New York, Academic Press, 1956.

KALLMANN, F. J.: *Heredity in Health and Mental Disorder*. New York, Norton, 1953.

———— and ANASTASIO, M. M.: Twin studies in the psychopathology of suicide. *J. Heredity, 37*:179, 1946.

KALMUS, H.: Defective colour vision, p.t.c. tasting and drepanocytosis in samples from fifteen Brazilian populations. *Ann. Hum. Genetics, 21*:313-317, 1957.

————: *Variation and Heredity*. London, Routledge, 1958.

KAPLAN, B. A.: Environment and human plasticity. *Am. Anthropol., 56*:780-800, 1954.

KEANE, A. H.: *Man: Past and Present*. Cambridge: at the University Press, 1920.

KEEN, J. A.: A study of the differences between male and female skulls. *Am. J. Phys. Anthropol., n.s. 8*:65-79, 1950.

KEITH, A.: *The Antiquity of Man*, 2 vols. London, Williams & Norgate, 1925.

————: *Further Discoveries Relating to the Antiquity of Man*. London, Williams & Norgate, 1931.

————: *A New Theory of Human Evolution*. New York, Philosophical Library, 1949.

————: *Essays on Human Evolution*. London, Watts, 1946.

————: Foetalization as a factor in human evolution. In Keith's *A New Theory of Human Evolution*. London, Watts, 1949, pp. 192-201.

————: *An Autobiography*. London, Watts, 1950.

————: *Human Embryology and Morphology*, 6th ed. London, Arnold, 1948.

KENNEY, R. A.: Anatomical differences due to race or climate. In UNESCO Publication, Arid Zone Research VIII, *Human and Animal Ecology*. New York, Columbia Univ. Press, 1957, 83-84.

KITCHIN, F. D., *et al.*: P.T.C. taste response and thyroid disease. *Brit. Med. J., 1*: 1069-1074, 1959.

KLINEBERG, O.: *Race Differences*. New York, Harper, 1935.

———— (editor): *Characteristics of the American Negro*. New York, Harper, 1944.

KLUCKHOHN, C.: *Mirror for Man*. New York, Whittlesey House, 1949.

—— and KELLY, W. H.: The conception of culture. In (R. Linton, editor) *The Science of Man in the World Crisis*. New York, Columbia Univ. Press, 1945.

KLUVER, H.: *Behavior Mechanisms in Monkeys*. Univ. Chicago Press, 1955.

KOENIGSWALD, G. H. R. VON: *The South African Man-Apes and Pithecanthropus*. Washington, Carnegie Inst., Publication 530, 1942, p. 205-222.

——: The discovery of early man in Java and South China. In *Early Man in the East* (edited by W. W. Howells), Philadelphia, The Wistar Institute, 1949.

——: *Gigantopithecus blacki* von Koenigswald, A giant fossil hominoid from the pleistocene of Southern China. *Anthropol. Papers. Am. Mus. Nat. Hist.*, 43: 295-325, 1952.

——: *Meeting Prehistoric Man*. London, Thames & Hudson, 1956.

——: Meganthropus and the Australopithecinae. In *Third Pan-African Congress on Prehistory* (editors J. D. Clark and S. Cole). London, Chatto & Windus, 1957, pp. 158-160.

—— and WEIDENREICH, F.: The relationship between Pithecanthropus and Sinanthropus. *Nature*, 144:926-927, 1939.

KORN, N. and SMITH, H. R. (editors): *Human Evolution*. New York, Holt, 1959.

KRAUS, B. S. and WHITE, C. B.: Micro-evolution in a human population. *Amer. Anthropol.*, 58:1017-1043, 1956.

KRAUS, W. W.: Race crossing in Hawaii. *J. Heredity*, 32:371-378, 1941.

KRETSCHMER, E.: *Physique and Character*. New York, Harcourt, 1925.

KROEBER, A. L. and KLUCKHOHN, C.: Culture: A Critical Review of Concepts and Definitions. *Papers of the Peabody Museum of American Archaeology and Ethnology, Harvard University*, 47:viii-223, 1952.

KROGMAN, W. M. (editor): The growth of man. *Tabulae Biologicae*, 20:vi-963, 1942.

——: *A Guide-Outline for the Study of Physical Growth in Children*. Philadelphia, Philadelphia Center for Research in Child Growth, 1958.

——: Changing man. *J. Am. Geriatrics Soc.*, 6:242-260, 1958.

——: A Handbook of the Measurement and Interpretation of Height and Weight in the Growing Child. *Mon. Soc. Res. Child. Develop.*, 8:1-68, 1950.

——: The human skeleton in legal medicine. In S. A. Levinson (editor): *Symposium on Medicolegal Problems*. Philadelphia, Lippincott, 1949, pp. 1-100.

——: *A Bibliography of Human Morphology, 1914-1939*. Chicago, Univ. Chicago Press, 1941.

KROPOTKIN, P.: *Mutual Aid*. Boston, Porter Sargent, 1955.

KRZYWICKI, L.: *Primitive Society and Its Vital Statistics*. London, Macmillan, 1934.

KUNO, Y.: *Human Perspiration*. Springfield, Thomas, 1956.

KURTÉN, B.: Mammal migrations, Cenozoic stratigraphy, and the age of Peking Man and the Australopithecines. *J. Paleontology*, 31:215-227, 1957.

——: A Case of Darwinian selection in bears. *Evolution*, 11:412-416, 1958.

——: A differentiation index, and a new measure of evolutionary rates. *Evolution*, 12:146-157, 1958.

——: The life and death of the Pleistocene cave bear. *Acta Zoologica Fennica* 95, Helsinki-Helsingfors, 1959, pp. 59.

KURTZ, A. K. and EDGERTON, H. A.: *Statistical Dictionary of Terms and Symbols.* New York, Wiley, 1939.

LACAILLE, A. D.: Châtelperron: a new survey of its palaeolithic industry. *Archaeologia,* 92:95-119, 1947.

————: The stone industry of Singa—Abu Hugar. In *Fossil Mammals of Africa,* No. 2, British Museum (Natural History), 43-50, 1951.

LADELL, W. S. S.: The influence of environment in arid regions on the biology of man. In *Human and Animal Ecology,* UNESCO Publication, Arid Zone Research VIII, New York, Columbia Univ. Press, 1957, 43-99.

LANGER, W. L. (editor): *An Encyclopaedia of World History.* 3rd ed. Boston, Houghton Mifflin, 1952.

LASKER, G. W.: The effects of partial starvation on somatotype. An analysis of material from the Minnesota starvation experiment. *Am. J. Phys. Anthropol.,* n.s. 5:323-341, 1947.

————: Migration and physical differentiation. *Am. J. Phys. Anthropol.,* n.s. 4:273-300, 1946.

————: Mixture and genetic drift in ongoing human evolution. *Am. Anthropol.,* 54:433-436, 1952.

————: Human evolution in contemporary communities. *Southwest. J. Anthropol.,* 4:353-365, 1954.

LAUGHLIN, W. S. (editor). *Papers on the Physical Anthropology of the American Indian.* New York, Viking Fund, 1951.

———— and JØRGENSEN, J. B.: Isolate variation in Greenlandic eskimo crania. *Acta Gen. et Stat. Med.,* 6:3-12, 1956.

———— GRAY, M. P. and HOPKINS, C. E.: Blood group genetics of the Basques of Idaho. *Acta Gen. et. Stat. Med.,* 6:536-548, 1956.

LAWLER, S. D. and LAWLER, L. J.: *Human Blood Groups and Inheritance.* Harvard Univ. Press, Cambridge, Mass., 1957.

LAYRISSE, M.: Anthropological considerations of the Diego (Di^a) antigen. Possible application in the studies of Mongoloid and hybrid populations. *Am. J. Phys. Anthropol.,* n.s. 16:173-186, 1958.

———— and DE LAYRISSE, Z.: Frequency of the new blood group antigen Js^a among South American Indians. *Nature, 184*:640, 1959.

LEAKEY, L. S. B.: *Olduvai Gorge.* New York, Cambridge University Press, 1951.

————: *Adam's Ancestors,* 4th ed. London, Methuen, 1953.

————: A new fossil skull from Eyassi, East Africa. *Nature, 138*:1082, 1936.

————: Recent discoveries at Olduvai Gorge, Tanganyika. *Nature, 181*:1099-1103, 1958.

————: A new fossil skull from Olduvai. *Nature, 184*:491-493, 1959.

LEE, M. M. C., and LASKER, G. W.: The sun-tanning potential of human skin. *Human Biology, 31*:252-260, 1959.

LEHMANN, H.: Haemoglobin and its abnormalities. *Practitioner* (London), *178:* 198-214, 1957.

LEROI-GOURHAN, A.: *Prehistoric Man.* New York, Philosophical Library, 1957.

LESSA, W. A.: *An Appraisal of Constitutional Typologies.* American Anthropological Association Memoir, No. 62, 1943.

LEVIN, G.: Racial and inferiority characters in the human brain. *Am. J. Phys. Anthropol.,* 22:345-380, 1937.

LEVINE, P., LAYRISSE, M., ARENDS, T., SISCO, R. D.: The Diego blood factor. *Nature*, 177:40-41, 1956.

LEWIS, J. H.: *The Biology of the Negro*. Chicago, Univ. Chicago Press, 1942.

LEWIS, M., KAITA, H. and CHOWN, B.: The blood groups of a Japanese population. *A. J. Hum. Genetics*, 9:274-283, 1957.

LI, C. C.: *Population Genetics*. Univ. Chicago Press, 1955.

————: *Introduction to Statistical Inference*. Ann Arbor, Michigan, Edwards Bros., 1957.

LIBBY, W. J.: *Radiocarbon Dating*, 2nd ed. Univ. Chicago Press, 1955.

LINTON, R. (editor): *The Science of Man in the World Crisis*. New York, Columbia Univ. Press, 1944.

———— (editor): *Most of the World: The Peoples of Africa, Latin America, and the East Today*. New York, Columbia Univ. Press, 1949.

LIVINGSTONE, F. B.: Anthropological significance of sickle-cell gene distribution in West Africa. *Am. Anthropol.*, 60:533-562, 1958.

LONGHEM, JR., J. J. VAN: Nomenclature of the rhesus typing sera. *Bull. World Health Organization*, 2:215-225, 1949.

LOTSY, J. P. and GODDIJN, W. A.: Voyages of exploration to judge of the bearing of hybridization upon evolution. I. South Africa. *Genetica*, 10:viii-315, 1928.

LOWIE, R. H.: Intellectual and cultural achievements of human races. In *Scientific Aspects of the Race Problem*, New York, Longmans, 1941, p. 189-249.

————: *The History of Ethnological Theory*. New York, Farrar & Rinehart, 1937.

LUGG, J. W. H.: Taste thresholds for phenylthiocarbamide of some populations. *Ann. Hum. Genetics*, 21:244-253, 1957.

MACALISTER, R. A. S.: *A Textbook of European Archaeology*. Cambridge and New York, Cambridge Univ. Press, 1921.

MACCURDY, G. G.: *Human Origins*, 2 vols. New York, Appleton, 1924.

———— (editor): *Early Man*. Philadelphia, Lippincott, 1930.

MACGOWAN, K.: *Early Man in the New World*. New York, Macmillan, 1950.

MACINNES, D. G.: Notes on the East African Miocene primates. *J. East Africa Uganda Natur. Hist. Soc.*, 18:141-148, 1943.

MCBURNEY, C. B.: *The Stone Age of Northern Africa*. Baltimore, Md., Penguin Books, 1959.

———— TREVOR, J. C. and WELLS, L. H.: The Haua-Fteah fossil jaw. *J. Roy. Anthropol. Inst.*, 83:71-85, 1953.

MCCOWN, T. D. and KEITH, A.: *The Stone Age of Mount Carmel*. Oxford, The Clarendon Press, 1939.

MACY, I. G. and KELLY, H. J.: *Chemical Anthropology*. Univ. Chicago Press, 1957.

M'GONIGLE, G. C. M. and KIRBY, J.: *Poverty and Public Health*. London, Victor Gollancz, 1936.

MAINLAND, D.: *Elementary Medical Statistics*. Philadelphia, Saunders, 1952.

MALEZ, M.: Die Höhle Veternica, eine neue paläolithische Fundstelle in Kroatien. *Bull. Scient.* (Jugoslavia), 3:11, 1956.

MANUILA, A.: Recherches sérologiques et anthropologiques ches les populations de la Roumanie et des régions voisines: Contribution a l'étude du problème Dinarique. *Arch. Jul. Klaus-Stiftung f. Vererbungsf. Sozialanthropolo. u. Rassenhygiene*, 32:219-357.

————: Blood groups and disease—hard facts and delusions. *J.A.M.A., 167:* 2047-2053, 1958.

MARDER, V. J., and CONLEY, C. L.: Electrophoresis of hemoglobin on agar gels. *Bull. Johns Hopkins Hosp.,* 105:77-88, 1959.

MARTIN, H.: *The Sheltering Desert.* New York, Nelson, 1958.

MARTIN, R.: *Lehrbuch der Anthropologie,* 2nd edition, 3 vols. Jena, Fischer, 1928. Third edition edited by Karl Saller, began to appear in parts, issued by the same publisher, in 1956.

MATUS, S.: The mongol spot in the Cape Coloured. *S. Afr. Med. J.,* 12 April 1941.

MAY, J. M.: *The Ecology of Human Disease.* New York, MD Publications, 1959.

MAYR, E.: *Systematics and the Origin of Species.* New York, Columbia Univ. Press, 1942.

————: Taxonomic categories in fossil hominids. *Cold Spring Harbor Symposia on Quantitative Biology,* 15:109-118, 1950.

———— (editor): *The Species Problem.* Washington, D.C. American Association for the Advancement of Science, 1957.

———— LINSLEY, G. E. and USINGER, R. L.: *Methods and Principles of Systematic Zoology.* New York, McGraw-Hill, 1953.

MEGGERS, B. J. (editor): *Evolution and Anthropology: A Centennial Appraisal.* Washington, D.C., The Anthropological Society of Washington, 1959.

MEREDITH, H. V.: Relation between socioeconomic status and body size in boys seven to ten years of age. *Am. J. Dis. Child.,* 82:702-709, 1951.

MERRITT, E. L.: *Analytical Photogrammetry.* New York, Pitman, 1958.

MERTON, B. B.: Taste sensitivity to PTC. *Acta Genetica et Statistica Medica, 8:* 114-128, 1958.

MERTON, R. K., and MONTAGU, M. F. ASHLEY: Crime and the anthropologist. *Am. Anthropol.,* 42:384-408, 1940.

METTLER, F. A.: *Culture and the Structural Evolution of the Nervous System.* New York, American Museum of Natural History, 1956.

MEWHINNEY, H.: *A Manual for Neanderthals.* Austin, Univ. Texas, 1957.

MIDDLETON, J.: On fluorine in bones, its source, and its application to the determination of the geological age of fossil bones. *Proc. Geol. Soc. Lond.,* 4:431-433, 1844.

MILLER, JR., G. S.: The controversy over human "missing links." *Smithsonian Report for 1928,* Smithsonian Institution, Washington, D.C., 1929, 413-465.

MOHR, J.: Taste sensitivity to phenylthiourea in Denmark. *Ann. Hum. Genetics,* 21:282-286, 1957.

MONGE, C.: *Acclimatization in the Andes.* Baltimore, Johns Hopkins Press, 1948.

————: Biological basis of behavior. In A. L. Kroeber (editor): *Anthropology Today.* Univ. Chicago Press, 1953, 127-144.

MONTAGU, M. F. ASHLEY: A cursory examination of the relations between physical and social anthropology. *Am. J. Phys. Anthropol.,* 26:41-61, 1940.

————: *Edward Tyson, M.D., F.R.S. (1650-1708): and the Rise of Human and Comparative Anatomy in England.* Philadelphia, American Philosophical Society, 1943.

————: The intelligence of northern Negroes and southern whites in the first World War. *Am. J. Psychol.,* 48:161-188, 1945.

————: On the relation between body size, waking activity, and the origin of social life in the primates. *Am. Anthropol.,* 44:141-145, 1944.

————: Physical anthropology and anatomy. *Am. J. Phys. Anthropol.*, 27:261-271, 1941.

————: The premaxilla in the primates. *Quart. Rev. Biol.*, 10:32-59, 181-208, 1935.

————: The premaxilla in man. *J. Am. Dent. A.*, 23:2043-2057, 1936.

————: The medio-frontal suture and the problem of metopism in the primates. *J. Roy. Anthropol. Inst.*, 67:157-201, 1937.

————: Genetics and the antiquity of man in the Americas. *Man*, 43:131-135, 1943.

————: *Man's Most Dangerous Myth: The Fallacy of Race*, 3rd edition. New York, Harper, 1952.

————: The tarsian hypothesis and the descent of man. *J. Roy. Anthropol. Inst.*, 60:335-362, 1930.

————: The origin and nature of social life and the biological basis of cooperation. *J. Soc. Psychol.*, 29:267-283, 1949.

————: *On Being Human*. New York, Schuman, 1950.

————: *Darwin, Competition, and Cooperation*. New York, Schuman, 1952.

————: *The Natural Superiority of Women*. New York, Macmillan, 1953.

————: The Barcombe Mills cranial remains. *Am. J. Phys. Anthropol.*, n.s. 9: 417-426, 1951.

————: The Piltdown mandible and cranium. *Am. J. Phys. Anthropol.*, n.s. 9: 464-470, 1951.

————: The Piltdown nasal turbinate and bone implement: some questions. *Science*, 119:884-886, 1954.

————: Time, morphology, and neoteny in the evolution of man. *Amer. Anthropol.*, 57:13-27, 1955.

————: The Kanam mandible. *Amer. Anthropol.*, 59:335-339, 1957.

————: Neoteny, and the evolution of the human mind. *Explorations* (University of Toronto), No. 6, 85-90, 1956.

————: The Natchez innominate bone. *Human Biology*, 27:193-201, 1955.

————: *The Direction of Human Development*. New York, Harper, 1955.

————: *Anthropology and Human Nature*. Boston, Porter, Sargent, 1957.

————: *The Reproductive Development of the Female*. New York, Julian Press, 1957.

————: *Human Heredity*. New York, World Publishing Co., 1959.

————: *Man: His First Million Years*. New York, New American Library, 1958.

———— and Merton, R. K.: Crime and the anthropologist. *Am. Anthropol.*, 42: 384-408, 1940.

———— and Oakley, K. P.: The antiquity of Galley Hill man. *Am. J. Phys. Anthropol.*, n.s. 7:363-384, 1949.

———— Steen, E. S.: *Anatomy and Physiology*, 2 vols. New York, Barnes & Noble, 1959.

Montoye, H. J.: *The Longevity and Morbidity of College Athletes*. Phi Epsilon Fraternity, Indianapolis, Indiana, 1957.

Moor-Jankowski, J. K.: La prépondérance du groupe sanguin O et du facteur Rhésus négatif chez les Walser de Suisse. *J. Gén. Hum.*, 3:25-70, 1954.

———— and Huser, H. J.: Seroanthropological investigations in the Walser and Romanish isolates of the Swiss Alps. Proc. 6th Congr. Interna. Soc. Blood Transf., Boston, 1956, *Bibl. Haem.*, 7:215-219, 1958.

Morant, G. M.: *The Races of Central Europe.* New York, Norton, 1939.

————: Studies of Palaeolithic Man. *Ann. Eugenics,* 1:257-276, 1926; 2:318-381, 1927; 3:337-360; 4:109-214, 1930.

————: The practical application of physical anthropology. *Zeit. f. Morph. u. Anthropol.,* 119:196-204, 1958.

Moroney, M. G.: *Facts from Figures.* Baltimore, Penguin Books, 1951.

Moullec, J. and Fine, J. M.: Frequencies of the haptoglobin groups in 406 French blood donors. *Nature,* 184:196-197, 1959.

Mourant, A. E.: *The Distribution of the Human Blood Groups.* Springfield, Thomas, 1954.

————: Blood groups and human evolution. *Proc. Brit. A. Adv. Sci.,* No. 50, 1956, 1-13.

————: *The ABO Blood Groups.* Springfield, Thomas, 1958.

Movius, Jr., H. L.: Lower paleolithic archaeology in Southern Asia and the Far East. In *Early Man in the Far East* (edited by W. W. Howells), p. 17-81, Philadelphia, The Wistar Institute, 1949.

————: Palaeolithic archaeology in Southern and Eastern Asia, exclusive of India. *J. World Hist.,* 2:258-282, 520-553, 1955.

Muller, H. J., Little, C. C. and Snyder, L. H.: *Genetics, Medicine, and Man.* Ithaca, New York, Cornell Univ. Press, 1947.

Myrdal, G.: *An American Dilemma: The Negro Problem and American Democracy.* 2 vols. New York, Harper, 1944.

Nabours, R. K.: Emergent evolution and hybridism. *Science,* 71:371-375, 1930.

Nasmyth, G.: *Social Progress and the Darwinian Theory.* New York, Putnam, 1916.

Negus, V.: *The Comparative Anatomy and Physiology of the Nose and Paranasal Sinuses.* Baltimore, Williams & Wilkins, 1958.

Newman, H. H.: *Multiple Human Births.* New York, Doubleday, Doran, 1940.

————, Freeman, F. N. and Holzinger, K. H.: *Twins: A Study of Heredity and Environment.* Chicago, Univ. Chicago Press, 1937.

Newman, M. T.: The application of ecological rules to the racial anthropology of the aboriginal New World. *Amer. Anthropol.,* 55:309-327, 1955.

Nissen, H. W.: A field study of the Chimpanzee. *Compt. Psychol. Monogr.,* 8: serial no. 36, 1931.

Notes and Queries on Anthropology, 6th ed. London, Routledge, 1951.

Nyman, M.: Über Haptoglobinbestimmung im Serum, Normalkonzentration und Verhaltnis zu Smithies Serumgruppen. *Clin. Chim. Acta,* 3:111, 1958.

Oakley, K. P.: A definition of man. *Science News* (London), Penguin Books, No. 20, May 1951, 68-81.

————: Tools or brains—which came first? *The Listener* (London), Dec. 19, 1957, 1027-1028.

————: The earliest tool-makers and the earliest fire-makers. *Antiquity,* 30:4-8, 1-2-107, 1956.

————: *Man the Tool-Maker,* 4th ed. London, British Museum (Natural History), 1958. Chicago, Univ. Chicago Press, 1958.

————: Dating fossil men. *Mem. & Proc. Manchester Lit. & Phil. Soc.,* 98: 1-18, 1956/57.

————: Swanscombe man. *Proc. Geol. Assoc.,* 63:271-300, 1952.

———— and Hoskins, C. R.: New evidence on the antiquity of Piltdown Man. *Nature,* 165:379-382, 1950.

————— and MONTAGU, M. F. ASHLEY: A reconsideration of the Galley Hill skeleton. *Bull. Brit. Museum Natur. Hist.*, 1:25-48, 1949.

OLIVER, J. A., MACKAY, I., and GOT, C.: Serum haptoglobins in hepatobiliary disease. *Brit. M. J.*, 1:1454-1456, 1959.

OLIVIER, G. and PINEAU, H.: Détermination du sexe par le poids des os. *Bull. et Mém. de la Soc. d'Anthrop. Paris*, 9:329-339, 1958.

OLSON, E. C. and MILLER, R. C.: *Morphological Integration.* Univ. Chicago Press, 1958.

OTTENSOOSER, F.: Blood groups, races and prehistory. *Hum. Biol.*, 27:253-257, 1955.

OWEN, J. A., MACKAY, I., and GOT, C.: Haptoglobins in hepatobiliary disease. *Br. Med. J.*, 1:1454-1456, 1959.

PARNELL, R. W.: *Behavior and Physique.* London, Arnold, 1958.

PATERSON, D. G.: *Physique and Intellect.* New York, Century Co., 1930.

PATTE, É.: *Les Neanderthaliens.* Paris, Masson, 1955.

PATTEN, W.: *The Grand Strategy of Evolution.* Boston, Badger, 1920.

PATTERSON, B.: The geologic history of the non-hominid primates in the Old World. *Hum. Biol.*, 26:191-209, 1954.

PEACOCK, L. J. and ROGERS, C. M.: Gestation period and twinning in chimpanzees. *Science*, 129:959, 1959.

PEARL, R.: *Introduction to Medical Biometry and Statistics*, 3rd edition, Philadelphia, Saunders, 1940.

—————: *The Rate of Living.* New York, Knopf, 1928.

—————: The search for longevity. *Scient. Monthly*, 46:462-483, 1938.

————— and MOFFET, E. W.: Bodily constitution and human longevity. *Proc. Nat. Acad. Sciences*, 25:609-616, 1939.

—————: *Man the Animal.* Bloomington, Indiana, Principia Press, 1946.

PEARSON, K.: Relationship of intelligence to size and shape of the head and other mental and physical characters. *Biometrika*, 5:105-106, 1906.

PEI, W. C.: Giant ape's jaw bone discovered in China. *Amer. Anthropol.*, 59:834-838, 1957.

PENNIMAN, T. K.: *A Hundred Years of Anthropology*, 2nd ed. New York, Macmillan, 1952.

PERLA, D. and MARMORSTON, J.: *Natural Resistance and Clinical Medicine.* Baltimore, Williams & Wilkins, 1941.

PETERSEN, W. R.: *The Patient and the Weather*, 4 vols. Ann Arbor, Michigan, Edwards Bros., 1934-1938.

PIGGOTT, S.: *Approach to Archaeology.* London, Black, 1959.

PIVETEAU, J.: *Primates et Paléontologie Humaine. Traité De Paléontologie*, 7:1-657. Paris, Masson et Cie., 1957.

PONS, J.: Taste sensitivity to phenylthiourea in Spaniards. *Hum. Biol.*, 27:153-160, 1955.

QUENSTEDT, W. and A.: *Fossilium Catalogus. Hominidae Fossiles.* 's-Gravenhague, Funk, 1936.

RANSON, S. W.: *The Anatomy of the Nervous System*, 7th edition. Philadelphia, Saunders, 1939.

RAO, C. R.: *Advanced Statistical Methods in Biometrical Research.* New York, Wiley, 1952.

REID, R. R. and MULLIGAN, H. H.: Relation of cranial capacity to intelligence. *J. Roy. Anthropol. Inst.*, 53:322-332, 1923.

RIFE, D. C.: *Dice of Destiny*, 2nd ed. Columbus, Ohio, Long's College Book Co., 1947.

ROBERTS, D. F.: Body weight, race and climate. *Am. J. Phys. Anthropol.*, n.s. 11:533-558, 1953.

————: Basal metabolism, race and climate. *J. Roy. Anthropol. Inst.*, 82:169-183, 1952.

————: An ecological approach to physical anthropology. *Actes Congr. IV Internat. Sci. Anthropol. et Ethnol.*, 1:145-148, 1952

ROBERTS, D. F. and WEINER, J. S. (editors): *The Scope of Physical Anthropology and its Place in Academic Studies*. London, Institute for Biology, 1958.

ROBERTS, J. A.: Surnames and blood groups, with a note on a probable remarkable difference between North and South Wales. *Nature*, 149:138, 1942.

ROBERTS, J. FRASER: *An Introduction to Medical Genetics*, 2nd ed. New York, Oxford Univ. Press, 1959.

————: The contribution of genetics to physical anthropology. *J. Roy. Anthrop. Inst.*, 88:115-129, 1958.

ROBINSON, J. T.: Telanthropus and its phylogenetic significance. *Am. J. Phys. Anthropol.*, n.s. II:445-501, 1953.

————: *The Dentition of the Australopithecinae*. Transvaal Museum Memoir No. 9, Transvaal Museum, Pretoria, 1956.

————: Occurrence of stone artefacts with Australopithecus at Sterkfontein. *Nature*, 180:521-524, 1957.

————: A bone implement from Sterkfontein. *Nature*, 184:583-585, 1959.

————: Cranial cresting patterns and their significance in the Hominoidea. *Am. J. Phys. Anthropol.*, n.s. 16:397-428, 1959.

RODENWALDT, E.: *Die Mestizen auf Kisar*, 2 vols. Batavia, 1927.

ROE, A. and SIMPSON, G. G. (editors): *Evolution and Behavior*. New Haven, Yale Univ. Press, 1958.

ROMER, A. S.: *Man and the Vertebrates*, 4th ed. Baltimore, Penguin Books, 1958.

ROWAN, W.: *The Riddle of Migration*. Baltimore, Williams & Wilkins, 1931.

ROWE, C. W.: Genetics vs. physical anthropology in determining racial types. *Southwest. J. Anthropol.*, 2:197-211, 1950.

RUCH, T. C.: *Bibliographica Primatologica*. Springfield, Thomas, 1941.

————: *Diseases of Laboratory Primates*. Philadelphia, Saunders, 1959.

SALDANHA, P. H.: Taste thresholds for phenylthiourea among Japanese. *Ann. Hum. Genetics*, 22:380-384, 1958.

SANDERS, B. S.: *Environment and Growth*. Baltimore, Warwick & York, 1934.

SCHEINFELD, A.: *The New You and Heredity*. Philadelphia, Lippincott, 1950.

————: *Women and Men*. New York, Harcourt, 1944.

————: The mortality of men and women. *Scientific American*, 198:22-28, 1958.

SCHENKE, E. T. and McMASTERS, J. H.: *Procedures in Taxonomy*, 3rd ed. California, Stanford Univ. Press, 1956.

SCHULTZ, A. H.: Fetal growth of man and other primates. *Quart. Rev. Biol.*, 1:493-495, 1926.

————: The skeleton of the trunk and limbs of higher primates. *Human Biol.*, 2:381-383, 1930.

————: Die Körperproportionen der erwachsenen Primaten, mit spezieller Berücksichtigung der Menschenaffen. *Anthropol. Anz., 10*:154-185, 1933.

————: Characters common to higher primates and characters specific for man. *Quart. Rev. Biol., 11*:259-283, 425-455, 1936.

————: Ontogenetic specializations of man. *Arch. Julius Klaus-Stiftung, 24:* 197-216, 1949.

————: Die Bedeutung der Primatenkunde für das Verstandnis der Anthropogenese. *Deut. Ges. f. Anthropol.,* 13-28, Gottingen, 1957.

————: Past and present views of man's specializations. *Irish J. Med. Sc.,* 341-356, 1957.

————: The physical distinctions of man. *Proc. Am. Phil. Soc., 94*:428-449, 1950.

SCHWESINGER, G. C.: *Heredity and Environment.* New York, Holt, 1930.

SCOTT, E. M., GRIFFITH, I. V. and HOSKINS, D. D.: Lack of abnormal hemoglobins in Alaskans Eskimos, Indians, and Aleuts. *Science, 129*:719-720, 1959.

SCOTT, J. H.: The variability of cranial and facial dimensions in modern skulls. *Brit. Dent. J., 94*:27-31, 1953.

SELIGMAN, C. G.: *Races of Africa,* 3rd ed. New York, Oxford Univ. Press, 1957.

SELLARDS, E. H.: *Early Man in America.* Austin, Univ. Texas Press, 1952.

SEMPLE, N. M., SIMMONS, R. T. and GRAYDON, J. J.: Blood group frequencies in natives of the Central Highlands of New Guinea, and in the Bainings of New Britain. *Med. J. Austral.,* 365, 371, Sept. 8, 1956.

SHAPIRO, H. L.: Descendants of the mutineers of the bounty. *Mem. Bernice P. Bishop Museum* (Honolulu), 9:1-106, 1929.

————: *The Heritage of the Bounty.* New York, Simon & Schuster, Inc., 1936.

———— and HULSE, F.: *Migration and Environment.* New York, Oxford Univ. Press, 1940.

SHELDON, W. H.: *The Varieties of Human Physique.* New York, Harper, 1940.

————: *The Varieties of Human Temperament.* New York, Harper, 1942.

————: *Varieties of Delinquent Youth.* New York, Harper, 1949.

————: *Atlas of Men.* New York, Harper, 1954.

SHEPHERD, R. H., SHOLL, D. A. and VIZOZO, A.: The size relationship subsisting between body length, limbs and jaws in man. *J. Anat., 83*:296-302, 1949.

SHERRINGTON, C.: *Man on His Nature.* New York, Macmillan, 1941.

SHETTLES, L. B.: Biological sex differences with special reference to disease, resistance, and longevity. *J. Obst. & Gynaec. Brit. Emp., 45*:288-295, 1958.

SIMMONS, R. T., GRAYDON, J. J. and SRINGAM, S.: A blood group genetical survey in Thais, Bangkok. *Am. J. Phys. Anthropol.,* n.s. *12*:407-412, 1954.

————: GRAYDON, J. J. and SEMPLE, N. M.: A blood group genetical survey in Australian aborigines. *Am. J. Phys. Anthropol.,* n.s. *12*:599-606, 1954.

————: GRAYDON, J. J., SEMPLE, N. M., and FRY, E. I.: A blood group genetical survey in Cook Islanders, Polynesia, and comparisons with American Indians. *Am. J. Phys. Anthropol.,* n.s. *13*:667-690, 1955.

————: GRAYDON, J. J., SEMPLE, N. M. and SWINDLER, D. R.: A blood group genetical survey in West Nakanai, New Britain. *Am. J. Phys. Anthropol.,* n.s. *14*:275-286, 1956.

———— and GRAYDON, J. J.: A blood group genetical survey in Eastern and Central Polynesians. *Am. J. Phys. Anthropol., 15*:357-366, 1957.

————, Semple, N. M., Cleland, J. B. and Casley-Smith, J. R.: A blood group genetical survey in Australian aborigines at Haast's Bluff, Central Australia. *Am. J. Phys. Anthropol.*, 15:547-554, 1957.

Simpson, G. G.: The principles of classification and a classification of mammals. *Bull. Am. Museum Natur. Hist.*, 85:xvi-350, 1945.

————: *The Major Features of Evolution.* New York, Columbia Univ. Press, 1953.

————: *The Meaning of Evolution.* New Haven, Yale Univ. Press, 1949.

————, Pittendrigh, C. S. and Tiffany, L. H.: *An Introduction to Biology.* New York, Harcourt Brace, 1957.

————, Roe, A. and Lewontin, R. C.: *Quantitative Zoology.* New York, Mc-Graw-Hill, 1960.

Singer, R.: The Saldanha skull from Hopefield, South Africa. *Amer. J. Phys. Anthropol.*, n.s. 12:346-362, 1954.

————: The Boskop "race" problem. *Man*, 58:173-178, 1958.

Skerlj, B.: The role and position of Neanderthal man in human evolution. *Acta Archaeologica*, 8:347-368, 1956.

————: Were Neanderthalers the only inhabitants of Krapina? *Bulletin Scientifique*, 4:44, 1958.

Smith, G. Elliot: *The Evolution of Man*, 2nd edition. New York, Oxford, 1927.

Smithies, O.: Zone electrophoresis in starch gels: group variations in the serum proteins of normal human adults. *Biochem. J.*, 61:629, 1955.

————: Variation in human serum β-globulins. *Nature*, 180:1482-83, 1957.

Snedecor, G. W.: *Statistical Methods*, 5th edition. Ames, Iowa, Collegiate Press, 1956.

Snyder, L. H.: The effects of selection and domestication on man. *J. Nat. Cancer. Inst.*, 15:759-769, 1954.

————: Fifty years of medical genetics. *Science,* 129:7-13, 1959.

Snyder, L. L.: *Race.* Chicago, Ziff-Davis, 1939.

Sonntag, C. F.: *The Morphology of the Apes and Man.* London, Bale, 1924.

Sorsby, A. (editor): *Clinical Genetics.* St. Louis, Mosby, 1953.

Spier, L.: Growth of Japanese children born in America and in Japan. *Univ. Washington Pub. Anthropol.*, 3: 1929.

Spuhler, J. N.: An estimate of the number of genes in man. *Science, 108*:279, 1948.

Spuhler, J. N. (editor): The evolution of man's capacity for culture. *Human Biology, 31*:1-73, 1959.

———— and Kluckhohn, C.: Inbreeding coefficients of the Ramah Navaho population. *Hum. Biol.*, 25:295-317, 1953.

Steggerda, M.: The inheritance of hair form. *Eugenical News, 16*:56-57, 1931.

————: *The Maya Indians of Yucatan.* Washington, Carnegie Inst., Publication 531, 1941.

Stein, L.: *The Infancy of Speech and the Speech of Infancy.* London, Methuen, 1949.

Stern, B. J.: *Society and Medical Progress.* Princeton, Princeton Univ. Press, 1941.

Stern, C.. *Principles of Human Genetics.* 2nd ed. San Francisco, Freeman, 1960.

————: The problem of complete Y-linkage in man. *Am. J. Hum. Genetics,* **9:** 147-166, 1957.

STEWARD, J. H. (editor): *Handbook of South American Indians.* Washington, D.C., Bureau of American Ethnology, 1945-50, 6 vols.

———— and FARON, L. C. (editors): *Native Peoples of South America.* New York, McGraw-Hill, 1959.

STEWART, T. D.: Antiquity of man in America demonstrated by the fluorine test. *Science, 113:*391-392, 1951.

STIRTON, R. A.: *Time, Life and Man.* New York, Wiley, 1959.

STRANDSKOV, H. H.: The distribution of human genes. *Scientific Monthly, 52:* 203-215, 1942.

————: The genetics of human populations. *Am. Naturalist, 76:*156-164, 1942.

STRATTON, F. and RENTON, P. H.: *Practical Blood Grouping.* Springfield, Thomas, 1959.

STRAUS, JR., W. L.: The riddle of man's ancestry. *Quart. Rev. Biol., 24:*200-223, 1949.

————: Pithecanthropus in Africa. *Science, 123:*498, 1956.

————: Oreopithecus bambolii. *Science, 126:*345-346, 1957.

————: Saldanha man and his culture. *Science, 125:*973-974, 1957.

———— and CAVE, A. J. E.: Pathology and posture of Neanderthal man. *Quart. Rev. Biol., 32:*348-363, 1957.

STRONG, L. C., *et al.*: Parental age and characteristics of the offspring. *Ann. N. Y. Acad. Sc., 57:*453-613, 1954.

STUCKERT, R. J.: African ancestry of the white American population. *Ohio J. Sci., 58:*155-160, 1958.

STURTEVANT, W. C.: *Anthropology as a Career.* Washington, D.C., Smithsonian Institution, 1958.

SULLIVAN, L. R.: The pygmy races of man. *Natur. Hist., 19:*687-695, 1919.

————: *Essentials of Anthropometry. A handbook for Explorers and Museum Collectors.* New York, American Museum of Natural History, 1928.

SUNDERMAN, F. W. and BOERNER, F.: *Normal Values in Clinical Medicine.* Philadelphia, Saunders, 1959.

SUSSMAN, L. N., MEYER, L. H. and CONARD, R. A.: Blood groupings in Marshallese. *Science, 129:*644-645, 1958.

SUTTON, H. E., *et al.*: Serum protein differences between Africans and Caucasians. *Nature, 178:*1287, 1956.

SWANSCOMBE COMMITTEE: Report on the Swanscombe skull. *J. Roy. Anthropol. Inst., 58:*17-98, 1938.

SYMPOSIUM: *Origin and Evolution of Man.* Cold Spring Harbor, L.I., *Cold Spring Harbor Symposia on Quantitative Biology,* XV:vii-425, 1950.

SZILARD, L.: On the nature of the aging process. *Proc. Nat. Acad. Sci., 45:* 30-45, 1959.

TANNER, J. M.: *Growth at Adolescence.* Springfield, Thomas, 1955.

TAX, S., *et al.*: *An Appraisal of Anthropology Today.* Univ. Chicago Press, 1953.

THAMBIPILLAI, V.: Taste threshold for thiophenyl-urea in Malay school children. *Ann. Eug., 20:*232-238, 1956.

THIEME, F. P.: The geographic and racial distribution of ABO and Rh blood types and tasters of PTC in Puerto Rico. *Am. J. Hum. Genetics, 4:*94-112, 1952.

THOMA, A.: Métissage ou transformation? Essai sur les hommes fossiles de Palestine. *L'Anthropologie*, 61:470-502, 1957; 62:30-52, 1958.

THOMAS, JR., W. L. (editor): *Man's Role in Changing The Face of the Earth*. Univ. Chicago, Press, 1956.

THOMPSON, A. and BUXTON, L. H. D.: Man's nasal index in relation to certain climatic conditions. *J. Roy. Anthropol. Inst.*, 53:92-122, 1923.

THOMPSON, CHARLES H. (editor): The physical and mental abilities of the American Negro. *J. Negro Education*, 3:317-564, 1934.

THOMPSON, E. T. (editor): *Race Relations and the Race Problem*. Durham, N.C., Duke Univ. Press, 1939.

THORNDIKE, E. L.: *Human Nature and the Social Order*. New York, Macmillan, 1940.

TINDALE, N. B.: Survey of the half-caste problem in South Australia. *Proc. Roy. Geographical Soc., South Australian Branch*, Session 1940-1941, p. 66-161.

TJIO, J. H. and PUCK, T. T.: The somatic chromosomes of man. *Proc. Nat. Acad. Sci.*, 44:1229-1237, 1958.

TOBIAS, P. V.: On a Bushman-European hybrid family. *Man*, No. 287, 1-4, 1954.

———: Les Boschimans Auen et Naron de Ghanzi. *L'Anthropologie*, 59/60:235 sq, 1955/56.

———: On the survival of the Bushman. *Africa*, 26:174-186, 1956.

———: Some aspects of the biology of the Bantu-speaking African. *The Leech*, pp. 3-12, Aug. 1958.

———: Physical anthropology and somatic origins of the Hottentots. *African Studies*, 14:1-15, 1955.

TODD, T. WINGATE: Cranial capacity and linear dimensions. *Am. J. Phys. Anthropol.*, 6:97-194, 1923.

——— and LINDALA, A.: Dimensions of the body, whites and American Negroes of both sexes. *Am. J. Phys. Anthropol.*, 12:35-119, 1928.

——— and LYON, D. W.: Cranial suture closure; its progress and age relationship. Part IV. Ectocranial closure in adult males of Negro stock. *Am. J. Phys. Anthropol.*, 8:149-168, 1925.

——— and GORDOR, L. VAN: The quantitative determination of black pigmentation in the skin of the American Negro. *Am. J. Phys. Anthropol.*, 4:239-260, 1921.

——— *et al.:* The color top method of recording skin pigmentation. *Am. J. Phys. Anthropol.*, 11:187-204, 1928.

TROTTER, M.: Hair growth and shaving. *Anat. Rec.*, 37:373-379, 1928.

——— and GLESTER, G. C.: Estimation of stature from long bones of American whites and Negroes. *Am. J. Phys. Anthropol.*, n.s. 10:463-514, 1952.

TUCKER, W. B. and LESSA, W. A.: Man: a constitutional investigation. *Quart. Rev. Biol.*, 15:265-289, 1940.

TURNER, R.: *The Great Cultural Traditions*, 2 vols. New York, McGraw-Hill, 1941.

VALLOIS, H. V.: The Fontéchevade fossil men. *Am. J. Phys. Anthropol.*, n.s. 7: 339-362, 1949.

———: La mandibule humaine fossile de la Grotte du Porc-Epic près. Dire-Daoua (Abyssinie). *L'Anthropol.*, 55:231-238, 1951.

———: La capacité cranienne cher les Primates supérieurs et le "Rubicon cérébral. *C.r. des Sci. de l'Acad. des Sci.*, 238:1349-1351, 1954.

————: The pre-Mousterian human mandible from Montmaurin. *Amer. J. Phys. Anthropol.*, n.s., *14*:319-323, 1956.

————: Neanderthals and praesapiens. *J. Roy. Anthropol. Inst.*, *84*:111-130, 1954.

————: La Grotte de Fontéchevade. Pt. 2. Anthropologie. *Arch. l'Inst. Pal. Hum., Paris*, Memoire No. 29, 5-164, 1958.

———— and Movius, Jr., H. (editors): *Catalogue Des Hommes Fossiles.* XIXᵉ Congrès Géologique International, Faculté des Sciences, Alger, French North Africa, 1952.

Voss, H.: *Bibliographie des Menschenaffen (Schimpanse, Orang, Gorilla).* Jena, Fischer, 1955.

Waddington, C. H.: *The Strategy of the Genes.* New York, Macmillan, 1957.

Walker, E. P.: *The Monkey Book.* New York, Macmillan, 1954.

Wallace, B.: Genetic studies of population. *Eugenics Quart.*, *1*:10-15, 1954.

———— and Dobzhansky, Th.: *Radiation, Genes, and Man.* Holt, 1959.

Wallis, W. D.: *Culture and Progress.* New York, Whittlesey House, 1930.

————: Variability in race hybrids. *Am. Anthropol.*, *40*:680-697, 1938.

Washburn, S. L.: Thinking about race. *Science Education*, *28*:65-76, 1944.

————: Sex differences in the pubic bone. *Am. J. Phys. Anthropol.*, n.s. *7*:425-432, 1949.

————: Australopithecines: the hunters or the hunted? *Amer. Anthropol.*, *59*:612-614, 1957.

————: The new physical anthropology. *Trans. N.Y. Acad. Sc.*, *13*:298-304, 1951.

Watson, E. H. and Lowrey, G. H.: *Growth and Development of Children*, 3rd ed. Chicago, Year Book Pub., 1959.

Weckler, J. E.: The relations between Neanderthal man and *Homo sapiens.* *Amer. Anthropol.*, *56*:1003-1025, 1954.

Weidenreich, F.: Some problems dealing with ancient man. *Am. Anthropol.*, *42*:373-383, 1940.

————: The "Neanderthal man" and the ancestors of "*Homo sapiens.*" *Am. Anthropologist*, *45*:39-48, 1943.

————: The skull of Sinanthropus Pekinensis: a comparative study on a primitive hominid skull. *Palaeontologica Sinica*, n.s., D, whole series, No. 127, 1943.

————: The Keilor skull: A Wadjak type from Southeast Australia. *Am. J. Phys. Anthropol.*, n.s. 3:21-32, 1945.

————: Giants and early man from Java and South China. *Anthropol. Papers Am. Museum Nat. Hist.*, *40: 1;* 1-134, 1945, New York.

————: The paleolithic child from the Teshik-Tash cave in Southern Uzbekistan (Central Asia). *Am. J. Phys. Anthropol.*, n.s., *3*:151-163, 1945.

————: *Apes, Giants, and Man.* Chicago, Univ. Chicago Press, 1946.

————: The trend of human evolution. *Evolution*, *1*:221-236, 1947.

————: Interpretations of the fossil material. In *Early Man In the Far East* (edited by W. W. Howells), p. 149-157, Philadelphia, The Wistar Institute, 1949.

————: *Anthropological Papers of Franz Weidenreich 1939-1948.* (Compiled by S. L. Washburn and D. Wolffson.) New York, The Viking Fund, Inc., 1950.

————: Morphology of Solo Man. *Anthropol. Papers Am. Mus. Nat. His.*, *43*:205-290, 1951.

Weiner, J. S.: *The Piltdown Forgery.* New York, Oxford Univ. Press, 1955.

————: Nose shape and climate. *Am. J. Phys. Anthropol.*, n.s., *12*:1-3, 1954.

———— and Zoutendyk, A.: Blood-group investigation on Central Kalahari Bushmen. *Nature, 183*:843-844, 1959.

———— *et al.*: Further contributions to the solution of the Piltdown problem. *Bull. Brit. Mus. (Nat. Hist.), 2*:227-287, 1955.

————, Oakley, K. P. and Clark, W. E. Le Gros: The solution of the Piltdown problem. *Bull. Brit. Mus. (Nat. Hist.), 2*:141-146, 1953.

Weinert, H.: Africanthropus, der neue Affenmenschfund in Ostafrika. *Ztschr. Morphol. u. Anthropol., 38*:18-24, 1939.

Wells, L. H.: The fossil human skull from Singa. In *Fossil Mammals of Africa*, No. 2, British Museum (Natural History), 1951, 29-42.

————: The Border Cave Skull. *Am. J. Phys. Anthropol.*, n.s., *8*:241-243, 1950.

————: 'Human,' 'Hominine,' 'Hominid.' *Man*, *59*:30-31, 1959.

Wendorf, F., Krieger, A. D., Albritton, C. C. and Stewart, T. D.: *The Midland Discovery*. Austin, Univ. Texas Press, 1955.

Wendt, H.: *In Search of Adam*. Boston, Houghton Mifflin, 1956.

White, L.: The concept of culture. *Am. Anthropol., 61*:227-251, 1959.

Whyte, L. L.: *The Next Development in Man*. New York, Holt, 1948.

————: *The Unitary Principle in Physics and Biology*, Holt, 1949.

Wiener, A. S.: The Rh factor and racial origins. *Science, 96*:407-408, 1939.

————: *Blood Groups and Transfusion*. Springfield, Thomas, 1943.

————: Rh Glossary. *Laboratory Digest*, p. 1-6, May, 1949.

———— and Wexler, I. B.: Blood group paradoxes. *J.A.M.A.*, p. 1074, Dec. 15, 1956.

————: *Heredity of the Blood Groups*. New York, Grune & Stratton, 1958.

Wilber, C. G.: Physiological regulations and the origin of human types. *Human Biology, 29*:329-336, 1957.

Wilder, H. H.: *A Laboratory Manual of Anthropometry*. Philadelphia, Blakiston, 1920.

————: *The Pedigree of the Human Race*. New York, Holt, 1926.

Wilson, T. M.: On the presence of fluorine as a test for the fossilization of animal bones. *Amer. Naturalist, 29*:301-317, 439-456, 719-725, 1895.

Woo Ju-Kang: Human fossils found in China and their significance in human evolution. *Scientia Sinica, 5*:289-297, 1956.

————: New materials of *Dryopithecus* from Keiyuan, Yunnan. *Vertebrata Palasiatica, 2*:38-42, 1958.

————: Tzeyang paleolithic man—earliest representative of modern man in China. *Am. J. Phys. Anthropol.*, n.s. *16*:459-471, 1959.

———— and Chow Min-Chen: New materials of the earliest primate known in China. *Vertebrata Palasiatica, 1*:267-272, 1957.

Woodward, A. S.: *The Earliest Englishman*. London, Watts & Co., 1948.

Woodworth, R. S.: *Heredity and Environment*. New York, Social Science Research Council, 1942.

Wormington, H. M.: *Prehistoric Indians of the Southwest*. Colorado Museum of Natural History, Denver, 1947.

————: *Ancient Man in North America*, 4th ed. revised. Denver Museum of Natural History, 1957.

Wright, S.: The roles of mutation, inbreeding, crossbreeding, and selection in evolution. *Proc. Sixth Int. Congress Genetics, 1*:356-366, 1932, Ithaca, New York.

WUNDERLY, J.: The Keilor fossil skull: anatomical description. *Mem. Nat. Museum*, Melbourne No. *13;* 57-69, 1943.

YERKES, R. M.: *Chimpanzees.* New Haven, Yale Univ. Press, 1943.

———— and A. W.: *The Great Apes.* New Haven, Yale Univ. Press, 1934.

YULE, G. Y. and KENDALL, M. G.: *An Introduction to the Theory of Statistics,* 14th edition. London, Griffin & Co., 1950.

ZEUNER, F. E.: *Dating the Past,* 4th ed. New York, Longmans, 1957.

————: Time rates of organic evolution. *Bull. Nat. Inst. Science of India*, No. 7, New Delhi, 1955, pp. 276-289.

ZUCKERMAN, S.: *The Social Life of Monkeys and Apes.* New York, Harcourt, 1932.

————: *Functional Affinities of Man, Monkeys, and Apes.* New York, Harcourt, 1933.

INDEX

A

A culture, term defined, 3

A society, term defined, 3

Abbevillian tools, illustrations of, 180

Abbie, A. A., 306, 315, 710; neonatal skulls of primates, illustrated, 302; suggested common primate stem, illustrated, 305

Adapidae, genera of, 95

Adaptation, and man, 488-498

Addair, J., 513

Adriatic, *See* Dinaric

Afalou man, remains of, 265

Africanthropus, craniogram of, 207

Africanthropus njarasensis, debate over family group of, 192; description of fragments, 191; fragments of skulls found, 190, 191; problem of status of, 192

African Pygmy, *See* Negrillo

Agglutinins, defined, 327

Agglutination, production of, 328

Agglutinogens, defined, 327

Ainu, 447-448; characteristics of, 447; home now, 447; possible routes of migration, 447; resemblance to Australian aboriginal, 447

Aird, I., on blood groups and peptic ulcers, 378-379; on blood groups and stomach cancer, 378

Albritton, C. C., 294, 737

Alimen, H., 710

Allee, Warder C., 410, 710

Allen, F., 357, 391, 392, 415, 710; first description of Kidd blood groups, 360; on Diego blood group phenotypes, 362

Allison, A. C., 368, 374, 376, 710; on Duffy blood groups, 359; on haptoglobin groups, 381; on P blood groups, 356; on PTC tasting, 386; on testing of phenotypes, 347; work on Kell blood groups, 357; work on Lutheran blood groups, 358

Allopatric populations, defined, 407

Alpine, characteristics of, 451-453; home of, 451; origin of, 453; origin of name, 451; origin of brachycephalization, 451

American Indian, basic traits of, 465-466; character gradients, 466; characteristics of, 465; migrations of, 466

Anagale gobiensis, illustration, 29

Anaptomorphidae, genera of, 94

Anastasio, M. M., 507, 723

Andamanese, cranial capacity, 435; description of, 434-435; home of, 434; photo of, 433, 434; skull of, illustration, 437

Anderson, J. T., 677, 678; on PTC testing, 386

Andrewartha, H. G., 411, 710

Andrews IV, James M., 673

Angel, J. L., 543, 710; anthropometric recording blanks, illustration, 597; cranial recording blanks, 615; cranial recording blank, illustration, 612-613

Anthropoidea, 47-91; divisions of, 33-34; main divisions of, chart, 75; suborder of primates, 33

Anthropoids, average cranial capacities, 458-459; comparison of brains, jaws, and skull of with man, 227

Anthropologist, cultural, *See* Cultural Anthropologist; physical, *See* Physical Anthropologist

Anthropology, defined, 3; directories relating to, 680; periodicals relating to, 680-686; physical, scope and definition, 3-21; social, defined, 3

Anthropometer, description of, 560; use of, 560

Anthropometry, basic instruments, illustrated, 559; defined, 555; historical data needed, 557; indices, 569-572; recording blanks used, illustration, 594, 596-597, 612-613; subdivisions of, 556

Fontéchevade—*continued*
capacity of, 252; fronto-naso-orbital fragment of skull I, illustrated, 249; cranial capacity, 246; description of, 245-246; finding of, 244-245; importance of, 248; photo of skull II, 248; type man, 246, 248
Forbes, H. O., 150, 718
Forbes, R. M., 676
Ford, E. B., 412, 718
Forest Negro, characteristics of, 422; home of, 422; relationship to pygmies, 422
Forssman, O., 679
Fox, A. L., 718
France, Anatole, cranial capacity of, 255
Frankel, T., 677
Franzen, R., 663, 677
Frazier, Franklin, 705
Franzblau, A. N., 633, 718
Freeman, F. N., 502, 503, 553, 729
Friedemann, T. E., 679
Frizzi, E., on cranial capacities, 458
Fry, E. I., 732
Fudenberg, H., 357
Fukuoka, G., on PTC tasting, 386
Fyleman, R., 91, 718

G

Galagidae, *See* Bush Baby
Galago crassicaudatus, *See* Bush Baby
Galago Baby, *See* Bush Baby
Galagoides, *See* Bush baby, dwarf
Galatius-Jensen, F., 718; on haptoglobin groups, 381
Gall bladder, constitution and, 513
Galley Hill Skeleton, 234-242; description of, 237; excavation of, 236-237; finding of, 235-236; fluorine content of, 240-242, 286; illustrated, 238, 239; nitrogen content, 286
Galloway, A., 216, 289, 718
Galton, D. A. G., 412, 718
Galton, Francis, 718; *Inquiries Into Human Faculty and its Development,* 501; value of twin method of study, 501
Gametes, defined, 522-523
Garn, Stanley M., 130, 151, 416, 472, 654, 661, 662, 676, 677, 678, 714, 718; area variations of hair in male, 573; on correlation of teeth to body size, 115; on hair form, 573; *Race,*

Garn—*continued*
311; stages in areolar development of white female, 579
Gastric ulcer, relationship of blood group O to, 378
Gastro-intestinal disease, and constitution, 513
Gates, R. R., 434, 552, 718
Gavan, J. A., 629, 719
Gazin, C. L., 151, 719
Gelada Baboon, photo, 68
Gellhorn, G., 514
Gelling, J. W., 712
Genes, and genotype equilibria, 687-691; and mind, 480; and populations, 687-691; and the "half-caste," 477-478; blood genes as genetic indicators, 364-377; blood trait genes as ethno-serological indicators, 365-366; causing sickle cell anemia, 373; conditions reported as due to lethal, 527; crossing over of chromosomes, 325; defined, 330; determining frequency of, 332-333; discontinuous and continuous variations, 326; distribution of subgroups A and AB, 367; elliptocytosis and the Rh gene complex, 365; environment and conditions of expression, 475-476; equilibrium in a genetically stable population, 687; examples of gene frequency, 690-691; expressivity of, 526; genotypes and phenotypes of series O, A_1, A_2, B, 366; hybridization, 476-477; hereditary onycho-osteodysplasia, 365; incompletely sex linked, 523; linkage defined, 325; linked genes, 325; mechanisms governing inheritance of blood traits, 365; Muller on racial genetic differences, 494; mutation of, 325-326; penetrance of, 526; possible combinations in a single mating, 475; principle of gametic purity or segregation, 324-325; proportions of genotypes in nine possible matings, 689; random mating population, 687; role in making person individualist, 475; sample genetic pedigree chart, 627; sex linked, 522-523; studies on crosses, 477; traits due to incompletely sex-linked, 523; variations due to mutation and recombination, 326; variations in genetic system, 476; viability of, 526
Genet-Varcin, E., 719

H

Hydrometry, 657-659
Hylobates lar, *See* White-handed Gibbon
Hylobatinae, characteristics of, 74-79

I

Ikin, E. W., 713; blood groups of the Basque People, 370; discoverer of Henshaw antigen He, 363; on Duffy blood groups, 359; on Kidd blood groups, 360; on Lewis blood groups, 361; on P blood groups, 356; on testing of phenotypes, 347; work on Kell blood groups, 357; work on Lutheran blood groups, 358
Illyrian, *See* Dinaric
Indices, comparing two measurements, 570; defined, 569-570; formula for, 570; most commonly used, 570-572
Indo-Dravidians, characteristics of, 460; gypsies or Romanies, 460
Indonesian-Malay, characteristics of, 466, 468; home of, 468
Infantile paralysis, constitution and, 513
Ingram, V. M., 413, 722
Ingwavuma skull, artifacts of Pietersburg industry, 261; cranial capacity, 261; description of, 261; photo of, 262, 263
Irano-Afghan Mediterranean, 450
Ischizu,   , on distribution of blood types M, N, and MN, 345
Isolates, class, 387; defined, 387; religious, 387
Isolation, defined, 397
Isserlis, cranial capacity of females, 604
Ito, P. K., 722
Ivanow, A. N., on bradygenesis, 309
Iverson, C. A., 679

J

Jacobs, M., 722
Jadin, J., on distribution of blood types M, N, and M, 345
Jahn, E. F., 719
Java Macaque Monkey, photo, 66
Java Monkey, photo, 66
Jenks, A. E., Pre-Columbian Indian types, 280, 281
Jenness, D., 290, 722
Jennings, H. S., 504, 723
Jepson, G. L., 94, 723
Jerison, H. J., 723
Johnson, L. H., 723

Jokl, E., 550, 715
Jolly, Keith, discoverer of Saldanha Man fossil, 187
Jones, D. F., 717
Jones, F. Woods, 47, 91, 151, 723; *Man's Place Among the Mammals,* 197; on man's descent from australopithecines, 135; on tarsiers and man, 102; on tree-shrews, 29
Jonson, B., 723; distribution of subgroups A and AB, 367; on P blood groups, 356
Jonxis, J. H. P., 413, 723
Jørgensen, J. B., 595, 725
Jumping Shrew, diagram of brain of, 104
Junqueira, P. C., on Diego blood group phenotypes, 362; on Duffy blood groups, 359; on testing of phenotypes, 347; work on Kell blood groups, 357; work on Lutheran blood groups, 358

K

Kabat, E. A., 723
Kabir, Humayun, 705
Kaita, H., 726
Kallmann, F. J., 507, 552, 723
Kallsen, R., on Duffy blood groups, 359; on MNSs phenotypes, 347; work on Lutheran blood groups, 358
Kalmus, H., 584, 721, 723; *Genetics,* 692; *Heredity and Variation,* 692; on PTC tasting, 386
Kanam mandible, description of, 256; finding of, 256; photo of, 258; radioactivity of, 256
Kanjera skulls, finding of, 256, 258
Kaplan, B. A., 552, 723
Karsten,   , on Wadjak skulls, 182
Keane, A. H., 472, 723
Keen, J. A., 615, 723
Keilor skull; character of, 183; cranial capacity, 182; craniogram of skull of, 178; comparison with Wadjak skull, 182; transverse diagram of skull, 179
Keith, A., 185, 290, 291, 304, 316, 723, 726; on brain volumes, 313; on cerebral growth and development, 301; on cranial capacities, 458, 459; *The Antiquity of Man,* portrait, 18; the Piltdown Committee, 226
Kell Blood Groups, 355-358; discovery of, 355-356; discovery of second antibody, 356-357; discovery of the third